Alan M...

November 6th 1981

Reviewed for Clinical Edannology

BIOREGULATORS
OF REPRODUCTION

P & S BIOMEDICAL SCIENCES SYMPOSIA Series

HENRY J. VOGEL, Editor

College of Physicians and Surgeons
Columbia University
New York, New York

Henry J. Vogel (Editor). *Nucleic Acid–Protein Recognition,* 1977

Arthur Karlin, Virginia M. Tennyson, and Henry J. Vogel (Editors).
Neuronal Information Transfer, 1978

Benvenuto Pernis and Henry J. Vogel (Editors). *Cells of Immunoglobulin
Synthesis,* 1979

Benvenuto Pernis and Henry J. Vogel (Editors). *Regulatory T Lymphocytes,* 1980

Georgiana Jagiello and Henry J. Vogel (Editors). *Bioregulators of
Reproduction,* 1981

BIOREGULATORS
OF REPRODUCTION

Edited by

GEORGIANA JAGIELLO
HENRY J. VOGEL

College of Physicians and Surgeons
Columbia University
New York, New York

1981

ACADEMIC PRESS

A Subsidiary of Harcourt Brace Jovanovich, Publishers

New York   London   Toronto   Sydney   San Francisco

ACADEMIC PRESS, INC.
111 Fifth Avenue, New York, New York 10003

United Kingdom Edition published by
ACADEMIC PRESS, INC. (LONDON) LTD.
24/28 Oval Road, London NW1 7DX

Library of Congress Cataloging in Publication Data
Main entry under title:

Bioregulators of reproduction.

   (P & S biomedical sciences symposia series)
   Includes bibliographies and index.
   1. Reproduction. 2. Biological control systems.
I. Jagiello, Georgiana. II. Vogel, Henry James,
Date. III. Series.
QP251.B567   599.01'6   81-7906
ISBN 0-12-379980-5   AACR2

PRINTED IN THE UNITED STATES OF AMERICA

81 82 83 84   9 8 7 6 5 4 3 2 1

Contents

Cellular Aspects of Sexual Differentiation of the Brain

C. DOMINIQUE TORAN-ALLERAND

An Experimental Approach to Female Mammalian Meiosis: Differential Chromosome Labeling and an Analysis of Chiasmata in the Female Mouse

PAUL E. POLANI, JOHN A. CROLLA, AND MARY J. SELLER

Problems in Interspecies Comparisons in Studies in Molecular Reproductive Biology

DEBRA J. WOLGEMUTH

The Ovarian and Extraovarian Control of Meiosis: The Role of Haplodins

A. B. FAJER

PART II GERM CELL PRODUCTION

Production of Germ Cells and Regulation of Meiosis

A. G. BYSKOV AND J. GRINSTED

Programming of Gene Expression during Mammalian Oogenesis

PAUL M. WASSARMAN, JEFFREY D. BLEIL,

STEPHANIE M. CASCIO, MICHAEL J. LaMARCA,

GAIL E. LETOURNEAU, SUZANNE C. MROZAK, AND

RICHARD M. SCHULTZ

Association of Nucleoprotein Transitions with Chromatin Changes during Rat Spermatogenesis

MARVIN L. MEISTRICH, PATRICIA K. TROSTLE, AND

WILLIAM A. BROCK

PART III GONADOTROPINS

The Brain and Gonadotropin Secretion in the Primate

MICHEL FERIN

The Biosynthesis of Gonadotropin-Releasing Hormone

JAMES L. ROBERTS, BETH SCHACHTER, AND MARIAN EVINGER

Structure of the Human Gonadotropin Genes

JOHN C. FIDDES AND HOWARD M. GOODMAN

Inhibition of Testicular and Ovarian Functions by LHRH Agonists

FERNAND LABRIE, ALAIN BÉLANGER, CARL SEGUIN,
LIONEL CUSAN, GEORGES PELLETIER, FLEUR-ANGE LEFEBVRE,
PAUL A. KELLY, LOUISE FERLAND, JERRY J. REEVES,
ANDRÉ LEMAY, AND JEAN-PIERRE RAYNAUD

TLCK-Binding Proteins in Freshly Harvested and Cultured Porcine Granulosa Cells

PATRICK J. McILROY, ANDREW R. LaBARBERA,
AND ROBERT J. RYAN

PART IV NONSTEROIDAL GONADAL HORMONES

Selective Suppression of Follicle-Stimulating Hormone by Folliculostatin: A Proposed Ovarian Hormone

ROSEMARY R. GRADY, RUTH T. SAVORY-MOORE, AND
NEENA B. SCHWARTZ

In Pursuit of Physiological Inhibitors of and From the Ovary

DARRELL N. WARD

Gonadostatins and Gonadocrinin: Peptides From the Gonads Regulating the Secretion of Gonadotropins

SHAO-YAO YING, NICHOLAS LING, PETER BÖHLEN, AND
ROGER GUILLEMIN

Dissociation of Luteal Progesterone and Relaxin Secretion: Modulation by Ovarian Factors

GERSON WEISS AND LAURA T. GOLDSMITH

PART V IN VITRO FERTILIZATION

In Vitro Fertilization in the Treatment of Human Infertility

ALEXANDER LOPATA, IAN W. JOHNSTON, IAN J. HOULT,
AND ANDREW L. SPEIRS

Current Problems in *in Vitro* Fertilization and Embryo Transfer

PIERRE SOUPART

Factors Affecting Mammalian *in Vitro* Fertilization

B. JANE ROGERS

Regulation of Epididymal Steroid Metabolizing Enzymes

B. ROBAIRE, H. SCHEER, AND C. HACHEY

Sperm–Egg Recognition and Binding in Mammals

BELA J. GULYAS AND ELI D. SCHMELL

Membrane-Bound Sperm-Specific Antibodies: Their Role in Infertility

RICHARD BRONSON, GEORGE COOPER, AND
DAVID L. ROSENFELD

PART VI POST-FERTILIZATION PHENOMENA

Regulation of Pronuclear Development

FRANK J. LONGO

Control of Cell Fate during Early Mouse Embryogenesis

MICHAEL I. SHERMAN

List of Participants

NANCY J. ALEXANDER, Oregon Regional Primate Center, Beaverton, Oregon 97006

DEBORAH D. ANDERSON, Immunogenetics Department, Sidney Farber Cancer Institute, Boston, Massachusetts 02115

GLENN ARMSTRONG, Department of Pathology, College of Physicians and Surgeons, Columbia University, New York, New York 10032

MYLES ASTOR, Department of Pathology, College of Physicians and Surgeons, Columbia University, New York, New York 10032

LINDA ATKINSON, The Ford Foundation, New York, New York 10017

WESLEY G. BEAMER, Jackson Laboratory, Bar Harbor, Maine 04609

J. M. BEDFORD, Department of Obstetrics and Gynecology, Cornell Medical College, New York, New York 10021

ALAIN BÉLANGER, Department of Molecular Endocrinology, Le Centre Hospitalier de l'Université Laval, Quebec G1V 4G2, Canada

SUSAN K. BENNETT, Oregon Regional Primate Center, Beaverton, Oregon 97006

STEVEN BIRKEN, Department of Medicine, College of Physicians and Surgeons, Columbia University, New York, New York 10032

MARK P. BIRKENBACH, College of Physicians and Surgeons, Columbia University, New York, New York 10032

EMILY BLAKE, Department of Human Genetics and Development, College of Physicians and Surgeons, Columbia University, New York, New York 10032

WILLIAM A. BLANC, Department of Pathology, College of Physicians and Surgeons, Columbia University, New York, New York 10032

MELANIE BLANK, Department of Human Genetics and Development, College of Physicians and Surgeons, Columbia University, New York, New York 10032

JEFFREY D. BLEIL, Medical Research Council, Laboratory of Molecular Biology, Cambridge CB2 2QH, England

PETER BÖHLEN, Laboratories of Neuroendocrinology, The Salk Institute for Biological Studies, La Jolla, California 92138

SUSAN BRAUNHUT, Department of Pathology, College of Physicians and Surgeons, Columbia University, New York, New York 10032

WILLIAM A. BROCK, Department of Experimental Radiotherapy, The University of Texas System Cancer Center, M. D. Anderson Hospital and Tumor Institute, Houston, Texas 77030

RICHARD A. BRONSON, Division of Human Reproduction, Department of Obstetrics and Gynecology, North Shore University Hospital, Manhasset, New York 11030

A. G. BYSKOV, The Finsen Laboratory, The Finsen Institute, 2100 Copenhagen Ø, Denmark

LINDA T. CAHILL, Division of Pediatric Endocrinology, New York Hospital-Cornell Medical Center, New York, New York 10021

ROBERT E. CANFIELD, Department of Medicine, College of Physicians and Surgeons, Columbia University, New York, New York 10032

PHILIP C. CARON, Department of Pathology, College of Physicians and Surgeons, Columbia University, New York, New York 10032

PETER CARROLL, Immunogenetics Department, Sidney Farber Cancer Institute, Boston, Massachusetts 02115

STEPHANIE M. CASCIO, Department of Biological Chemistry, and Laboratory of Human Reproduction and Reproductive Biology, Harvard Medical School, Boston, Massachusetts 02115

CHING-LING CHEN, Center for Reproductive Sciences, College of Physicians and Surgeons, Columbia University, New York, New York 10032

GEORGE COOPER, Division of Human Reproduction, Department of Obstetrics and Gynecology, North Shore University Hospital, Manhasset, New York 11030

JOHN A. CROLLA, Paediatric Research Unit, The Prince Philip Research Laboratories, Guy's Hospital Medical School, University of London, London SE1 9RT, England

LIONEL CUSAN, Department of Molecular Endocrinology, Le Centre Hospitalier de l'Université Laval, Quebec G1V 4G2, Canada

EVELYN DEVINE, Division of Medical Genetics, Mount Sinai School of Medicine, New York, New York 10029

INGE DYRENFURTH, Department of Obstetrics and Gynecology, College of Physicians and Surgeons, Columbia University, New York, New York 10032

JAMES EBERWINE, Department of Biochemistry, College of Physicians and Surgeons, Columbia University, New York, New York 10032

TRUDY EDELIST, Department of Pathology, College of Physicians and Surgeons, Columbia University, New York, New York 10032

ISIDORE S. EDELMAN, Department of Biochemistry, College of Physicians and Surgeons, Columbia University, New York, New York 10032

ANKE A. EHRHARDT, Department of Psychiatry, College of Physicians and Surgeons, Columbia University, New York, New York 10032

PAUL EHRLICH, Department of Medicine, College of Physicians and Surgeons, Columbia University, New York, New York 10032

MAX EISENBERG, Department of Biochemistry, College of Physicians and Surgeons, Columbia University, New York, New York 10032

ANNE M. ETGEN, Department of Biology, Rutgers University, New Brunswick, New Jersey 08903

MARIAN EVINGER, Center for Reproductive Sciences, College of Physicians and Surgeons, Columbia University, New York, New York 10032

A. B. FAJER, Department of Physiology, University of Maryland, Baltimore, Maryland 21201

JYE-SIUNG FANG, Department of Human Genetics and Development, College of Physicians and Surgeons, Columbia University, New York, New York 10032

MURIEL FEIGELSON, Department of Obstetrics and Gynecology, Roosevelt Hospital, New York, New York 10019

MICHEL FERIN, Institute for Reproductive Sciences and Departments of Physiology and Obstetrics and Gynecology, College of Physicians and Surgeons, Columbia University, New York, New York 10032

LOUISE FERLAND, Department of Molecular Endocrinology, Le Centre Hospitalier de l'Université Laval, Quebec G1V 4G2, Canada

JOHN C. FIDDES, Cold Spring Harbor Laboratory, Cold Spring Harbor, New York 11724

LUTHER E. FRANKLIN, Biology Department, University of Houston, Houston, Texas 77004

JOHN J. FURTH, Department of Pathology, University of Pennsylvania School of Medicine, Philadelphia, Pennsylvania 19104

ALLEN H. GATES, Division of Genetics, University of Rochester Medical Center, Rochester, New York 14642

CONNIE GEE, Center for Reproductive Sciences, College of Physicians and Surgeons, Columbia University, New York, New York 10032

LAUREL E. GLASS, Department of Anatomy, University of California Medical School, San Francisco, California 94143

GABRIEL C. GODMAN, Department of Pathology, College of Physicians and Surgeons, Columbia University, New York, New York 10032

LAURA T. GOLDSMITH, Department of Obstetrics and Gynecology, New York University School of Medicine, New York, New York 10016

BERNARD GONDOS, Department of Pathology, University of Connecticut, Farmington, Connecticut 06032

HOWARD M. GOODMAN, Howard Hughes Medical Institute Laboratory, Department of Biochemistry and Biophysics, University of California, San Francisco, California 94143

ROSEMARY R. GRADY, Department of Biological Sciences, Northwestern Univesity, Evanston, Illinois 60201

J. GRINSTED, The Finsen Laboratory, The Finsen Institute, 2100 Copenhagen Ø, Denmark

ROGER GUILLEMIN, Laboratories for Neuroendocrinology, The Salk Institute for Biological Studies, La Jolla, California 92138

BELA J. GULYAS, National Institute of Child Health and Human Development, National Institutes of Health, Bethesda, Maryland 20205

C. HACHEY, Department of Pharmacology and Therapeutics and of Obstetrics and Gynecology, McGill University and The Royal Victoria Hospital, Montreal, Quebec H3G 1Y6, Canada

JOHN L. HALL, Division of Cell Surface Immunogenetics, Memorial Sloan-Kettering Cancer Center, New York, New York 10021

MARILYN S. HAMILTON, Department of Pediatrics, Harvard Medical School, Boston, Massachusetts 02115

ULRICH HÄMMERLING, Sloan-Kettering Institute for Cancer Research, New York, New York 10021

KAREN HEIN, Department of Pediatrics, College of Physicians and Surgeons, Columbia University, New York, New York 10032

WYLIE HEMBREE, Department of Obstetrics and Gynecology, College of Physicians and Surgeons, Columbia University, New York, New York 10032

IAN J. HOULT, Department of Obstetrics and Gynecology, University of Melbourne, and Reproductive Biology Unit, Royal Women's Hospital, Carlton, Victoria 3053, Australia

ROGER JACOBS, Department of Obstetrics and Gynecology, College of Physicians and Surgeons, Columbia University, New York, New York 10032

GEORGIANA JAGIELLO, Center for Reproductive Sciences, College of Physicians and Surgeons, Columbia University, New York, New York 10032

IAN W. JOHNSTON, Department of Obstetrics and Gynecology, University of Melbourne and Reproductive Biology Unit, Royal Women's Hospital, Carlton, Victoria 3053, Australia

SANDRA KAMMERMAN, Department of Medicine, New York University School of Medicine, New York, New York 10016

MICHAEL KATZ, Department of Pediatrics, College of Physicians and Surgeons, Columbia University, New York, New York 10032

PAUL A. KELLY, Department of Molecular Endocrinology, Le Centre Hospitalier de l'Université Laval, Quebec G1V 4G2, Canada

COLLINS F. KELLOGG, JR., Department of Pathology, College of Physicians and Surgeons, Columbia University, New York, New York 10032

MARIANNE KELLOGG, Columbia University, New York, New York 10027

ABRAHAM L. KIERSZENBAUM, Department of Anatomy and Laboratories for Reproductive Biology, University of North Carolina at Chapel Hill, Chapel Hill, North Carolina 27514

SAMUEL S. KOIDE, The Population Council, Center for Biomedical Research, The Rockefeller University, New York, New York 10021

MASANOBU KOMATSU, Department of Obstetrics and Gynecology, Hiroshima University School of Medicine, Hiroshima, Japan

ADELE B. KOSTELLOW, Department of Physiology, Albert Einstein College of Medicine, New York, New York 10461

ANDREW R. LABARBERA, Department of Cell Biology, Mayo Graduate School of Medicine, Rochester, Minnesota 55901

FERNAND LABRIE, Department of Molecular Endocrinology, Le Centre Hospitalier de l'Université Laval, Quebec G1V 4G2, Canada

MICHAEL J. LaMARCA, Department of Biology, Lawrence University, Appleton, Wisconsin 54911

FLEUR-ANGE LEFEBVRE, Department of Molecular Endocrinology, Le Centre Hospitalier de l'Université Laval, Quebec G1V 4G2, Canada

ANDRE LEMAY, Laboratory of Reproductive Endocrinology, Hôpital St. François d'Assise, Quebec G1L 3L5, Canada

PHYLLIS C. LEPPERT, Department of Obstetrics and Gynecology, College of Physicians and Surgeons, Columbia University, New York, New York 10032

GAIL E. LETOURNEAU, Department of Biological Chemistry and Laboratory of Human Reproduction and Reproductive Biology, Harvard Medical School, Boston, Massachusetts 02115

SEYMOUR LIEBERMAN, Department of Obstetrics and Gynecology, College of Physicians and Surgeons, Columbia University, New York, New York 10032

NICHOLAS LING, Laboratories for Neuroendocrinology, The Salk Institute for Biological Studies, La Jolla, California 92138

DANIEL M. LINKIE, Department of Obstetrics and Gynecology, College of Physicians and Surgeons, Columbia University, New York, New York 10032

HERBERT H. LIPOWSKY, Department of Physiology, College of Physicians and Surgeons, Columbia University, New York, New York 10032

FRANK J. LONGO, Department of Anatomy, University of Iowa, Iowa City, Iowa 52242

ALEXANDER LOPATA, Department of Obstetrics and Gynecology, University of Melbourne, and Reproductive Biology Unit, Royal Women's Hospital, Carlton, Victoria 3053, Australia

DAVID K. MCCLINTOCK, Lederle Laboratories, Pearl River, New York 10965

BRUCE MCEWEN, The Rockefeller University, New York, New York 10021

ROBERT W. MCGAUGHEY, Department of Zoology, Arizona State University, Tempe, Arizona 85282

PATRICK J. MCILROY, Department of Cell Biology, Mayo Graduate School of Medicine, Rochester, Minnesota 55901

KENNETH W. MCKERNS, International Society for Biomedical Endocrinology, Blue Hill Falls, Maine 04615

PALMA ANN MARONE, Department of Pathology, College of Physicians and Surgeons, Columbia University, New York, New York 10032

MARIE-FRANCE MAYLIÉ-PFENNINGER, Department of Anatomy, College of Physicians and Surgeons, Columbia University, New York, New York 10032

MARVIN L. MEISTRICH, Department of Experimental Radiotherapy, M. D. Anderson Hospital and Tumor Institute, Texas Medical Center, Houston, Texas 77030

HEINO F. L. MEYER-BAHLBURG, Department of Psychiatry, College of Physicians and Surgeons, Columbia University, New York, New York 10032

DOROTHY A. MILLER, Department of Human Genetics and Development, College of Physicians and Surgeons, Columbia University, New York, New York 10032

ORLANDO J. MILLER, Department of Obstetrics and Gynecology, College of Physicians and Surgeons, Columbia University, New York, New York 10032

GENE A. MORRILL, Department of Physiology, Albert Einstein College of Medicine, New York, New York 10461

MONTROSE J. MOSES, Department of Anatomy, Duke University Medical Center, Durham, North Carolina 27710

SUZANNE C. MROZAK, Department of Biological Chemistry and Laboratory of Human Reproduction and Reproductive Biology, Harvard Medical School, Boston, Massachusetts 02115

SUSUMU OHNO, Division of Biology, City of Hope National Medical Center, Duarte, California 91010

MOHAMED OSMAN, Department of Pathology, College of Physicians and Surgeons, Columbia University, New York, New York 10032

GEORGES PELLETIER, Department of Molecular Endocrinology, Le Centre Hospitalier de l'Université Laval, Quebec G1V 4G2, Canada

PAUL E. POLANI, Paediatric Research Unit, The Prince Philip Research Laboratories, Guy's Hospital Medical School, University of London, London SE1 9RT, England

JEAN-PIERRE RAYNAUD, Centre de Recherches Roussel-UCLAF, Romainville 93230, France

JERRY J. REEVES, Department of Molecular Endocrinology, Le Centre Hospitalier de l'Université Laval, Quebec G1V 4G2, Canada

RICHARD A. RIFKIND, Memorial Sloan-Kettering Cancer Center, New York, New York 10021

BERNARD ROBAIRE, Department of Pharmacology and Therapeutics and of Obstetrics and Gynecology, McGill University and The Royal Victoria Hospital, Montreal, Quebec H3G 1Y6, Canada

JAMES L. ROBERTS, Center for Reproductive Sciences and Department of Biochemistry, College of Physicians and Surgeons, Columbia University, New York, New York 10032

B. JANE ROGERS, Department of Obstetrics and Gynecology, John A. Burns School of Medicine, Kapiolani-Children's Medical Center, Honolulu, Hawaii 96826

DAVID L. ROSENFELD, Division of Human Reproduction, Department of Obstetrics and Gynecology, North Shore University Hospital, Manhasset, New York 11030

EDWINA RUDAK, MRC Unit of Reproductive Biology, Edinburgh EH3 9EW, Scotland

ROBERT J. RYAN, Department of Cell Biology, Mayo Graduate School of Medicine, Rochester, Minnesota 55901

EDWARD J. SACHAR, Department of Psychiatry, College of Physicians and Surgeons, Columbia University, New York, New York 10032

RUTH T. SAVORY-MOORE, Department of Biological Sciences, Northwestern University, Evanston, Illinois 60201

BETH SCHACHTER, Center for Reproductive Sciences, College of Physicians and Surgeons, Columbia University, New York, New York 10032

H. SCHEER, Department of Pharmacology and Therapeutics and of Obstetrics and Gynecology, McGill University and The Royal Victoria Hospital, Montreal, Quebec H3G 1Y6, Canada

JOEL SCHINDLER, Roche Institute for Molecular Biology, Nutley, New Jersey 07110

ELI D. SCHMELL, National Institute of Child Health and Human Development, National Institutes of Health, Bethesda, Maryland 20205

RICHARD M. SCHULTZ, Department of Biology, University of Pennsylvania, Philadelphia, Pennsylvania 19104

NEENA B. SCHWARTZ, Department of Biological Sciences, Northwestern University, Evanston, Illinois 60201

CARL SEGUIN, Department of Molecular Endocrinology, Le Centre Hospitalier de l'Université Laval, Quebec G1V 4G2, Canada

MARY J. SELLER, Paediatric Research Unit, The Prince Philip Research Laboratories, Guy's Hospital Medical School, University of London, London SE1 9RT, England

MICHAEL I. SHERMAN, Roche Institute of Molecular Biology, Nutley, New Jersey 07110

R. V. SHORT, MRC Unit of Reproductive Biology, Edinburgh EH3 9EW, Scotland

PIERRE SOUPART, Department of Obstetrics and Gynecology, Vanderbilt University Medical Center, Nashville, Tennessee 37232

LINDA A. SPATZ, Department of Pathology, College of Physicians and Surgeons, Columbia University, New York, New York 10032

ANDREW L. SPEIRS, Department of Obstetrics and Gynaecology, University of Melbourne, and Reproductive Biology Unit, Royal Women's Hospital, Carlton, Victoria 5053, Australia

DWIGHT W. STAPLETON, Division of Biology, City of Hope Research Institute, Duarte, California 91010

WENG KONG SUNG, Center for Reproductive Sciences, College of Physicians and Surgeons, Columbia University, New York, New York 10032

TERUKO TAKETO, The Population Council, The Rockefeller University, New York, New York 10021

DONALD F. TAPLEY, Office of the Dean, College of Physicians and Surgeons, Columbia University, New York, New York 10032

C. DOMINIQUE TORAN-ALLERAND, Center for Reproductive Sciences and Department of Neurology, College of Physicians and Surgeons, Columbia University, New York, New York 10032

LAURA L. TRES, Department of Anatomy, Laboratories for Reproductive Biology, University of North Carolina at Chapel Hill, Chapel Hill, North Carolina 27514

PATRICIA K. TROSTLE, Department of Experimental Radiotherapy, The

University of Texas System Cancer Center, M. D. Anderson Hospital and Tumor Institute, Houston, Texas 77030

RAYMOND L. VANDE WIELE, Department of Obstetrics and Gynecology, College of Physicians and Surgeons, Columbia University, New York, New York 10032

HENRY J. VOGEL, Department of Pathology, College of Physicians and Surgeons, Columbia University, New York, New York 10032

RUTH H. VOGEL, Department of Pathology, College of Physicians and Surgeons, Columbia University, New York, New York 10032

STEPHEN S. WACHTEL, Division of Cell Surface Immunogenetics, Memorial Sloan-Kettering Cancer Center, New York, New York 10021

DARRELL N. WARD, Department of Biochemistry, University of Texas, M. D. Anderson Tumor Institute, Houston, Texas 77030

PAUL M. WASSARMAN, Department of Biological Chemistry and Laboratory of Human Reproduction and Reproductive Biology, Harvard Medical School, Boston, Massachusetts 02115

WILLIAM B. WEHRENBERG, Department of Obstetrics and Gynecology, College of Physicians and Surgeons, Columbia University, New York, New York 10032

GERSON WEISS, Department of Obstetrics and Gynecology, New York University School of Medicine, New York, New York 10016

DAVID G. WHITTINGHAM, MRC Mammalian Development Unit, Wolfson House, London NW1 2HE, England

RICHARD WISSLER, College of Physicians and Surgeons, Columbia University, New York, New York 10032

DEBRA J. WOLGEMUTH, Department of Human Genetics and Development, Center for Reproductive Sciences, College of Physicians and Surgeons, Columbia University, New York, New York 10032

SHAO-YAO YING, Laboratories for Neuroendocrinology, The Salk Institute for Biological Studies, La Jolla, California 92138

Jacob Furth (1896–1979)*

In a sense it is appropriate that you have chosen to include a commemoration to Jacob Furth in this symposium on Bioregulators of Reproduction. If he had lived just one year longer, he would have been with you. He would have been sitting in one of the first few rows, for in his later years his hearing was not too good, and he did not want to miss a thing: neither recent evidence putting an old theory to rest nor new data and new techniques holding forth the prospect of new theories and new discoveries. After all, he would only have been 84. Literally, to his dying day, he was interested in the present and future of science. He intended to write an autobiography, but even at the age of 83 there was one more experiment to be done.

While his research was primarily related to pathological processes, notably neoplasia, he was firmly convinced that it was through the study of a disease process that information concerning normal physiology would be obtained. I recall him once citing a remark of Landsteiner to the effect that "Every idea I (Landsteiner) have had came from an observation made at the autopsy table." Jacob Furth also believed the converse: that an understanding of normal physiology is required in order to elucidate the nature of pathological processes.

His studies on and with endocrine tumors and the studies by other investigators on and with these tumors or cell lines derived from these tumors increasingly led to more basic research. He followed these studies with great interest and understanding. It is more than time that separates his studies on the receptor analysis of Paratyphoid B published in 1922 (1) with his Harvey lecture entitled "Pituitary Cybernetics and Neoplasia" delivered in 1967 (2).

Jacob Furth's studies with hormone-secreting tumors go back to his Cornell years in the early 1940's when he studied a functioning granulosa cell tumor in mice (3). At this time his major research interest was not endocrine tumors but leukemia. Trained as an immunologist

* Commemorative remarks delivered at the symposium on Bioregulators of Reproduction.

he shifted to leukemia research in 1927. (There was no NIH at that time, and the shift was prompted by a then anonymous grant to Eugene Opie to study this disease.)

Within a few years of Roentgen's discovery of x-rays, two major occupational hazards had been discovered: induction of carcinoma on the exposed hands and leukemia. Jacob Furth used irradiation to induce leukemia in his experimental animals. However, remembering the advice of Eugene Opie, Jacob Furth did not terminate the experiment after the primary objective, the development of leukemia, had been attained but he maintained the surviving animals until "natural" death ensued. These studies led to the observation that a single exposure can trigger the development of a large number of neoplastic and non-neoplastic diseases (4,5).

Endocrine tumors so obtained were thoroughly studied. I will only cite one experiment which illustrates the use he made of these tumors. The MET.W15, a mammotropic pituitary tumor, was used to provide hormone to determine the responsiveness of various mammary tumors placed in organ cultures. It was observed that the hormone invariably stimulated DNA synthesis of hormone-responsiveness tumors and normal mammary glands but not of autonomous tumors (6).

He was over 70 when these experiments were done and it was for others to take these hormone-secreting tumors and put them in cell culture. It was for others to extend research on hormones and hormone-secreting tumors, research which is now at the point where a cloned cDNA coding for human growth hormone can be grown in a 750-liter culture (7).

As Jacob Furth pointed out in his autobiographical essay: "While progress in science sometimes results from the insight of a genius or from serendipity, more often it evolves from the toil of a vast number of investigators, each building upon another's contributions. Most of these investigators become casualties of progress, the stars of one era fade into oblivion in the light of the new knowledge in a new era" (8).

Jacob Furth possessed insight, profited from serendipity, and contributed a considerable number of building blocks to the edifice of science. His contributions to our understanding of normal and pathologic processes span six decades. He has many former students who have carried on his work, and many others who were inspired by him. Particularly worthy of note is one individual, Mark Furth, a grand-nephew, who will in a year or so return the name of Furth to the Faculty roster of Columbia University.

While we commemorate Jacob Furth we should not grieve, for he was fortunate in living a long life and to be active in the Golden Age of

American Science. He was fortunate in having a wife who, while pursuing a career of her own, was devoted to him. To his sons and to the children of his sons he was a loving father and grandfather. (The sons, when they were small, did not know that few fathers worked twelve-hour days and invariably talked shop to dinner guests.) That his sons continued in medical research was, although never expressed to them, a continuing source of satisfaction.

The star dies but the light goes on.

John J. Furth

REFERENCES

1. Furth, J. (1922) Rezeptorenanalyse und Variations versuche mit B. Paratyphus Aertryck. Z. *Immunitätsforsch.* **35,**162.
2. Furth, J. (1969) Pituitary cybernetics and neoplasia. *Harvey Lect.* **63,**47.
3. Furth, J. and Boon, M. G. (1945) Liver changes associated with a transplantable granulosa cell carcinoma in mice. *Proc. Soc. Exp. Biol. Med.* **58,**112.
4. Furth, J., Haron-Ghera, N., Curtis, H. J., and Buffett, R. F. (1959) Studies on the pathogenesis of neoplasms by ionizing radiation. I. Pituitary tumors. *Cancer Res.* **19,**550.
5. Haron-Ghera, N., Furth, J., Buffett, R. F., and Yokoro, K. (1959) Studies on the pathogenesis of neoplasms by ionizing radiation. II. Neoplasms of endocrine organs. *Cancer Res.* **19,**1181.
6. Takizawa, S., Furth, J. J., and Furth, J. (1970) DNA synthesis in autonomous and hormone responsive tumors. *Cancer Res.* **30,**206.
7. *Federal Register* (1980) **45,**28909.
8. Furth, J. (1976) The making and missing of discoveries: An autobiographical essay. *Cancer Res.* **36,**871.

Preface

The biological regulation of reproductive processes, in the context of this volume, has a history of some six decades. Thus, since the early 1920's, the field witnessed steady progress, until the 1970's saw a surge of advances in the biochemistry of the pituitary hormones, the releasing factors, and the receptors of these hormones. Explorations of binding proteins for androgens were successful, and investigations into the hormonal control of gene expression in reproductive tissues brought remarkable new insights.

With these and related advances as a background, a symposium on "Bioregulators of Reproduction" was held at Arden House, on the Harriman Campus of Columbia University, from June 6 through June 8, 1980. The meeting was the fifth of the P & S Biomedical Sciences Symposia. The proceedings are contained in this volume.

The participants were welcomed by Dr. Donald F. Tapley, Dean of the College of Physicians and Surgeons (P & S) which sponsors the symposia. Dr. Tapley spoke on the historical role of reproductive biology at P & S. The earliest textbook on obstetrics and gynecology in North America, "The Compendium of the Theory and Practice of Midwifery," containing a passage on ovarian structure, was published in 1807 by Dr. Samuel Bard, the first dean of this medical school.

Our sincere thanks go to Dr. Roger V. Short who delivered the Opening Address. The contributions of the session chairmen, Dr. Susumu Ohno, Dr. Paul E. Polani, Dr. Robert E. Canfield, Dr. Darrell N. Ward, and Dr. Short, are gratefully acknowledged. A session was also chaired by one of us (G. J.).

Several colleagues from P & S, Dr. William A. Blanc, Dr. Robert E. Canfield, Dr. Isidore S. Edelman, Dr. Andrew G. Frantz, Dr. Michael Katz, Dr. Seymour Lieberman, Dr. Ines Mandl, Dr. Orlando J. Miller, Dr. Ralph M. Richart, Dr. Richard A. Rifkind, Dr. Edward J. Sachar, and Dr. Raymond L. Vande Wiele, kindly agreed to serve as honorary hosts.

Dr. Ruth H. Vogel has made much appreciated contributions to the organization of the symposium and to the preparation of this volume.

Georgiana Jagiello
Henry J. Vogel

OPENING ADDRESS

Reproductive Regulation

R. V. SHORT

MRC Unit of Reproductive Biology
Edinburgh, Scotland

Since this work is devoted to biological regulatory mechanisms that control reproduction, it seems appropriate to begin with some discussion of the most important regulatory mechanisms which will not be referred to by any of the other contributors.

The first chapter of Genesis, verses 3–5, gives us a clue as to the most important regulatory mechanism of all:

> And God said, let there be light: and there was light. And God saw the light, that it was good: and God divided the light from the darkness. And God called the light Day, and the darkness he called Night.

There could be no more succinct reminder of the fact that circadian rhythms have existed since the beginning of time, preceding the appearance of the first forms of life on earth. It is, therefore, hardly surprising to find that circadian rhythms are a fundamental property of almost all forms of living matter, from single cells to complex animals (1). Many mammals have keyed in to these circadian rhythms to regulate various aspects of their reproductive cycle. Thus in the female rat, ovulation occurs at a set time of day. But even more ingenious and important are the devices by which a host of birds and mammals in temperate and polar regions of the globe have used annual changes in daylength to restrict their reproductive activity to certain seasons of the year, thereby ensuring that their young are born at the most propitious time.

The precise mechanism by which this primeval circadian clock is used to time the circannual cycle is proving a fascinating although incredibly complex area of investigation (2). This is not a new problem. Early man also gave the matter much thought, and even produced a calculating machine to predict the time of the summer solstice. Stonehenge, the most famous of all megalithic monuments, was built in Wiltshire, England, starting in about 2800 B.C. (3). The central axis of the henge is orientated around sunrise on midsummer day, which is

1

BIOREGULATORS OF REPRODUCTION

the only day of the year on which the sun rises directly over the heel-stone when viewed from the center of the henge (Fig. 1).

The earth, spinning about its tilted axis, takes a full year to orbit the sun, and it is this tilt that causes the changing day lengths at different seasons of the year. These changes are imperceptible in equatorial regions, and most accentuated in the polar regions. Since sunlight regulates temperature and hence climate, it is hardly surprising to find that tens, hundreds, probably thousands of species of amphibians, reptiles, birds, and mammals depend on photoperiod as the environmental stimulus that regulates their reproductive activity (2). In contrast to dependent variables like ambient temperature or food availability, which fluctuate unpredictably from year to year, daylength, the proximate variable, is absolutely constant year in and year out, and hence provides a completely predictable timing device for the regulation of reproductive activity.

Fig. 1. Dawn on midsummer day at Stonehenge, with the sun rising directly over the heelstone. This megalithic monument in Wiltshire was built in about 2800 B.C., and one of its functions was to time the summer solstice. Variations in day length represent perhaps the most important bioregulatory mechanism for the control of reproduction in all forms of life. (Reproduced by gracious permission of Her Majesty Queen Elizabeth II.)

It was Descartes in 1677 (4) who proposed that the pineal gland was the seat of the soul, and although the pineal has since been called by some "the graveyard of endocrinologists," recent evidence in several mammalian species shows that the pineal unquestionably plays a key role in the timing of circadian and hence circannual rhythms (5). It seems to function as a neuroendocrine transducer, translating a light-derived neural input from the eyes into a systemically mediated endocrine response in the form of daily alterations in the peripheral concentration of the pineal's main secretory product, melatonin. But the pathway by which light reaches the pineal to trigger this endocrine response is bizarre in the extreme. Light is perceived by the retina, and a neural stimulus is transmitted via the retinohypothalamic tract to the suprachiasmatic nucleus within the hypothalamus. The suprachiasmatic nucleus seems to function as a circadian oscillator with an inherent rhythm approximately 24 hours in duration, which is entrained by the photoperiod. Nerve fibers leaving the suprachiasmatic nucleus pass down the cervical spinal cord, leave in the thoracic outflow, reascend the neck in the cervical sympathetic trunk, and synapse with postganglionic fibres in the superior cervical ganglion, near the bifurcation of the carotids. Postganglionic fibers then pass to the pineal gland itself, and if the pineal is deprived of its autonomic innervaton, it is incapable of synthesizing and secreting normal amounts of melatonin (5).

In temperate regions of the world, mammals with short gestation lengths can both mate and give birth during the summer months, and we refer to them as "long day breeders." However, if the gestation period is more extended, it may be necessary to mate during the autumn or winter to ensure a summer birth; such animals are referred to as "short day breeders." The ferret and the hamster are good examples of long day breeders, and the sheep and the red deer are good examples of short day breeders. In both groups, the pineal seems to exert an inhibitory effect on reproduction, since denervation or extirpation of the pineal makes it impossible for these animals to switch off their reproductive activity outside the breeding season. The precise way in which the pineal gland brings about this reproductive inhibition has still to be determined, but our own results in sheep would suggest that systemic melatonin, or maybe some other pineal hormone, acts back on the hypothalamus to inhibit the frequency of pulsatile discharge of gonadotropin releasing hormone (GnRH) (6). However, this inhibitory effect is quite complex, and seems to depend on the time during the 24 hours at which the melatonin levels are elevated; it is as if a state of resonance must exist between the suprachiasmatic nucleus and the pineal before the latter's inhibitory effects can become manifest.

Man, and his closest living relatives, the gorilla, chimpanzee, and orangutan, show no evidence of light-controlled seasonal variations in reproductive activity, probably reflecting the equatorial origins of all four species. However, it would be a mistake to dismiss the human pineal gland as having nothing to do with reproduction, since there are marked circadian variations in the pattern of gonadotropin secretion in children at the time of puberty that could be pineally mediated.

By far the most important bioregulator of human reproduction is lactational amenorrhoea. This was inadvertently illustrated by Leonardo da Vinci in his diagram of human intercourse, in which he shows a duct connecting the uterus to the nipple, probably because at that time it was believed that milk was manufactured from the menses, a logical deduction, since everybody knew that lactating women seldom menstruated (see Fig. 2). Today, breast feeding seems to exert remarkably little inhibitory effect on reproduction in Western women, and this is because of relatively trivial cultural alterations in breast feeding practices. In human hunter–gatherer communities, with no access to artificial forms of contraception, and no cultural taboos on intercourse during lactation, births are normally spaced about 4 years apart. That this is due to the contraceptive effects of lactation is demonstrated by the fact that if the suckling infant dies, the birth interval is considerably reduced. The prolonged duration of lactational amenorrhoea in these hunter–gatherer societies seems to be due to the very high suckling frequencies; the baby is put to the breast several times an hour during the day, with each feed lasting only 1 or 2 minutes, and sleeps beside its mother at night, often feeding from her while she is still asleep (7). When the infant sucks the nipple, afferent nerve impulses pass up to the hypothalamus, where they alter sensitivity to steroidal feedback, inhibit GnRH and hence pituitary gonadotropin secretion, and raise prolactin secretion. The net result is an inhibition of ovarian follicular development, and the more frequent the sucking stimulus, the more profound the inhibition. In Western society, we have drastically reduced the suckling frequency by advising women to feed once every 4 hours, instead of four times an hour, and by putting the baby in a cot at night and encouraging women to abandon night-time feeds as soon as possible. It is small wonder that in the process we have lost the contraceptive effects of breast feeding, which hitherto represented the most important natural constraint on human fertility.

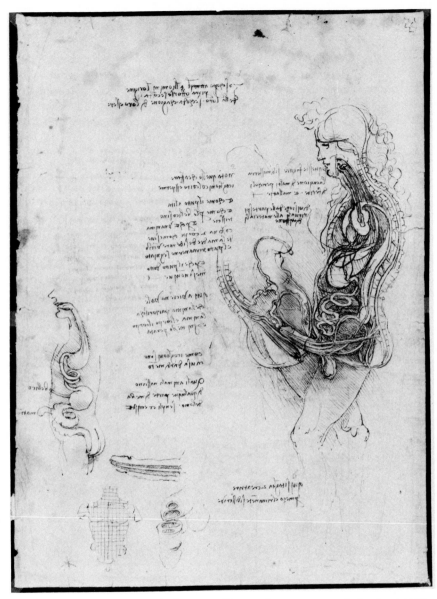

Fig. 2. Leonardo da Vinci's drawing of human intercourse, made in about 1492–1494. The duct connecting the uterus to the nipple was thought to carry the blood of the retained menses up to the breast for the formation of milk, since it was known that menstruation did not occur in lactating women. Lactational amenorrhoea is the most important bioregulator of human reproduction, although drastic reductions in the suckling frequency in many developed countries have markedly reduced its effectiveness. A return to more natural patterns of breast feeding could have a major impact on the birth rate and on infant health in many developing countries. (Reproduced by gracious permission of Her Majesty Queen Elizabeth II.)

Perhaps it is not too late to re-educate women in developing countries; we must persuade them to retain their traditional breast feeding practices, rather than trying to emulate the faddish, and foolish, bottle feeding regimes of Western society. A little bit of encouragement from Church and State for this, the most natural of all forms of family planning, could have a profound demographic impact, and in addition would achieve significant improvements in infant health. It could easily halve the birth rate in many developing countries, which is more than can be said for most of the existing contraceptive techniques.

But its failing lies in its very simplicity. No drug, no technology is required, only advice, coupled with a ban on the importation of bottles and powdered milk from Western nations. Hardly an appealing project for a technology-oriented developed nation to initiate. And yet what could be more important? It underlies the dilemma of Science today; the massive problems facing mankind are essentially very simple ones, requiring very simple practical solutions. But the myopia of specialization means that the scientist is often ill-equipped to tackle them.

REFERENCES

1. Rusak, B., and Zucker, I. (1979) *Physiol. Rev.* **59**, 449–526.
2. Follett, B. K., and Follett, D. E., eds. (1981) "Biological Clocks in Seasonal Reproductive Cycles." Wright, Bristol.
3. Daniel, G. (1980) *Sci. Am.* **243**, 64–76.
4. Descartes, R. (1677) "Tractatus de Homine, et de Formatione Foetus." Elsevirium, Amstelodami.
5. Reiter, R. J. (1980) *Endocr. Rev.* **1**, 109–131.
6. Lincoln, G. A., and Short, R. V. (1980) *Recent Prog. Horm. Res.* **36**, 1–52.
7. Short, R. V. (1980) *J. Reprod. Fertil. Suppl.* **28**, 3–11.

PART I

SEX DIFFERENTIATION
AND DETERMINATION

H-Y Antigen in Primary Sex Determination

STEPHEN S. WACHTEL AND JOHN L. HALL
Division of Cell Surface Immunogenetics
Memorial Sloan-Kettering Cancer Center
New York, New York

LINDA T. CAHILL
Division of Pediatric Endocrinology
New York Hospital–Cornell Medical Center
New York, New York

INTRODUCTION

H-Y antigen was discovered 25 years ago with the observation that intrastrain male skin grafts are rejected by female mice whereas skin grafts exchanged among the other sex combinations are tolerated (1). Presence of H-Y was established for male tissues other than skin, by observing rejection of those tissues directly, or by measuring ability of those tissues to sensitize female mice against secondary male skin grafts. For example, accelerated rejection of male skin grafts in female mice that had been primed with injections of spermatozoa signaled presence of H-Y antigen in the spermatozoa (2,3).

While surveying mouse antisera for sperm-reactive antibodies in 1971, Ellen Goldberg (4) discovered a serologic assay for H-Y that has since found wide applicability in our laboratory: sera from male-grafted female mice were cytotoxic for mouse sperm in the presence of rabbit complement. Specificity for the reaction was demonstrated by the serologic technique of absorption. The antisera were pooled and divided into equal portions. One portion was unabsorbed; one portion was absorbed with female cells (H-Y⁻); and one, with male cells (H-Y⁺). Next, the three portions were reacted with mouse sperm in the cytotoxicity test. Positive absorption, indicating that the absorb-

9

BIOREGULATORS OF REPRODUCTION
Copyright © 1981 by Academic Press, Inc.
All rights of reproduction in any form reserved.
ISBN 0-12-379980-5

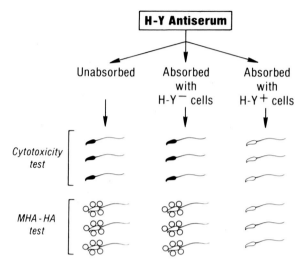

Fig. 1. H-Y typing by absorption. H-Y⁺ cells selectively remove H-Y antibodies from H-Y antiserum which now loses its capacity for reaction with target sperm cells. This causes fall in proportion of stained sperm in the cytotoxicity test, and a corresponding fall in the proportion of labeled (rosetted) cells in the MHA·HA test [From Silvers and Wachtel (6). Copyright 1977 by the American Association for the Advancement of Science.]

ing cells had selectively removed the relevant antibodies, was manifested as a fall in cytotoxic titer.

For technical reasons, only sperm and male epidermal cells proved to be satisfactory targets in the cytotoxicity test for H-Y, and in another assay for H-Y, the mixed hemadsorption hybrid antibody (MHA·HA) test (5). Yet H-Y could be demonstrated in the other male tissues by absorption in either of these systems (Fig. 1) (6).

PHYLOGENETIC CONSERVATISM OF H-Y: A TESTIS-INDUCING FUNCTION IN MAMMALS

In 1973 Silvers and Yang (7) reported that female mice could be sensitized against skin grafts from syngeneic male mice by injections of lymphoid cells from male rats; on that basis they proposed homology of male-specific antigens of mouse and rat. So the question arose whether cells of the male rat would absorb mouse H-Y antibodies in serological tests. The answer was yes. Mouse H-Y antisera lost their reactivity in both the cytotoxicity test and MHA·HA test when they were first absorbed with cells of the male rat.

Mouse H-Y antisera likewise lost their reactivity when they were absorbed with cells of the male guinea pig, the male rabbit, and man (Fig. 2) (8). This indicated that H-Y was widespread and perhaps ubiquitous among the mammals. We now asked whether the molecule might be found in other, nonmammalian species.

In birds, it is the female that is the heterogametic (XY) sex, and it is

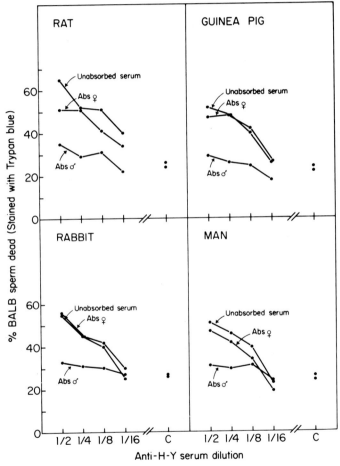

Fig. 2.   Absorption of mouse H-Y antiserum by cells from mammalian species in the sperm cytotoxicity test. Abs denotes absorption with cells of indicated sex (spleen cells of rat, guinea pig, and rabbit; blood leukocytes of man). C denotes control, showing background cytotoxicity in suspensions containing complement and inbred BALB sperm, but no antiserum. Comparative fall in cytotoxicity signifies presence of H-Y antigen in absorbing cells; see Fig. 1. [From Wachtel *et al.* (8).]

the female whose cells absorb H-Y antibodies. In amphibians both male and female heterogametic species occur: *Rana pipiens*, the leopard frog, is an XY male species; in that species male cells absorb mouse H-Y antibodies. *Xenopus laevis*, the South African clawed frog, is a female heterogametic species; in that species female cells absorb mouse H-Y antibodies (reviewed in 9). In view of the exquisite sensitivity of the antibody–antigen interaction, these observations implied occurrence of a common or cross-reacting "antigen" in species representing widely divergent pathways of vertebrate evolution. Widespread conservatism of a sex-associated cell surface molecule implied, moreover, a vital sex-associated role for the molecule. On that basis we proposed that H-Y antigen is the inducer of the testis in male heterogametic species such as the mouse, and that cross-reactive H-W antigen is the corresponding inducer of the ovary in female heterogametic species such as the chicken (10).

Under normal circumstances the indifferent mammalian gonad becomes a testis when the Y chromosome is present, and an ovary when the Y is absent. The newly formed testis secretes androgens and antimullerian hormone. The androgens stimulate development of the wolffian ducts and male external genitalia. The antimullerian hormone blocks development of the uterus and tubes, and cephalad portion of the vagina. In the absence of the testis, the embryo develops as a female whether or not a Y chromosome is present. Thus the sex-determining role of the mammalian Y chromosome is limited to the induction of the testis; further male differentiation is governed by testicular secretions. It follows that the sex-determining role of Y chromosome associated H-Y antigen should also be limited to the induction of the testis.

The model requires that H-Y must be present in order for testicular differentiation to commence. Accordingly, we set out to test the scheme by studying expression of H-Y in subjects whose gonadal sex failed to coincide with their karyotype or secondary sex phenotype.

H-Y AND TESTICULAR DIFFERENTIATION *IN VIVO*

XX MALES

Males with a female sex chromosome constitution are known for several species including mouse, goat, dog, and man. Human 46,XX males were first described in 1964. More than 80 cases have been reported since then. These subjects have small azospermic testes. Facial hair is generally scant and female-like breast development is not uncommon, occurring in 9 of 28 cases (32%) reviewed by de la Chapelle (11) for instance. Psychosexual orientation is male.

As to the cause of sex-reversal in XX males, Y-to-X chromosome translocation has been implicated in at least 11 cases in which one of the X chromosomes is larger than the other. In other XX males, there is little evidence of any chromosomal rearrangement. The condition has been inherited as an autosomal dominant trait in some instances, and as an autosomal recessive trait in others (implying presence of "inactive" or hypoactive testis determinants in the mother); and this raises the question of locus of the structural testis-determining gene (reviewed in 12).

One of the traits that all XX males seem to manifest in common is H-Y antigen. In all species, XX males have been typed H-Y$^+$, whatever the mode of inheritance of testis determining (H-Y) genes.

XX TRUE HERMAPHRODITES

Individuals with testicular and ovarian tissue are called "true hermaphrodites." In many cases these individuals have ambiguous external genitalia; male and female structures may coexist internally. For example, in the 46,XX patient reported by Saenger et al. (19) there was a hypertrophic clitoris, fused labio-scrotal folds, and a single perineal opening; surgical exploration revealed a hypoplastic uterus, left ovary with epididymis, and right ovotestis with epididymis. This is a representative case; the most common gonad in human true her-

TABLE I
H-Y Antigen in XX Males

Species	Mode of inheritance	H-Y phenotype	Reference
Mouse	Autosomal dominant $(Sxr)^a$	+	(13)
Goat	Autosomal recessive $(P)^b$	$+^c$	(14)
Dog	Autosomal^d	+	(15)
Human	Y-X interchange	+	(12)
Human	Autosomal recessive	+	(16)

[a] Sxr is the sex-reversed mutant described in Cattanach et al. (17).

[b] XX goats that are homozygous for the autosomal dominant gene, Polled (hornlessness), have testes (18).

[c] There is some indication of reduced levels of H-Y in the tissues of XX,P/P billy goats.

[d] It is not clear at present whether this is a dominant or recessive gene.

maphroditism is the ovotestis, and the most common karyotype is 46,XX (see review in 20).

We have studied XX true hermaphrodites in man and in dogs. All were H-Y⁺. Statistical analyses in human XX true hermaphrodites indicate H-Y phenotypes intermediate between those of normal male and female controls. The intermediate H-Y phenotype is most striking in the ovotestis, an H-Y⁺/H-Y⁻ mosaic tissue. Thus, cells cultured from the ovarian moiety of a human XX ovotestis were typed H-Y⁻ and those cultured from the testicular moiety were typed H-Y⁺ (21). Since H-Y has been detected in somatic tissues of the XX true hermaphrodite (blood, skin, fascia), these findings imply selective exclusion of the molecule from the developing ovary in XX gonads containing "functional" H-Y genes.

XY FEMALES

The Scandinavian wood lemming *Myopus schisticolor* is notable for a skewed sex ratio with a preponderance of females (4 : 1). Almost half have the male karyotype (32,XY), yet these "sex-reversed" females are H-Y⁻ and have normal, fertile ovaries. The XY female condition is inherited as an X-linked trait. There are moreover two kinds of X chromosomes in the wood lemming, recognizable by their distinctive staining characteristics; one in XY males, and one (X*) in X*Y females and X*X females (22). This indicates that there is a gene on the X chromosome of the wood lemming that functions during testicular differentiation, and suggests that similar genes may occur on the X chromosome of the other mammalian species including man.

The suggestion is borne out in the study of Bernstein *et al.* (23): an additional band was located on the short arm of the X chromosome (Xp⁺) in an Xp⁺Y human female and in her Xp⁺Y fetal female sibling. Degenerative ovaries were present in the Xp⁺Y female; normal ovaries, in the Xp⁺Y female fetal sib; both females were typed H-Y⁻. [X-linked inheritance has also been implicated in three 46,XY females reported by German *et al.* (24) and in two 46,XY sibs (H-Y⁻) reported by Ghosh *et al.* (25).]

Failure of H-Y antigen synthesis in subjects with a Y chromosome is not always attributable to failure or mutation of X-chromosomal genes. In the case reported by Rosenfeld *et al.* (26) H-Y was suppressed in a female with dysgenetic ovaries and 46,XYp⁻ karyotype. In this case the X chromosome was apparently intact. It was the short arm of the Y that was affected (deleted, hence Yp⁻), evidence of Y-chromosomal H-Y genes that function during testicular differentiation.

Of all 46, XY human females that have so far been studied for H-Y, some two-thirds have typed H-Y$^+$ (see 27, for example). Anomalous presence of H-Y in XY females who lack testes might seem paradoxical at first sight, but the paradox is easily resolved, for there is now considerable evidence for the occurrence of an H-Y gonadal receptor (see Fig. 3) (28). Thus, for example, H-Y is secreted in testicular Sertoli cells and bound in cells of the male or female gonad, but not in cells of the extragonadal tissues (29). Accordingly 46,XY gonadal dysgenesis in females with the H-Y$^+$ cellular phenotype (as determined in somatic cells) could represent functional absence of the H-Y inducer molecule due to mutation of a receptor determinant, whereas 46,XY gonadal dysgenesis in females with the H-Y$^-$ phenotype most probably represents functional absence due to mutation of an *inducer* determinant (one that could be located in either of the sex chromosomes). The end result is the same. In the functional absence of the testis inducer, XY gonads organize ovaries, fertile as in the wood lemming, degenerative as in man (Table II).

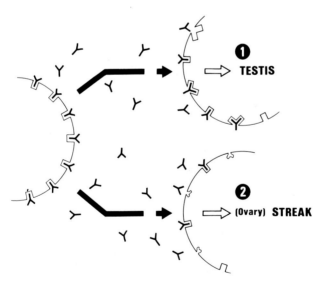

Fig. 3.   Receptor failure as a cause of XY gonadal dysgenesis in man. Left: Cell of the indifferent gonad (with membrane associated H-Y) secretes molecules of testis-inducer. Right: Molecules engage specific receptors of target cell 1 which is now induced for testicular differentiation. Receptor is unavailable in target cell 2. Indifferent XY gonad bearing cells of type 2 may initiate ovarian differentiation, but follicles degenerate, thereby giving rise to "streak gonad." [From Wachtel *et al.* (28). Reproduced by permission.]

TABLE II
Functional Absence of H-Y Antigen in XY Females

Species	Gonads	Sex chromosomes	H-Y phenotype	Reference
Wood lemming	Fertile ovaries	X*Y	−	(22)
Horse	Small fertile ovaries[a]	XY	±	(30)
Human	Ovaries	Xp$^+$Y	−	Fetus in (23)
Human	Dysgenetic ovaries	XYp$^-$	−	(26)
Human	"Streak" gonads	XY	+	Case #7 in (27)

[a] This unusual mare, referred for "infertility," had left and right ovaries of 2 × 2 cm, an "underdeveloped uterus," and a 64,XY (male) karyotype in blood and skin fibroblasts. She gave birth to a normal XX filly 1 year after original referral. H-Y was detected in blood cells of the XY mare, but statistical evaluation revealed intermediate phenotype compared with that of corresponding cells from normal XY stallions and normal XX mares.

A SPECIAL CASE: THE BOVINE FREEMARTIN

It is a known fact, and, I believe, is understood to be universal, that when a cow brings forth two calves, and that one of them is a bull-calf, and the other a cow to appearance, the cow-calf is unfit for propagation; but the bull-calf becomes a very proper bull. They are known not to breed: they do not even shew the least inclination for the bull, nor does the bull even take the least notice of them. This cow-calf is called in this country a *free martin;* and this singularity is just as well known among the farmers as either cow or bull [from John Hunter, 1779 (31)].

Thus it has long been recognized that, among cattle, females born as the twin of a bull are sterile. Though female with respect to external appearance, the freemartin may be masculinized internally: development of the mullerian ducts is often suppressed; development of the wolffian ducts may be induced. The gonads are often stunted, and in extreme cases may organize small testes; these may produce substantial amounts of androgen. It follows that masculinization of the internal genitalia may be due to androgen secreted in the freemartin herself (32).

Heterosexual twinning among the Bovidae is notable for the establishment of a common chorionic vasculature. For that reason Lillie (33) suggested that transformation of the freemartin is due to "hormones" secreted in the bull and borne in the serum to the susceptible female. This "hormonal theory" is weakened, however, because androgens injected into pregnant cows may influence the secondary sex characteristics of developing female embryos, but they do not affect primary sex, i.e., differentiation of the ovary (34).

The discovery of XX/XY chimerism in heterosexual twins led to the "cellular theory" of freemartinism according to which transformation of the female is due to colonizing XY cells (35). The initial observation of H-Y in the freemartin gonad was accordingly attributed to soluble H-Y released by migrant XY cells and bound by receptors in XX cells (36). However, it was demonstrated soon after (37) that the freemartin stigmata were precluded if vascular connections between male and female twin fetuses were disrupted between days 37 and 45 of gestation, *after* the establishment of XX/XY chimerism.

On the basis of current findings we now believe that Lillie's humoral theory may be vindicated, for we have evidence that H-Y antigen circulates as a component of the fetal bull serum, and that it is transmitted through the common vasculature into the cow twin where it is bound by gonadal receptors. In preliminary experiments, engagement of radioactive H-Y antigen and its fetal ovarian receptor is inhibited by serum of the fetal bull or the fetal freemartin, but not by serum of the normal fetal cow.

H-Y AND TESTICULAR DIFFERENTIATION *IN VITRO*

TESTICULAR CELLS LYSOSTRIPPED OF H-Y ANTIGEN FORM FOLLICULAR AGGREGATES

Under conditions of slow rotation, cells in suspension have the capacity to reaggregate, thereby forming structures characteristic of the tissue from which they arose. Sertoli cells of the newborn mouse (or rat) testis, for example, reaggregate to form structures reminiscent of the testicular tubule. But when they are exposed to H-Y antibody, the cells organize follicle-like aggregates resembling the follicles that abound in the neonatal ovary (38,39).

In this system, female-like aggregation of male gonadal cells may be attributed to removal of H-Y antigen from the membranes of the male cells in the presence of specific antibody. In cases of antibody excess, cell-surface antigen–antibody complexes migrate to a polar cap of the cell, where they are internalized and digested by autophagic lysosomes; hence H-Y cell surface antigen is said to be "lysostripped" by its specific antibody.

The lysostripping experiment provides a striking parallel of Nature's experiment with gonadal cells in the XY female wood lemming. In both cases, H-Y is removed from the membrane of XY gonadal cells, and in both cases the result is ovarian differentiation in a tissue that might otherwise form a testis.

OVARIAN CELLS EXPOSED TO H-Y FORM TUBULAR AGGREGATES

After the lysostripping experiments described above, the question arose whether dispersed ovarian cells could organize testicular structures in the presence of H-Y antigen. To answer the question, dispersed ovarian cells of the newborn rat were cultured in medium containing "free" H-Y released by newborn rat testicular cells. After incubation for 18 hours under conditions of slow rotation, the XX ovarian cells organized long tubular structures containing germ cells (40).

In related experiments, LH/hCG receptors were detected in newborn XX ovarian cells exposed to H-Y antigen (41). The LH/hCG receptors are found in the rat testis immediately at birth, but they do not usually appear in the rat ovary until 6 to 8 days later.

PRECOCIOUS TESTICULAR TRANSFORMATION INDUCED IN XX INDIFFERENT GONADS IN ORGAN CULTURE

Perhaps the most dramatic evidence of a testis-inducing role of H-Y is provided in the recent organ culture experiments of Ohno *et al.* (42) using indifferent XX gonads of the fetal cow (27 mm crown-rump length). After three days' exposure to a concentrated source of human H-Y, "complete" testicular differentiation was observed, commencing with the appearance of seminiferous tubules, and climaxing after 5 days with the development of the tunica albuginea, the thick outer covering of the testis. Neither germ cells nor Leydig cells were apparent in the converted XX testis, but the cells of the tubules resembled postpubertal Sertoli cells. (The H-Y antigen in this study was from the concentrated medium of cultured XY 'Daudi' cells; see below.)

BIOCHEMISTRY OF H-Y

THE "THREE STATES" OF H-Y

From the foregoing discussion it may be inferred that H-Y antigen occurs in at least three states: (a) as a stable portion of the cell membrane, as in male somatic cells; (b) as a free circulating molecule, as in the medium of testicular cell preparations; and (c) bound to its gonadal receptor, as in the normal testis. Yet the scheme raises a question: How is a secreted molecule maintained on the plasma membrane of somatic cells in the absence of a specific receptor?

Based on numerous reports indicating close physical association of

H-Y antigens and cell surface antigens of the major histocompatibility complex (MHC), Ohno (43) suggested that cell surface components of the MHC (H-2 in the mouse, HLA in man) serve as nonspecific anchorage sites for H-Y and indeed for all organogenesis-directing proteins.

The MHC is made up of a system of genetic loci; these include (at opposite ends of the complex) H-2D and H-2K of the mouse, corresponding to HLA-A and HLA-B of man. The H-2D and H-2K loci govern presence of serologically detectable polypeptides of about 45,000 MW. One end of these polypeptides is buried in the lipid portion of the cell membrane, and the other end is "free" at the cell surface. The free end associates noncovalently with another cell surface molecule, beta-2-microglobulin (β_2m), a polypeptide of about 12,000 MW, coded by a gene that is not part of the MHC. At the level of the cell surface, therefore, the MHC may be viewed as comprising a heavy chain (H-2D or H-2K) and a light chain (β_2m).

Depending on the manner in which they are extracted from the cell surface, H-2 components may associate in solution to form two identical covalently linked heavy chains and two light chains; or alternatively a soluble fragment of a heavy chain in association with a single light chain. It follows that cell surface H-2 may consist of a single heavy chain in association with a single molecule of β_2m; or two heavy and two light chains; or some combination thereof.

Thus MHC molecules are excellent candidates for the carriers of H-Y on the cell surface: (a) they themselves are anchored in the plasma membrane; (b) they proffer an exposed cell surface site for interaction with one another, with β_2m, and by implication with other molecules such as H-Y; (c) like H-Y, they are ubiquitous, occurring in all tissues; and (d) as noted above, there are indications of physical association of H-Y and antigens of the MHC (to cite one example: cell-mediated cytotoxicity of H-Y incompatible target cells is H-2 restricted). According to Ohno's scheme, then, newly synthesized H-Y resides on the cell membrane in association with dimers of MHC-β_2m.

DAUDI CELLS AS A SOURCE OF FREE H-Y

A corollary is that in the mutational absence of its MHC-β_2m carrier, H-Y could not reside on the membrane, and would be secreted instead. There is a cultured cell line from a Burkitt lymphoma called Daudi that has lost HLA and β_2m. When tested serologically, Daudi cells absorbed considerably less H-Y antibody than was absorbed by cells from other male lymphomas that had not lost HLA and β_2m.

When they were cocultured with HLA($+$) β_2m($+$) cells of the female HeLa D98 line, the capacity to absorb H-Y antibody was regained in resulting (HeLa x Daudi) somatic cell hybrids; this was correlated with restoration of HLA and β_2m (44).

Whereas the data seem to confirm association of H-Y and HLA-β_2m, the question is by no means settled. Fellous and colleagues (45) detected H-Y in the Chevalier cultured Burkitt lymphoma despite loss of HLA (and retention of β_2m); Geib et al. (46) reported that H-Y and H-2 antigens of the mouse thymocyte were redistributed independently in response to specific antibody; and Flaherty et al. (47) mapped H-2D^b and H-2K^b relatively distant from H-Y on the mouse thymocyte; in that case, H-Y and H-2D^b were *approximated* in response to H-Y antibody.

The question of cell surface association of MHC and H-Y may be unanswered, but the fact is that cultured Daudi cells are an excellent source of soluble H-Y antigen. On exposure to Daudi culture medium, fetal ovarian cells adopt the H-Y$^+$ cellular phenotype (they absorb H-Y antibody); binding of secreted Daudi proteins to fetal ovarian cells is blocked by testicular cell preparations, known to contain soluble H-Y; and as noted above, Daudi supernatant induces testicular differentiation in XX indifferent gonads of the bovine fetal calf *in vitro*.

PRELIMINARY CHARACTERIZATION

Release of H-Y has permitted characterization of the secreted molecule. Nagai et al. (48) metabolically labeled Daudi proteins with tritiated lysine (^{3}H-lys). SDS polyacrylamide gel electrophoresis profiles of Daudi-secreted proteins revealed a mixture of polypeptides, one of which manifested a MW of about 18,000. The 18,000 MW polypeptide reacted specifically with dissociated bovine fetal ovarian cells as follows: targets (including gonadal and extragonadal cells) were incubated with labeled Daudi supernatant fluid and then solubilized for measurements of bound cpm. Counts in the somatic target cells (e.g., spleen) were only 25% of those in the gonadal (ovarian) target cells, indicating lower binding affinity of the former for labeled molecules.

The results indicate selective adsorption of cpm to ovarian cells, representing in this case uptake of the 18,000 MW polypeptides. However, complete uptake of the 18,000 MW peptide was not observed, raising the question whether a population of 18,000 MW Daudi-secreted molecules may lack receptor binding affinity. Even when the culture medium was absorbed twice with separate batches of ovarian cells, concentration and ultracentrifugation of the residuum yielded a precipitate comprising 18,000 MW molecules almost exclusively (48).

We have approached the initial characterization of H-Y using cultured Sertoli cells from inbred BALB mice. The Sertoli-cell proteins were labeled with tritiated leucine (^{3}H-leu). Next the Sertoli cell medium was reacted with mouse H-Y antiserum (or with normal mouse serum) and the resulting complexes precipitated with goat anti-mouse Ig. The visible precipitates were then solubilized and run on cylindrical or slab gels; three peaks resulted (Fig. 4), one representing high MW proteins that had barely entered the gel, one representing a polypeptide of MW 31,000 and one, a polypeptide of MW 16,500, the last corresponding to the 18,000 MW polypeptide identified in the Daudi supernate. However, in initial tests with NMS we obtained similar but smaller profiles, raising questions of the specificity and resolution of the technique.

Early indications are that these difficulties (due perhaps to non-

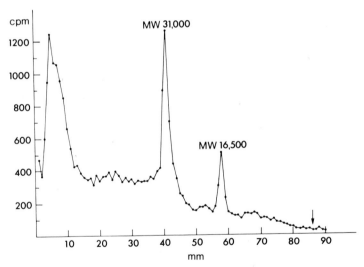

Fig. 4. SDS gel electrophoresis profile of secreted Sertoli cell proteins after immunoprecipitation with H-Y antibody. After solubilizing the labeled precipitate in SDS buffer (5% β-mercaptoethanol) and heating to 90°C for 3 minutes, the sample was run on SDS polyacrylamide gel (10% acrylamide). The gel was then sliced and the slices individually solubilized for counting. Position of migration front is indicated by arrow. Radioactive MW standards were run on separate gel treated in the same manner. When electrophoresis was performed using 5.6% acrylamide gels, the small peak ran at 18,000 MW. [For details of the technique see Hall and Wachtel (49).]

specific reactivity of the goat antiserum, and/or to subsequent over-loading of the gels with excessive immunoglobulin) could be obviated by substitution of *Staphylococcus* protein A for the goat anti-mouse Ig. The point is that protein A, which reacts with the Fc portion of the mouse antibody should eliminate nonspecific immunoprecipitation and thereby provide clear-cut controls.

As a further step in characterization, we studied membrane-bound H-Y in mouse Sertoli cells. Tyrosine residues of Sertoli cell surface proteins were radioiodinated using lactoperoxidase (a catalyst which does not penetrate the membrane). The cell surface was then solubi-lized with detergent, and the resulting lysate reacted with either H-Y antiserum or NMS. Next we performed a two-dimensional electro-phoresis of the precipitate: isoelectric focusing in one direction, and SDS polyacrylamide gel in the other. Preliminary trials in this system yielded precipitates with both immune and normal antisera, but poly-peptides of 18,000 MW and 31,000 MW were precipitated only with H-Y antiserum (49).

SUMMARY

The contention that H-Y induces the mammalian testis has with-stood extensive testing in a wide variety of experimental conditions. XX males and XX true hermaphrodites have testes and are H-Y$^+$, whereas fertile XY females lack testicular tissue and are H-Y$^-$. *In vitro*, Daudi secreted H-Y antigen induces testicular organogenesis in XX gonads of the fetal calf, whereas H-Y *antibody* blocks testicular re-organization of dispersed XY Sertoli cells inducing them to organize follicles instead.

Indications are that there is a gonad-specific H-Y antigen receptor. Ovarian cells exposed to supernatant of the dissociated testis take up H-Y and thus bind H-Y antibody. Specific uptake of H-Y does not occur in the extragonadal tissues. We infer that H-Y antigen is se-creted during development and bound by specific receptors in cells of the indifferent gonad, and that reaction of H-Y and its receptor triggers a program of testicular organogenesis in XY or XX gonads, both of which possess the specific receptor.

Availability of Daudi-secreted H-Y has permitted initial characteri-zation of the molecule, a polypeptide of approximately 18,000 MW, corresponding to the cell surface polypeptide recovered by immuno-precipitation of the solubilized mouse Sertoli cell plasma membrane.

ACKNOWLEDGMENTS

Supported in part by grants from the National Institutes of Health: AI-11982, CA-08748, HD-00171, HD-10065; grant RF 77042 from the Rockefeller Foundation; and grant 6-247 from the March of Dimes Birth Defects Foundation. We thank Ms. Virginia Barsky for preparation of the manuscript.

REFERENCES

1. Eichwald, E. J., and Silmser, C. R. (1955) *Transplant. Bull.* **2**, 148–149.
2. McLaren, A. (1962) *Nature (London)* **195**, 1323–1324.
3. Katsh, G. F., Talmage, D. W., and Katsh, S. (1964) *Science* **143**, 41–43.
4. Goldberg, E. H., Boyse, E. A., Bennett, D., Scheid, M., and Carswell, E. A. (1971) *Nature (London)* **232**, 478–480.
5. Koo, G. C., Stackpole, C. W., Boyse, E. A., Hammerling, U., and Lardis, M. (1973) *Proc. Natl. Acad. Sci. U. S. A.* **70**, 1502–1505.
6. Silvers, W. K., and Wachtel, S. S. (1977) *Science* **195**, 956–960.
7. Silvers, W. K., and Yang, S. L. (1973) *Science* **181**, 570–572.
8. Wachtel, S. S., Koo, G. C., Zuckerman, E. E., Hammerling, U., Scheid, M., and Boyse, E. A. (1974) *Proc. Natl. Acad. Sci. U. S. A.* **71**, 1215–1218.
9. Wachtel, S. S., and Koo, G. C. (1981) *In* "Mechanisms of Sex Differentiation in Animals and Man" (C. R. Austin and R. G. Edwards, eds.), Academic Press, New York (in press).
10. Wachtel, S. S., Ohno, S., Koo, G. C., and Boyse, E. A. (1975) *Nature (London)* **257**, 235–236.
11. de la Chapelle, A. (1972) *Am. J. Hum. Genet.* **24**, 71–105.
12. Wachtel, S. S., and Bard, J. (1981) *In* "The Intersex Child" (N. Josso, ed.). Karger, Basel (in press).
13. Bennett, D., Mathieson, B. J., Scheid, M., Yanagisawa, K., Boyse, E. A., Wachtel, S. S., and Cattanach, B. M. (1977) *Nature (London)* **265**, 255–257.
14. Wachtel, S. S., Basrur, P., and Koo, G. C. (1978) *Cell* **15**, 279–281.
15. Selden, J. R., Wachtel, S. S., Koo, G. C., Haskins, M. E., and Patterson, D. F. (1978) *Science* **201**, 644–646.
16. de la Chapelle, A., Koo, G. C., and Wachtel, S. S. (1978) *Cell* **15**, 837–842.
17. Cattanach, B. M., Pollard, C. E., and Hawkes, S. G. (1971) *Cytogenetics* **10**, 318–337.
18. Hamerton, J. L., Dickson, J. M., Pollard, C. E., Grieves, S. A., and Short, R. V. (1969) *J. Reprod. Fertil., Suppl.* **7**, 25–51.
19. Saenger, P., Levine, L. S., Wachtel, S. S., Korth-Schutz, S., Doberne, Y., Koo, G. C., Lavengood, R. W., German, J. L., and New, M. I. (1976) *J. Clin. Endocrinol. Metab.* **43**, 1234–1239.
20. van Niekerk, W. A. (1974) *In* "True Hermaphroditism. Clinical Morphologic and Cytogenetic Aspects," pp. 6–16. Harper, New York.
21. Winters, S. J., Wachtel, S. S., White, B. J., Koo, G. C., Javadpour, N., Loriaux, L., and Sherins, R. J. (1979) *N. Engl. J. Med.* **300**, 745–749.
22. Herbst, E. W., Fredga, K., Frank, F., Winking, H., and Gropp, A. (1978) *Chromosoma* **69**, 185–191.

23. Bernstein, R., Koo, G. C., and Wachtel, S. S. (1980) *Science* **207**, 768–769.
24. German, J., Simpson, J. L., Chaganti, R. S. K., Summitt, R. L., Reid, L. B., and Merkatz, I. R. (1978) *Science* **202**, 53–56.
25. Ghosh, S. N., Shah, P. N., and Gharpure, H. M. (1978) *Nature (London)* **276**, 180–181.
26. Rosenfeld, R. G., Luzzatti, L., Hintz, R. L., Miller, O. J., Koo, G. C., and Wachtel, S. S. (1979) *Am. J. Hum. Genet.* **31**, 458–468.
27. Wolf, U. (1979) *Hum. Genet.* **47**, 269–277.
28. Wachtel, S. S., Koo, G. C., de la Chapelle, A., Kallio, H., Heyman, J. M., and Miller, O. J. (1980) *Hum. Genet.* **54**, 25–30.
29. Muller, U., Aschmoneit, I., Zenzes, M. T., and Wolf, U. (1978) *Hum. Genet.* **43**, 151–157.
30. Sharp, A. J., Wachtel, S. S., and Benirschke, K. (1980) *J. Reprod. Fertil.* **58**, 157–160.
31. Hunter, J. (1779) *Philos. Trans. R. Soc. London,* **69**, 279–293.
32. Short, R. V., Smith, J., Mann, T., Evans, E. P., Hallett, J., Fryer, A., and Hamerton, J. L. (1969) *Cytogenetics* **8**, 369–388.
33. Lillie, F. R., (1916) *Science* **43**, 611–613.
34. Jost, A. (1965) *In* "Organogenesis" (R. L. de Haan and H. Ursprung, eds.), pp. 611–628. Holt, New York.
35. Fechheimer, N. S., Herschler, M. S., and Gilmore, L. O. (1963) *In* "Genetics Today" (S. J. Geerts, ed.), Vol. 1, p. 265. Macmillan, New York.
36. Ohno, S., Christian, L. C., Wachtel, S. S., and Koo, G. C. (1976) *Nature (London)* **261**, 597–599.
37. Vigier, B., Locatelli, A., Prepin, J., du Mesnil du Buisson, F., and Jost, A. (1976) *C. R. Hebd. Seances Acad. Sci.* **282**, 1355–1358.
38. Ohno, S., Nagai, Y., and Ciccarese, S. (1978) *Cytogenet. Cell Genet.* **20**, 351–364.
39. Zenzes, M. T., Wolf, U., Gunther, E., and Engel, W. (1978) *Cytogenet. Cell Genet.* **20**, 365–372.
40. Zenzes, M. T., Wolf, U., and Engel, W. (1978) *Hum. Genet.* **44**, 333–338.
41. Muller, U., Zenzes, M. T., Bauknecht, T., Wolf, U., Siebers, J. W., and Engel, W. (1978) *Hum. Genet.* **45**, 203–207.
42. Ohno, S., Nagai, Y., Ciccarese, S., and Iwata, H. (1979) *Recent Prog. Horm. Res.* **35**, 449–470.
43. Ohno, S. (1977) *Immunol. Rev.* **33**, 59–69.
44. Beutler, B., Nagai, Y., Ohno, S., Klein, G., and Shapiro, I. M. (1978) *Cell* **13**, 509–513.
45. Fellous, M., Gunther, E., Kemler, R., Wiels, J., Berger, R., Guenet, J. L., Jakob, H., and Jacob, F. (1978) *J. Exp. Med.* **147**, 58–70.
46. Geib, R., Goldberg, E. H., and Klein, J. (1977) *Nature (London)* **270**, 352–354.
47. Flaherty, L., Zimmerman, D., and Wachtel, S. S. (1979) *J. Exp. Med.* **150**, 1020–1027.
48. Nagai, Y., Ciccarese, S., and Ohno, S. (1979) *Differentiation* **13**, 155–164.
49. Hall, J. L., and Wachtel, S. S. (1980) *Mol. Cell. Biochem.* (in press).

Associative Recognition of Testis-Organizing H-Y Antigen and Immunological Confusion

SUSUMU OHNO AND DWIGHT W. STAPLETON

Division of Biology
City of Hope Research Institute
Duarte, California

On one hand, the proposed role of H-Y antigen as the primary sex determiner of mammals (1) appeared to have been confirmed by the following: Studies on exceptional individuals of various mammalian species indicated that the primary (gonadal) sex of mammals, in a very strict sense, is determined not so much by the presence or absence of the Y but by the expression or nonexpression of H-Y antigen: Witness H-Y antigen (+) XX males in man (2), the dog (3), the goat (4), and the mouse (5) as well as H-Y antigen (−) fertile XY would lemming ♀ (6). Indeed, human H-Y antigen identified as a discrete protein species induced precocious testicular transformation in organ cultured XX bovine embroynic indifferent gonads (7,8).

On the other hand, however, with the increasing use of rat H-Y antibody, usually titrated on Raji human male Burkitt lymphoma cells, the disturbing reports of H-Y antigen (−) man and H-Y antigen (+) women among sexual transversites and others began to appear (9). In this report, we shall first establish that human testis-organizing protein, functionally so identified, does carry H-Y antigenic determinants. Then it should be pointed out that T cell receptors as well as humoral antibodies of the mammalian immune system never recognize H-Y antigen by itself, but in association with ubiquitously expressed MHC (major histocompatibility) antigens. Consequently, H-Y antibodies occasionally confuse (H-Y + altered self MHC) antigenic complexes with unaltered self or allo-MHC antigens.

BIOREGULATORS OF REPRODUCTION
Copyright © 1981 by Academic Press, Inc.

H-Y ANTIGENIC DETERMINANTS ON HUMAN TESTIS-ORGANIZING PROTEIN

In the mutational absence of H-Y antigen's proposed plasma membrane anchorage sites (10), β_2-microglobulin (−), HLA (−) Daudi human male Burkitt lymphoma cells are incapable of stably maintaining H-Y antigen on their plasma membrane (11,12). Instead, they excrete it to the culture medium (7). In our previous reports, human H-Y antigen, so excreted, was functionally identified as a series of extremely hydrophobic polymers made of MW 16,500–18,000 subunit linked by interchain disulfide bridges (8). Unoccupied, gonad-specific H-Y receptor sites residing on the plasma membrane of bovine fetal ovarian cells selectively absorbed these MW 18,000 × n polymers, and this H-Y antigen–receptor interaction induced the precocious testicular transformation in XX bovine embryonic indifferent gonads (7,8).

H-Y antigen and several other hydrophobic protein subunits excreted by Daudi cells have a characteristically slow turnover rate; a half life of greater than 20 hours. Accordingly the preferential labeling of these hydrophobic proteins was easily accomplished by the following means: Daudi cells were first kept in 10% FCS (Ig-free fetal calf serum) added RPMI 1640 culture medium (10^6 cells/0.6 ml) in which cold lysine was totally replaced by 6 μCi/ml of [³H]lysine (2.1 Ci/mmol specific activity) for a period of 16 hours. These labeled Daudi cells were then allowed to excrete their proteins into FCS-free, cold lysine containing RPMI 1640 during the period between 20 and 36 hours after [³H]lysine incorporation. The MW 18,000 H-Y antigen subunit comprised 40% of the preferentially labeled hydrophobic protein subunits.

Since MW 18,000 × n polymers were the most hydrophobic of all when such a culture medium was concentrated precisely 6.5- to 6.7-fold by ultrafiltration using a dialysis tube (6.4 mm diameter, 24 Å average pore radius), the subsequent ultracentrifugation at 100,000 g for 1 hour selectively precipitated 70% of the available MW 18,000 × n polymers (8). No other protein subunits were discernible in the precipitates (Fig. 1). Once precipitated, these nearly pure MW 18,000 × n polymers became irreversibly water insoluble, their reprecipitation from the suspension no longer requiring the use of an ultracentrifuge.

In each of our H-Y antibody absorption tests, the MW 18,000 × n precipitates excreted by 70 × 10^6 Daudi cells during a 16-hour period were resuspended in 12.5 μl of 1/2 diluted mouse H-Y antibody raised

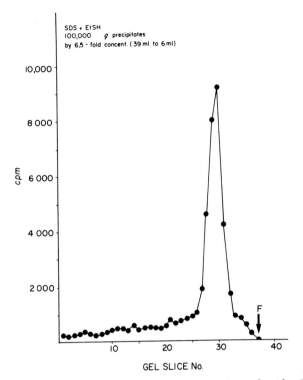

Fig. 1. SDS-polyacrylamide gel electrophoresis (5.6% acrylamide, 0.4 × 9.2 cm tube, 2 hours at 2 mA/tube) profile of the 100,000 g precipitates produced as a result of a 6.5-fold concentration of the Daudi culture medium. A 1.0% SDS-pretreatment of 12 hours at an ambient temperature followed by an additional 8 hours at 37°C included 5% (V/V) EtSH (β-mercaptoethanol). Only one peak of MW 18,000 subunit is seen. 65 × 10⁶ Daudi cells contributed to the amount of precipitates shown. F, The migration front marked by pyronin Y dye.

in B6 females by weekly injections of male B6 spleen cells, and incubated for 45 minutes on ice. After removing the precipitates by 50,000 g refrigerated centrifugation for 30 minutes, the residual cytotoxicity that remained in the supernatant was titated on BALB/c tail epidermal cells in the presence of guinea pig complements. Agarose absorbed guinea pig sera were selected on the basis of their negligible anti-mouse-epidermal cytotoxicity. Results of a series that used a good H-Y antibody are depicted in Fig. 2. This particular anti-H-Y serum was nearly free of anti-epidermal activity, thus, its cytotoxicity toward female epidermal cells was barely perceptible (Fig. 2a). The nearly complete removal of its male specific cytotoxocity contained in 12.5 μl of this antibody 1/2 diluted required absorption with 20 × 10⁶

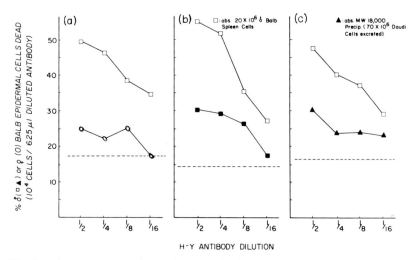

Fig. 2. The cytotoxicity of a good H-Y antibody titrated on male ($\square,\triangle$) and female ($\bigcirc$) BALB epidermal cells before and after absorption. The complement control killing level of each experiment is indicated by a broken horizontal line. In the case of Fig. 2a, the complement control killing levels of male and female targets were nearly identical. (a) The male specific cytotoxicity of this good H-Y antibody before absorption. (b) Absorption with 20×10^6 male BALB spleen cells ($\blacksquare$). (c) The absorption with the MW 18,000 $\times$ n precipitates ($\blacktriangle$) excreted by 70×10^6 Daudi cells during the 16-hour period just as effectively removed this H-Y antibody's male specific cytotoxicity as 20×10^6 male BALB spleen cells.

male BALB spleen cells (Fig. 2b). The absorption capacity of the MW 18,000 $\times$ n precipitates contributed by 70×10^6 Daudi cells was at least equal of that of the above number of male BALB spleen cells (Fig. 2c). A further increase either in the number of male BALB spleen cells or in the amount of Daudi excreted MW 18,000 $\times$ n precipitates failed to remove the residual cytotoxicity towards male BALB epidermal cells seen in Figs. 2b and 2c. Thus, the absorption achieved in Figs. 2b and 2c was considered as complete. Figures 2a, b, and c are also instructive indemonstrating the extent of day-to-day variabilities in the epidermal cytotoxicity test of the same H-Y antibody using the same source of guinea pig complements. A series depicted in Fig. 3 deliberately used a bad H-Y antibody heavily contaminated with anti-self-epidermal antibody. Accordingly, this antibody killed only 105 or so more male than female epidermal cells at all dilutions (Fig. 3a). When absorbed with Daudi excreted MW 18,000 $\times$ n precipitates, this antibody lost only its anti-H-Y activity, thus, bringing its male cell killing to the female epidermal cell killing level (Fig. 3b). We believe that with the above demonstration of H-Y antibody

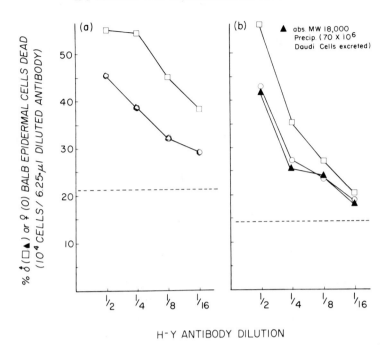

H⁻Y ANTIBODY DILUTION

Fig. 3. This time a bad H-Y antibody heavily contaminated with anti-self-epidermal antibody was used. (a) In the unabsorbed state, this antibody was cytotoxic to both male and female epidermal cells. 10% or so more killing of male cells at 1/2 and 1/4 dilutions, accounting for the presence of H-Y antibody. (b) The absorption with the Daudi excreted MW 18,000 × n precipitates merely reduced the male cell killing to the female cell killing level.

absorption capacity, we have conclusively identified that the testis-organizing H-Y antigen of man functionally so identified and the immunologically identified H-Y antigen on the male plasma membrane are one and the same.

THE ALTERED SELF OR ASSOCIATIVE RECOGNITION OF H-Y ANTIGEN BY THE IMMUNE SYSTEM

The altered self recognition of viral antigens on the target plasma membrane was originally discovered by Zinkernagel and Doherty in 1974 (13). The original interpretation of the phenomenon was that *killer* T cells do not recognize viral antigens per se on the infected target plasma membrane, but a specific perturbation or perturbations of self MHC antigens caused by their association with viral antigens;

"altered self" (13). This concept has subsequently been proven to be correct and applies as well to H-Y antigen and other so-called minor histocompatibility antigens on the plasma membrane. Since the sound viral strategy to escape immunological persecution by the host is to disguise their antigens as selves of the host, the discrimination between selves and nonselves became a main preoccupation of the host immune system which chose to monitor other antigens present on the plasma membrane via genetically polymorphic MHC antigens; H-2D and H-2K antigens of the mouse and HLA-A, HLA-B, and HLA-C antigens of man. The humoral immune response by B cells is, as a rule, T cell dependent being under the control of *helper* and *suppressor* T cells. Thus, the concept of "altered self" applies to the humoral immune response as well. However, MHC antigens involved are not the ubiquitous ones noted above but Ia (IA to IJ) antigens in the case of the mouse and HLA-DW antigens in the case of one.

The reason that the mammalian genome is endowed with two or more gene loci for ubiquitously expressed MHC antigens (e.g., H-2D and H-2K of the mouse) is found in the fact that a given viral antigen demonstrates different associative affinities to polymorphic MHC antigens and that cytotoxic T cell receptors preferentially recognize (alien antigen + altered self MHC) antigen complexes of higher associative affinities. This is very true of the cell mediated immune response against H-Y antigen. In H-2^b (H-2D^b H-2K^b) mice, it has been shown that H-Y antigen on the male plasma membrane preferentially associates with H-2D^b in the presence of testosterone and not with H-2K^b. Indeed, anti-H-Y cytotoxic T cells raised in female H-2^b mice recognize only (H-Y + altered self H-2D^b) antigen complex and no other combination (14).

CONFUSION BETWEEN ALTERED SELF MHC AND UNALTERED SELF OR ALLO-MHC

Inasmuch as each ubiquitously expressed MHC molecule must be endowed with just so many conformational alternatives, it will be no surprise if an altered form of one MHC antigen comes to resemble another MHC antigen of the species in the unaltered form. Thus, the T cell receptor's preference to recognize more of the altered self MHC and less of an alien antigen such as H-Y itself should cause problems of confusion. I have just noted that anti-H-Y female cytotoxic female T cells of the H-2^b mouse preferentially react against (H-Y + altered H-2D^b) antigen complex on the male plasma membrane. When such anti-

H-Y cytotoxic T cells were cloned and then propagated, aside from their proper male target cells carrying H-2D^b, they indiscriminately lysed male and female cells alike of H-2^d haplotype offered as targets (15). It appeared that anti-H-Y receptor of the above noted cytotoxic T cells confused (H-Y + altered self H-2D^b) antigen complex with unaltered H-2D^d (Fig. 4).

The fact that male and female cells carrying H-2D^d are lysed equally in the above experiment further indicates that either H-Y and H-2D^d and/or H-2K^d are incapable of association, or by association,

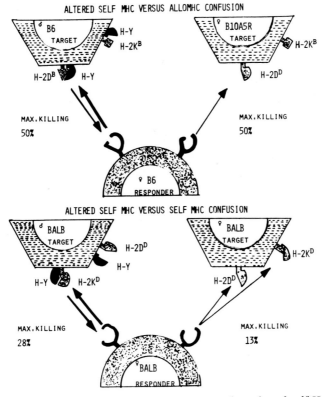

Fig. 4. Anti-H-Y cytotoxic T cells of the mouse confuse altered self H-2 antigens with unaltered allo- or self-H-2 antigens; the cause of autoimmune response? Top: Anti-H-Y cytotoxic female H-2^b T cells confuse (H-Y + altered H-2D^b) antigen complexes with unaltered allo-H-2D^d, thus, indiscriminately lysing male and female H-2D^d cells alike presented as the targets. Bottom: *In vitro* raised anti-H-Y cytotoxic T cells of H-2^d female mice have difficulty in distinguishing (H-Y + altered H-2K^d) antigen complexes from unaltered H-2D^d and/or H-2K^d antigens of the self, thus, lysing one-third as much female H-2^d cells (self) as their proper male target.

H-Y antigen alters H-2D^d only inperceptibly. As shown in Figure 2, when anti-H-Y cytotoxic female T cells of the H-2^d haplotype were raised *in vitro,* it recognized not (H-Y + H-2D^d), but (H-Y + altered self H-2K^d) antigen complexes on the male target. But by association, H-Y antigen apparently altered even H-2K^d very little, for such anti-H-Y cytotoxic T cells lysed nearly half as much of the self (H-2^d female cells) as their intended male targets (16).

THE SAME V$_H$ GENE IS UTILIZED BOTH BY T CELL RECEPTOR AND HUMORAL ANTIBODY DIRECTED AGAINST THE SAME ANTIGEN

The reader may ask "What possible connection is there between confusions by anti-H-Y T cell receptor and the descriminating power of humoral H-Y antibody?" Thus, we should point out that against the same antigen, both T cell receptors and humoral antibodies utilize the same V$_H$ (heavy chain variable region) as their antigen binding sites.

An increasing number of evidences indicate that while T cell receptors contain neither immunoglobulin light chains nor immunoglobulin heavy chain constant regions, their antigen binding sites are supplied by V$_H$ (immunoglobulin heavy chain variable region) genes. We shall cite the most convincing demonstration only. V$_H$ Ig-1^b is a V$_H$ gene allotype (allele) of the mouse. The anti-NP(4-hydroxy-3-nitrophenacetyl) humoral antibody of V$_{\lambda L}$V$_H$NP^b phenotype exhibits a unique heteroclicity in that this antibody raised against NP demonstrates a far greater binding affinity to a related hapten NIP (4-hydroxy-5-iodo-3-nitrophenacetyl). Anti-NP T cell receptor of the same mouse also exhibited the same heteroclicity toward NIP (17).

However, in the case of anti-NP humoral antibodies, the above noted heteroclicity is the property of V$_{\lambda L}$V$_H$NP^b and not of V$_{\kappa L}$V$_H$NP^b as already inferred. Thus, the question arises as to how V$_H$NP^b of the T cell receptor alone, without help from the λ-class light chain, can express this heteroxlicity? We propose the solution in Fig. 5–8. In the mammalian genome, three unlinked clusters of genes specify Ig (immunoglobulin) κ-class light chains, λ-class light chains, and several classes of heavy chains. Inasmuch as each cluster is divided into two subclusters separated by a million or more base pairs of void, the one made of numerous V genes for antigen binding sites, and the other made of a small number of C (constant region) genes, it was earlier realized that in order to specify each Ig transcript containing one each of V and C coding sequences, one of the numerous V's must somehow be brought to the proximity of the C. In the case of κ-class as well as λ-class light chains, the above essential has recently been shown to be accomplished by a pretranscriptional coding sequence fusion between one of the V's and one of the several J's(18,19). Since these 5 or so short J coding sequences are likely to have been derived from the hydrophobic leader (HyL) sequence of the C when the C was specifying an independent β_2-microglobulin-like peptide (20), a cluster of them accompany the C. Accordingly, a single V + J coding sequence fusion event causes that V + J, remaining unattached J's and the C coding sequence to be included in the same transcript. When one of each of the V's and J's are brought together by a V + J fusion enzyme, the cardinal signal sequence $\frac{CCACAGTG}{GGTGTCAC}$ at the end of V and its complementary sequence $\frac{CACTGTGG}{GTGACACC}$ at the head of each J initiate side-wise base pairing between then to form the cross configuration at the V and J coding sequence junction on DNA. The resulting V + J coding sequence fusion presumably discards a million or more base pairs of DNA.

The situation is a little different in the Ig heavy chain gene cluster, for it was found that anti-phosphorylcholine V_H's of mouse myeloma antibodies first fuse with very short D coding sequences good only for 5 amino acid residues, and only then does the fusion between V + D and J occur (21). Why do anti-phosphorylcholine V_H's bother to undergo prefusion with D_H's, while anti-Dextran V_H's seem to undergo direct fusion with J_H's? Our view is that since the anti-phosphorylcholine B cell response is T cell dependent, the former V_H's have to be used not only by immunoglobulin heavy chains but also as antiphosphorylcholine receptors by *helper* and *suppressor* T cells. Thus, $V_H + D_H$ pretranscriptional fusions occuring in the B cell nucleus represents an irreversible commitment by that V_H to be utilized as the antigen binding site of immunoglobulin heavy chains.

What occurs in the nucleus of antiphosphorylcholine T cells? We have noted that the last 31 base pairs of the first intervening sequence separating HyL (hydrophobic leader) coding sequence from $V_H S107$ remained identical with the corresponding bases of $V_H M603$, and so are the first 11 base pairs of these two anti-phosphorylcholine V_Hs specifying Gly·Ile·Asn·Cys· that are to be discarded together with 15 amino acids of HyL (21). Furthermore, the above noted conserved sequence shared in common by $V_H S107$ and $V_H M603$ can engage in extensive side-wise base pairing with the fusion signal of $V_H S107$ intended for the fusion with D_H that begins with the modified cardinal fusion

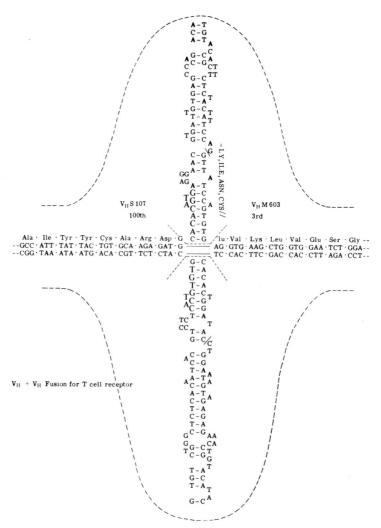

Fig. 5. Tandem pretranscriptional fusion of two antiphosphorylcholine V_H genes in the T cell nucleus. The upstream fusion signal sequence that begins with the core sequence $\frac{ACACAGTG}{TGTGTCAC}$ (in big capital letters) of V_HS107 can engage in extensive sidewise base pairing with the base sequence immediately proximal to the GTG codon for Val. of the second position of V_HM603. Bases of noncoding sequences are shown in italics and so are the first four amino acid residues specified by V_HM603 that are discarded together with hydrophobic leader amino acid residues. We believe that the antigen binding site of T cell receptors are furnished by such tandemly fused V_H's directed against the same antigen (see Fig. 7). This figure does not imply that in the V_H gene cluster of the mouse genome, V_HM603 is in a position closer to the C_H gene cluster than V_HS107. The order $V_HS107 + V_HM603$ was forced by the fact that the latter's upstream fusion signal sequence is not known as of this date.

signal $\frac{\text{ACACAGTG}}{\text{TGTGTCAC}}$ (Fig. 5). Thus, it became evident that the fusion enzyme that causes $V_H + D_H$ pretranscriptional fusion as the first step in the Ig heavy chain transcript formation can also cause the tandem fusion of V_HS107 and V_HM603 or presumably vice versa, depending upon their relative positions in the V_H gene cluster. The beauty of such a pretranscriptional tandem fusion of two V_H's lies in the probability that it likely involves two recent duplicates of each other because of the similarity in their fusion signal sequence, thus, the two V_H's involved in tandem fusion are likely to be directed against the same antigen; phosphorylcholine in the case of V_HS107 and V_HM603. By having two V_H's in tandem as their antigen binding site, the discriminatory power of T cell receptors is elevated to the equivalent of at least Ig LH dimers (Fig. 6 and 9).

Anti KLH (keyhole limpet hemocyanin) receptors excreted by *suppressor* T cells of H-2^b mice have been shown to contain the antigen binding site and I-J^b antigenic determinants in unseparable coupling; their combined molecular weight being in the range of 50,000 (22). Although there exists no a priori reason why the pretranscriptional tandem fusion of V_H's should stop after the union of two, the T cell receptor molecular weight noted above precludes the involvement of three or more V_H's in the antigen binding site of T cell receptors. After the $V_H + D_H$ pretranscriptional fusion in the B cell nucleus, V_HS107 contributes the amino acid sequence up to Asp of the 101st position to Ig heavy chains. After the tandem pretranscriptional fusion with another upstream V_H in the T cell nucleus, the translation of V_HS107 sequence in processed *messenger* can continue until the chain terminating codon UGA, thus, adding 8 extra amino acid residues beyond the 101st Asp (Fig. 8). Conversely, immediately beyond GAU for the 101st Asp, one finds the upstream splicing signal CAC ACA·G/ U GAG AG which differs from the 14-base-long prototype splicing signal sequence CC ACA·G/ GU GAG AG only by one substitution and one deletion (20). 41 bases further downstream, one finds the equally respectable downstream splicing signal *CCA ACA G/A· GG*; bases of an intervening sequence in italics (Fig. 8). The future extension of the sequence data on the germ-line V_HS107 may show that the resulting splicing adds 20 or so amino acid residues beyond the 101st Asp. In the schematic drawings of Figs. 6 and 7, the amino acid sequence beyond the 101st Asp was indicated as J_{TR} (T-cell receptor junction) sequence in that through this junction sequence the antigen binding site of T cell receptor is joined to one of the subunits of I-J and other I-like antigens (Fig. 7).

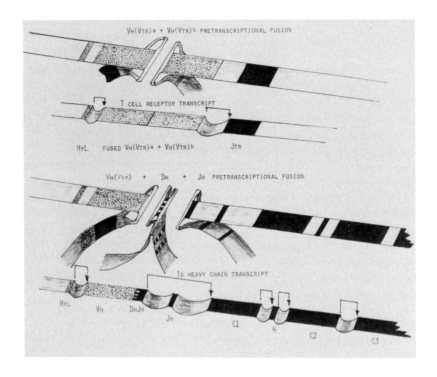

Fig. 6. Differential uses of the same $V_H(V_{TR})$ gene as the antigen binding site of T cell receptors (Top) as well as of Ig heavy chains. HYL, Hydrophobic leader sequence; J_{TR}, T cell receptor carboxyl terminal coding sequence; D_H, the short coding sequence of Ig heavy chain that specifies only 5 amino acid residues; J_H, junction coding sequence of Ig heavy chain specifying about 15 amino acid residues; C1, C2, C3, Ig heavy chain constant region coding sequences; each is good for about 110 amino acid residues; H, hinge region coding sequence good for another 14 amino acid residues. In Ig μ heavy chain, this is displaced by another C. Top: In the T cell nucleus, the upstream fusion signal sequence of $V_H(V_{TR})a$ engages in extensive side-wise base pairing with the base sequence immediately proximal to $V_H(V_{TR})b$ coding sequence (see Fig. 7). The resulting pretranscriptional fusion, by eliminating HyL of the latter, links two $V_H(V_{TR})$ coding sequences directed against the same antigen together. The T cell receptor transcripts thus produced are processed by eliminating intervening sequences. In translation of the processed *messenger*, the T cell receptor gains an extra carboxyl terminal amino acid sequence either because a splicing unites $V_H(V_{TR})b$ with J_{TR} coding sequences (see top of Fig. 8) or because the translation $V_{H\hat{V}TR}b$ continues until encountering the chain terminating codon (see Bottom of Fig. 8). Bottom: In the B cell nucleus, the same $V_H(V_{TR})a$ now called $V_H(V_{tr})$ first undergo the pretransciptional fusion with D_H. The second fusion between $V_H(V_{tr}) + D_H$ and J_H brings the former in the proximity of Ig C_H (heavy chain constant region) gene cluster, thus, Ig heavy chain transcript is produced. It is a choice of fusion partners, $V_H(V_{TR})b$ or D_H, which determines the fate of $V_H(V_{TR})b$.

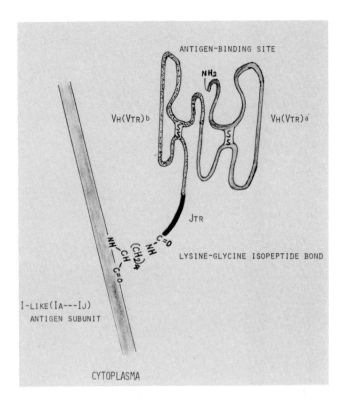

Fig. 7. The schematic illustration of T cell receptors. This scheme is heavily influenced by the finding of Tada's group on *suppressor* T cell receptors. Its antigen binding site is furnished by two V_H's directed against the same antigen tandemly fused together such as anti-phosphorylcholine V_HS107 and V_HM603 (Figs. 5 and 6). The sufficient antigen binding affinity as well as specificity is too much to ask of V_H monomers. But V_H dimers may be sufficient to display even the peculiar heteroclicity associated with V_HNP^b of the mouse. T cell receptor's preoccupation with associative recognition of altered self as well as allo-MHC antigens may be explicable by the fact that the amino terminus of the second V_H is not free. The two alternative sources of J_{TR} carboxyl terminal amino acid sequence are shown in Fig. 8. I believe that J_{TR} and one or the other subunit of I-like antigens are linked together by the isopeptide bond; here shown as lysine–glycine.

In view of the unseparable coupling between the antigen binding site and I-J antigenic determinants observed in *suppressor* T cell receptors (22), I propose that the isopeptide linkage between the two; ubiquitin and histone H-2A are linked by the lysine—glycine isopeptide bond (Fig. 7). It must be this linkage with the I-like antigen sub-

(1) FURTHER TRANSLATION

V_HM603-LIKE + V_HS107

            101st   102nd

---Tyr . Tyr . Cys . Ala . Arg . Asn . G//1u . Val . Lys . Leu . Val . Glu . Ser --------
---UAU. UAC. UGU. GCA. AGA. AAU. G//AG. GUA. AAG. CUG. GUG. GAA. UCU------

      202nd

---Cys . Ala . Arg . Asp//ALA , THR, SER , ASP , ARG , THR, SER , LEU ,
---UGU. GCA. CGA. GAU//GCA. CAC. AGU. GAG. AGG. ACG. UCA. UUG. $\boxed{UGA}$ GCCCAGCACAA---
      + D_H

(2) SPLICING

V_HM603-LIKE + V_HS107

            101st   102nd

---Tyr . Tyr . Cys . Ala . Arg . Asn . G//1u . Val . Lys . Leu . Val . Glu . Ser --------
---UAU. UAC. UGU. GCA. AGA. AAU. G//AG. GUA. AAG. CUG. GUG. GAA. UCU------

      202nd

---Cys . Ala . Arg . Asp//ALA , THR, AR-
---CGU. GCA. CGA. GAU//GCA. CAC. AG/ U GAG AG GACGUCAUUG UGA GCC CAG CAC
      + D_H

                   -G , GLY

AAA CCU CCA UUG CAG GGG UGU UCU GGA CCA ACA G/A . GG (END OF THE SEQUENCE DATA)

Fig. 8. Two alternative sources of J_{TR} when V_HS107 of the mouse as the down stream partner of V_H + V_H fusion is transcribed and translated in T cells. Top row: The continuous translation of V_HS107 beyond Asp of the 202nd (101st position in Ig heavy chains) can add 8 extra amino acid residues as J_{TR} before the translation is stopped by the chain terminating codon UGA (boxes). Bottom row: Conversely, the base sequence immediately beyond GAU codon for the above noted Asp contains a pair of prototype-like splicing signals (bases conserved from the prototype sequence CC ACA G/GU GAG AG are underlined). This splicing can create J_{TR} of an indeterminant length; at least longer than 4 amino acid residues.

unit that anchors T cell receptors to the plasma membrane and confers the unique property of MHC associative recognition to T cell receptors.

HUMORAL H-Y ANTIBODY ALSO SEES (H-Y + ALTERED MHC) ANTIGEN COMPLEXES

Reflecting the same origin of their V_H's, humoral H-Y antibodies also appear to recognize not H-Y antigen itself but (H-Y + altered MHC) antigen complexes, as do anti-H-Y T cell receptors. Nevertheless, while some H-Y antibodies appear to recognize less of evolutionary conserved H-Y antigen and more of altered MHC antigens, the opposite may be true of other H-Y antibodies.

A good example of the former was found in human H-Y antibody reported by Goulmy et al. (23). Of male and female human cells of various HLA haplotypes offered as its cytotoxic targets, this antibody lysed only male human cells carrying HLA-A-2 antigenic determinants. Yet, this was not anti-HLA-A-2 antibody, for it was not cytotoxic toward female HLA-A-2 cells. Furthermore, the absorption of the male specific cytotoxicity of this antibody was possible only by male HLA-A-2 cells. This human H-Y antibody was apparently not recognizing H-Y antigen per se but a significant alteration that H-Y antigen induced on the HLA-A-2: true altered self.

By contrast, mouse H-Y antibody appears to represent the latter, for its male specific cytotoxicity can be absorbed out by male cells of all mammalian species (24). Yet, the cytotoxicity of this antibody toward appropriate male mouse targets (spermatozoa and epidermal cells) demonstrates very pronounced H-2 dependence: male cells of $H-2^b$ and $H-2^d$ haplotypes are susceptible to lysis, while those of $H-2^k$ are resistant (25). Thus, it would appear that even mouse H-Y antibody does not see H-Y antigen alone but (H-Y + H-2) antigen complexes.

Indeed anti-(H-Y + $H-2^b$) antibodies raised in $H-2^b$ female mice appears to confuse the above (H-Y + $H-2^b$) antigen complex with unaltered $H-2K^k$ antigen. H-Y antibody of the above type can be IgM or IgG, and the antibody of both classes demonstrate nearly an identical cytotoxic potency; a maximal 60% killing of male epidermal cells or spermatozoa 1/8th antibody dilution. Yet the male specific cytotoxicity of IgM H-Y antibody can be absorbed out with only 1/12th as many male cells as the number required for absorption of IgG H-Y antibody: 0.32×10^6 male mouse spleen cells/μl versus 4.0×10^6 cells/μl (compare Table I of Beutler et al., 11, to Fig. 2a). As shown in Fig. 9, we

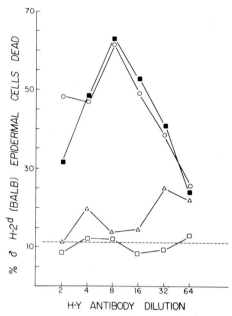

Fig. 9. One example showing that mouse H-Y antibody raised in H-2^b females may confuse the antigenic determinants of H-2K^K with the combined antigenic determinants of H-Y + H-2D^b. The male specific cytotoxicity of this antibody titrated on male H-2^d (BALB) epidermal cells can be completely absorbed out by 0.5 × 10^6 male H-2^d (BALB) or H-2^b (C57BLACK6) spleen cells/μl antibody. 3.22 × 10^6 female H-2^k (C3H) spleen cells but not of H-2^d or H-2^{b}/μl of antibody also completely absorbed out its male specific cytotoxicity. ■, Unabsorbed H-Y antibody. ○, Absorbed with 3.6 × 10^6 female H-2^d spleen cells/μl. △, Absorbed with 3.22 × 10^6 female H-2^k spleen cells/μl. □, Absorbed with 0.5 × 10^6 male H-2^d spleen cells/μl.

have found that the male specific cytotoxicity of IgM H-Y antibody can be greatly reduced by absorption with a very large number (3.0 × 10^6/μl) of female mouse cells of either H-2D^k H-2K^k (C3H) or H-2D^{b}H-2K^k (B10A-2R) haplotypes, while the same number of H-2^b (B6) or H-2^d (BALB) female cells did not show an appreciable adsorption; thus, establishing the cross reactivity between (H-Y + H-2^b) antigen complex and unaltered H-2K^k. Since the comparable experiment on IgG H-Y antibody would have required the use of 37.0 × 10^6 female H-2K^k cells/μl. The experiment proved impractical.

SUMMARY

On one hand, human testis-organizing protein functionally so identified does carry H-Y antigenic determinants readily detectable by mouse H-Y antibody. Nevertheless, the fact is that neither T cell receptors nor humoral antibodies of the mammalian immune system recognize H-Y antigen per se. Instead, they invariably recognize (H-Y + altered MHC) antigen complexes. Whenever ambiguous results are obtained on sexually abnormal individuals, it is important to remember that H-Y antibody sometimes confuses certain unaltered MHC antigens with (H-Y + altered MHC) antigen complexes, and that H-Y antigen, not in strong association with any of the MHC antigens of certain haplotypes, may not be recognized by H-Y antibody.

REFERENCES

1. Wachtel, S. S., Ohno, S., Koo, G. C., and Boyse, E. A. (1975) *Nature (London)* **257**, 235–236.
2. Wachtel, S. S., Koo., G. C., Berg, W. R., Thaler, H. T., Dillarad, G. M., Rosenthal, I. M., Dosik, H., Gerald, P. S., Saenger, P., New, M., Lieber, E., and Miller, O. J. (1976) *N. Engl. J. Med.* **295**, 750–754.
3. Selden, J. R., Wachtel, S. S., Koo, G. C., Haskins, M. E., and Patterson, D. F. (1978) *Science* **210**, 644–646.
4. Wachtel, S. S., Basrur, P., and Koo, G. C. (1978) *Cell* **15**, 279–281.
5. Bennett, D., Boyse, E. A., Mathieson, B. J., Scheid, M., Wachtel, S. S., Yanagisawa, K., and Cattanach, B. M. (1977) *Nature (London)* **265**, 255–257.
6. Wachtel, S. S., Koo, G. C., Ohno, S., Gropp, A., Dev, V. G., Tantravahi, R., Miller, D. A., and Miller, O. J. (1976) *Nature (London)* **264**, 638–639.
7. Ohno, S., Nagai, Y., Ciccarese, S., and Iwata, I. (1979) *Recent Prog. Horm. Res.* **35**, 449–476.
8. Nagai, Y., Ciccarese, S., and Ohno, S. (1979) *Differentiation* **13**, 155–164.
9. Eicher, W., Spoljar, M., Cleve, H., Murken, J.-D., Richter, K., and Rutkowski, S. S. (1979) *Lancet* **2**, 1137–1138.
10. Ohno, S. (1977) *Immunol. Rev.* **33**, 59–69.
11. Beutler, B., Nagai, Y., Ohno, S., Klein, G., and Shapiro, I. (1978) *Cell* **13**, 509–513.
12. Fellous, M., Günther, E., Kemler, R., Wiels, J., Berger, R., Guenet, J. L., Jakob, H., and Jacob, F. (1978) *J. Exp. Med.* **148**, 58–70.
13. Zinkernagel, R. M., and Doherty, P. D. (1974) *Nature (London)* **251**, 547–549.
14. Simpson, E., and Gordon, R. D. (1977) *Immunol. Rev.* **35**, 59–75.
15. von Boehmer, H., Hengartner, H., Nabholz, M., Lernhardt, W., Schreier, M. H., and Haas, W. (1979) *Eur. J. Immunol.* **9**, 592–597.
16. Matsunaga, T., and Ohno, S. (1980) *Transplant. Proc.* (in press).
17. Cramer, M., Krawinkel, U., Melchers, I., Imanishi-Kari, T., Ben-Neriah, T., Givol, D., and Rajewsky, K. (1979) *Eur. J. Immunol.* **9**, 332–338.

18. Sakano, H., Hüppi, K., Heinrich, G., and Tonegawa, S. (1979) *Nature (London)* **280,** 288–294.
19. Seidman, J. G., Max, E. E., and Leder, P. (1979) *Nature (London)* **280,** 370–375.
20. Ohno, S. (1980) *Differentiation* **16,** 1–15.
21. Early, P., Huang, H., Davis, M., Calame, K., and Hood, L. (1980) *Cell* **19,** 981–992.
22. Taniguchi, M., Saito, T., and Tada, T. (1979) *Nature (London)* **278,** 255–258.
23. Goulmy, E., Bradley, B. A., van Leeuwen, A., Lansberg, Q., Munro, A., Termijtelen, A., and van Rood, J. T. (1977) *Tissue Antigens* **10,** 248.
24. Wachtel, S. S., Koo, G. C., and Boyse, E. A. (1975) *Nature (London)* **254,** 270–272.
25. Scheid, M., Boyse, E. A., Carswell, E. A., and Old, L. J. (1972) *J. Exp. Med.* **135,** 938–955.

Cellular Aspects of Sexual Differentiation of the Brain

C. DOMINIQUE TORAN-ALLERAND

Center for Reproductive Sciences
(IISHR) and Department of Neurology
Columbia University
College of Physicians and Surgeons
New York, New York

For of course , said Mr. Foster, in the vast majority of cases fertility is merely a nuisance . . . but we want to have a good choice. And of course one must always leave an enormous margin of safety. So we allow as many as 30 per cent of the female embryos to develop normally. The others get a dose of male sex hormone every twenty-four metres for the rest of the course. Result: they're decanted as free-martins—structurally quite normal (except, he had to admit, that they *do* have just the slightest tendency to grow beards), but sterile, guaranteed sterile. [Aldous Huxley (1932). *Brave New World*].

INTRODUCTION

It is generally believed that the gonadal hormones exert a dual influence on the vertebrate central nervous system (CNS); an inductive or organizational influence during development and an excitatory or activational one in the adult. Exposure of the developing brain to the presence or absence of these hormones results in the differentiation of a broad spectrum of neuroendocrine and behavioral responses, which are congruent with the genetic sex. This process is referred to as sexual differentiation of the brain.

The most extensively studied and most clear-cut gender-specific differences in brain function are those concerned with reproductive physiology and sexual, or mating, behavior. The adult female exhibits ovarian cycles, a cyclical release of gonadotrophins, and fluctuating gonadal hormone levels; the male on the other hand, does not. In subprimate mammals, moreover, the gender-specific and stereotyped,

43

hormonally dependent patterns of sexual behavior are generally cyclical in the female but not in the male. It is widely accepted that these functional differences are due to differences in the neural substrates which regulate pituitary activity and sexual behavior.

The basic concepts of sexual differentiation have been shown to exist in numerous mammalian and nonmammalian species from fish to primates. In all these species, while the genotype determines the nature of the gonad present, whether a testis or an ovary, the subsequent sexually dimorphic development of both the external genitalia and the brain is dependent on the later influence of the gonadal hormones.

Sexual differentiation of the brain is thought to result from exposure of the CNS to testicular androgens during a very restricted or "critical" period of neural differentiation during which the tissue is competent and sufficiently plastic to respond permanently to the hormone and after which it is refractory or responds in a reversible manner. The phenomenon of sexual differentiation actually consists of two separate processes, both of which are dependent on androgen. One, termed *masculinization* refers to the development and potentiation of male characteristics. The other, termed *defeminization*, relates to the suppression of female characteristics.

Although many of the concepts of sexual differentiation are derived from experiments with rodents, the most extensively studied animal model, it should always be kept in mind that, despite the obvious difficulties in extrapolation from one species to another, the underlying principles of hormonal action are probably valid generally. However, the neural functions affected, the anatomical loci involved, the timing of the critical period, and even the very hormone(s) responsible may vary widely among species. In many animals, including man, in whom the critical period occurs prenatally, experimental hormonal manipulation may also affect the genitalia. In the rodent, on the other hand, while differentiation of the reproductive system occurs prenatally, that of the brain takes place largely postnatally, from the late fetal through the first 5 postnatal days. Thus, it is possible in rodents to modify the brain experimentally without affecting the genitalia whose normal structure and function are requisites for normal sexual behavior.

The hypothalamus appears to have an endogenous rhythm of hormone release and sexual behavior, which is characteristic of the adult female but absent in the male. This is summarized in Fig. 1. During the critical period, the expression of this intrinsic rhythmicity is permanently and irreversibly suppressed in the neonatal male by expo-

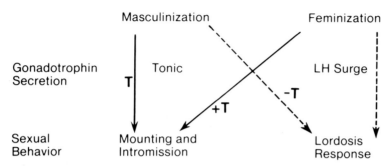

Fig. 1. Current view of sexual differentiation of brain function with respect to reproductive physiology and sexual behavior, and its exclusive dependence on androgen.

sure to androgens, which cause the masculinization of postpubertal sexual behavior and the noncyclic or tonic pattern of gonadotrophin release (see 1,2 for review). The permanent postpubertal alterations in reproductive function induced by neonatal androgenization of the rodent brain has led to the concept that regardless of genetic sex, the newborn brain, though sexually undifferentiated and bi-potential, is intrinsically organized to support the cyclical or female pattern. Thus, androgenization of the neonatal female and castration of the neonatal male have been shown to profoundly disturb the development of those regulatory mechanisms underlying the gender-specific responses. Thus, neonatally androgenized females are rendered anovulatory and sterile; exhibit a masculinized (tonic) pattern of gonadotrophin release; and there is both an absence of female behavior and an increased display of male behavior (3,4). Males, castrated neonatally during the critical period, will both support ovulation of ovarian grafts consequent to the cyclical release of gonadotropins and exhibit a female pattern of sexual receptivity in the presence of a normal male.

Prenatal endogenous androgen secretion by the fetal testis from the 14th day of gestation onward has been found, moreover, to have profound consequences for the sexual differentiation of reproductive behavior in male and female rats (5–7) and mice (8). The frequency of masculine sexual behavior exhibited by normal female rats and mice has been related to their intrauterine proximity to a male fetus (7,8); female rats born in a litter with few or no males having a lower probability of exhibiting masculine behavior than those born in litters containing four or more males (9,10). The apparent importance of such prenatal androgen influences is suggested by the female hamster who, unlike the female rat and mouse, does not normally exhibit masculine behavior (6). Born of a relatively shorter gestation (16 days versus 22 days for the rat), the female hamster is apparently not significantly exposed to fetal testicular effects; sexual differentiation in this species being an entirely postnatal phenomenon. Prenatal anti-androgen treatment with flutamide (5) or cyproterone acetate (11,12), furthermore, has been shown to increase feminine sexual behavior in both males and females. This further supports the view that prenatal androgen exerts a defeminizing influence on the development of female sexual behavior and suggests a prenatal component of sexual differentiation in both sexes.

While it is generally accepted that androgen is necessary for differentiation of the male brain, nothing is known about the steroid requirements, if any, for the normal development of the female brain. The prevailing dogma generally holds that androgen alone is the determining factor, feminization being viewed as emerging passively in the absence of such hormonal induction and to represent the expression of the brain's presumed intrinsic or unmodified pattern of neural organization. It is generally assumed that the neonatal female rodent brain is protected from excessive estrogenization (i.e., masculinization), by the high perinatal levels of maternal estrogens through extracellular sequestration by binding to α-fetoprotein (AFP), the high-affinity estrogen-binding plasma protein of the developing rodent (13,14). Testosterone, on the other hand, with no such affinity for AFP, remains free to exert its effects.

POSSIBLE MODES OF STEROID ACTION

The fundamental biochemical processes by which androgen mediates its irreversible effects are not fully known. Considerable evidence, however, has accumulated to suggest that its initial mode of action may involve local intraneuronal conversion through aromatization to estradiol-17β in such target regions as the hypothalamus, the preoptic area (POA), and the amygdala (15–18). These are regions of the brain which have all been implicated in the neural control of reproductive function and behavior (see 19, for review) and which contain both high-affinity, distinct androgen-, and estrogen-binding macromolecules ("receptors"), as shown by ^{3}H-steroid autoradiography (20,21) and by receptor assay (13,22–28), as well as high levels of aromatizing enzymes (18). A variety of different experiments in the rodent have suggested that local conversion of testosterone to estradiol-

17β and subsequent binding of estradiol to putative receptors may be requisite events for the initiation of masculinization of the brain. The importance of estradiol has been shown in a number of ways. Intrahypothalamic implants of testosterone or estradiol have been found to be equally effective in eliciting masculinization of reproductive function (29). The nonaromatizable androgens such as 5α-dihydrotestosterone (DHT), on the other hand, appear to be ineffective (30,31) or only partially so (32). Testosterone-induced (33–35) and estrogen-induced (36) masculinization can be blocked by anti-estrogens which compete with estradiol for the receptor sites. The masculinizing effects of both endogenous and exogenous testosterone, furthermore, have been attenuated by aromatizing enzyme inhibitors (34,35,37,38).

SEXUAL DIMORPHISM OF BRAIN STRUCTURE

The permanent and irreversible nature of the steroidal effects and their mediation by receptors has suggested that androgen may influence the structural organization of the CNS through alterations in neuronal genomic expression. Since steroid effects are believed to be mediated through specific receptors, however, their primary action, rather, may be at the molecular level, altering responsiveness to afferent inputs perhaps through modulations of the levels of enzymes controlling synaptic transmission (39) or by alterations in membrane properties. A critical and as yet unresolved issue, therefore, is whether or not the gonadal steroids can induce meaningful structural changes in the neural substrate as a result of cellular interations. That the gonadal hormones may induce morphological changes in the CNS of many species has been supported by increasingly numerous examples of steroid-dependent, structural dimorphism in such physiologically significant, steroid receptor-containing regions of the adult brain as the hypothalamus, the POA, and the amygdala. The morphological consequences of exposure to steroid are summarized in Table 1.

Although the precise sexually dimorphic function subserved by these morphological differences in mammals is unknown, with the single exception perhaps of the dimorphic motoneuron nucleus of the rat spinal cord (40), which is involved in penile motor function, inferential evidence based on the cytological nature of the differences has led to the hypothesis that gender-specific differences in neural connectivity or circuitry, perhaps at the local level, may form the substrate for sexual differentiation. Despite such demonstrations of neural plasticity and reorganization of neuropil, the morphological

TABLE I
Steroid-Dependent Sexual Dimorphism in the CNS

• NEURONAL NUCLEAR, NUCLEOLAR, and SOMAL SIZE	Preoptic Area	rat
	Ventromedial N. Amygdala	monkey
	Telencephalic Song NN.	songbird
• NEURONAL ORGANELLES	Arcuate N. Suprachiasmatic N.	rat
	Preoptic Area	hamster
• SYNAPTIC VESICLES SYNAPTIC TERMINALS	Arcuate N.	rat
• SYNAPTIC ORGANIZATION	Preoptic Area Arcuate N.	rat
• DENDRITIC SPINES	Hippocampus	mouse
	Telencephalic Song NN.	songbird
• DENDRITIC BRANCHING PATTERNS	Preoptic Area Suprachiasmatic N.	hamster
	Telencephalic Song NN.	songbird
• VOLUME BRAIN NUCLEUS	Telencephalic Song NN.	songbird
	Preoptic Area Spinal Cord	rat

differences merely represent the final results of the steroidal effects. They tell little about the underlying cellular mechanisms which produced them.

GONADAL HORMONES AND BRAIN DEVELOPMENT
IN VITRO

In tissue culture studies designed to elucidate some aspects of these problems, I have been studying the role of the gonadal steroids in the differentiation and development of the newborn mouse hypothalamus and preoptic area. This is an approach to investigating the cellular aspects that may underlie the developmental responses to these hormones during the process of sexual differentiation.

Estradiol-17β and testosterone both induce an accelerated and progressively intense selective proliferation of neuronal processes (neurites) from specific regions of the hypothalamus/preoptic area *in vitro*. The response is most marked in the POA and infundibular/ventral premamillary regions (Fig. 2) (41) and is characterized in its extreme by the formation of extensive neuritic arborizations or plexuses of very fine fibers. There is a strong correlation between the pattern and regional localization of this response and the presence and topo-

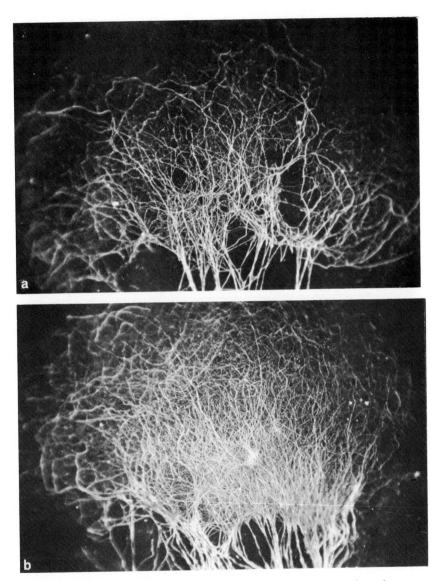

Fig. 2. Morphological concomitant of a dose–response effect in an homologous explant pair from the POA 13 days *in vitro*. The surface area covered does not differ significantly but the differences in neuritic density are striking, suggesting steroidal induction of branching. (a) Control (normal horse serum, estradiol ~200 pg/ml; (b) estradiol 100 ng/ml and normal serum. Holmes', darkfield (× 25). [Reprinted by permission from *Brain Research* (41).]

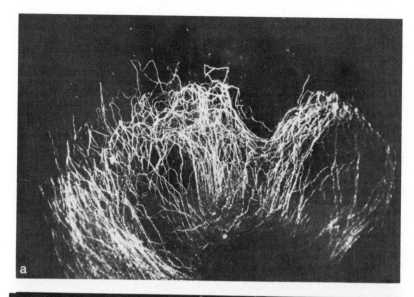

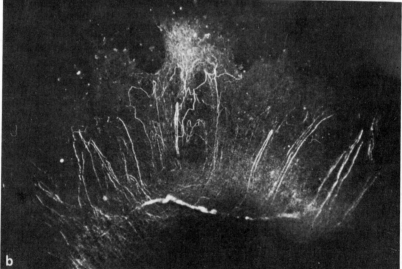

Fig. 3. The importance of estradiol per se. Homologous pair of explants from the POA, 22 days *in vitro*, exposed to normal serum containing either (a) antibodies to BSA or (b) antibodies to estradiol-17β/BSA. Note the striking reduction in neuritic outgrowth following physiological inactivation of the estradiol. Holmes', darkfield (× 15.8). [Reprinted by permission from *Brain Research* (41).]

graphic distribution of nuclear receptors for estradiol or its metabolites as shown by [³H]estradiol autoradiography (42). The topography of the labeled cells is similar to that seen in the developing rat (20) and mouse (43); namely, the bed nucleus of the stria terminalis, the medial POA, and the arcuate, the ventromedial, and the ventral premamillary nuclei of the hypothalamus. Localized areas of steroid responsive neuritic proliferation appear to emanate from regions containing labeled cells. Nonresponsive regions such as the anterior hypothalamus contain isolated or no labeled cells. The pattern of the response and its regional localization suggest induction of neuritic branching perhaps only in neurons containing the steroid receptor.

The developmental importance and specificity of estradiol is emphasized by the demonstration (41,44) that reducing the availability of the steroid to the cultures by pretreating the serum component of the nutrient medium by physical or immunochemical means or with an anti-estrogen (CI-628), which competes with estradiol for the receptor, elicits a reduction and retardation of neuritic outgrowth (Fig. 3) only in those regions previously shown to be responsive to steroid. This and the apparent failure of testosterone alone (41) to elicit the neuritic response has led to the hypothesis that in the rodent of both sexes, neurons may require an intracellular source of estradiol of non-androgen origin for the induction of *both* male and female patterns of sexual differentiation.

POSSIBLE BASIS FOR SEXUAL DIFFERENTIATION

These *in vitro* observations suggest that regions containing estrogen receptors respond to varying levels of estrogen by variations in the rate and extent of the growth of their neurites. This suggests that steroidal influences on neuritic growth patterns may play a role in the neurogenesis of sexual differentiation by so influencing the dendritic development and synaptic distribution of target neurons as to result in fundamentally different, gender-specific patterns of neural circuit organization.

The numerous reported examples of the sexually dimorphic cytological features of the adult brain shown in Table I may be viewed, perhaps, as the ultimate morphogenetic consequence of the steroid-induced differences in neuronal development and neuritic interactions. The trophic effects of steroids, particularly those of estradiol, could thus influence significantly not only the patterning of developing target neural circuits, but the cytological aspects of their component cellular constituents as well.

The tissue culture studies also suggest that the absence of androgen imprinting may not be sufficient for the emergence of the female pattern of neural organization. Masculine and feminine patterns may *both* require active induction by estrogen.

The question thus arises as to the possible source of such estrogen. As mentioned above the developing female rodent brain is generally assumed to be protected from the high, perinatal levels of estrogen by extracellular sequestration of estradiol through binding to AFP (14). AFP is present in milligram levels throughout development, a concentration calculated as sufficient to bind all available circulating estradiol (45). The extent to which functional inactivation occurs however, is not really known. This is particularly important in view of the fact that it has been shown that steroids covalently linked to steroid-binding proteins retain the ability to react with their receptors (46).

THE POSSIBLE ROLE OF α-FETOPROTEIN

In this regard some additional autoradiographic findings in the cultures may be pertinent. A number of cells exhibited the estradiol label in the cytoplasm and *not* in the nucleus (42). While this discrete and unusual localization may represent a normally present class of cytoplasmic receptors, an intriguing possibility is that it may also represent estradiol binding to intraneuronal AFP. Several studies have shown an intracellular pool of AFP of unknown functional significance in soluble extracts of fetal and neonatal rats (14) and mice (47). Its intraneuronal localization has been confirmed within the central and peripheral nervous systems of the developing rat (48,49) and human fetus (50) by immunoperoxidase cytochemistry.

In some of my recent experiments (51) the first evidence for the widespread intraneuronal localization and coexistence of immunoreactive plasma proteins, AFP, albumin, and transferrin within the same neurons of the late fetal and postnatal mouse brain but not of the adult has been found by combined direct and indirect, double label immunofluorescence cytochemistry (Fig. 4).

The intraneuronal localization and coexistence of AFP and albumin, both of which are estrophilic, may have profound implications for the process of sexual differentiation of the brain. Their intracellular presence, during development only, forces one to reconsider the extent to which the developing brain is actually protected from expo-

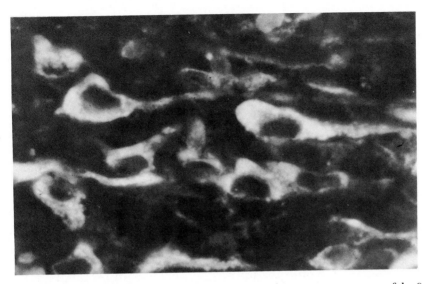

Fig. 4. Immunofluorescent localization of mouse α-fetoprotein in neurons of the 8-day-old female mouse mid-brain ($\times$ 200).

sure to maternal estrogens by the extracellular AFP (14). On the contrary, neuronal uptake, perhaps by endocytosis, of such estrogen-binding proteins as AFP and albumin must bring estradiol *into* the cell. There is, moreover, a difference of several orders of magnitude [K_d AFP 10^{-8} M; estradiol 10^{-10-11} M; (52)] between the affinity constants for the binding of estradiol by AFP and by its receptor. Intracellular dissociation of the plasma protein–estradiol complexes consequent to the greater affinity of estradiol for its receptor could thus liberate the steroid for subsequent nuclear translocation. Such a mechanism might thus provide certain neurons of both sexes with the intracellular source of estradiol of nonandrogen origin referred to above. These observations also suggest that these plasma proteins may have an important role as mediators or modulators of the intraneuronal transport of steroids and other bound growth-promoting substances into the developing brain.

This question, furthermore, becomes increasingly interesting and the problem compounded, however, if one looks at the topographic distribution of the AFP and albumin immunoreactivity. Localization and coexistence of these plasma proteins (as well as transferrin) was observed in cell groups throughout the brains of both sexes and appeared to be limited to neurons only. AFP-, albumin-, and transferrin-containing neurons were widely distributed throughout the cerebral cortex, septum, basal ganglia, hippocampus, hypothalamus, brain stem, cerebellum, and medulla. The numbers of labeled neurons in any given region increased with its development. In the hypothalamus, preoptic area, and the amygdala, however, certain nuclear regions, known to contain estradiol-concentrating cells by [³H]estradiol autoradiography, were rendered anatomically distinctive by the complete or almost complete and bilaterally symmetrical absence of fluorescence (51,53). These regions include the medial preoptic area, the suprachiasmatic, the arcuate, the ventromedial, and the ventral premamillary nuclei of the hypothalamus, and the medial and cortical amygdaloid nuclei. The significance of these observations is unknown. It is unlikely that it is artifactual since it has been repeatedly observed in both sexes of different ages as well as in the newborn rat. The topographic distribution of the absence of fluorescence by its association with presumed target regions of estrogen during the critical period for sexual differentiation raises intriguing questions not only regarding the possible multiplicity of functions of estradiol-binding proteins but about such aspects as selective uptake and metabolism, and possible local synthesis as well.

SEXUAL DIFFERENTIATION OF THE MALE AND FEMALE BRAIN

Although the female neural phenotype is assumed to result normally from a female genotype *and* the absence of androgen exposure, the tissue culture and AFP studies suggest, on the contrary, a mechanism by which estradiol per se could exert a positive developmental and feminizing action on the CNS. As summarized in Fig. 5, in the genetic female or neonatally castrated male, exposure of the brain to the very low trophic levels of estradiol, originating perhaps from the intracellular dissociation of the plasma protein–estradiol complexes, may result in a given pattern of neural organization. Intraneuronal aromatization of testosterone to estradiol could, on the other hand, produce a more localized and concentrated effect and the resultant synergistic or additive stimulus to neuritic development might induce a different or what would be termed male pattern of neural differentiation.

The importance of estradiol to neuritic development *in vitro* may have relevance for the *in vivo* state. This is suggested by a number of recent observations, which demonstrate a steroid-induced trophic enhancement of dendritic differentiation, neuritic proliferation and of synaptogenesis in the arcuate nucleus of the hypothalamus of the neonatally treated female rat (54,55) and mouse (56), in the deaf-

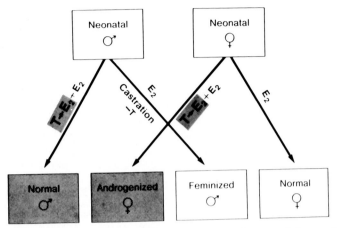

Fig. 5. Proposed view of sexual differentiation of the brain and the need for both estrogen and androgen.

ferented arcuate nucleus of the adult female rat (57), and in the steroid receptor-containing telencephalic regions of the songbird brain (58,59).

None of this, however, is meant to imply that testosterone per se, as well as the nonaromatizable androgens may not also exert an as-yet-unknown pre- and/or postnatal influence of their own. Putative androgen receptors have been detected in the hypothalamus, the preoptic area, and the cerebellum of embryonic and neonatal rats and mice (21,28,60,61) of both sexes, and confirmed, in a sense, by the reduced binding noted in the androgen-insensitive, *Tfm* mutant mouse (60,61).

Finally, whether this response to estradiol is solely related to the process of sexual differentiation or whether it represents, rather, a general requirement of neurons at specific or critical developmental stages is unknown. The extensive distribution of the AFP-and albumin-containing neurons, shown by immunofluroescence in regions containing few or no estradiol receptors, makes it unlikely that estradiol effects in such cells could be mediated by classical receptors. The possibility that estrogen could here exert nonreceptor-mediated membrane or other effects should, however, be at least considered.

ACKNOWLEDGMENTS

The skilled technical assistance of Mr. Hubert Cummins, Mrs. Myrna Retino, and Mr. Manuel Urena is gratefully acknowledged in various aspects of the author's investigations. The author's research was supported in part by the National Institutes of Health (HD-08364); the National Science Foundation (BNS 77-0859); the March of

Dimes Birth Defects Foundation; the W. T. Grant Foundation; and a National Institute of Mental Health Research Scientist Development Award (MH-00192) and by institutional funds from the Rockefeller Foundation and the Mellon Foundation.

REFERENCES

1. Gorski, R. A. (1973) *Prog. Brain Res.* **39**, 149–163.
2. Toran-Allerand, C. D. (1978) *Am. Zool.* **18**, 553–565.
3. Barraclough, C. A., and Gorski, R. A. (1961) *Endocrinology* **68**, 68–79.
4. Barraclough, C. A. (1967) *In* "Neuroendocrinology" (L. Martini and W. F. Ganong, eds.), Vol. 2, pp. 61–99. Academic Press, New York.
5. Gladue, B. A., and Clemens, L. G. (1978) *Endocrinology* **103**, 1702–1709.
6. Clemens, L. G., Gladue, B. A., and Coniglio, L. P. (1978) *Horm. Behav.* **10**, 40–53.
7. Weisz, J., and Ward, I. L. (1980) *Endocrinology* **106**, 306–316.
8. Gandleman, R., VomSaal, F. S., and Reinish, J. M. (1977) *Nature (London)* **266**, 722–724.
9. Clemens, L. G., and Coniglio, L. P. (1971) *Am. Zool.* **11**, 617.
10. VomSaal, F. S., and Bronson, F. H. (1980) *Science* **208**, 597–599.
11. Nadler, R. (1969) *Horm. Behav.* **1**, 53–64.
12. Ward, I. L., and Renz, F. J. (1972) *J. Comp. Physiol. Psychol.* **78**, 349–355.
13. MacLusky, N. J., Chaptal, C., and McEwen, B. S. (1979) *Brain Res.* **178**, 129–142.
14. McEwen, B. S., Plapinger, L., Chaptal, J., and Wallach, G. (1975) *Brain Res.* **96**, 400–407.
15. Naftolin, F., Ryan, K. J., and Petro, Z. (1971) *J. Clin. Endocrinol. Metab.* **33**, 368–370.
16. Weisz, J., and Gibbs, C. (1974) *Neuroendocrinology* **14**, 72–86.
17. Reddy, V. V. R., Naftolin, F., and Ryan, K. J. (1974) *Endocrinology* **94**, 117–121.
18. Lieberburg, I., and McEwen, B. S. (1975) *Brain Res.* **85**, 165–170.
19. McEwen, B. S., Davis, P. G., Parson, B., and Pfaff, D. W. (1979) *Annu. Rev. Neurosci.* **2**, 65–112.
20. Sheridan, P. J., Sar, M., and Stumpf, W. E. (1974) *Endocrinology* **93**, 1386–1390.
21. Sheridan, P. J., Sar, M., and Stumpf, W. E. (1974) *Am. J. Anat.* **140**, 589–593.
22. Barley, J., Ginsburg, M., Greenstein, B. D., MacLusky, N. J., and Thomas, P. J. (1974) *Nature (London)* **252**, 259–260.
23. MacLusky, N. J., Chaptal, C., Lieberburg, I., and McEwen, B. S. (1976) *Brain Res.* **114**, 158–165.
24. Attardi, B., and Ohno, S. (1976) *Endocrinology* **99**, 1279–1290.
25. Westley, B. R., and Salaman, D. F. (1977) *Brain Res.* **119**, 375–388.
26. MacLusky, N. J., Lieberburg, I., and McEwen, B. S. (1979) *Brain Res.* **178**, 143–160.
27. Vito, C. C., and Fox, T. O. (1979) *Science* **204**, 517–519.
28. Vito, C. C., Wieland, S. J., and Fox, T. O. (1979) *Nature (London)* **282**, 308–310.
29. Christensen, L. W., and Gorski, R. A. (1978) *Brain Res.* **146**, 325–340.
30. Luttge, W. G., and Whalen, R. E. (1970) *Horm. Behav.* **1**, 265–281.
31. McDonald, P. G., and Doughty, C. (1974) *J. Endocrinol.* **61**, 95–103.
32. Gerall, A. A., McMurray, M. M., and Farrell, A. (1975) *J. Endocrinol.* **67**, 439–445.
33. Doughty, C., and McDonald, P. G. (1974) *Differentiation* **2**, 275–285.
34. McEwen, B. S., Lieberburg, I., and Krey, L. C. (1977) *Horm. Behav.* **9**, 249–263.

35. Vreeburg, J. T. M., van der Vaart, P. D. M., and van der Schoot, P. (1977) *J. Endocrinol.* **74**, 375–382.
36. Doughty, C., Booth, J. E., McDonald, P. G., and Parrott, R. F. (1975) *J. Endocrinol.* **67**, 459–460.
37. Booth, J. E. (1977) *J. Endocrinol.* **72**, 53–54.
38. Lieberburg, I., Wallach, G., and McEwen, B. S. (1977) *Brain Res.* **128**, 176–181.
39. Luine, V. N., Khylschevskaya, R. I., and McEwen, B. S. (1975) *Brain Res.* **86**, 293–306.
40. Breedlove, S. M., and Arnold, A. P. (1979) *Neurosci. Abstr.* **5**, 1479.
41. Toran-Allerand, C. D. (1980) *Brain Res.* **189**, 413–427.
42. Toran-Allerand, C. D., Gerlach, J. L., and McEwen, B. S. (1980) *Brain Res.* **184**, 517–522.
43. Stumpf, W. E., Narbaitz, R., and Sar, M. (1980) *J. Steroid Biochem.* **12**, 55–64.
44. Toran-Allerand, C. D. (1976) *Brain Res.* **106**, 407–412.
45. Ruoslahti, E., and Seppälä, M. (1979) *Adv. Cancer Res.* **29**, 275–346.
46. Rao, B. R., Patrick, T. B., and Sweet, F. (1980) *Endocrinology* **106**, 356–362.
47. Attardi, B., and Ruoslahti, E. (1976) *Nature (London)* **263**, 685–687.
48. Benno, R. H., and Williams, T. H. (1978) *Brain Res.* **142**, 182–186.
49. Trojan, J., and Uriel, J. (1979) *C. R. Hebd. Seances Acad. Sci., Ser. D* **289**, 1157–1160.
50. Mollgard, K., Jacobsen, M., Jacobsen, G. K., Clausen, P. P., and Saunder, N. R. (1979) *Neurosci. Lett.* **14**, 85–90.
51. Toran-Allerand, C. D. (1980) *Nature (London)* **286**, 733–735.
52. Linkie, D. M., and LaBarbera, A. R. (1979) *Life Sci.* **25**, 1665–1674.
53. Toran-Allerand, C. D. (1980) *Neurosci. Abstr.* **6**, 381.
54. Matsumoto, A., and Arai, Y. (1976) *Neurosci. Lett.* **2**, 79–82.
55. Arai, Y., and Matsumoto, A. (1978) *Psychoneuroendocrinology* **3**, 31–45.
56. Nichizuka, M. (1978) *Brain Res.* **31**, 31–40.
57. Matsumoto, A., and Arai, Y. (1979) *Cell Tissue Res.* **198**, 427–433.
58. Nottebohm, F., and Arnold, A. P. (1976) *Science* **194**, 211–213.
59. Gurney, M. E., and Konishi, M. (1980) *Science* **208**, 1380–1382.
60. Fox, T. O. (1975) *Proc. Natl. Acad. Sci. U. S. A.* **72**, 4303–4307.
61. Fox, T. O. (1977) *Brain Res.* **128**, 263–273.

An Experimental Approach to Female Mammalian Meiosis: Differential Chromosome Labeling and an Analysis of Chiasmata in the Female Mouse

PAUL E. POLANI, JOHN A. CROLLA, AND
MARY J. SELLER
Paediatric Research Unit
The Prince Philip Research Laboratories
Guy's Hospital Medical School
University of London
London, England

The genetically more important events of meiosis—namely, those related to synapsis of homologous chromosomes, crossing over, and recombination of linked genes, including gene conversion and chiasma formation—take place during the meiotic prophase. This process, in most female mammals, occurs solely, or almost solely, during embryonic life (1–5) in keeping with Waldeyer's "dogma."

The driving forces behind the embryonic initiation of female meiosis seem to reside partly in the chromosomal and genic constitution of the germ cells themselves, and partly (and probably more importantly) in environmental epigenetic controlling influences related to the architecture of the gonad (which is, of course, under genetic control) and in short range chemical stimuli derived from paragonadal embryonic tissues (6–8).

It is clear that experimental work on female mammalian meiosis aimed, for example, at studying its controlling mechanisms or at altering, say, the physical and chemical circumstances within which the essential steps of the meiotic prophase take place, must be directed at

59

BIOREGULATORS OF REPRODUCTION
Copyright © 1981 by Academic Press, Inc.
All rights of reproduction in any form reserved.
ISBN 0-12-379980-5

the ovary during early embryonic development *in utero*. However, the situation poses difficult methodological problems, and creates serious constraints on experimental procedures, because of the interaction of these procedures with the mother, the placenta, and the fetus, with their own metabolic activities and their ability to act as barriers and screens that are difficult or impossible to quantify.

In the light of these considerations, we decided to develop a technique of *in vitro* maturation of the fetal ovary so that we should be in a position to exercise a direct influence on the meiotic prophase. As one of our first objectives was a study of chiasmata and their detailed relationship to crossing over, we had to ensure that the embryonic ovary grown *in vitro* could then be made to mature *in vivo*. We planned to obtain, in this way, oocytes at first or second meiotic divisions, the chromosomes of which might be studied in detail. To these ends we (9) adopted and extended a technique originally described by Blandau *et al.* (10), Rumery *et al.* (11), and Rumery and Blandau (12) of *in vitro* culture and subsequent transplantation of embryonic ovaries. For a number of practical and theoretical reasons the mouse was the experimental animal selected.

The technique will be described and examined in detail, and its usefulness will be exemplified by work we have done using bromodeoxyuridine (BUdR) to label meiotic chromosomes for studies on chiasmata and crossing over. The BUdR technique was first introduced by Zakharov and Egolina (13). They found that bifilary substitution of chromosomal thymidine by BUdR through two rounds of DNA synthesis diminished the staining affinity of chromosomes and could, therefore, result in differentiation of the two chromatids, one with monofilary and the other with bifilary substitution. The technique was improved by Latt (14), who used the fluorescent dye Hoechst 33258, and by Perry and Wolff (15), who produced "harlequin" chromosomes by subsequent Giemsa staining (fluorescence plus Giemsa, or FPG technique). Others contributed to further developments and to applications of the technique, for example, Kato (16) [see review by Wolff (17)].

It is obvious that the technique is a very discriminative tool for studies of chromatid exchanges, and many workers on experimental meiosis must have thought of applying it to investigate chiasmata and crossing over. Though we developed our *in vitro/in vivo* technique of female meiosis largely to this end, we had in mind other work on chiasmata, to include, for example, the effects of physical and chemical agents on their formation and maintenance, and thus an attack on problems related to the mechanical function of chiasmata and, therefore, on nondisjunction. Many other problems related to mammalian meiosis, more specifically to female meiosis, could be handled.

MATERIALS AND TECHNIQUES

ANIMALS

1. A Strong closed colony random-bred.
2. CBA/H-T6T6 inbred (brother–sister matings).
3. Congenic mice (supplied by Medical Research Council Laboratory Animals Centre, Carshalton, Surrey): C3H/He agouti, wild type at the albino locus and C3H/He albino (cc) obtained by breeding the C3H/He agouti (CC) inbred mice to the inbred ICFW albino (cc) strain, thus incorporating into the former the albino locus from the latter (18). Both the agouti and the albino animals are maintained by brother–sister mating.

FETAL OVARY CULTURE TECHNIQUE

60 mm plastic petri dishes were used, containing a strip of bacto-agar, partially immersed in nutrient medium with the following composition: HAM F10 (Gibco Biocult) with 20% donor calf serum, plus L-glutamine (added prior to use) and penicillin and streptomycin. Strips of agar in the culture dishes were preconditioned in the medium for at least 12 hours before use.

Fetal mouse ovaries were set up in organ culture on the agar strips. The day of gestation was calculated by calling the day on which a plug was first seen d 1, or alternatively, d 0, and hereafter the double notation will be used. For labeling experiments, e.g., after BUdR, the ovaries were removed from the agar strips, mostly after 24 hours, and placed on fresh agar in dishes preconditioned in complete medium. For ovaries explanted on d 14 (d 13), the total culture time *in vitro* was 8 d (d of setting-up = 0), changing medium once, or occasionally twice, during this period.

The cultures were incubated at 37°C in humidified incubators, in 5% CO_2 in air. To the basic medium were added, as required, BUdR, either cold or tritium-labeled ([³H]BUdR), or tritiated thymidine ([³H]TdR). Together with BUdR we often used deoxycytidine (dC), which is alleged to diminish the toxicity of BUdR (19,20), and strict light precautions were taken at all stages of culture, during transplantation and metaphase preparation.

[^{3}H]BUdR and [^{3}H]TdR (Radiochemical Centre, Amersham, Buckinghamshire) had specific activities of 0.5 Ci mM^{-1}. The former was used in concentrations of 0.05 μCi ml^{-1} of culture medium ($\approx$30 ng BUdR ml^{-1}). The latter was used at the concentration of 1 μCi ml^{-1} in some experiments, but in others in concentrations ranging from this to 1 pCi ml^{-1}. Cold BUdR (Sigma) was used at a concentration of 6.5 nM ml^{-1} (2 μg ml^{-1}) and dC at a concentration of 3 nM ml^{-1} (0.68 μg ml^{-1}).

OVARIAN TRANSPLANTS

Heterotopic. Under ether anesthesia the *in vitro* grown ovaries were transplanted (generally in pairs) under the left kidney capsule of young adult females spayed 2 to 3 weeks beforehand. The ovaries were removed, ova harvested, and metaphases processed, after 19 days (day of transplant = 0). These transplants were mostly of A ovaries into CBA recipients.

Orthotopic. The procedure was essentially that outlined by Jones and Krohn (21). The recipients were spayed at the time of transplant by right ovariectomy with tubal ligation, while the left ovary was removed from its bursa, paying special attention to hemostasis, and the transplant(s) matured *in vitro* put in its place. This procedure was used for (major) histocompatible and for congenic transplants (agouti ovary into albino recipient).

METAPHASE AND PROPHASE PREPARATIONS AND STAINING

Ova were collected, prepared, and routinely stained according to techniques previously described (22). Preparations of prophase oocytes were obtained by placing the ovaries in 0.7% sodium citrate for not less than 35 minutes at room temperature (diplotenes were better spread after incubation at 37°C). After rapid removal of citrate solution in 3:1 ethanol/acetic acid fixative on a microscope slide, the tissue was kept for 20 to 40 seconds in 45% acetic acid and dissociated mechanically; within 90 seconds the resulting cell suspension was spread over the center of the slide and about 3 to 4 small droplets of fixative were immediately dropped from a height of 5 to 6 cm. Time was allowed between drops for the fixative to evaporate almost completely. Gentle blowing on the slide or, after the last drop, waving it, helped more rapid evaporation of fixative and better spreading of cells.

After BUdR incorporation the cells were stained in Hoechst 33258 (Farbwerke Hoechst Ag., Frankfurt (M)), benzimidazole dye prepared from a 10 μg l^{-1} stock solution with 2% KCl and diluted at the time of use one part in 100 with 2% KCl (final concentration of dye 0.1 μg ml^{-1}). After staining for 10 minutes and rinsing in 2% KCl the preparation was mounted temporarily in 2% KCl and examined by fluorescence microscopy. Subsequently, after exposure to daylight for 24 hours to 3 days (depending on weather), the cells were stained in 10% Giemsa solution (Gurr: Hopkin and Williams, Chadwell Heath, Essex), washed in phosphate buffer at pH 6.8 (same suppliers) for 10–15 minutes, checked for staining quality, and, if this was satisfactory, the preparation was passed through xylol and mounted in Xam.

AUTORADIOGRAPHY

Standard techniques were adopted, using Kodak fine grain autoradiographic stripping Plate AR10, Kodak D19 Developer (powder, made up in distilled water as per manufacturer's instructions), and Kodak Rapid Fixer solution A (prepared as 1 part of fixative to 3 of water). The floating solution consisted of 40 g sucrose and 0.02 g KBr (both Analar reagents quality), prepared with 2 liters of distilled water immediately before use. Autoradiographic exposure following [^{3}H]BUdR was 6 weeks. For [^{3}H]TdR the exposure time varied between 2 weeks for high, and 6–8 weeks for low radioactivity.

HISTOLOGY

Whole ovaries (either post-culture or post-transplant) were fixed at once in buffered glutaraldehyde for 4 hours, at room temperature, or overnight. After washing in phosphate buffer with glucose at pH 7.4, the specimens were post-fixed in osmium tetroxide for 1 hour. They were then dehydrated through graded ethyl alcohol solutions (10% to absolute, 20 minutes in each) and placed in propylene oxide (2 changes, 15 minutes each). Subsequently they were put in equal volumes of the oxide and of resin for $2\frac{1}{2}$ hours at room temperature. After a change in resin, they were embedded in neat resin and incubated at 60°C overnight. Sections were cut at 2 μm and stained in toluidine blue, methylene blue, or paragon.

RESULTS

TECHNICAL

Three sets of *heterotopic "heterochronic" transplant* experiments were carried out, in which *in vitro* matured embryonic ovaries were transplanted under the kidney capsule of previously spayed young adult females: CBA into CBA, A into CBA, and A into A.

In general, successful explants were characterized by a growth of the embryonic ovary *in vitro* which, for example, over a period of about 8 days when the explant was on day 14 (d 13) of gestation, was well comparable to the *in vivo* growth rate between the age at which explantation was carried out and term. Histologically the germ cells had mostly reached the dictyate stage (Fig. 1). In many ways the histological findings are comparable to those of Blandau and Odor (23).

The meiotic metaphases (M I and M II) obtained after transplantation and *in vitro* maturation were of as high quality as those that could be obtained *in vivo* (Fig. 2). Most of them were M I, as we aimed our

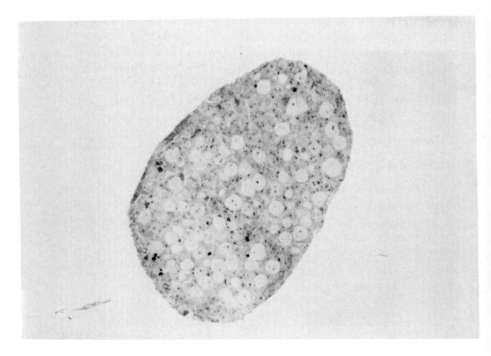

Fig. 1.   A fetal ovary (× 140), matured *in vitro* from d 14 (d 13) for 8 days (see text).

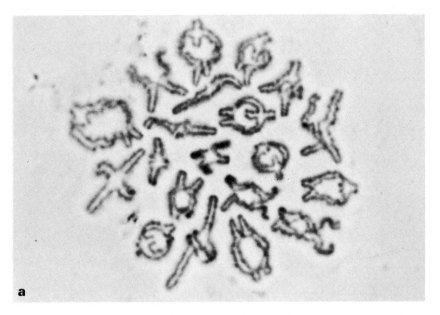

Fig. 2a. First meiotic metaphase ($n = 20$) from a primary oocyte of an ovary matured *in vitro* at the embryonic stage and transferred heterotopically to a spayed female ($\times 800$).

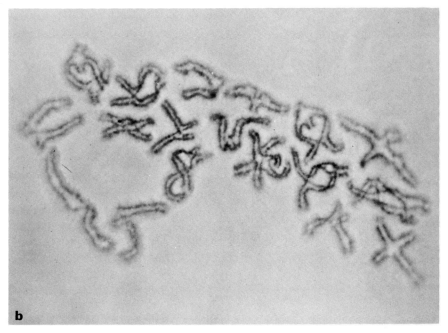

Fig. 2b. Incomplete oocyte ($n = 19$) obtained in the same way. The missing chromosome was out of the field of view ($\times 1200$).

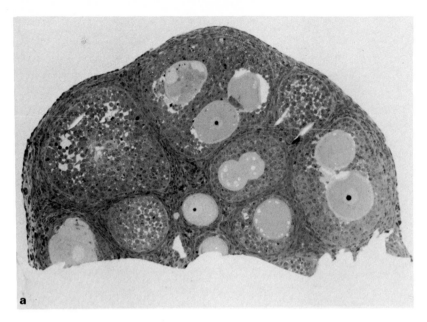

Fig. 3a. An ovary (× 125) grown *in vitro* from d 14 (d 13) for 8 days, and subsequently transplanted orthotopically and removed after 28 days (see text).

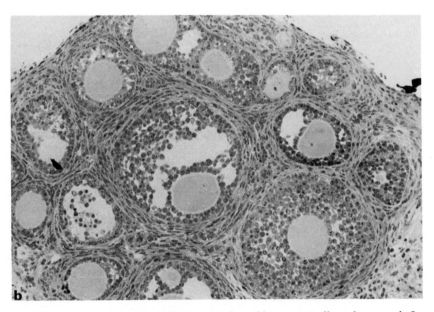

Fig. 3b. A similar ovary (× 125), but transplanted heterotopically and removed after 19 days. Figures 3a and 3b show numerous, mainly Graafian, follicles.

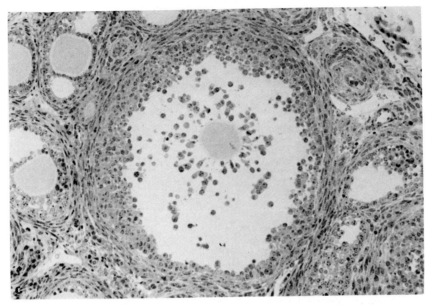

Fig. 3c. A single Graafian follicle (× 125) from a heterotopically matured ovary, showing the oocyte with a first meiotic metaphase plate at 4 o'clock (for fixation, etc., see Techniques).

technique at obtaining these cells. In a few instances the heterotopically transplanted ovaries released spontaneously primary oocytes with their germinal vesicle broken down (Fig. 3C), or even with a polar body, and from these we obtained M II.

While all of the first and last groups of transplants (Table I) were successful, the success rate was approximately four out of every five for the group A into CBA, in which the donor tissue differed from that of the recipient at the major histocompatibility locus [where the difference is a recombinational one (24)] and at least at some minor loci (25). The problem of the relatively good survival ability of histoincompatible endocrine grafts is discussed by Krohn (26,27).

In the three sets of transplants the proportions of mature ova per transplant (namely, ova without follicular cells or with a few such cells unevenly and incompletely surrounding the oocyte) were appreciably different, but the proportions of metaphases obtained from them were fairly uniform, and around 40%. The yield of meiotic metaphases per transplant was highest in the A into A, and lowest in the CBA into CBA, groups. The results also show that the production of metaphases is not as favorable in the *in vitro/in vivo* system as it is under more

TABLE I
Heterotopic Transplants of *in Vitro* Matured Ovaries[a]

In vitro ovary/spayed female	Transplants		"Mature" ova		Metaphases		
	Total	Successful	Total	Per successful transplant	Total	Per successful transplant	Per 100 ova
CBA/CBA	6	6	46	7.7	16	2.7	34.8
A/CBA	23	19	497	26.2	207	10.9	41.6
A/A	3	3	95	31.6	37	12.3	38.9
In vivo controls: A	9	—	326	36.2	154	17.1	47.2

[a] Usually ovaries were transplanted in pairs, and almost all metaphases were M I (see text).

natural circumstances *in vivo*, although the differences are not great. In the *in vivo* A controls the yield for 9 animals was an average of 17.1 metaphases per pair of ovaries. However, a small number of *in vivo* CBA controls yielded far fewer metaphases.

The *in vitro* matured ovaries were also transplanted orthotopically. Successful orthotopic ovarian transplantation [see Woodruff (28)] was first achieved by Robertson (29,30) in the mouse because of its favorable anatomy, and the original technique (31) was modified by Jones and Krohn [21; see Krohn (32)] and was used here.

It is clear that attempts to extrapolate the results of *in vitro* experiments to an *in vivo* situation rest on the quality of the germ cells in the experimental situation: its best estimate is their fertilizability as shown by the production of offspring. Of the possible ways, this is most naturally done if the ovaries are transplanted orthotopically, and the transplant is tested by mating its recipient.

We conducted three sets of experiments, using unilateral orthotopic transplantation of fetal ovaries grown *in vitro* from day 14 (d 13) for 8 days immediately after (bilateral) spaying. When we transplanted orthotopically nonsyngeneic ovaries (A into CBA, as in our original experiments), we were unable to mate the recipients successfully, due to the transient nature of the ovarian transplant [for a discussion on the ovarian bursa or "capsule" as a "privileged site", see Krohn (26)]. We then transplanted A ovaries into A spayed recipients. To date seven A strain animals have had *in vitro* matured embryonic A ovaries transplanted into the left ovarian bursa. The bursal cavity is considerably larger than the transplanted "fetal" ovaries, so that on all occasions we transplanted two or three ovaries. On two occasions we assessed the potential of a variant technique, where the ovaries were first grown heterotopically under the kidney capsule for 19 days and subsequently transplanted to the ovarian site. Although in this way the transplanted ovaries fit the vacant bursa much more closely, the technique did not seem to offer other advantages over straight transplantation, and is, of course, more laborious.

All nine grafts were judged to be successful, although the only measure of success at this stage was the external vaginal appearance and mating behaviour. Successful orthotopic grafts matured very well, and showed plentiful primordial and Graafian follicles, about 3 to 4 weeks after transplantation (Fig. 3A). Heterotopic grafts also allowed good ovarian follicle maturation (Fig. 3B) to take place, and showed no evidence of graft rejection, even between histoincompatible mouse strains.

Orthotopically grafted females were put to young adult males of the same strain. Nine of these showed plugs, and four of the latter produced one liveborn litter each. One female produced two stillborn litters, with two young in each litter. The average number of offspring per litter was 3.8, and it is worth noting that gestation was, on average, $1\frac{1}{2}$ days longer than in controls, and that the newborn were somewhat heavier than controls of the same strain. With the exception of the one female with two stillborn litters, none of the other transplanted females have littered more than once, though apart from this their reproductive performance to date compares favorably to that of ordinary orthotopic transplants, summarized by Krohn (26,27). Thus, when we transplanted A ovaries into A donors, we were successful. However, whether the male was albino (as in the A strain) or agouti (as in the CBA strain), we could not exclude the possibility that in at least some experiments the offspring were derived from an ovarian remnant incompletely removed from the recipient site. Clearly a test of the system could only be provided by transplanting an *in vitro* matured ovary, histocompatible with but genetically distinguishable from the recipient. Mainly because of ease of scoring, and also because of the ability to score by fetal inspection during a pregnancy which could then be allowed to continue, we selected a coat-and-eye color marker. Because a syngeneic strain with the appropriate mutation at the albino locus was not available, we used a congenic strain. The donor ovary was agouti, and both the recipient and her mate were albino, ensuring that any agouti animal (or dark-eyed fetus) could in practice derive only from the *in vitro* matured orthotopically transplanted ovary.

With this system we have carried out six transplants. So far two pregnancies have resulted. Inspection of the embryos by laparotomy

PAUL E. POLANI *et al.*

TABLE II
Tritiated Thymidine Labeling Experiments[a]

% of labeled
pachytene and
diplotene cells

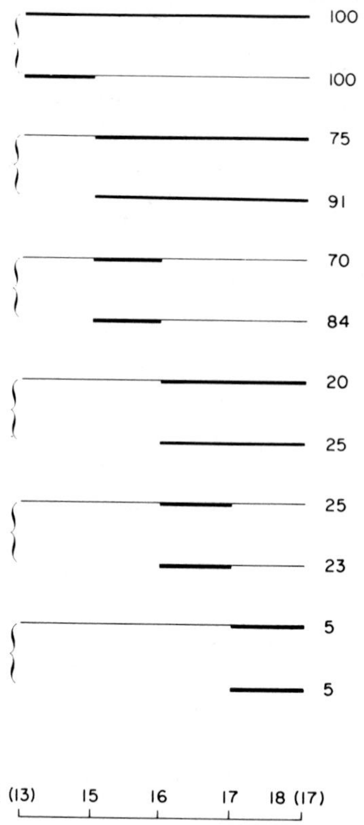

100
100
75
91
70
84
20
25
25
23
5
5

14 (13)   15   16   17   18 (17)

[a] The thick lines indicate the length of time during which the *in vitro* ovaries were exposed to this, at a concentration of [³H]TdR of 1 μCi ml^{-1} (specific activity 0.5 Ci mM^{-1}). The thin lines indicate culture in nonsupplemented medium (see Techniques), and the scale at the foot of the table indicates days of gestation.

at d 16 (d 15) of the first pregnancy showed one absorption and four live fetuses with dark eyes and normal growth and development. The pregnancy continued after the operation, but an act of cannibalism at term prevented us from studying this litter further. The second litter, which was born recently, consisted of four black-eyed newborns, clearly agouti. The length of gestation for this animal was not recorded, but the young at birth appeared larger than normal.

DNA labeling experiments are basic to an understanding of the fundamental germ-cell dynamics in our system, and were an essential prelude to—among others—the BUdR substitution experiments used for the study of chiasmata.

The results in Table II show that the proportion of labeled pachytene and diplotene cells at the end of *in vitro* incubation vary, depending on the day of exposure of the fetal ovaries to [³H]TdR. However, they do not differ when one compares embryonic ovaries set up in culture from day 14 (day 13) with those removed from the embryo on the day on which labeling was started. The proportions of cells estimated to be labeled on the different days of gestation are given in Fig. 4. These may be extrapolated to the proportions of *oocytes* that might be labeled, but even with low radiation doses the toxicity of the radioactive label to the maturing oocyte is clearly shown in Table III. In the light of this, when one is dealing with schedules capable of labeling less than 100% of pachytene/diplotene stages, and especially with relatively high radiation exposures, differential survival of unlabeled or incompletely labeled oocytes can be expected, and the effect on oocyte survival of labeling the follicular cells has also to be taken into consideration.

We based our attempt to label the chromatids differentially with BUdR on these findings. However, the addition to the culture medium of BUdR on day 14 (day 13) in a concentration of 0.3 μg BUdR

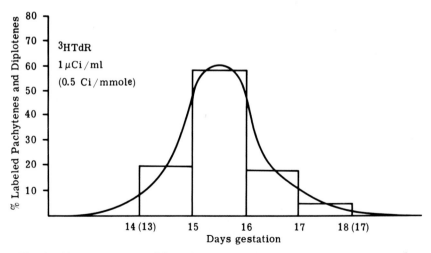

Fig. 4. Histogram prepared from the results given in Table II showing calculated tritium labeling frequencies of pachytene and diplotene cells at the end of *in vitro* culture of embryonic ovaries (see text) ([³H]TdR 1 Ci ml⁻¹; specific activity 0.5 Ci mM⁻¹).

TABLE III

In Vitro Ovaries Were Exposed to Different Radiation Concentrations of [³H]TdR for 24 Hours after Removal on Day 14 (Day 13)

Concentration of [³H]TdR ml⁻¹ *in vitro*	Heterotopic transplants A → CBA (successful)	"Mature" ova fixed per transplant	Ova % of control
10^{-6} Ci	3 (2)	2	6.5
10^{-8} Ci	3 (3)	11	35.5
10^{-10} Ci	3 (2)	13	41.9
10^{-12} Ci	3 (3)	23	74.2
Control	2 (2)	31	100.0

TABLE IV

Tritiated BUdR Labeling Experiments with a Low Concentration of BUdR and Low Radioactivity[a]

In vitro [³H]BUdR (13) (days) (17) 14 15 16 17 18	M I/M II analyzed (heterotopic transplants A into CBA)	Autoradiography Positive (%)	Negative (%)
⟶	29 (3)	96.5	3.5
⟶	70 (9)	97.1	2.9
⟶	10 (3)	100.0	0.0
⟶	49 (8)	96.0	4.0
⟶	118 (16)	49.1	50.9
⟶	39 (3)	10.0	90.0

[a] The solid lines indicate the time at which the ovaries maturing *in vitro* were exposed to [³H]BUdR (0.05 μCi ml⁻¹; specific activity 0.5 Ci mM⁻¹; BUdR concentration 30 ng ml⁻¹). The thin lines indicate culture in nonsupplemented medium (see Techniques).

ml^{-1} did not result in chromatid differentiation at meiotic metaphase. Tritiated BUdR labeling experiments with a low concentration of BUdR and low radioactivity (Table IV) show that 100% labeling could be achieved by labeling from day 14 (day 13). However, these findings do not indicate what proportion of cells went through one or more DNA synthesis cycles in the presence of BUdR, and thus had monofilary or bifilary chromatid substitutions. One may assume that it is the cells with bifilary substituted chromatids which, when committed to meiosis, will yield metaphases with differentially labeled chromatids suitable for an analysis of chiasmata, but this view may not be entirely correct (33).

BUdR LABELING FOR THE STUDY OF CHIASMATA

By using different BUdR concentrations to label the chromatids of human lymphocytes differentially in culture, we found that the optimal concentration of BUdR was 2 μg (6.5 nM) ml^{-1} of medium. The mitotic index was only moderately impaired. At meiosis, within the limits of small numbers the chiasma frequency observed per bivalent was average. This suggests that BUdR at this concentration does not upset, one way or another, chiasma formation. The value per bivalent in those cells whose bivalents were differentially labeled was 1.33 ± 0.032 chiasmata for 166 bivalents, and 1.31 ± 0.039 for the 136 clearly labeled bivalents used in the analysis (see below). These compare well to A oocytes, with 1.35 ± 0.037 chiasmata per bivalent in young females *in vivo*, and 1.33 ± 0.052 in *in vitro/in vivo* transplanted ovaries. The results when the above concentration of BUdR was used in the *in vitro/in vivo* system are shown in Table V. The

TABLE V
Fetal Ovaries Were Explanted on Day 14 (Day 13), and Exposed in Culture to 2 μg ml^{-1} BUdR for Periods of Time between 12 and 24 hours

Labeling time (hours)	Transplants	(M I)	M I per transplant	Differentially stained M I	Percentage of M I differentially stained
12,16,20	13	(20)	1.54	2	10.0
24	185	(83)	0.44	16[a]	19.3
Total	198	(103)	0.52	18	17.5

[a] Nine out of 16 good quality M I, which yielded 136 labeled and well analyzable configurations (15.1/M I), out of 166 configurations (18.4/M I) (see text).

yield of M I per transplant (0.52) is low compared to 10.9 for A transplants into CBA, and with the *in vivo* results of about 17.1 for A strain females (Table I). Less than one in every five metaphases had differentially stained bivalents, and only about half these metaphases had most or all bivalents well stained differentially. These yielded 136 configurations for analysis (Table VI). Among the side-by-side configurations are listed 6 doubtful "overlapped crosses" (34), in which the centromeres could not be identified confidently. Unlike side-by-side monochiasmate configurations, cross configurations have their centromeres co-oriented at opposite arms of the cross. The informative crosses display the point of breakage and reunion of homologous chromatids, which is hidden in the noninformative crosses (compare Fig. 5B to 5C). The former are derived from dark-to-light side-by-side association, while the latter arise from the association and hidden (and thus in this context assumed, because invisible) crossing over by breakage and reunion between similarly BUdR-labeled (and differentially stained) homologous chromatids. Assuming that light and dark homologous chromatids associate at random, among the single-chiasma bivalents, the total number of light-to-dark side-by-side associations, plus the informative crosses (together with the terminal associations whose aligned homologous chromatids are identically stained), should equal the rest: we find 47 of the former types, and 49 of the latter, in agreement with expectation. We have arbitrarily included "terminal associations" among the monochiasmate configurations. However, in none of the four dark-to-dark or light-to-light associations was there terminal isolabeling, such as would result from a very short terminal or terminalized chiasma (see below). In this sense there is no *evidence* here of a crossover, and thus of a previous chiasma, though there is a limit to the resolution of even BUdR labeling. This must be especially the case with the rather short and generally condensed mammalian meiotic chromosomes.

Given that there is no chromatid interference, diagonal (three-strand) double chiasma configurations should approximate in number the other two groups together, half of which should be reciprocal (two-strand doubles) and half complementary (four-strand doubles). One can see that the expectation is reasonably fulfilled.

Attention should be drawn to a special type of side-by-side configuration in which the dark and light chromatids, respectively, are at the center of the configuration and appear actually to cross each other while the two "outside" chromatids are complementary to each other, and are made up of dark joined to light threads, and are cross overs (Fig. 5D). This type of configuration is interpreted as arising from a

TABLE VI

The Types of 136 Labeled Configurations Analyzed[a]

Monochiasmate (?) bivalents (total: 96)									Dichiasmate (?) bivalents (total: 40)			
Side-by-side and ?[b]		Total	"Co-oriented" (cross)		Total	Terminal associations		Total	Reciprocal	Comple-mentary	Diagonal	Other with terminal associations
L/D[c]	D/D or L/L		Inform-ative	Noninform-ative		L/D	D/D or L/L					
21	24	45	22	21	43	4	4	8	10	8	14	8

[a] See Table V.
[b] Configurations in which the position of the centromeres could not be identified (see text).
[c] L, Lightly stained chromatids; D, darkly stained chromatids.

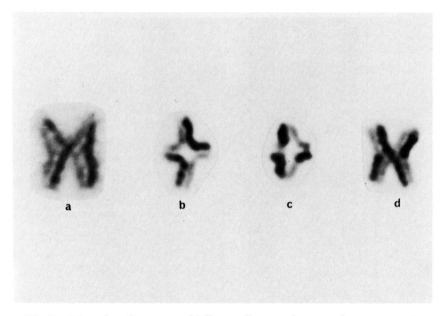

Fig. 5. Selected configurations of differentially stained meiotic chromosomes. Configurations a and d' have centromeres oriented north and configurations b and c have centromeres oriented north and south respectively. Configuration A shows a chiasma between dark and light homologous chromatids, the homologues lying side-by-side. Configuration b shows a noninformative cross. Configuration c shows an informative cross, with the points of crossing over at about 10 and 4 o'clock, respectively. Configuration d shows a "resolved" chiasma, i.e., the point of the crossover exchange (see text).

dark-to-light side-by-side association of homologous chromatids with chiasma formation, "flipping over" of one centromeric end over the other, thus revealing a "resolved chiasma" in the outside chromatids, through its recombinational consequences. We have found 12 visible "resolved chiasmata" both among the monochiasmate and the dichiasmate bivalents. Given an equal number of hidden ones, their total proportions would be about 18% of the scored configurations, or 14% of chiasmata.

A further point of interest resides in the frequency of sister chromatid exchanges (SCE). We have found 13 in the 136 bivalents (0.096 per bivalent), including two in the same chromatid of two configurations. This could be estimated to be equivalent to about 2 SCE per somatic metaphase (or 0.05 SCE per chromosome).

DISCUSSION

We have already discussed technical points related to culture of the embryonic ovaries and grafting. The congenic transplantation experiments are the nearest approach we could use to a syngraft situation. Their object is to enable us to obtain ova and litters over an extended period of the life of transplanted females.

We have already stressed the sensitivity of oocytes to, for example, radiation from the tritium label. This was put on a quantitative basis by Baker and McLaren (35). They gave repeated injections of [³H]TdR to pregnant mice, at concentrations of 4–400 μCi per dose, and analyzed oocyte loss, which was proportional to concentration, in their offspring. We have already commented on the toxicity of BUdR in the concentrations we had to use to obtain differential labeling and staining of chromatids of meiotic metaphases. This is reflected in relatively small numbers of metaphases obtained per transplant (Table V). This effect was present in spite of efforts to minimize exposure of labeled ovaries to light (36), and the use of dC (see Techniques). Our impression is that the latter was in no way helpful. As a thymidine analog BUdR is alleged to act as a mutagen because of the apparent greater ease with which it can undergo tautomeric shifts, with consequent infidelity of DNA replication. Also, it has been shown that BUdR can affect the transcription process of mammalian cells (37). It is known that growing mouse oocytes are active in RNA synthesis and presumably DNA transcription (38). At the end of the growth period they may contain proportionally as much RNA as a mature amphibian oocyte, yet by contrast RNA synthesis is resumed shortly after fertilization (39,40). At the other end of oocyte development chromosomal DNA-directed synthesis is active during a great deal of the meiotic prophase (41). Thus the BUdR would seem *prima facie* capable of seriously affecting oocyte metabolism, growth, and survival. Clearly in parallel it could exercise similar detrimental effects on the somatic cells of the developing ovary, and also in this way affect oocyte growth and maturation.

The relatively low proportion of differentially labeled and stained metaphases, and the relatively fewer in which all or most of the bivalents are well differentiated, may be a reflection of an incomplete labeling due to asynchrony of premeiotic DNA synthesis. It might also be surmised that this rather low proportion may be due to a low proportion of oogonia going through two cycles of DNA replication in the presence of BUdR, and thus presenting bifilary as well as monofilary

BUdR-substituted chromatids. However, attempts to label *in vitro* ovaries explanted on d 13 (d 12) failed, because of failure of germ cells and ovaries to grow. Allen (33), on evidence from the Armenian hamster, concludes that monofilary substitution with BUdR during spermatogonial DNA synthesis is adequate to reveal differential fluorescence of chromatids.

The *BUdR labeling experiments* have at least three objectives relevant to chiasmata: (1) their nature, (2) the terminalization, and (3) SCE at meiosis. Before developing the *in vitro* labeling method, we had done experiments—but without success—on *in vivo* labeling the bivalents of male mice (using repeated injections of BUdR (42), as well as with the Tablet method (43). Equally without positive results were experiments aimed at *in vivo* labeling fetal female germ cells by repeated BUdR injection of pregnant females at 13 (12) to 15 (14) days of gestation. Since this work was begun, BUdR labeling and analyses of monochiasmate bivalents and of meiotic SCE in a grasshopper have been published (34,44,45), and occasional BUdR labeling of male mouse meiotic metaphases (almost always the XY pair only) has been described (42). Allen (33) has recently reported on meiotic studies of the Armenian hamster, almost exclusively an analysis of its peculiarly interesting XY bivalents, while, by using a continuous infusion technique, Kanda and Kato (46) have obtained information on both monochiasmate bivalents and SCE in the male mouse. A further objective, therefore, of the female mouse meiosis *in vitro/in vivo* experiments is a comparison with other species, and especially with male mice.

Chiasmata are now practically universally accepted as originating from a "breakage and reunion" recombinational event between two of the four homologous chromatids, and resulting in crossing over. This is in line with the original cytological interpretation of Janssens (47), to whose chiasmatype hypothesis Morgan and his school at Columbia subscribed to explain the results of their genetic work with *Drosophila ampelophila* (48,49). The alternative cytological view of chiasmata stems from Granata's (50) cytological observations, and his clear-cut indications that chiasmata are the site of a change of chromatid partnership: on the one side of a chiasma sister- and on the other side homologous-chromatids would be associated in pairs at diplotene (51). In this view chiasmata are not related to crossing over [whose nature was not clearly explained by it: see Wenrich (52)]. However, it was later considered (53) that this hypothesis of chiasma formation—which came to be known as the Classical hypothesis—might be compatible with breakage and reunion. An extension of the strictly classical view was thus hypothesized (54). Support for this "extended classical hypothesis" was considered to lie in the reduction of chiasmata between diplotene and diakinesis (53), but the support was later withdrawn (55,56), when chiasma terminalization came to account for the said reduction. Efforts were directed from then on to find support for partial chiasmatypy. What may be termed "indirect" support stems from a number of observations, especially, but not only, the behavior of morphologically marked homologs at diplotene *and* at anaphase I/metaphase II [see, for example, Whitehouse (57)], and the correspondence between map lengths calculated from chiasmata and from genetic data (58,59).

More direct and visual support for breakage and reunion came from the work of Taylor (60), using tritiated thymidine to label the meiotic chromosomes, which was backed by different ingenious applications of this method by Peacock (61), Jones (62), and others. Taylor's results proved, for the first time visibly, that there is exchange of homologous chromatids, as required by the genetic findings, and in keeping with partial chiasmatypy. However, there are problems with [³H]TdR labeling. The technique has relatively poor resolution, so that, in general, labeling switch points had to be assessed at anaphase I and especially M II, namely, after first meiotic metaphase chromosome separation; this can, therefore, make distinction between homologous cross over exchanges and SCE difficult. Yet, clearly, in these circumstances support for a chiasma breakage and reunion hypothesis of chiasmata rests on a satisfactory one-to-one correspondence between chiasma frequency and switch point data. In spite of the above reservations on [³H]TdR labeling, by correlating chiasma frequency with cross over points, the "direct" evidence in support of partial chiasmatypy has been accepted as compelling.

The work with BUdR extends these findings with regard to informative crosses (Fig. 5C). Our results, like those of others (discussed below), support at the strictly cytological level the chiasmatype hypothesis, also when considered vis-a-vis the "extended" classical view. However, the type of configuration that is clearly absolutely against a classical view of a chiasma is to be seen in Fig. 5A, as a direct comparison with Fig. 1c of Granata (50) plainly shows (see also his Fig. 1e, on the make-up of a "classical" cross). It can be seen that the association between a dark and a light chromatid, at what must be considered an interstitial chiasma, respects the principle of strict homology, so that both north and south of the chiasma the pairwise associated chromatids are sisters.

Unlike Taylor (60) and others whose work was discussed above, we were able to estimate directly the chiasma frequency in the differentially labeled configurations. The value is very close to that observed in females both *in vivo* and in the *in vitro/in vivo* system. Other workers too (see below) find that BUdR labeling does not affect chiasma frequency.

Terminalization of chiasmata, first suspected by Darlington (56), is an important and controversial problem [see, for example, Henderson (63)], both practically and theoretically. Its two main and interlocked features are, first, a change of position of chromatid association from that at which the original chiasma and crossing over had occurred; and, second, a decrease in the numbers of chiasmata due to some being assimilated through chiasma movement toward the chromosome ends. We have failed to obtain, so far, any clear evidence for full terminalization, but in two dichiasmate configurations with two subterminal chiasmata it was obvious that one of the associations at least had terminalized, i.e., the position of cross over was more proximal than that of association. Tease and Jones (34) found no evidence of terminalization in the male grasshopper when they considered the monochiasmate bivalents, and the same applies to the monochiasmate bivalents in the male mouse studied by Kanda and Kato (46). Conversely, Allen (33), in the Armenian hamster, found evidence of chiasma terminalization, i.e., of a difference in position of visible cross over points compared to zone of association of X and Y chromosomes; he also noted that there was probably terminalization and elimination of one chiasma from a usually dichiasmate autosomal bivalent. He did not consider that the observed "terminalization" was an artifact resulting from stretch due to the air drying technique, a possibility raised by Tease and Jones (34).

As we have already mentioned, in spite of the nonexistence of direct evidence for this, we have included the terminally associated bivalent with the monochiasmate ones. It is clear that at least some terminal associations are chiasmata in the ordinary sense of the word and that this can be demonstrated by BUdR labeling and chromatid differentiation in rather elongated bivalents [see, for example, Fig. 5 of Tease and Jones (34); Allen (33)]. The topic of terminal associations is of great cytogenetic interest, and is highly relevant to the problems of homologue association, recombinational events, and the mechanical function of chiasmata [see the clear discussion by White (64)]. It has added importance in view of the association of axial elements and of synaptonemal complexes with the nuclear membrane at telomeric chromosome ends, and the fact that here is where chromosome synapsis appears to start [see, for example, Counce and Meyer (65) in *Lo-*

custa, and Moses (66) in the Chinese hamster]. Finally, it is clear that telomeres have an unusual DNA make-up (67), as well as an important place in the history of chromosome genetics (68,69).

We have observed a small proportion of *sister chromatid exchanges*. Interest has centered on these ever since Beadle and Emerson (70) concluded that they must be very rare, as meiotic events, from their observations on female meiosis in *Drosophila*. However, Schwartz (71), studying a ring chromosome, produced evidence in maize for sister-strand exchanges at meiosis. Taylor (60), using tritium labeling, suggested that they were probably rare in *Romalea microptera*, while Peacock (61), instead, using a similar method to Taylor's, thought that they were common in *Goniaea australasiae*. Jones (62) made a thorough study of the problem in *Stethophyma grossum*, using tritium-labeled configurations, and now, with Tease (44), the matter has been investigated in *Locusta migratoria* after BUdR substitution. In a total of 161 SCE they found that there was a clear correlation with chromosome length, and that the distribution of exchanges was clearly random. They gathered some evidence that some of the SCE were meiotic, rather than premeiotic, in origin. Also, they believe that most of the exchanges are BUdR-derived. The overall frequency per medium-sized bivalent they estimated to be 0.279 (0.893 for the larger bivalents), a value in keeping with the somatic cells of female *Locusta*, but about three times greater than the value (0.096) we obtained. Kanda and Kato (46) found a value of 0.073 SCE per bivalent, similar to ours. These values match with those in mouse spermatogonia, but not with those in bone marrow cells (72). Davidson *et al.* (73) have recently suggested that SCE are largely independent of the BUdR in the chromosomal DNA, but correlate with its concentration in the medium. Clearly this observation has to be taken into account when trying to assess differences in SCE produced by different techniques and regimes of labeling [see, for example, cultured mouse fibroblasts; Allen and Latt (72)].

A few additional comments on numbers are required to compare further our results with those from other mammals and grasshoppers. Kanda and Kato (46) present an analysis of 338 configurations from 52 young male mice, of which 235 (plus 2) were monochiasmate (92, or 39% of them, informative), 76 were end-to-end (29 associating light or dark chromatids, but without a visible exchange), and 25 were the end-to-end XY pair. These are remarkable because the association of the two sex chromosomes with each other was always of dark to light "homologous" chromatids, where a crossing over exchange, if it existed, would be hidden. If so, it follows that side-by-side pairing of X and Y would be between identically labeled chromatids. In addition, 21 univalents, without exchange, were observed. Allen (33) studied the differentially stained sex bivalent of 141 primary and 84 secondary spermatocytes of two young Armenian hamsters treated with BUdR, and found that 48% showed exchange of label. By contrast, in 239 cells from two old males, the visible pattern was found in only 28%, suggesting that crossing over between X and Y decreases with age. On the basis of the proportion of sex univalents found, he too did not think that BUdR labeling affects chiasma formation. Tease and Jones (34) analyzed 326 monochiasmate bivalents from the testes of five locusts implanted with BUdR tablets. Of these, 136 carried visible cross over exchanges, and 9.5% were anomalous, while the remaining bivalents were not informative. The visible exchanges were detected mostly in open crosses, but some were in "overlapped" crosses. Chiasma frequency was apparently unaffected by the treatment.

Figure 5D shows a configuration to which we have already drawn attention. Differential staining patterns such as this, which we have called "resolved chiasmata," have not been commented on in the papers just reviewed, and seem somewhat peculiar. These chiasmata correspond precisely to Janssens' original (1909) interpretation, that the chiasma is the point where two homologous chromatids cross each other *without* break and reunion; the two "qui passent sans chiasma au contraire sont ceux qui ont subi une soudure secondaire." This differs in detail from the interpretation that the point of chiasma is the very spot where homologous chromatids have actually broken and have cross-united [see, for example, Wilson and Morgan (74); especially Morgan's Fig. 7D (after Janssens 1919); compare our Figs. 5A to 5D]. The impression given both in the monochiasmate and in the dichiasmate bivalents in which such a "resolved" chiasma is seen, is that the elements of the bivalents hang together in spite of the fact that the chiasma itself appears to be resolved. The question then is, what keeps the chromosomes of the bivalent from falling apart? The need for a chiasma binder has been discussed (75), and it has been thought that perhaps remnants of the synaptonemal complex may act as a binder (76), or that the synaptonemal complex may in some way subserve sister chromatid cohesiveness (77). Moens (78), from studies of the meiotic prophase in the rat, believes that the lateral elements of the complex cross over at chiasma points after they break and rejoin (79). But the problem raised by the pattern under discussion, and, indeed, by other configurations, seems different to us. It can be said that it looks as if sister chromatids (and through them, the bivalents) are still held together, though the original chiasma, now visible as the point of cross over exchange, has opened up and disappeared. The inference is that the mechanical function of the chiasma must have lapsed at the point of exchange. So what binds together the chromatids, and thus the bivalents? Obviously there must be a persistent "attraction" of sister chromatids which does not allow the homologs to fall apart. Searching for what may underlie the holding together of sister chromatids, we are led to wonder whether, for example, the axial elements (considered to be precursors of the lateral elements of the synaptonemal complex) might subserve this cementing function. We would be tempted to postulate that the axial elements would persist and bind to each other, as an *unbroken* spine or hinge, sister chromatids (and, through them, bivalents), even when the centromeres have co-oriented and the chromatids have formed, for example, a cross. The axial elements would provide the continuous chromosomal skeleton that lends stability to the bivalent, and maintains it until chromatid attraction lapses, possibly through enzymatic action or co-incident with the disappearance of the nuclear membrane and important changes of the vascular properties of the nucleoplasm. Indeed, we are tempted to speculate further, and suggest that the familiar lack of chromatid duality of leptotene and zygotene chromosomes, which has been a source of difficulty in the early interpretation of meiosis and crossing over, depends, also, on a tight association of sister chromatids, attributable to the axial elements—in a sense, another view of the precocity of meiosis. In fact, a fundamental question about axial elements was posed by Moses (80), when he asked whether they are components of all replicated chromosomes, or whether they are exclusive (or perhaps modified?) meiotic structures.

To return to the postulated postpachytene, and also postdiplotene, mechanical function of the axial elements: while there is evidence that these axes are present, largely as single filaments, at early zygotene (66), and then join as "homologous pairs" to form part of the synaptonemal complex, there is no evidence as to their fate when the complex disappears at the end of pachytene. During pachytene axial elements are organized into the lateral elements of the synaptonemal complex, and these disappear after mid-pachytene, at least in *Locusta* males, and when they are viewed with conventional electron microscopy techniques to serially reconstruct the synaptonemal complex (81). The studies which have made use of the spreading technique of Counce and Meyer (65) seem to have been done on primary spermatocytes, mostly at zygotene and pachytene, and seldom at diplotene, stages. So, even apart from lack of detailed information on axial elements in the later stages of the meiotic prophase in the male, that of the female—and specifically that of the female mammal—does not seem to have been scrutinized. The peculiar nature of female mammalian meiosis may well be associated with, and related to, differences in this, as in other important aspects of chromosome behavior

SUMMARY

A new experimental technique for the study of female meiosis is described in detail. Its potential is examined in the light of a number of parameters investigated experimentally. The method permits us to influence, in a direct way, the germ cells that mature and are committed to meiosis during embryonic ovarian development *in vitro*. The last premeiotic DNA synthetic rounds of maturing oogonia, and all stages of the meiotic prophase up to the resting dictyate stage take place during the *in vitro* phase of the procedure. Subsequent heterotopic transplantation to spayed females is a simple way of allowing ovarian maturation and oocyte growth to proceed so that primary and secondary oocytes may be harvested and examined, and their chromosomes studied. Orthotopic transplantation is possible in the mouse, and has allowed us to test also the functional competence of the *in vitro* matured ovaries and their oocytes. This was successfully demonstrated by using congenic strains and genetically marked explanted and transplanted ovaries: after mating to normal males, genetically marked young were produced.

A first application of the technique for the visual recognition of recombinational (cross over) events is described. *In vitro* incorporation of 5-bromodeoxyuridine and subsequent study of chiasmata and of crossing over occurring in relation to them was possible. The findings with this method gave, not only unequivocal, direct cytological support to the partial chiasmatype hypothesis, but also revealed some peculiarities of chiasma behavior which may be special to female mammalian meiosis.

ACKNOWLEDGMENTS

We acknowledge with gratitude the financial support of the Spastics Society, and a grant by an anonymous donor. We thank Mr. M. Crowder for his expert histological work, and Miss H. Wilson and Miss F. Moir for their assistance.

REFERENCES

1. Brambell, F. W. R. (1927) *Proc. R. Soc. London, Ser. B* **101**, 391–409.
2. Borum, K. (1961) *Exp. Cell Res.* **24**, 495–507.
3. Franchi, L. L., Mandl, A. M., and Zuckerman, S. (1962) *In* "The Ovary" (S. Zuckerman, A. M. Mandl, and P. Eckstein, eds.), Vol. 1, pp. 1–88. Academic Press, New York.
4. Baker, T. G. (1972) *In* "Reproduction and Biology" (H. Bolin and S. K. Glosser, eds.), pp. 398–437. Excerpta Medica, Amsterdam.
5. Zuckerman, S., and Baker, T. G. (1977) *In* "The Ovary" (S. Zuckerman and B. J. Weir, eds.), 2nd ed., Vol. 1, pp. 47–67. Academic Press, New York.
6. Byskov, A. G., and Saxén, L. (1976) *Dev. Biol.* **52**, 193–200.
7. Byskov, A. G. (1979) *Ann. Biol. Anim., Biochim., Biophys.* **19**, B4, 1251–1261.
8. McLaren, A. (1980) *Nature (London)* **238**, 688–689.
9. Polani, P. E., Crolla, J. A., Seller, M. J., and Moir, F. (1979) *Nature (London)* **278**, 348–349.
10. Blandau, R. J., Warrick, E., and Rumery, R. E. (1965) *Fertil. Steril.* **16**, 705–715.
11. Rumery, R. E., Phinney, E., and Blandau, R. J. (1971) *In* "Methods in Mammalian Embryology" (J. C. Daniel, Jr., ed.), pp. 472–495. Freeman, San Francisco, California.
12. Rumery, R. E., and Blandau, R. J. (1976) *J. Morphol.* **149**, 421–436.
13. Zakharov, A. F., and Egolina, N. A. (1972) *Chromosoma* **38**, 341–365.
14. Latt, S. A. (1973) *Proc. Natl. Acad. Sci. U.S.A.* **70**, 3395–3399.
15. Perry, P., and Wolff, S. (1974) *Nature (London)* **251**, 156–158.
16. Kato, H. (1974) *Nature (London)* **251**, 70–72.
17. Wolff, S. (1977) *Annu. Rev. Genet.* **11**, 183–201.
18. Festing, M. F. W. (1979) "Inbred Strains in Biomedical Research," pp. 104–114. Macmillan, New York.
19. Meuth, M., and Green, H. (1974) *Cell* **2**, 109–112.
20. Davidson, R. L., and Kaufman, E. R. (1978) *Nature (London)* **276**, 722–723.
21. Jones, E. C., and Krohn, P. L. (1960) *J. Endocrinol.* **20**, 135–146.
22. Polani, P. E., and Jagiello, G. A. (1976) *Cytogenet. Cell Genet.* **16**, 505–529.
23. Blandau, R. J., and Odor, D. L. (1972) *In* "Oogenesis" (J. D. Biggers and A. W. Schuetz, eds.), pp. 301–320. University Park Press, Baltimore, Maryland.
24. Klein, J. (1975) "Biology of the Mouse Histocompatibility-2 Complex: Principles of Immunogenetics Applied to a Single System," pp. 118–121. Springer-Verlag, Berlin and New York.
25. Altman, P. L., and Katz, D. D., eds. (1979) "Inbred and Genetically Defined Strains of Laboratory Animals," Part 1, pp. 21–23. Fed. Am. Soc. Exp. Biol., Bethesda, Maryland.
26. Krohn, P. L. (1965) *Br. Med. Bull.* **21**, 157–162.
27. Krohn, P. L. (1977) *In* "The Ovary" (S. Zuckerman and B. J. Weir, eds.), 2nd ed., Vol. 2, pp. 101–128. Academic Press, New York.
28. Woodruff, M. F. A. (1960) "The Transplantation of Tissues and Organs," pp. 494–503. Thomas, Springfield, Illinois.
29. Robertson, G. G. (1940) *Proc. Soc. Exp. Biol. Med.* **44**, 302–309.
30. Robertson, G. G. (1945) *Proc. Soc. Exp. Biol. Med.* **59**, 30–33.
31. Russell, W. L., and Hurst, J. G. (1945) *Proc. Natl. Acad. Sci. U.S.A.* **31**, 267–273.
32. Krohn, P. L. (1962) *Proc. R. Soc. London, Ser. B* **157**, 128–147.
33. Allen, J. W. (1979) *Chromosoma* **74**, 189–207.

34. Tease, C., and Jones, G. H. (1978) *Chromosoma* **69**, 163–178.
35. Baker, T. G., and McLaren, A. (1973) *J. Reprod. Fertil.* **34**, 121–130.
36. Kao, F. T., and Puck, T. T. (1968) *Proc. Natl. Acad. Sci. U.S.A.* **60**, 1275–1281.
37. Hill, B. T., Tsuboi, A., and Baserga, R. (1974) *Proc. Natl. Acad. Sci. U.S.A.* **71**, 455–459.
38. Moore, G. P. M., Lintern-Moore, S., Peters, H., and Faber, M. (1974) *J. Cell Biol.* **60**, 416–422.
39. Wassarman, P. M., and LeTourneau, G. E. (1976) *Nature (London)* **261**, 73–74.
40. Woodland, H. R., and Graham, C. F. (1969) *Nature (London)* **221**, 327–332.
41. Bakken, A. H., and McClanahan, M. (1978) *Chromosoma* **67**, 21–40.
42. Allen, J. W., and Latt, S. A. (1976) *Nature (London)* **260**, 449–451.
43. Allen, J. W., Shuler, C. F., Mendes, R. W., and Latt, S. A. (1977) *Cytogenet. Cell Genet.* **18**, 231–237.
44. Tease, C. (1978) *Nature (London)* **272**, 823–824.
45. Tease, C., and Jones, G. H. (1979) *Chromosoma* **73**, 75–84.
46. Kanda, N., and Kato, H. (1980) *Chromosoma* **78**, 113–121.
47. Janssens, F. A. (1909) *Cellule* **25**, 387–411.
48. Morgan, T. H. (1911) *Science* **34**, 384.
49. Morgan, T. H., Sturtevant, A. H., Muller, H. J., and Bridges, C. B. (1915) "The Mechanism of Mendelian Heredity," pp. 131–135. Constable, London.
50. Granata, L. (1910) *Arch. Zellforsch.* **5**, 182–214.
51. Newton, W. C. F., and Darlington, C. D. (1929) *J. Genet.* **21**, 1–15.
52. Wenrich, D. H. (1917) *J. Morphol.* **29**, 471–518.
53. Darlington, C. D. (1929) *J. Genet.* **21**, 17–56.
54. Sax, K. (1930) *J. Arnold Arbor., Harv. Univ.* **11**, 193–220.
55. Darlington, C. D. (1930) *Proc. R. Soc. London, Ser. B* **107**, 50–59.
56. Darlington, C. D. (1931) *J. Genet.* **24**, 65–96.
57. Whitehouse, H. L. K. (1973) "Towards an Understanding of the Mechanism of Heredity," 3rd ed., p. 118. Arnold, London.
58. Beadle, G. W. (1932) *Genetics* **17**, 481–501.
59. Darlington, C. D. (1937) "Recent Advances in Cytology," 2nd ed., pp. 249–301. Churchill, London.
60. Taylor, J. H. (1965) *J. Cell Biol.* **25**, 57–67.
61. Peacock, W. J. (1970) *Genetics* **65**, 593–617.
62. Jones, G. H. (1971) *Chromosoma* **34**, 367–382.
63. Henderson, S. A. (1969) *In* "Handbook of Molecular Cytology" (A. Lima-de-Faria, ed.), pp. 326–357. North-Holland Publ., Amsterdam.
64. White, M. J. D. (1973) "Animal Cytology and Evolution," 3rd ed., pp. 166–170. Cambridge Univ. Press, London and New York.
65. Counce, S. J., and Meyer, G. F. (1973) *Chromosoma* **44**, 231–253.
66. Moses, M. J. (1977) *Chromosoma* **60**, 99–125.
67. Cavalier-Smith, T. (1974) *Nature (London)* **250**, 467–470.
68. Muller, H. J. (1932). *Proc. Int. Congr. Genet., 6th, 1932* Vol. 1, pp. 213–256.
69. Muller, H. J. (1938). *Collecting Net* **13**, 181–195, 198 (reprinted in "Studies in Genetics—The Selected Papers of H. J. Muller." Indiana Univ. Press, Bloomington, 1926).
70. Beadle, G. W., and Emerson, S. (1935) *Genetics* **20**, 192–206.
71. Schwartz, D. (1953) *Genetics* **38**, 251–260.
72. Allen, J. W., and Latt, S. A. (1976) *Chromosoma* **58**, 325–340.
73. Davidson, R. L., Kaufman, E. R., Dougherty, C. P., Ouellette, A. M., Di Folco, C. M., and Latt, S. A. (1980) *Nature (London)* **284**, 74–76.

74. Wilson, E. B., and Morgan, T. H. (1920) *Am. Nat.* **54**, 632, 193–219.
75. Maguire, M. P. (1974) *J. Theor. Biol.* **48**, 485–487.
76. Maguire, M. P. (1978) *Chromosoma* **65**, 173–183.
77. Maguire, M. P. (1978) *Exp. Cell Res.* **112**, 297–308.
78. Moens, P. B. (1978) *Can. J. Genet. Cytol.* **20**, 567–597.
79. Moens, P. B. (1977) *In* "Cell Biology: A Comprehensive Treatise" (L. Goldstein and D. Prescott, eds.), Vol. 1, pp. 93–108. Academic Press, New York.
80. Moses, M. J. (1968) *Annu. Rev. Genet.* **2**, 363–412.
81. Moens, P. B. (1973) *Cold Spring Harbor Symp. Quant. Biol.* **38**, 99–107.

Problems in Interspecies Comparisons in Studies in Molecular Reproductive Biology

DEBRA J. WOLGEMUTH*

Department of Molecular Cell Biology
The Rockefeller University
New York, New York

INTRODUCTION

The bulk of existing information on the molecular biology of oogenesis, fertilization, and early embryonic development has been obtained from experiments using nonmammalian species (reviewed in 1). The large size and ease with which large numbers of oocytes and early embryos can be obtained has made sea urchins and several amphibia the favorites of investigators interested in the subcellular biochemistry of development. Only recently (within the last 10 years) have mammalian systems become amenable for similar studies and the vast majority of these studies have focused on the mouse (reviewed in 2). The principle reason for this breakthrough has been the development of technology permitting biochemical analyses at the microanalytical level. For example, incorporation of radiolabeled precursors of high specific activity followed by high resolution gel electrophoresis has been used to monitor synthetic activities during specific stages of oogenesis, fertilization, and early embryogenesis; the underlying goal of such investigations being an understanding of the role of differential gene expression in regulating these processes.

However, the emergence of such qualitative and increasingly quantitative data from mammalian systems has also brought into focus surprising differences in the molecular developmental biology among mammalian species thus far studied. "Surprising" is used in the sense

* Present address: Department of Human Genetics and Development, Center for Reproductive Sciences, College of Physicians and Surgeons, Columbia University, New York, New York.

BIOREGULATORS OF REPRODUCTION
Copyright © 1981 by Academic Press, Inc.
All rights of reproduction in any form reserved.
ISBN 0-12-379980-5

that while perhaps few investigators would have been startled by notable differences in, for example, DNA synthesis following fertilization in organisms as diverse as sea urchin and mouse, less predicted was the observation of considerable differences in protein synthesis in early embryonic development in mouse and rabbit (discussed below). As a way of calling attention to the opinion that caution should be used in extrapolation of the experimental results obtained from one mammalian species to the formulation of generality of the phenomena involved, a few examples will be discussed. Greatest experimental detail will be presented in an example with which the author is most familiar, that of the organization and quantitation of genes for ribosomal RNA during mammalian oogenesis. Several additional examples drawn from the literature and particularly relevant to the theme of this symposium will be cited.

RIBOSOMAL RNA GENE ORGANIZATION AND QUANTITATION DURING OOGENESIS

The phenomenon of amplification of the genes for ribosomal RNA in oocytes was first shown in *Xenopus laevis* (3,4) and has been well-documented cytologically and biochemically in a wide variety of non-mammalian species (5). This transient alteration in gene copy number may occur at various stages during oogenesis but is typically most pronounced during late pachytene to diplotene of meiotic prophase I. The level of increase of ribosomal RNA genes ranges from a two- to fivefold increase seen in certain molluscs (6) to the dramatic 1000-fold increase seen in *Xenopus laevis* (3,4).

A frequently observed cytological manifestation of these extra genes is the presence of multiple small nucleoli in addition to the large, main nucleolus(i). It was the observation of small, nucleolus-like structures in mammalian oocytes that led to the speculation that oocytes of higher organisms might also amplify their genes for rRNA during oogenesis (7). These structures were observed in human fetal oocytes, most notably in late pachytene and early diplotene stages (7,8). Examples of early diplotene human oocytes containing these structures are shown in Fig. 1. Recently, similar structures were noted in oocytes of another mammal, the baboon (*Papio cynecephalus*), during late diplotene stage of meiosis (9).

Although the observation of these small RNA-containing bodies which cytologically (7,8) and ultrastructurally (10) resemble primary nucleoli except for size was highly suggestive of the presence of extra

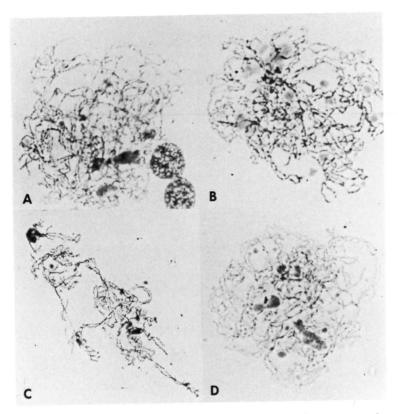

Fig. 1. Human diplotene nuclei with primary nucleoli and varying numbers of small nucleolus-like bodies. Note variation in size, shape, number, and intranuclear distribution of these putative micronucleoli. All preparations were from a 26-week-old fetus, stained with toluidine blue and viewed with phase optics. Each nucleus contains one or more primary nucleoli and multiple micronucleoli.

genes coding for rRNA, a more definitive demonstration lay in cytological molecular hybridization experiments. Ribosomal RNA was purified from a human tissue culture cell line, labeled *in vitro* to high specific activity with ^{125}I, and hybridized *in situ* to cytological preparations of fetal oocytes from second trimester human ovaries (8) and third trimester baboon ovaries (9). It was first established that most of the small, nucleolus-like bodies were indeed true micronucleoli (i.e., containing DNA sequences complementary to rRNA) as evidenced by their ability to hybridize rRNA *in situ*. Examples of such labeled micronucleoli from human oocytes are shown in Fig. 2.

Whether these structures were indicative of an increase in rRNA

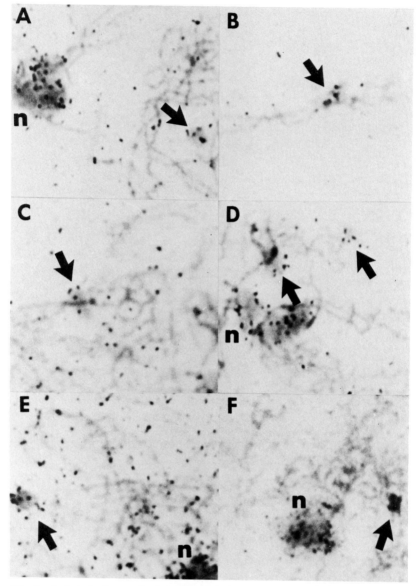

Fig. 2. Labeled micronucleoli in human diplotene oocytes. Portions of posthybridization autoradiographs of human diplotene oocyte nuclei from a 26-week-old fetus. Hybridization was with ^{125}I-RNA, specific activity, 1×10^8 dpm/μg; 16 hours; 38°C (see reference 11). Arrows indicate the small, nucleolus-like structures which labeled after hybridization *in situ* with rRNA. Primary nucleoli are denoted by (n). Exposure time A–D, 3½ days; E–F, 6 days. Giemsa stain; bright light optics.

gene number was examined with this combined biochemical–cytological approach by using a quantitative analysis of rRNA–DNA hybridization *in situ* (12). Quantitation of the rRNA genes in oocytes at
various stages of meiotic prophase showed that both human (13) and
baboon (9) oocytes contained slightly elevated (~fourfold) levels of
rRNA genes in diplotene stages. Although this represents a relatively
low level of amplification, it is well within the ranges so far observed
(5) and is of particular significance in extending the generality of this
phenomenon to include mammals. Finally, recent ultrastructural and
Ag^+-staining evidence has suggested that micronucleoli are indeed
active in rRNA synthesis (10).

Given the observation of rRNA gene amplification in organisms as
phylogenetically diverse as man and molluscs, it was tempting to
speculate that micronucleoli and extra rRNA templates would be a
common feature of all mammalian oocytes. Since perhaps the best
studied of all mammalian species is the mouse, the mouse oocyte in
meiotic prophase was examined. To date, we have been unsuccessful
in visualizing micronucleoli similar to those seen in human and baboon and in demonstrating the presence of extra rRNA genes, nor are
we aware of any reports in the literature to this effect (discussed in
11). In a study on nucleoli in mouse oocytes during meiotic prophase,
Stahl *et al.* (14) present no data for the existence of micronucleoli. Finally, biochemical studies by Jahn *et al.* (15) suggested that the growing mouse oocyte was capable of synthesizing rRNA at sufficiently
high rate such that no extra rRNA templates would be necessary to
produce the amount of rRNA stored in the oocyte cytoplasm. Although
kinetic studies have not been performed on other mammals, it is clear
that there are obvious cytological and biochemical differences in the
behavior of rRNA genes during meiosis in oocytes of mice and men.

GENE EXPRESSION DURING EARLY MAMMALIAN DEVELOPMENT

In order to understand the possible role of selective gene activation
in development and differentiation, patterns of gene expression have
been analyzed at both transcriptional and translational levels. Experimental approaches have included examining the effect of inhibitors of
RNA (either mRNA or rRNA) synthesis or protein synthesis at specific
stages following fertilization on subsequent development. Recently,
direct analysis of newly synthesized proteins in mouse and rabbit at
various stages of early embryogenesis has provided evidence for the

synthesis of developmentally stage-specific sets of proteins. As reviewed by Sherman (16), these newly synthesized proteins fall into subsets as follows: (a) those synthesized prior to fertilization and during early cleavages; (b) proteins synthesized after fertilization and only during a few cleavages; (c) proteins that appear during the 8-cell to blastocyst stage; and (d)proteins that appear first at late morula, following compaction.

Within this overall scheme there lie remarkable differences between patterns of gene expression between, for example, amphibia and mammals, and further, even among the few mammals so far examined (1,16). For example, in rabbit, the first clear example of embryo-specific proteins was seen at the 8- to 12-cell stage (17), in contrast to the major changes in the synthetic patterns of polypeptides occurring shortly after fertilization in the mouse (18,19). Interestingly, with respect to the question of the time of resumption of significant levels of rRNA synthesis by the early embryo, rabbit and *Xenopus laevis* are more similar (128-cell stage and 64-cell stage, respectively) (1,16) than is rabbit to mouse (2- to 4-cell stage). Even the lengths of time for cell division vary greatly between mouse and rabbit: by 96 hours a fertilized rabbit egg will have given rise to almost 1000 cells (20) whereas a fertilized mouse egg will have produced about 64 cells (21). The complexitity of these differences among species was noted by Van Blerkhom (22) who commented that "the stage of development when the embryo is capable of supplying its own genetic information may vary significantly among species."

SPECIFIC STRUCTURAL COMPONENTS OF MAMMALIAN OOCYTES

Concomitant with the recent interest in defining gene products following fertilization and during early embryogenesis has been a renewed effort to biochemically define the oocyte itself. The zona pellucida is an oocyte component which has become increasingly feasible to study biochemically because of technical advances in mass isolation and *in vitro* labeling to high specific activity. This acellular envelope surrounds the follicular oocyte and is believed to be composed predominantly of glycoproteins in the three mammals in which it has been best characterized—mouse, pig, and rabbit. In the mouse, electrophoretic analysis of *in vitro* labeled or nonlabeled isolated zonae revealed the presence of three major glycoproteins, which migrated as relatively discrete bands of molecular weights of approximately 200,000, 120,000, and 83,000 (23,24). Little or no evidence has been obtained for the existence of even limited heterogeneity of the glycoproteins within the three general size classes. In contrast, biochemical studies of mass-isolated, unlabeled pig zonae pellucidae have revealed that while there are also three major size classes of glycoproteins (of molecular weight ranges of 45,000–120,000, 80,000–100,000, and 85,000–120,000), unlike the situation in mouse, there is extensive microheterogeneity within each class (25,26). Such microheterogeneity, presumably due to heterogeneity of the carbohydrate moieties of the glycoproteins, was recently noted among the major size classes of glycoproteins of purified rabbit zonae pellucidae (26). Until more species are examined under identical isolation procedures it is impossible to infer which is the more widely found situation. It is of interest to note, however, that the porcine zona pellucida has been reported to share antigenic determinants with the human zona (27,28).

CONCLUDING COMMENTS

There are numerous additional examples in the literature of differences among mammals in events of oogenesis, fertilization, and early embryogenesis ranging from differences in the frequency of occurrence of spontaneous activation of oocytes with subsequent parthenogenic development (see Whittingham, 29) to differences in chromosome morphology during identical stages of meiotic prophase (see Baker, 30). A recurrent theme that emerges is that while the mouse is clearly the best studied mammal, it is often the most apparently "atypical." With its well-studied genetic aspects and its experimental malleability, the mouse will undoubtedly continue to serve as an excellent system for studies in mammalian reproductive biology. However, it is hoped that the examples discussed in this chapter will emphasize that caution should be used in the extent to which information obtained in the mouse is extrapolated to other mammals, including humans. It is further hoped that the next few years will see more attention being paid to comparative studies among mammals in areas of reproductive biology.

ACKNOWLEDGMENTS

Special thanks are extended to Dr. Bonnie S. Dunbar of the Population Council at The Rockefeller University for making available unpublished data and to Drs. Georgiana Jagiello, Ann S. Henderson, and Kimball C. Atwood for their support during the studies which yielded the date shown in Figs. 1 and 2.

REFERENCES

1. Davidson, E. H. (1976) "Gene Activity in Early Development." Academic Press, New York.
2. Sherman, M. I. (1979) *Annu. Rev. Biochem.* **48**, 443–470.
3. Brown, D. D., and Dawid, I. B. (1968) *Science* **160**, 272–280.
4. Gall, J. G. (1968) *Proc. Natl. Acad. Sci. U.S.A.* **60**, 553–560.
5. Tobler, H. (1975) *In* "The Biochemistry of Animal Development" (R. Weber, ed.), Vol. 3, pp. 91–123. Academic Press, New York.
6. Kidder, G. M. (1976) *Dev. Biol.* **49**, 132–142.
7. Stahl, A., Luciani, J.-M., Devictor, M., Capodano, A.-M., and Gagne, R. (1975) *Humangenetik* **26**, 315–327.
8. Wolgemuth-Jarashow, D. J., Jagiello, G. M., and Henderson, A. S. (1977) *Hum. Genet.* **36**, 63–68.
9. Wolgemuth, D. J., Jagiello, G. M., and Henderson, A. S. (1980) *Dev. Biol.* **78**, 598–604.
10. Hartung, M., Mirre, C., and Stahl, A. (1979) *Hum. Genet.* **52**, 295–308.
11. Wolgemuth-Jarashow, D. J. (1977) Ph. D. Dissertation, Columbia University, New York.
12. Wolgemuth-Jarashow, D. J., Jagiello, G. M., Atwood, K. C., and Henderson, A. S. (1976) *Cytogenet. Cell Genet.* **17**, 137–146.
13. Wolgemuth, D. J., Jagiello, G. M., and Henderson, A. S. (1979) *Exp. Cell Res.* **118**, 181–190.
14. Stahl, A., Mirre, C., Hartung, M., Knibiehler, B., and Navarro, A. (1977) *Chromosomes Today* **6**, 255–264.
15. Jahn, C. L., Barran, M., and Bachvaroua, R. (1976) *J. Exp. Zool.* **197**, 161–169.
16. Sherman, M. I. (1979) *Annu. Rev. Biochem.* **48**, 443–470.
17. Van Blerkhom, J., and McGaughey, R. (1978) *Dev. Biol.* **63**, 151–164.
18. Van Blerkhom, J., and Brockaway, G. (1975) *Dev. Biol.* **44**, 148–157.
19. Levinson, J., Goodfellow, P., Vandeboncour, M., and McDevitt, H. (1978) *Proc. Natl. Acad. Sci. U.S.A.* **75**, 3332–3336.
20. Daniel, J. C. (1964) *Am. Nat.* **98**, 85–87.
21. Barlow, P. W., Owen, D. A., and Graham, C. F. (1972) *J. Embryol. Exp. Morphol.* **27**, 431–445.
22. Van Blerkhom, J. (1979) *Dev. Biol.* **72**, 188–194.
23. Bleil, J., and Wasserman, P. M. (1980) *Dev. Biol.* **76**, 185–202.
24. Bleil, J., and Wasserman, P. M. (1980) *Proc. Natl. Acad. Sci. U.S.A.* **77**, 1029–1033.
25. Dunbar, B. S., Wardrip, N. J., and Hedrick, J. L. (1980) *Biochemistry* **19**, 356–365.
26. Dunbar, B. S., and Sammons, D. W. (1980) *J. Cell Biol.* **87**, 743a.
27. Sacco, A. G. (1977) *Biol. Reprod.* **16**, 164–173.
28. Shivers, C. A., and Dunbar, B. S. (1977) *Science* **197**, 1082–1084.
29. Whittingham, D. G. (1980). *In* "Recent Progress in Reproduction," Vol. 2. Oxford Univ. Press, London and New York (in press).
30. Baker, T. G. (1970) *Adv. Biosci.* **6**, 7–23.

The Ovarian and Extraovarian Control of Meiosis: The Role of Haploidins

A. B. FAJER

Department of Physiology
University of Maryland School of Medicine
Baltimore, Maryland

INTRODUCTION

Meiosis can be defined functionally as the series of events that marks the end of the diploid life of the germ cells. The main role of meiosis is to reduce the number of chromosomes from $2n$ to the haploid, $1n$, in preparation for the fusion of the gametes and the maintenance of chromosomal number of the species.

In most species the first meiotic division is characterized by the formation of the synaptonemal complex (1), recombination between homologous chromosomes and the nondivision of the kinetochores. In the female, the first division is interrupted at the diplotene stage of the prophase, to continue only before ovulation. The second meiotic division is a typical cell division and occurs after fertilization.

Meiosis assures genetic variability by the cited exchange of material between maternal and paternal chromosomes and the random distribution of the chromosomes during the metaphase and anaphase of the first division. For a discussion on the relation between the crossing over of chromosomes and the pachytene stage of the meiotic prophase see Stern and Hotta (2).

A common observation in mammalian ovaries is the great extent of the degeneration of germ cells during the mitotic cycles that precede meiosis as well as during all stages of the first meiotic division. By this degenerative process, presumably due to various causes but grouped

BIOREGULATORS OF REPRODUCTION

under the name of atresia, a large number of oogonia, oocytes, and follicles are eliminated.

In contrast to what happens in the testis, where the undifferentiated spermatogonia do not enter meiosis, all oogonia eventually go through meiosis. This phenomenon and atresia lead as a consequence to the reduction and limitation of the number of oocytes available at puberty and during the length of the reproductive life.

In contrast to mitosis, meiosis is not a cyclic event in the life of the germ cell. Furthermore, once committed to meiosis a cell cannot revert to mitosis. What this commitment means on a cellular level is not known.

Though mammalian meiosis is very similar in both sexes, the time table by which it develops and the results are very different: four viable spermatocytes in the male, one oocyte and three polar bodies in the female.

Our knowledge of the genetic consequences of meiosis is well established and the structural alterations of the chromosomes during meiosis have been studied in great detail (3).

In spite of the wealth of morphological and genetic data, our understanding of the mechanisms involved is limited. There is a scarcity of data on the cellular metabolism related to the unique events of meiosis as opposed to the metabolism that supports the cell during the mitotic cycle (4).

In early studies on sexual differentiation, relatively little attention was given to meiosis itself, and to the fate of the germ cells in relation to the somatic elements of the gonad. More recently observations in the freemartin and in male–female chimeras drew attention to the conditions that affect the survival of the germ cells and the onset of meiosis.

Few bovine freemartin fetuses show any meiotic cells before day 88 of pregnancy and germ cells have disappeared by day 186 without entering meiosis (5).

In the case of male XX-XY chimeric mice it was postulated that some groups of germ cells show meiosis during the fetal period, not because of their genotype but because of the influence of the XX somatic cells that surround them (6).

There are many practical reasons for the lack of more experimental data on cells in meiosis. The male germ cells are more easily available but the complexity of the germinal line in the testis still hinders the complete isolation of cells at the various stages of the prophase (7). In the female, meiosis occurs during a short period of fetal life or at birth in relatively few species—rabbit, hamster, ferret, vole, dog. In all cases the prophase of the first division ends shortly after birth and this timing restricts the availability of material for more extensive studies. In addition, isolated germ cells have not been maintained adequately *in vitro*.

In the female, meiosis is arrested at the diplotene stage of the prophase. The primordial follicle is then formed with the association of follicular cells and many events—cell growth, formation of the zona pellucida, follicle growth—attest to the fact that the cell in meiosis can be a very active cell.

Progress has been made in the study of DNA synthesis during meiosis. It was observed that there is a lengthening by a factor of 2 or 3 of the S phase of the cell cycle preceeding meiosis (8). There is also a small—0.3%—but constant DNA synthesis during the zygotene and pachytene, in plants and animals (male) (2). More recently three proteins typical of meiosis and involved in the chromosomic events were described in lillium and in mammalian spermatocytes; an endonuclease, an unwinding protein (U), and a renaturating protein (R) (9).

In spite of the similar early chromosomic events in male and female meiosis, little is known about the mechanisms that relate to the onset of meiosis and determine the differences between male and female in their commitment to meiosis at the time of ovarian differentiation or at puberty.

In the ovary the problem can be dissociated into three main parts:

1. What makes the oogonia shift from mitosis to meiosis? What are the signs, metabolic or otherwise, at this shift?
2. What arrests the nuclear events at the diplotene stage of the prophase of the first division?
3. What makes the oocytes of some follicles resume meiosis?

I will concern myself mainly with the first question.

CONTROL OF THE ONSET OF MEIOSIS

In amphibia and birds (10) female germ cells can be seen in meiosis at extraovarian sites, presumably far from the influence of the somatic cells of the ovary. In some prosimian species, nests of oogonia do not enter meiosis before birth but show meiosis during adult life (11).

In the ovary the shift from mitosis to meiosis is very sharp (12). It does not seem possible to hasten experimentally the initiation of meiosis. In the rabbit, it is not possible to show induction of meiosis by 3-day-old ovaries with meiotic cells on fetal ovaries obtained 2 weeks before the expected onset of meiosis (13).

In the hamster I have observed that meiosis can be induced in ovaries obtained only 1 day before the normal initiation *in vivo* (14).

In insects, experiments have strongly suggested that ecdysteroids secreted by the thoracic gland are involvedl in the initiation of meiosis in the testis of the locust *Schistocerea gregaria* (15) and the ovary of a riduvidid bug *Panstrongylus megistus* (16). In studies involving the left ovary of the chicken the results tend to indicate that the onset of meiosis depends on cells of the ovarian cortex (17). It has been shown in the mouse, hamster, and the rat that the onset of meiosis is dependent on cells in the ovary and the periovarian tissue.

THE RETE OVARII

The rete ovarii is formed by cells from the mesonephros. Morphological studies have indicated that the rete is an important source of follicular cells of the cat, mink, ferret (18), and mouse (19). In other studies involving sheep (20) and mice (21), the mesonephros is described as the exclusive source of the somatic cells of the ovary.

In the hamster, the extraovarian rete is easily detected as an epithelial formation in the hilar zone but its importance as a source of follicular cells has not been studied in detail (22). In the rat, as in other species, the role of the mesonephros is less dominant (23).

In mouse transplantation experiments it was clear that the external portion of the rete was most important for the formation of the primordial follicles (24). If all somatic cells of the mouse ovary are derived from the mesonephros, there are differences among the various cells of the rete ovarii.

MEIOSIS IN THE MOUSE

It has been accepted that ovaries removed before the onset of meiosis become sterile with degeneration of the germ cells after a few days in culture (25,26). Meiosis proceeds normally if the explant is obtained at a later stage (25,27).

When mouse ovaries were grafted into a immunologically incompetent "nude mouse," only those explants retaining the "rete ovarii" developed primordial follicles. The ovarian pieces free of the rete ovarii lost most of the germ cells and few reached the zygotene stage (28). When these studies were extended to *in vitro* conditions, it was possible to demonstrate that older ovaries, or the medium in which older ovaries were maintained could induce meiosis in younger ovaries, obtained on day 11 post conception (meiosis in the mouse starts on day 12 post conception) (29). It was also demonstrated that 14 day fetal ovaries with the rete ovarii attached (30), pubertal testis or rete testis conditioned medium (31) could induce meiosis in fetal testis. Similar studies on the testis are not available in other species.

THE RAT OVARY

The importance of the extraovarian rete has been confirmed in the hamster (32), but not in the rat (33). An external rete ovarii cannot be seen in the rat on day 13 of gestation when the ovary lays directly on the mesonephros and cannot be separated from it. Later, on day 17 of gestation, the rete can be seen as a "cell system with extensive continuity between the mesonephric epithelium and the ovary" (34).

Ovaries removed with some of the underlying mesonephros on day 13 and 14 of pregnancy show germ cells in meiosis after 5 days and 4 days of culture, respectively (33). Meiosis *in vivo* starts on the 17th day of pregnancy. The addition of sex steroids, male inhibin, ram rete fluid, or antiestrogen do not seem to alter the course of meiotic prophase (5).

It was possible to demonstrate *in vitro* that the 5-day-old isolated hamster ovary can significantly accelerate the initiation of meiosis in 13-day-old rat ovary. Practically all germ cells have entered meiosis after 6 days of coculture, a majority having reached zygotene and pachytene stages (35). Quantitative studies, however, have not been done.

TIME-STUDY EXPERIMENTS IN THE HAMSTER

From the evidence presented, the observations in freemartins and chimeric mice and the experiments in the mouse, hamster, and rat as well as in insects and birds, have strongly indicated that somatic cells or their products influence the initiation of meiosis. In the ovary there seems to be a fixed stage of development in which meiosis can start. The male germ cells seem to be ready to initiate meiosis at the same time as the female germ cells, but the initiation of meiosis in the fetal testis *in vitro* was only clearly demonstrated in the mouse.

The studies cited previously give no indication of the dynamics of the process during the development of the ovary or the possible functional relations between ovary and the external rete ovarii.

In order to better understand these results (36), it is important to notice that instead of histological observation of the presence of meiotic cells and the most advanced stage reached, a more quantitative method was developed. In this method, the cells are dissociated after hypotonic treatment, stained, and counted. The distribution of oogonia and cells at various stages of the prophase is then analyzed statistically.

Hamster ovaries obtained on the 14th day of pregnancy become sterile and meiotic figures are not seen when maintained alone. However, if they are cultured together with older ovaries, germ cells survive and are capable of entering meiosis.

When these fetal ovaries are cultured for 7 days together with ovaries obtained from the 15th day of pregnancy to the 15th day postpartum the results show that the meiosis inducing capacity of the ovaries increases with age up to day 5 postpartum, remains stable until day 15, and falls abruptly soon thereafter. The number of cells in meiosis is lower than that seen *in vivo* at the same age but all phases of the prophase can be seen (Fig. 1).

Very different results are obtained when the fetal ovaries are cocultured with the periovarian tissue containing the remnants of the mesonephros or external rete ovarii. In this case there is a very sharp period of activity that peaks on day 5 postpartum. Fetal ovaries cul-

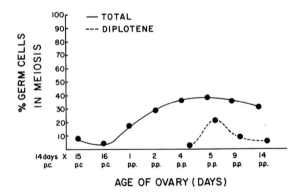

Fig. 1. Haploidin I (meiosis inducing) and haploidin M (meiosis maturing) activities of ovaries of different ages. p.c., Postconception; p.p., postpartum. The activity of haploidin I reaches a peak on day 5 p.p. and remains stable until 14 p.p. The maturing activity, broken line, (haploidin M) follows the pattern of the extraovarian tissue seen in Fig. 2.

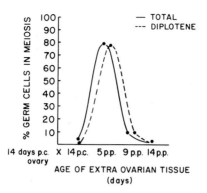

Fig. 2. Haploidin M (meiosis maturing) activity of the periovarian tissue. p.c., Post-conception; p.p., postpartum. Practically all germ cells reached the diplotene stage. The activity is short lasting in contrast to the haploidin I activity in the ovary. The maturing activity must increase considerably the weak meiosis inducing activity in the fetal ovary.

tured with day 5 rete ovarii show a very large number of cells in meiosis, most having reached the diplotene stage (Fig. 2).

The activity demonstrated by the periovarian tissues decreases rapidly after day 5 postpartum in contrast with the meiosis induction capacity still present in the older ovaries. In Figs. 1 and 2 it can be seen that when only cells in diplotene are taken into consideration the results obtained with ovaries and periovarian tissues are very similar.

The comparison of the two experiments brings to light two different actions; the capacity to initiate meiosis and the apparent ability to rush the cells to diplotene. The two actions are separated further by the time pattern that can be demonstrated.

Finally, when the fetal ovaries are cultured with ovaries attached to their external rete, the results show a great similarity with those seen with the rete alone, the notable difference being that the clearly demonstrated inducing activity of the ovary after day 5 postpartum is not seen. This fact would indicate that the rete becomes inhibitory. To test further this inhibitory activity of the external rete, the fetal ovaries were cultured simultaneously with 5-day-old ovaries and 12-day-old periovarian tissue. The results indicate that there is little reduction in the number of cells in meiosis but there is a very significant reduction in the number of cells reaching diplotene from 35 to 2% (37).

In summary, the time studies in the hamster have demonstrated a complicated regulation of the prophase of the first meiotic division. The results concerning the meiosis activity of the ovaries and extra ovarian tissues have broadened the observations in the mouse. The

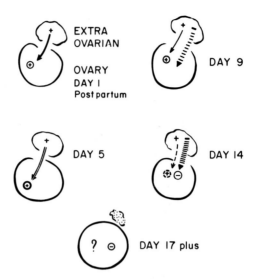

Fig. 3. Regulation of the prophase of the first meiotic divison in the hamster ovary. Day 1 postpartum (p.p.): Cells from the mesonephros that colonize the ovary and the cells in the extra ovarian tissues stimulate the germ cells to switch from mitosis to meiosis (haploidin I). Day 5 p.p.: The meiosis inducing activity is supplemented by a strong maturating action of the rete externa (haploidin M) indicated by the double arrow. The meiosis inducing activity of the ovary reaches its maximum. Day 9 p.p. and 14 p.p.: While the meiosis inducing activity of the haploidin I remains stable, the maturing action of haploidin M fades and is substituted by an inhibitory action of the periovarian tissues (haploidin S) as the prophase is arrested at the diplotene stage. Day 17 p.p.: Only the oocytes in the arrested stage that formed primordial follicles remain. Haploidins cannot be detected in the ovary or periovarian tissue.

finding of an inhibitory activity in older periovarian tissues was unexpected. There are no oogonia in 14-day-old ovaries and the inhibition of diplotene does not seem to serve any purpose. It can be speculated that this inhibitory activity may be related to the arrest at diplotene or to the degeneration of the germ cells during meiosis, two events for which we have no other reasonable explanation.

Based on the results described in this paper and those obtained in the mouse, Fig. 3 summarizes our ideas as to how the prophase is controlled.

HAPLOIDINS

From this rather limited amount of experimental data in the mouse and the hamster, the existence of various substances specifically involved in the onset, development and arrest of the meiotic process have been suggested (21,36). At this time, these substances are labeled meiosis inducing, meiosis inhibiting, and meiosis maturing. I would use this opportunity to propose a nomenclature that could serve as this field develops.

The substances involved in the process of meiosis could be called haploidins, since the main role of meiosis is the production of haploid cells.

At this time the following haploidins can be postulated:

Haploidin I: starts or allows the switch from mitosis
Haploidin M: accelerates the process to diplotene
Haploidin S: arrests meiosis at diplotene
Haploidin T: prevents meiosis in the fetal testis

Haploidin S could be similar or identical to the "oocyte maturation inhibitor" described in follicular fluid.

This scheme can clarify possible ways to handle the problem experimentally and indicate conceptual and methodological approaches that can be developed. As Joseph Conrad wrote:

> He who wants to persuade should put his trust not in the right argument but in the right word

It can be stated safely that the experimental research of the mechanisms of control of meiosis just started to bear fruit. The conditions are propitious for good progress in the near future.

ACKNOWLEDGMENT

This work was supported in part by a grant of the USPHS (National Institutes of Health—NICHD 13087).

REFERENCES

1. Moses, M. J. (1968) *Annu. Rev. Genet.* **2**, 263–412.
2. Stern, H., and Hotta, Y. (1973) *Annu. Rev. Genet.* **7**, 37–66.
3. Westergaard, M., and von Wettstein, D. (1972) *Annu. Rev. Genet* **6**, 71–110.
4. Brinster, R. L., and Harstad, H. (1977) *Exp. Cell Res.* **109**, 111–117.
5. Prépin, J., Vigier, B., and Jost, A. (1979) *Ann. Biol. Anim., Biochim., Biophys.* **19**(4B), 1263–1272.
6. Tarkowski, A. K. (1978) *In* "Genetic Mosaics and Chimeras in Mammals" (L. B. Russell, ed.), pp. 135–142. Plenum, New York.
7. Meistrich, M. L., and Trostle, P. K. (1975) *Exp. Cell Res.* **95**, 231–244.
8. Kofman-Alfaro, S., and Chandley, A. C. (1970) *Chromosoma* **31**, 404–420.
9. Stern, H., and Hotta, Y. (1980) *Mol. Cell. Biochem.* **29**, 145–158.

10. Firket, J. (1914) *Arch. Biol.* **29**, 201–351.
11. Kumar, T. C. A. (1968) *Proc. R. Soc. London, Ser. B* **169**, 167–176.
12. Mauléon, P. (1975) *Ann. Biol. Anim., Biochim., Biophys.* **15**, 725–738.
13. Byskov, A. G. (1979) *Ann. Biol. Anim., Biochim., Biophys.* **19**(4B), 1251–1262.
14. Fajer, A. B., Ances, I. G., Polakis, S. E., and Reese, A. H. (1977). *Gynecol. Invest.* **8**, 85–86.
15. Theresa Jones, R. (1978) *J. Cell Sci.* **31**, 145–163.
16. Furtado, A. (1979) *J. Insect. Physiol.* **25**, 561–570.
17. Erickson, G. F. (1974) *Dev. Biol.* **36**, 113–129.
18. Byskov, A. G. (1975) *J. Reprod. Fertil.* **45**, 201–209.
19. Byskov, A. G. (1978) *Biol. Reprod.* **19**, 720–735.
20. Zamboni, L., Bézard, J., and Mauléon, P. (1979) *Ann. Biol. Anim., Biochim., Biophys.* **19**(4B), 1153–1178.
21. Upadhyay, S., Luciani, J. M., and Zamboni, L. (1979) *Ann. Biol. Anim., Biochim., Biophys.* **19**(4B), 1179–1210.
22. Nakano, A. (1960) *Okajimas Folia Anat. Jpn.* **35**, 183–217.
23. Merchant-Larios, H. (1979) *Ann. Biol. Anim., Biochim, Biophys.* **19**(4B), 1219–1230.
24. Byskov, A. G., Skakkebaek, N. E., Stafanger, G., and Peter, H. (1977) *J. Anat.* **123**, 77–86.
25. Wolff, E. (1952) *C. R. Hebd. Seances Acad. Sci.* **234**, 1712–1714.
26. Challoner, S. (1975) *J. Anat.* **119**, 149–156.
27. Martinovitch, P. N. (1938) *Proc. R. Soc. London, Ser. B* **235**, 232–249.
28. Byskov, A. G. (1974) *Nature (London)* **252**, 396–397.
29. Byskov, A. G., and Saxen, L. (1976) *Dev. Biol.* **52**, 193–200.
30. Grinsted, J., Byskov, A. G., and Andreasen, M. P. (1979) *J. Reprod. Fertil.* **56**, 653–656.
31. Byskov, A. G. (1978) *Int. J. Androl., Suppl.* **2**, 29–38.
32. O, W. S., and Baker, T. G., (1976) *J. Reprod. Fertil.* **48**, 399–401.
33. Rivelis, C., Prépin, J., Vigier, B., and Jost, A. (1976) *C. R. Hebd. Seances Acad. Sci.* **282**, 1429–1434.
34. Stein, L. E., and Anderson, C. H. (1979) *Anat. Rec.* **193**, 197–212.
35. Fajer, A. B., and Prépin, J. (1980) Unpublished results.
36. Fajer, A. B., Schneider, J., McCall, D., Ances, I. G., and Polakis, E. S. (1979) *Ann. Biol. Anim., Biochim., Biophys.* **19**(4B), 1273–1278.
37. Fajer, A. B., and Conally, J. (1979) Unpublished results.

PART II

GERM CELL PRODUCTION

Production of Germ Cells and Regulation of Meiosis

A. G. BYSKOV AND J. GRINSTED

The Finsen Laboratory
The Finsen Institute
Copenhagen, Denmark

INTRODUCTION

The production of germ cells is dependent on multiple intrinsic and extrinsic factors that influence the germ cells and the gonads from early embryonic stages throughout life. The germ cells must settle within the gonadal anlage in order to survive and differentiate. The gonadal anlage must differentiate into testicular or ovarian tissue according to the genetic sex to create the right surroundings necessary for germ cell differentiation and for the establishment of the feedback mechanisms to the brain. A finely regulated interaction between somatic cells and germ cells controls the transformation by meiosis of the diploid germ cells to the halploid sperm or egg.

THE PRIMORDIAL GERM CELLS: THE GONIA

The primordial germ cells, the gonia, are undifferentiated, mitotically dividing germ cells of both sexes. The gonia were first recognized in the yolk sac endoderm (1). By amoeboid movements they travel through the hindgut and the dorsal mesentery to reach the gonadal ridge at the ventral part of the mesonephros (for review, see 2). During migration and after reaching the gonads the gonia continue to divide by mitosis. In the 8-day-old fetal rat only few gonia, all situated in extragonadal sites, are recognized (3). About 3 days later the gonads are populated by approximately 10,000 germ cells. After 2 more days,

BIOREGULATORS OF REPRODUCTION

when the gonadal sex becomes morphologically recognizable, the number increased to 20,000, and a day later to about 30,000 (4). Also, in other mammals, the number of germ cells increases rapidly, often exponentially during the early stages of gonadogenesis (mouse: 5; man: 6;7).

The male and female gonia are morphologically identical in spite of their cytogenetic difference. Even after the gonads achieve the characteristic structures of a testis or an ovary, the spermatogonia and ovogonia often remain alike for an extended period. The first obvious signs revealing their genetic divergence are a dissimilarity in proliferation and the stage of development where they commence meiosis.

THE PREMEIOTIC DIFFERENTIATION OF THE GERM CELLS

In the differentiated gonads the germ cells, which are still able to divide by mitosis, are called spermatogonia or prespermatogonia in the male and ovogonia or oogonia in the female. When the germ cells enter meiosis they are termed spermatocytes and ovocytes or oocytes, respectively. The final product of haploid germ cells are the spermium and the ovum (see, for example, 8;9).

Among female mammalian species two different patterns of gonadal and germ cell differentiation have been described as "immediate meiosis" and "delayed meiosis" (10). Immediate meiosis refers to germ cells that enter meiosis at the time of gonadal differentiation. In species with delayed meiosis, a time period of varying length, the "delay period," separates the time of sex differentiation and onset of meiosis.

The time schedule and patterns of multiplication that the male germ cells follow resemble those of their female counterparts, with immediate or delayed meiosis. Certain mechanisms, which influence the mitotic and meiotic kinetics, seem to work almost simultaneously in the developing testis and ovary of the same species.

THE OVOGONIA

Species with immediate and delayed meiosis are not only distinguished by the different timing of the meiotic initiation in respect to gonadal sex differentiation, but also by differences in ovarian morphology and hormone production.

The germ cells in species with immediate meiosis tend to be distributed equally or in larger groups within the ovarian tissue at the time when meiosis begins. No sex steroid hormones—or only small amounts—are secreted by these ovaries before the first follicles form. In species with delayed meiosis the germ cells are confined to cords during the delay-period, and sex steriod hormones, sometimes in large amounts, are produced by the ovaries during the delay-period. However, at the time when meiosis starts, the cords deteriorate, and the hormone level becomes low or unmeasurable (for review, see 10).

Both in species with immediate and delayed meiosis, a wave of mitosis among the ovogonia introduces the onset of meiosis (for review, see 11). In ovaries of fetal pigs and rabbits the delay-period is characterized by a rather low percent of mitosis of the ovogonia (Table I). However, shortly before meiosis starts the number of mitotic figures increases (Table I).

The rate of degeneration appears to be low in the population of ovogonia (4). The number of germ cells will, therefore, increase until meiosis has begun (7).

THE SPERMATOGONIA

The first signs of testicular differentiation include gathering of the gonia and their enclosure into testicular cords. Immediately thereafter a considerable amount of testosterone is produced by the testis.

The following pattern of proliferation and differentiation of the spermatogonia or prespermatogonia prior to spermatogenesis has

TABLE I
Germ Cells of Fetal and Immature Porcine Testes and Ovaries[a]

Age in days	Ovogonia	Spermatogonia	Mitosis ♀	Mitosis ♂	Meiosis ♀	Meiosis ♂	Number counted ♀	Number counted ♂
35 p.c.	96.1 (47.2)	97.5 (9.0)	3.0	2.2	0.9	0.3	235	321
42 p.c.	75.7 (62.9)	96.7 (15.8)	5.3	3.3	21.4	—	412	209
50 p.c.	59.1 (29.8)	98.8 (2.0)	2.7	1.2	38.2	—	655	246
76 p.c.	43.0 (36.5)	98.5 (2.4)	—	1.0	57.0	0.5	446	206
95 p.c.	2.0 —	99.7 (6.8)	—	0.3	98.0	—	202	311
56 p.p.	—	98.1 (0.9)	—	1.9	100	—	300	319
70 p.p.	—	97.7 (1.3)	—	1.6	100	—	300	306

[a] Distribution of spermatogonia/ovogonia, preloptotene (Number in parentheses), mitotic figures, and more advanced stages of the meiotic prophase expressed as percentages of total number of germ cells counted.

been described as prespermatogenesis (12). In the rat this pattern starts with a period of high mitotic activity during early testicular differentiation, followed by a resting period with few mitotic divisions and a seond wave of mitosis which introduces spermatogenesis at puberty.

In some species as the rat and the mouse the first wave of mitosis occurs shortly after gonadal sex differentiation (13;14). In both species it coincides in time with the onset of meiosis in the female gonad (immediate meiosis). In other species in which the females show delayed meiosis, the mitotic activity of the spermatogonia during the delay-period is rather low. However, simultaneously with the onset of meiosis in the female, a transient high mitotic activity is seen in the male germ cells (rabbit: 15; pig: Table I).

The second period with high mitotic activity among the spermatogonia occurs prior spermatogenesis (4).

In different species the first period of proliferation is followed by a wave of degeneration in the population of spermatogonia. In the fetal rat testis, where this proliferation occurs around day 17 to 18 (13), a large percent of the rat spermatogonia are dying during the following week (16). A similar pattern is seen in the neonatal rabbit in which the first wave of mitosis is seen at the time of birth (15). During the second week of life almost 50% of the spermatogonia in the rabbit are found dying in the center of the testicular cords.

The atretic boost of the spermatogonia coincide in time with a drastic decrease in the level of testicular testosterone (for review, see 17).

It would be interesting during this period to analyze the relationship between testosterone level—or sex steroid level—and germ cell kinetics and differentiation.

REGULATION OF MEIOSIS

Meiosis consists of two consecutive divisions, which transform the diploid germ cells to haploid gametes. Before entering meiosis the diploid germ cells pass through a premeiotic phase of DNA synthesis at the end of which the germ cells are equipped with a DNA amount of 4c. During the first meiotic division both the DNA content and the chromosomes are halved and the germ cell now has 2c DNA. In the second meiotic division only the DNA content, but not the chromosome number, is halved. Thus, the haploid gametes contain only 1c DNA and half a number of chromosomes compared to somatic cells.

The first meiotic prophase consists of five stages: preleptotene, leptotene, zygotene, pachytene, and diplotene. It is a unique prophase since homologous chromosomes in zygotene stage are paired, a process which is recognized as synaptonemal complexes. During this pairing the paternal and maternal genes are exchanged. In the male the first meiotic prophase is transitory although slow compared to the prophase of a mitosis (18). It leads directly to the first and second meiotic division followed by the complicated differentiation to a sperm. In the female only the first 4 stages are transitory, and the oocyte remains for a long time in the diplotene stage. Not before ovulation approaches, the ovocyte may enter the metaphase of the first meiotic division. The second meiotic division is normally finished before the ovum is fertilized.

In both sexes a high percent of the germ cells degenerate during the meiotic prophase. The preleptotene stage presents an ambiguous stage. In the ovary most germ cells in this stage have the capacity to continue in the meiotic prophase (19). But in the fetal and immature testes in which many germ cells enter preleptotene stage, they will not proceed further. These cells either die or may eventually return to an interphase stage (20). The pachytene stage may be the most traumatic phase of meiosis. More than half the peak germ cell population will degenerate, often in pachytene stage, during the meiotic prophase. In the human ovary, for example, only about 5% of the maximal number of germ cells present in fetal life remain at birth (7,21). Also in the mammalian testis the pachytene stage appears to be the most sensitive stage in spermatogenesis (17).

Although sex steroid hormones and gonadotropins are necessary in spermatocyte as well as in ovocyte differentiation, neither hormone is needed for or trigger initiation of meiosis. Experiments infer that the gonads produce two substances, one which induces meiosis, the meiosis-inducing substance, MIS, and another which prevents meiosis, the meiosis-preventing substance, MPS (22). The two substances might interact with one another and with sex steriod hormones in the regulation of meiosis (10).

MEIOSIS IN THE FEMALE

In all female mammals meiosis commences early, often in fetal life (23). It is typical that the first germ cells that enter the meiotic prophase are those situated in the basal central area of the gonad. Those cells are the first to come in contact with the mesonephric-derived rete cells, which seem to be responsible for induction of meiosis (24). Gradually also the more peripherally placed germ cells enter meiosis.

The time which elapses between the appearance of the first meiotic figures and when the last ovogonia enter meiosis varies greatly between species (for review, see 25). During development, therefore, species with larger ovaries often contain germ cells at different stages of differentiation. Mitotically dividing ovogonia may reside in the perpipheral areas; ovocytes in different stages of meiosis are situated closer to the center and small follicles may already be formed in the center of the ovary. This topographical observation initiated experiments which showed that the mesonephric-derived rete system in the developing ovary secreted the meiosis-inducing substance, MIS. *In vitro* studies of the fetal and neonatal hamster ovary indicate that the MIS activity of the rete system is transient: Fetal and neonatal rete systems up to day 5 postpartum (meiosis starts the first day after birth) induce meiosis in 14-day-old fetal hamster ovaries, whereas older rete systems have an inhibitory action on the onset of meiosis (26).

The arrest of ovocytes in diplotene stage is still not understood. However, in small and large graafian follicles the follicle fluid as well as the granulosa cells in culture inhibit maturation of large oocytes, i.e., resumption of meiosis (27). This inhibition is more pronounced in smaller follicles than in larger ones.

It is tempting to assume that the enclosure and separation from the surroundings of the diplotene oocyte results in the meiotic arrest.

MEIOSIS IN THE MALE

During normal testicular and germ cell differentiation the male germ cells do not enter and proceed through meiosis and commence spermatogenesis until puberty (for review, see 28). However, the male germ cells have the capacity to enter meiosis prematurely, as was observed in the fetal mouse testis: Spermatogonia left outside the newly formed testicular cords entered meiosis (leptotene and zygotene stages) when situated close to the developing epididymis or rete testis (14). However, these meiotic germ cells die within a few days; they do not proceed further than zygotene before they become pyknotic. Meiosis in fetal male germ cells can also be induced experimentally *in vitro*. This phenomenon is characteristically accompanied with impaired or total absence of testicular cords (29,30). It appears that the enclosure of the male germ cells ensures that meiosis does not occur until much later in life. The enclosure also provides the germ cells with a milieu in which they are able to survive. All germ cells left outside the cords will eventually die.

The fetal Sertoli cells enclosing the germ cells during early testicular development might be responsible for prevention of meiosis during fetal life (31).

The initiation of meiosis at puberty could be a result of decreasing activity or amount of MPS within the testis, as indicated by culture experiments. Meiosis is prevented in fetal mouse ovaries if they are cultured in media which previously served as culture media for fetal testicular tissues (32). However, media in which puberal bull testes or adult human testes had grown did not inhibit the initiation of meiosis in fetal mouse ovaries when cultured in these media. In contrast, the puberal and adult testes media contained substances that induced meiosis in fetal mouse testes (33). It is, therefore, suggested that spermatogenesis is initiated at puberty when the influence of MPS decreases and is overcome by MIS. MIS is present in epididymis and rete testis in fetal life as well as in adulthood. (33).

The architecture of the testicular cords presumably plays an important role in the regulation of germ cell kinetics. Studies of the human fetal testis describe two types of Sertoli cells: a dark meiosis-inducing cell (MI-cell) and a light meiosis-preventing cell (MP-cell). It was suggested that meiosis in the testis is controlled by alternating influences of these two cell types (34). It has been pointed out that the blood–testis barrier, which develops at puberty, is essential not only for the regulation of meiosis and spermatogenesis but also for the conservation of the germinal stem cell population in the basal compartment of the seminiferous cords (35,36).

CONCLUDING REMARKS

Being a germ cell is a luxurious as well as a dangerous business. Although this chapter almost exclusively describes events that take place within the gonads and not the numerous interactions of the rest of the body, it is obvious that the germ cells will succeed only if a series of factors are present at the right time and site.

Comparative studies of structure and physiology of the developing testis and ovary may be inspiring when control mechanisms of production and differentiation of germ cells are known.

ACKNOWLEDGMENTS

We wish to gratefully acknowledge Professor Nils Bjørkman, the Royal Veterinary and Agriculture University, Copenhagen, Dr. Inga Elisabet Hägerstrand and Professor

Karl Kristoffersen, the University Hospital of Odense, for providing fetal pig and fetal human gonads, respectively. In addition we wish to thank Anni Bang Mørch, John Post, and Lene Ahrenst for skilful technical assistance.

The work was supported by the Danish Medical Research Council No. 512-15090 and 512-16139, and by the Nordic Insulin Foundation, EURATOM contract No. 120-73-1, BIO-DK, King Christian the 10th Foundation and Martha and Erik Scheibel's Foundation.

REFERENCES

1. Witschi, E. (1948) *Contrib. Embryol. Carnegie Inst.* **32**, 67–80.
2. Hardisty, M. W. (1978) *In* "The Vertebrate Ovary" (R. E. Jones, ed.), pp. 1–45. Plenum, New York.
3. Eddy, E. M., and Clark, J. M. (1975) *In* "Electron Microscopic Concepts of Secretion" (M. Hess, ed.), pp. 151–167. Wiley, New York.
4. Beaumont, H. M., and Mandl, A. M. (1963) *J. Embryol. Exp. Morphol.* **11**, 715–740.
5. Mintz, B. (1959) *Arch. Anat. Microsc. Morphol. Exp.* **48**, 155–172..
6. Witschi, E. (1962) *In* "The Ovary" (H. G. Grady and D. E. Smidt, eds.), pp. 1–10. Williams & Wilkins, Baltimore, Maryland.
7. Baker, T. G. (1963) *Proc. R. Soc. London, Ser. B* **158**, 417–433.
8. Witschi, E. (1956) "Development of Vertebrates." Saunders, Philadelphia, Pennsylvania.
9. Byskov, A. G. (1980) *In* 'Mechanisms of Sex Differentiation in Animals and Man' (C. R. Austin and R. E. Edwards, eds.). Academic Press, New York (in press).
10. Byskov, A. G. (1979) *Ann. Biol. Anim., Biochim., Biophys.* **19**, 1251–1261.
11. Peters, H., and McNatty, K. P. (1980) "The Ovary." Granada Press.
12. Hilscher, W. (1970) *Andrology* **1**, 17–28.
13. Hilscher, B., Hilscher, W., Bülthoff-Ohnolz, B., Krämer, U., Birke, A., Pelzer, H., and Gauss, G. (1974) *Cell Tissue Res.* **154**, 443–470.
14. Byskov, A. G. (1978) *Ann. Biol. Anim., Biochim. Biophys.* **18**, 327–334.
15. Gondos, B., and Byskov, A. G. (1981) *Cell Tiss. Res.* (in press).
16. Franchi, L. L., and Mandl, A. M. (1964) *J. Embryol. Exp. Morphol.* **12**, 289–308.
17. Setchell, B. P. (1978) "The Mammalian Testis." Paul Elek, London.
18. Steinberger, E., and Steinberger, A. (1975) *In* "Handbook of Physiology" (R. E. Greep and E. B. Astwood, eds.), Vol. V, pp. 1–19. Williams & Wilkins, Baltimore, Maryland.
19. Luciani, J. M., Bézard, J., Devictor-Vuillet, M., and Mauléon, P. (1979) *Ann. Biol. Anim., Biochim., Biophys.* **19**, 1241–1250.
20. Luciani, J. M., Devictor, M., and Stahl, A. (1977) *J. Embryol. Exp. Morphol.* **38**, 175–186.
21. Block, E. (1952) *Acta Anat.* **14**, 108–123.
22. Byskov, A. G., and Saxén, L. (1976) *Dev. Biol.* **52**, 193–200.
23. Peters, H. (1970) *Philos. Trans. R. Soc. London* **259**, 91–101.
24. Byskov, A. G. (1975) *J. Reprod. Fertil.* **45**, 201–209.
25. Mauléon. P. (1979) *In* "Control of Ovulation" (D. B. Crighton, N. B. Haynes, G. R. Foxcroft, and G. E. Lamming, eds.), pp. 141–158. Butterworth, London.
26. Fajer, A. B., Schneider, J. A., McCatt, D., Ances, I. G., and Polakis, E. S. (1979) *Ann. Biol. Anim., Biochim., Biophys.* **19**, 1273–1278.

27. Tsafriri, A., Pomerantz, S. H., and Channing, C. P. (1976) *Biol. Reprod.* **14,** 511–516.
28. Gondos, B. (1977) *In* "The Testis" (A. D. Johnson and W. R. Gomez, eds.), pp. 1–37. Academic Press, New York.
29. Grinsted, J., Byskov, A. G., and Andreasen, M. P. (1979) *J. Reprod. Fertil.* **56,** 653–656.
30. Byskov, A. G., and Grinsted, J. (1981) *Science* (in press).
31. Jost, A., Magre, S., and Cressent, M. (1972) *Adv. Biosci.* **10,** 3–13.
32. Byskov, A. G. (1978) *Int. J. Androl., Suppl.* **2,** 29–38.
33. Grinsted, J., and Byskov, A. G. (1981) *Fertil. Steril.* (in press).
34. Wartenberg, H. (1978) *Andrologica* **10,** 1–21.
35. Dym, M., and Fawcett, D. W. (1970) *Biol. Reprod.* **3,** 308–326.
36. Setchell, B. P., and Waites, G. M. H. (1975) *In* "Handbook of Physiology" (R. O. Greep and E. B. Astwood, eds.), Vol. V, pp. 143–172. Williams & Wilkins, Baltimore, Maryland.

Programming of Gene Expression during Mammalian Oogenesis

PAUL M. WASSARMAN, JEFFREY D. BLEIL,[1]
STEPHANIE M. CASCIO, MICHAEL J. LaMARCA,[2]
GAIL E. LETOURNEAU, SUZANNE C. MROZAK,
AND RICHARD M. SCHULTZ[3]

*Department of Biological Chemistry and Laboratory
of Human Reproduction and Reproductive Biology
Harvard Medical School, Boston, Massachusetts*

INTRODUCTION

The process of oogenesis has traditionally been of intense interest to scientists since, for more than a century, it has been recognized that the mature egg contains a reserve of developmental potential upon which the progress of early embryogenesis depends (1,2). In general, it has been found that the genetic, nutritional, synthetic, energetic, and regulatory requirements of the early embryo are, indeed, met to varying degrees by the mature eggs of both mammalian and nonmammalian animal species (2).

While scientists may disagree as to the precise developmental period inferred by the term "oogenesis" (e.g., 3,4), we have aligned ourselves with Webster (5) who defines oogenesis very broadly as the "formation of the egg and its preparation for fertilization and development." Such a definition "embraces all those cellular, molecular, and physiological phenomena involved in producing a cell which is capa-

[1] Present address: Medical Research Council, Laboratory of Molecular Biology, Cambridge CB22QH, England.

[2] Present address: Department of Biology, Lawrence University, Appleton, Wisconsin 54911.

[3] Present address: Department of Biology, University of Pennsylvania, Philadelphia, Pennsylvania 19104.

BIOREGULATORS OF REPRODUCTION

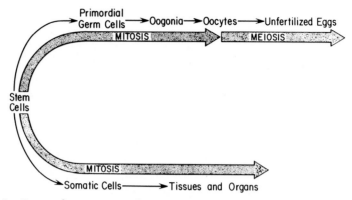

Fig. 1. Stages of oogenesis resulting in the transformation of stem cells into oocytes.

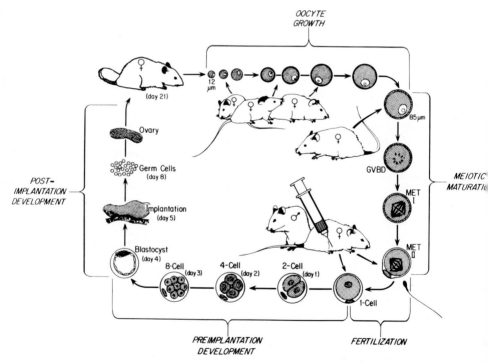

Fig. 2. Schematic representation of oogenesis and early embryogenesis in the mouse. Juvenile and sexually mature (adult) mice are depicted in order to indicate the sources of growing and fully grown oocytes, unfertilized eggs, and early embryos used in the experiments described in this chapter.

ble of expressing and maintaining the characteristics of the species"
(6).

In this chapter we review, principally, the results of our own investigations of the period of oogenesis during which the nongrowing mammalian oocyte is transformed into an unfertilized egg (Figs. 1 and 2). In particular, we have focused much of our attention on gene expression during this period of oogenesis, so as to be able to assess the manner and extent of the contribution of the mammalian egg to the successful development of the preimplantation embryo.

OOGENESIS IN THE MOUSE

Oogenesis in the mouse really begins with the formation of primordial germ cells (PGCs) in the 8-day-old embryo (3,4,7–9; Figs. 1 and 2). These large cells are found in that region of the allantois arising from the primitive streak; consequently, the embryonic rudiment of the allantois and the caudal end of the primitive streak may be considered the regions of PGC formation. The PGCs migrate into the endoderm and then along the dorsal mesentery to the genital ridges found in the roof of the coelom. These PGCs are the sole source of adult germ cells.

As early as day 12 of embryogenesis, after migration of the PGCs is complete, a few oogonia enter the preleptotene and then leptotene stage of the first meiotic prophase. It is during preleptotene that the final DNA synthesis takes place in preparation for meiosis. Oocytes progress rapidly through the leptotene and zygotene stages and by day 16 of embryogenesis nearly all oocytes are in the pachytene stage of the first meiotic prophase. The first oocytes in the diplotene stage of prophase are seen by day 18 of embryogenesis, with their chromosomes exhibiting the characteristic chiasmata; chromosome pairing, crossing-over, and recombination having been completed. By the time of parturition a few oocytes have entered the late diplotene, or so-called dictyate stage, and by day 5 postpartum nearly all primary oocytes have reached dictyate of the first meiotic prophase where they will remain until stimulated to resume meiosis.

Shortly after birth, the mouse ovary is populated with thousands of small, primary oocytes arrested in late prophase of meiosis. Commencement of oocyte growth is apparently regulated within the ovary, the number of oocytes entering the growth phase being a function of the size of the pool of nongrowing oocytes (10,11). The oocyte and its surrounding follicle grow coordinately, progressing through a series of definable morphological stages (12). The oocyte completes its growth in the adult mouse before the formation of the follicular antrum; consequently, the majority of follicle growth occurs after the oocyte has stopped growing (13). Growth is continuous, ending in ovulation of a mature oocyte (unfertilized egg) or degeneration (atresia) of the oocyte and its follicle (14).

In the adult mouse, the oocyte grows from a diameter of about 12 μm to a terminal diameter of about 85 μm. Each oocyte is contained within a cellular follicle which grows concomitantly with the oocyte, from a single layer of a few flattened cells to three layers of cuboidal granulosa cells (approximately 900 cells) by the time the oocyte has completed its growth (15). The theca is first distinguishable, outside of and separated by a basement membrane from the granulosa cells, when the granulosa layer is two cell layers thick (approximately 400 cells). During a period of several days, while the oocyte remains a constant size, the follicle cells undergo rapid division, increasing to more than 50,000 cells and resulting, finally, in a follicle greater than 600 μm in diameter. The follicle exhibits an incipient antrum when it is several layers thick (approximately 6,000 cells) and, as the antrum expands, the oocyte takes up an acentric position surrounded by two or more layers of granulosa cells; the innermost layer of cells becomes columnar in shape and constitutes the cumulus oophorous.

In the sexually mature female mouse, fully grown oocytes in Graafian follicles resume meiosis and complete the first meiotic reductive division just prior to ovulation. The resumption of meiosis can be mediated by a hormonal stimulus *in vivo* or simply by the release of oocytes from their ovarian follicles into a suitable culture medium *in vitro* (16). The oocytes undergo nuclear progression from dictyate of the first meiotic prophase (4C) to metaphase II (2C) and remain at this stage of meiosis in the oviduct, or in culture, until fertilization or parthenogenetic activation takes place. Progression from dictyate (oocyte) to metaphase II (unfertilized egg) is termed "meiotic maturation," a process characterized by dissolution of the nuclear (germinal vesicle, GV) membrane, condensation of diffuse chromatin into distinct bivalents, separation of homologous chromosomes and emission of the first polar body, and arrest of meiotic progression at metaphase II. Meiotic maturation is of fundamental importance in mammalian development, since it is only after reaching metaphase II that the cell is competent to be fertilized.

GROWTH OF MOUSE OOCYTES

Completion of oocyte growth in the mouse takes approximately 2 weeks, a relatively short period of time in comparison to the months or years required for completion of growth of oocytes in many nonmammalian animal species (2). During its growth phase, while continually arrested in dictyate of the first meiotic prophase, the mouse oocyte undergoes about a 350-fold increase in volume that is accompanied by an impressive ultrastructural reorganization of its organelles and inclusions. Progressive changes in the oocyte's nucleoli, ribosomes, mitochondria, endoplasmic reticulum, Golgi complex, and surface all support the idea that growth of the mouse oocyte involves not just tremendous enlargement of the cell, but extensive alterations in its overall metabolism as well (17). Such changes in the phenotype of the cell are presumably reflected in a changing pattern of gene expression during this period of oogenesis.

MEIOTIC MATURATION OF MOUSE OOCYTES

The time sequence for meiotic maturation of mouse oocytes *in vitro* can be approximated as follows: 1–5 hours, GV breakdown and chromosome condensation occur; 5–10 hours, chromosomes line up on the metaphase I spindle; and 10–15 hours, separation of homologous chromosomes, emission of the first polar body, and lining up of chromosomes on the metaphase II spindle take place (Fig. 2). Certain of these events can be visualized clearly by staining mouse oocytes undergoing meiotic maturation *in vitro* with an immunofluorescent anti-tubulin probe (18; Fig. 3). It should be noted that mouse oocytes matured and fertilized *in vitro* have developed into viable fetuses following transplantation to the uteri of foster mothers (19).

RELATIONSHIP BETWEEN OOCYTE GROWTH AND MEIOTIC MATURATION

Oocytes at various stages of growth can be isolated from the ovaries of juvenile mice, 3 to 21 days of age (20–24). The average diameter of these oocytes increases from about 12 to 75 μm as the age of the donor mice increases from 3 to 21 days; consequently, it is possible to obtain a population of oocytes at a given stage of growth (±5 μm) by choosing donors of a given age. Such oocytes are viable, based upon a variety of morphological and biochemical criteria, and can be successfully cultured *in vitro* for at least 24 hours in a chemically defined medium.

Examination of the ability of growing mouse oocytes to undergo spontaneous meiotic maturation *in vitro* (21) has revealed that oocytes recovered from mice younger than 15 days of age (approximately 12–55 μm in diameter) are unable to resume meiosis. On the other hand, oocytes recovered from mice 15 days of age or older (approximately

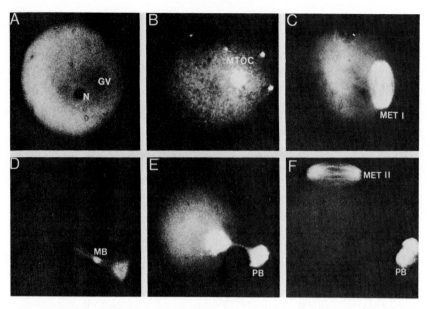

Fig. 3. Immunofluorescent staining of mouse oocytes and unfertilized eggs at various stages of meiotic maturation of oocytes *in vitro* as described by Wassarman and Fajiwara (18).

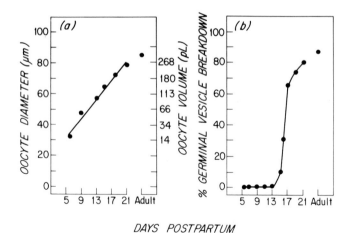

Fig. 4. Relationship between mouse oocyte size, ages of donor mice, and the ability of oocytes to resume meiosis *in vitro* as described by Sorensen and Wassarman (21) and Schultz and Wassarman (31).

60–75 μm in diameter) resume meiosis at a frequency that increases with the age of the donors (Fig. 4). Of the oocytes that resume meiosis *in vitro*, those from younger animals exhibit a high frequency of incomplete meiotic maturation with arrest after GV breakdown. Accordingly, the ratio of the number of oocytes that progress to metaphase II to the number that arrest following GV breakdown increases from 0.16 to 9.0 for 60 μm and fully grown (85 μm) oocytes, respectively. These results suggest that the ability to *resume* meiosis ("meiotic competence") is acquired at a specific stage of oocyte growth and that the ability to *complete* meiotic maturation is acquired subsequently.

GENE EXPRESSION DURING GROWTH AND MEIOTIC MATURATION OF MOUSE OOCYTES

In order to be able to relate phenotypic changes that characterize oocyte growth and meiotic maturation to changes in gene expression, we have examined the patterns and rates of synthesis of oocyte proteins during these periods of oogenesis. Such an analysis represents a first step toward understanding the regulation of oocyte growth and meiotic maturation in the mammal and, in addition, has permitted a comparison of oogenesis in mammalian and nonmammalian animal species at the molecular level.

EXPERIMENTAL APPROACHES

We have carried out experiments to determine whether or not absolute rates of synthesis of total oocyte proteins or specific oocyte proteins change during oocyte growth and meiotic maturation in the mouse. Because a change in the incorporation of a radioactively labeled amino acid ([^{35}S]methionine) into a protein with time (dI/dT) cannot be interpreted as a change in the *absolute* rate of protein synthesis (R) unless the specific activity of the amino acid pool (SA) is known, we have measured the sizes and specific activities of the free methionine pools in growing mouse oocytes. This has enabled us to convert *apparent* rates of protein synthesis into *absolute* rates, where $R = (dI/dT)/SA$.

To determine the size and specific activity of the oocyte's total methionine pool, we have used a modification of the procedure of Regier and Kafatos (25). This method is based upon the reaction of methionine with fluorodinitrobenzene (FDNB). The specific activity of [^{35}S]methionine is determined by reaction with [^{3}H]FDNB and mea-

suring the ratio of ^{35}S to ^{3}H in the resulting dinitrophenyl(DNP)-me-
thionine after purification by two-dimensional chromatography (Fig.
5). Because absolute rates determined by this method would be subject to serious error if a smaller compartment of the oocyte's methionine pool (i.e., "kinetic pool") actually served as precursor for protein
synthesis, we have also used a procedure analogous to that described
by Ecker (26). This method depends upon differential expansion of a
cell's amino acid pool, such that apparent rates of incorporation are al-

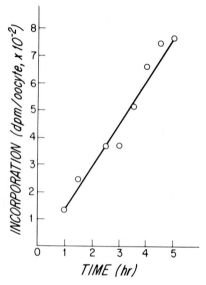

Fig. 5. Analysis of the sizes of total endogenous free methionine pools and absolute rates of protein synthesis in mouse oocytes, eggs, and embryos using the procedure described by Regier and Kafatos (25).

$$\text{Incorporation } (I) = \text{rate } (R) \times \text{specific activity } (SA) \times \text{time } (T)$$

where I(DPM) = incorporation of [^{35}S]MET into protein; R(mole/hr) = rate of incorporation of MET into protein; SA(DPM/mole) = specific activity of intracellular MET
pool; T(hr) = time of labeling, the formula is

$$R = \frac{dI/dT}{SA}$$

MET pool size:

$$\frac{SA_{exp}}{SA_{med}} = \frac{A}{(A + B)}$$

where A = moles of MET taken up into intracellular pool; B = size of endogenous
MET pool; SA_{exp} = specific activity of intracellular MET; SA_{med} = specific activity of
external MET (medium).

tered while absolute rates remain the same (Fig. 6). The rates of protein synthesis and sizes of free methionine pools determined by this "kinetic" method were found to be in excellent agreement with those determined by the [³H]FDNB method (24,27,28). This strongly suggests that the total intracellular free methionine pool serves as precursor for protein synthesis in mouse oocytes; a similar conclusion was drawn

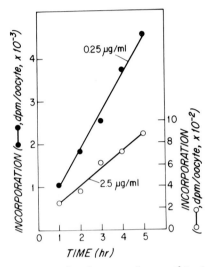

Fig. 6. Analysis of the sizes of endogenous free methionine "kinetic" pools and absolute rates of protein synthesis in mouse oocytes, eggs, and embryos using the procedure described by Ecker (26).

$$dI/dT = R \times SA$$
$$SA = L/P + G$$

where L(DPM) = [³⁵S]MET in acid-soluble fraction; P(moles) = size of endogenous MET pool; G(moles) = MET taken up into intracellular pool. The formula is

$$R = \frac{dI/dT}{L/(P + G)}$$

Therefore, under conditions of differential expansion of a cell's methionine pool, such that apparent rates of MET incorporation into protein are altered while absolute rates remain the same:

$$R = \frac{dI_1/dT}{\{L_1/(P + G_1)\}} \qquad R = \frac{dI_2/dT}{\{L_2/(P + G_2)\}}$$

Therefore,

$$\frac{dI_1/dT}{\{L_1/(P + G_1)\}} = \frac{dI_2/dT}{\{L_2/(P + G_2)\}}$$

Solve for P, the size of the endogenous ("kinetic") MET pool. Solve for R using P.

from results of experiments utilizing unfertilized eggs, as well as one and eight-cell mouse embryos (24,27,28).

High-resolution two-dimensional electrophoresis, as described by O'Farrell (29) and by LaMarca and Wassarman (30), has been used to examine changes in the patterns of protein synthesis during oocyte growth and meiotic maturation, and to determine absolute rates of synthesis of specific proteins (24,28,30). These procedures involve separation of radiolabeled proteins on polyacrylamide gels, first as a function of their isoelectric points and then as a function of their molecular weights. This results in the resolution of individual polypeptide chains and permits a qualitative appraisal of patterns of protein synthesis and a quantitative estimate of absolute rates of synthesis of specific proteins.

OVERALL PROTEIN SYNTHESIS DURING GROWTH OF MOUSE OOCYTES

Oocyte growth in the mouse is accompanied by the accumulation of about 30 ng of protein/cell, as well as by significant changes in the relative rates of synthesis of different oocyte proteins (24,31). As seen in Fig. 7, the overall pattern of proteins synthesized by growing oocytes 35 μm in diameter is significantly different from the pattern of proteins synthesized by oocytes 75 μm in diameter. For example, while polypeptides designated (A-E) are detected in 75 μm oocytes, they are absent in 35 μm oocytes. On the other hand, polypeptides (F-H), which are actively synthesized in 35 μm oocytes, are not detected in 75 μm oocytes; additional differences can be seen in regions of the gels designated J and K. These results simply illustrate overall differential gene expression, at the protein level, during oocyte growth.

During its growth phase the mouse oocyte undergoes a 350-fold increase in volume. The oocyte's intracellular methionine pool also increases about 350-fold during the growth phase, from 0.16 to 56 fmole/cell (Fig. 8A). Each doubling of oocyte volume is accompanied by a doubling of the size of the methionine pool, such that the concentration of intracellular free methionine remains constant at about 170 μM throughout oocyte growth. On the other hand, while the absolute rate of protein synthesis increases during oocyte growth, from 1.1 to 41.8 pg/hour per cell (Fig. 8B; Table I), the increase is only about 38-fold compared to the 350-fold increase in oocyte volume. Consequently, the absolute rate of protein synthesis, expressed on a unit volume basis, actually decreases during oocyte growth by about a factor of 10. It should be noted that we have found the absolute rate of

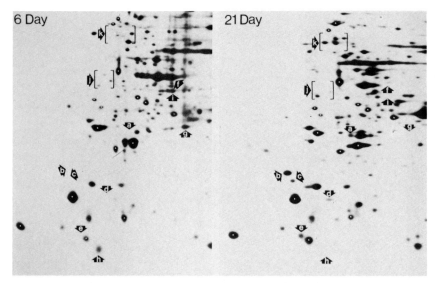

Fig. 7. High-resolution two-dimensional gel electrophoresis of [^{35}S]methionine-labeled proteins synthesized in growing mouse oocytes as described by Schultz *et al.* (24). Shown is a region of fluorograms depicting approximately 80 polypeptide chains synthesized in oocytes isolated from 6- and 21-day-old mice. Certain of the polypeptides, common to both fluorograms, are designated by a white dot so that they act as reference points with which to compare the fluorograms. The region of the fluorograms shown covers the pH range 4.5–6.5 and molecular weight range 12,000–125,000.

protein synthesis in fully grown oocytes to be the same using either denuded or cumulus-enclosed oocytes.*

Our measurements indicate that the preovulatory oocyte synthesizes and stores some 12.8 ng of protein; a value of some interest, since fully grown oocytes contain about 30 ng of protein (31). Therefore, the fully grown oocyte contains about twice as much protein as it is capable of synthesizing. This situation may reflect the presence of a "yolk-like" component in mouse oocytes which is synthesized elsewhere in the organism and taken up into oocytes by endocytosis. This would be analogous to the process of yolk accumulation in the amphibian, where as much as 80% of the total protein in fully grown oocytes is associated with yolk platelets; this protein is not synthesized by the oocyte, but by the liver (32). A number of studies have shown that mouse oocytes can selectively take up proteins from the blood (33–35), therefore, they at least have the capacity to accumulate a yolk

* Unpublished results of J. D. Bleil, S. M. Cascio, G. E. Letourneau, S. C. Mrozak, and P. M. Wassarman

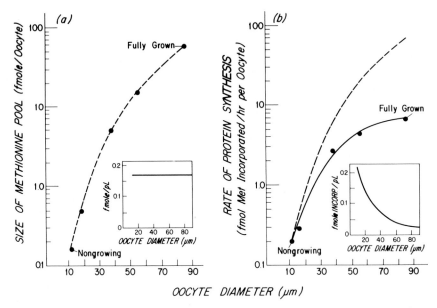

Fig. 8. Relationship between the diameter of growing mouse oocytes and sizes of the methionine pool (a) or absolute rates of protein synthesis (b) as described by Schultz *et al.* (24). The closed circles refer to the experimentally determined values for either methionine pool sizes (a) or absolute rates of protein synthesis (b). The broken lines are theoretical curves constructed by assuming a simple linear relationship between oocyte volume and either methionine pool size (a) or absolute rate of protein synthesis (b). Inset (a): Data converted to fmoles methionine/pl as a function of oocyte diameter. Inset (b): Data converted to fmoles methionine incorporated/pl as a function of oocyte diameter.

component made elsewhere. It remains to be determined, however, whether or not a specific protein(s) taken up by growing oocytes serves a nutritional function during early embryogenesis in the mouse.

TABLE I

Absolute Rates of Protein Synthesis and Sizes of Methionine Pool during Growth and Meiotic Maturation of Mouse Oocytes

Stage of oogenesis	Pool size (avg. ± SD) fmole Met/cell	Absolute rate (avg. ± SD) pg protein/hour per cell
Nongrowing oocyte (12 μm)	0.16 ± 0.08	1.10 ± 0.36
Fully grown oocyte (85 μm)	56 ± 19	41.8 ± 5.5
Unfertilized egg	74 ± 12	33.0 ± 2.2

OVERALL PROTEIN SYNTHESIS DURING MEIOTIC MATURATION OF MOUSE OOCYTES

Meiotic maturation, which involves the transformation of a fully grown oocyte into an unfertilized egg, is of fundamental importance in animal development. This relatively brief period of oogenesis includes not only meiotic events, but also the final metabolic steps that prepare the female gamete for fertilization and early embryogenesis (16,36).

As in the case of oocyte growth, meiotic maturation of mouse oocytes is accompanied by significant changes in the overall pattern of protein synthesis, as revealed by either one- or two-dimensional electrophoresis (31,37). We find that virtually all of the changes in protein synthesis observed take place *subsequent* to breakdown of the oocyte's GV, but are not dependent upon the occurrence of other morphological events, such as spindle formation or polar body emission; the latter conclusion is drawn from experiments utilizing drugs that specifically block meiotic maturation *in vitro* at specific stages of nuclear progression (38). The changes in protein synthesis do not take place in oocytes that fail to undergo GV breakdown spontaneously or in oocytes arrested at the GV stage by dibutyryl 3′:5′-cAMP. Such data suggest that mixing of the oocyte's nucleoplasm and cytoplasm may trigger many of the changes in protein synthesis that accompany meiotic maturation of mouse oocytes. Furthermore, these and other (39,40) results indicate that (a) fully grown mouse oocytes are poised to resume meiosis such that concomitant protein synthesis is not necessary for GV breakdown to take place. (b) Protein synthesis is necessary for a brief period just following GV breakdown for meiotic maturation to proceed to metaphase I. (c) The reprogramming of protein synthesis during meiotic maturation of mouse oocytes is directed by RNA templates already present in the oocyte's cytoplasm and does not require concomitant transcription.

Whereas, electrophoretic patterns of oocyte proteins synthesized during meiotic maturation reveal both increases and decreases in relative rates of synthesis of specific proteins, overall there is a significant decrease in the absolute rate of protein synthesis during meiotic maturation (27,28). As mouse oocytes proceed from dictyate of the first meiotic prophase to metaphase II, the absolute rate of protein synthesis decreases from 41.8 to 33.0 pg/hour per oocyte (Table I). The absolute rate of protein synthesis in fully grown mouse oocytes compares quite favorably with that reported for amphibian oocytes when these results are expressed as pg protein synthesized/hour per pl of cytoplasm (27). On the other hand, the more than 20% decrease in absolute rate of protein synthesis observed during meiotic maturation of mouse oocytes is in marked contrast to the substantial increase reported for progesterone-induced, maturing amphibian oocytes (41,42). It is possible that the modest decrease in protein synthesis during meiotic maturation of mouse oocytes reflects degradation of oocyte RNA, since the rate of RNA synthesis appears to decrease dramatically following GV breakdown (43).

SPECIFIC PROTEIN SYNTHESIS DURING GROWTH AND MEIOTIC MATURATION OF MOUSE OOCYTES

We have determined the rates of synthesis of several individual proteins and classes of proteins during growth and meiotic maturation of mouse oocytes. Such measurements have enabled us to identify specific examples of differential gene expression during these periods of oogenesis and, recently, to begin to relate the synthesis of particular proteins to the availability of corresponding messenger RNAs(see footnote p. 129).

Tubulin, Lactate Dehydrogenase, Histone-H4. The absolute rates of synthesis of tubulin, lactate dehydrogenase (LDH), and histone-H4 during oocyte growth and meiotic maturation have been calculated from the incorporation of [^{35}S]methionine into these proteins and the sizes of the intracellular methionine pool. These specific proteins were resolved from other radiolabeled oocyte proteins by high-resolution two-dimensional electrophoresis (29,30) and located by coelectrophoresis and staining of purified tubulin (24,28), LDH, or histone-H4 (see footnote on p. 129).

The absolute rate of tubulin synthesis increases from 0.40 to 0.60 pg/hour per oocyte as the oocyte grows from 40 to 85 μm in diameter; however, the percentage of total protein synthesis devoted to tubulin actually declines somewhat during this period, from 2.0 to 1.5% (Table II). During meiotic maturation the absolute rate of tubulin synthesis declines from 0.60 pg/hour per oocyte to 0.36 pg/hour per unfertilized egg, a 40% decrease in the rate of tubulin synthesis compared with a 21% decrease in the rate of total protein synthesis during the same period (Table II). Furthermore, although tubulin subunits are present in equimolar amounts in microtubules, the ratio of the rate of synthesis of the β subunit to that of the α subunit is significantly greater than 1 (1.4–2.6) at all stages of oocyte growth and meiotic maturation.

TABLE II
Relative Rates of Synthesis of Specific Proteins during Growth and
Meiotic Maturation of Mouse Oocytes

Stages of oogenesis	% of total protein synthesis						
	Tubulin			LDH		Histone-H4	Zona pellucida proteins
	α	β	Total	"Heart"	"Muscle"		
Growing oocyte (40–50 μm)	0.8	1.2	2.0	1.0	<0.05	0.07	>10
Fully grown oocyte (85 μm)	0.4	1.1	1.5	1.6	<0.1	0.05	<0.1
Unfertilized egg	0.3	0.8	1.1	<0.1	<0.1	0.04	<0.1

Synthesis of "heart-type" LDH increases dramatically during oocyte growth in the mouse, such that it represents 1.6% of total protein synthesis in fully grown oocytes (Table II). Therefore, the rate of synthesis of this enzyme is equivalent to that of the structural protein, tubulin. Unlike tubulin, however, the absolute rate of synthesis of LDH falls more than 15-fold during meiotic maturation, such that LDH synthesis in the unfertilized egg accounts for less than 0.1% of total protein synthesis (Table II). Measurements of "muscle-type" LDH indicate that, while it is synthesized during oocyte growth and meiotic maturation, it never represents more than 0.1% of total protein synthesis; consequently, only the H_3M and H_4 isozymes of LDH are detected on native gels of oocyte proteins stained for enzyme activity (see footnote on p. 129).

While histone-H4 synthesis is detectable in growing and fully grown mouse oocytes, it represents less than 0.1% of total protein synthesis (Table II). Therefore, similar to the situation in amphibian oocytes (44,45), histone synthesis in mouse oocytes is a relatively large component of total protein synthesis (see footnote on p. 129); however, unlike the amphibian, there is not a 50- to 100-fold increase in histone synthesis in unfertilized mouse eggs (Table II).

Ribosomal Proteins. The absolute rates of synthesis of specific ribosomal proteins have been determined by using a high-resolution two-dimensional gel electrophoresis procedure developed to resolve basic proteins with isoelectric points between 9.1 and 10.2 (30).Mouse oocyte ribosomal proteins were separated on such gels and observed rates of incorporation of [^{35}S]methionine into each of 12 representative ribosomal proteins were converted into absolute rates of synthesis.

The rates of synthesis of 12 different ribosomal proteins in growing mouse oocytes, 50 to 60 μm in diameter, represent from 0.005 to 0.054% of the rate of total protein synthesis. These values correspond to absolute rates of synthesis from 1.4 to 15.4 fg/hour per oocyte or, on a molar basis, 0.5 to 4.4 $\times$ 10^{-19} moles/hour per oocyte. Similarly, in fully grown oocytes, the 12 different ribosomal proteins are not synthesized at the same rates such that their synthesis represents from 0.04 to 0.071% of the rate of total protein synthesis. Conversion of these values into absolute rates of synthesis reveals that individual ribosomal proteins are synthesized at the rate of 1.6 to 30.4 fg/hour per oocyte or, on a molar basis, 0.6 to 8.7 $\times$ 10^{-19} moles/hour per oocyte. It is clear from these data that the synthesis of different ribosomal proteins is not under tight coordinate control, even though the proteins are present in ribosomes in equimolar amounts (46,47). Overall, these 12 ribosomal proteins are synthesized about 1.5 times as fast in fully grown oocytes as in growing oocytes 55 μm in diameter; however, in both cases their synthesis represents 0.25% of the rate of total protein synthesis in these oocytes. Since eukaryotic ribosomes contain 70 unique proteins (47), it can be estimated, based on the assumption that these 12 ribosomal proteins are representative of the total complement, that synthesis of ribosomal proteins accounts for 1.5% (i.e., 0.25% $\times$ 70/12) of total protein synthesis during oocyte growth and in fully grown oocytes (Table III). These results can be contrasted with those obtained using amphibian oocytes (48), where as much as 31.5% of the growing oocyte's total protein synthesis is devoted to ribosomal proteins. The fully grown amphibian oocyte, on the other hand, devotes only about 1.5% of its total protein synthesis to ribosomal proteins; a value comparable to that found for fully grown mouse oocytes.

At the time of GV breakdown and dissolution of the nucleolus, the initial morphological characteristics of meiotic maturation, the synthesis of ribosomal RNA ceases (43,49). Despite the absence of concomitant ribosomal-RNA synthesis, each of the 12 ribosomal proteins continues to be synthesized in unfertilized mouse eggs, albeit, in nearly every case at a reduced rate compared to fully grown oocytes (Table III). Synthesis of the total ribosomal protein complement in unfertilized eggs represents 1.1% of total protein synthesis (Table III). As in growing and fully grown oocytes, the individual ribosomal proteins are synthesized at different absolute rates, ranging from 0.3 to 4.9 $\times$ 10^{-19} moles/hour per egg.

TABLE III

Absolute Rates of Synthesis of Specific Ribosomal Proteins during Oogenesis in the Mouse

Ribosomal protein	Growing oocyte (55 μm), absolute rate		Fully grown oocyte, absolute rate		Unfertilized egg, absolute rate	
	fg/hour/oocyte	mole/hour/oocyte $\times 10^{19}$	fg/hour/oocyte	mole/hour/oocyte $\times 10^{19}$	fg/hour/egg	mole/hour/egg $\times 10^{19}$
S	13.5	4.1	16.5	5.0	16.2	4.9
1	9.6	1.7	9.6	1.7	5.4	1.0
2	7.2	1.4	6.3	1.3	6.2	1.2
3	5.4	1.7	11.7	3.7	4.9	1.6
4	6.6	3.1	15.4	7.2	5.9	2.7
5	2.4	0.6	3.2	0.8	3.1	0.8
6	15.4	4.4	30.4	8.7	15.0	4.3
7	1.4	0.5	1.6	0.6	1.2	0.4
8	2.2	0.9	4.6	1.9	3.0	1.2
9	2.1	1.0	2.3	1.0	0.7	0.3
10	3.4	1.5	3.0	1.4	1.4	0.6
11	2.1	1.0	2.3	1.1	0.7	0.3

Absolute rates of synthesis of total ribosomal protein complement during oogenesis in the mouse

Growing oocyte (55 μm) (pg/hour/oocyte)	Fully grown oocyte (pg/hour/oocyte)	Unfertilized egg (pg/hour/egg)
0.42 (1.5%)[a]	0.62 (1.5%)	0.37 (1.1%)

[a] Values in parentheses are the percentages of total protein synthesis devoted to ribosomal protein synthesis.

Zona Pellucida Proteins. The zona pellucida is a relatively thick, translucent, acellular coat that surrounds the plasma membrane of fully grown mammalian oocytes and performs a variety of vital biological functions during early mammalian development. The zona pellucida is laid down during growth of the ovarian follicle, remains throughout preimplantation development, and is finally shed as the blastocyst readies for implantation. Several lines of evidence suggest that the zona pellucida possesses a receptor for sperm, that it acts as a barrier to sperm penetration after fertilization, and that its presence is necessary for early development *in vivo*. The site of origin of the zona pellucida has been the subject of considerable interest for more than a century and, despite numerous studies, it had remained an unresolved issue to whether the zona pellucida originates from the oocyte, follicle cells, or both (16).

Recently (50), we showed that zonae pellucidae of mouse oocytes are composed of three different glycoproteins, designated as ZP1, ZP2, and ZP3, having apparent molecular weights of 200,000, 120,000, and 83,000, respectively (Table IV). This information permitted an examination of the site of synthesis of these proteins during follicular development (oocyte growth) and an estimation of the rates of synthesis of zona pellucida proteins (51). Denuded and follicle-enclosed mouse oocytes at various stages of growth were isolated and cultured *in vitro* in the presence of either [^{35}S]methionine or [^{3}H]fucose. Approximately 1.5% of the [^{35}S]methionine, and as much as 45% of the [^{3}H]fucose, incorporated into acid-insoluble material by denuded or follicle-enclosed oocytes is found associated with zonae pellucidae removed from the cultured oocytes. Incorporation of [^{35}S]methionine into zona pellucida proteins is depressed to less than $\frac{1}{50}$th when denuded oocytes are cultured in the presence of puromycin, and secretion of zona pellucida proteins can be demonstrated by pulse–chase experiments. Electrophoretic analyses of radiolabeled proteins present in oocytes, zonae pellucidae, and follicle cells reveal

TABLE IV
Characteristics of the Zona Pellucida Proteins from
Unfertilized Mouse Eggs

Protein	CHO	MW ($\times 10^{-3}$)	pI	% (ng/zona)	Disulfides	Receptor activity
ZP1	+	200	5.9	<35 (<1.6)	Inter	No
ZP2	+	120	4.3	>50 (>2.3)	Intra	No
ZP3	+	83	3.7	<15 (<0.7)	?	Yes

that denuded oocytes synthesize and secrete zona pellucida proteins, whereas, no evidence has been obtained to suggest that follicle cells synthesize these proteins. Furthermore, denuded oocytes, ranging in diameter from 48 to 68 μm, incorporate both [^{35}S]methionine and [^{3}H]fucose into zona pellucida proteins during culture *in vitro*, whereas, zonae pellucidae removed from fully grown oocytes (85 μm) are not radiolabeled to a significant extent (Fig. 9). More than 95% of the [^{3}H]fucose incorporated into oocyte proteins is found in ZP1, ZP2, and ZP3, indicating that the zona pellucida proteins are the major class of proteins glycosylated during oocyte growth; this observation is consistent with our finding that ZP1, ZP2, and ZP3 represent the

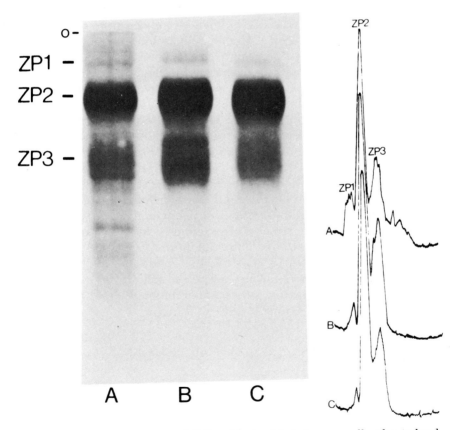

Fig. 9. Gel electrophoresis of [^{35}S]methionine-labeled zonae pellucidae isolated from mouse oocytes at various stages of growth as described by Bleil and Wassarman (51). Shown are fluorograms and corresponding densitometer tracings of zonae pellucidae isolated from 68 μm (lane A), 54 μm (lane B), and 48 μm (lane C) oocytes. o, Origin.

bulk of the glycoprotein present in fully grown mouse oocytes (see footnote on p. 129). These results provide strong biochemical evidence supporting the idea that the zona pellucida originates from the mammalian oocyte itself, rather than from the surrounding follicle cells. Estimates made of the rates of synthesis of zona pellucida proteins in growing mouse oocytes indicate that more than 10% of the oocyte's total protein synthesis is devoted to ZP1, ZP2, and ZP3 (Table III); this is a conservative estimate and more accurate measurements will probably result in a significantly higher percentage.

In further experiments, ZP1, ZP2, and ZP3 were purified from zonae pellucidae isolated individually from mouse oocytes, unfertilized eggs, and two-cell embryos and each of the glycoproteins was then tested for its ability to interfere with the binding of sperm to eggs *in vitro* (52). Solubilized zonae pellucidae isolated from unfertilized eggs, but not from two-cell embryos, reduce binding of sperm to as little as 10% of control values. Similarly, ZP3 purified from zonae pellucidae of unfertilized eggs reduces the binding of sperm to eggs *in vitro* to an extent comparable to that observed with solubilized zonae pellucidae (Table 4). On the other hand, ZP3 purified from zonae pellucidae of two-cell embryos has no significant effect on the extent of sperm binding, consistent with the inability of solubilized zonae pellucidae from two-cell embryos to affect sperm binding. In no case do purified ZP1 or ZP2 interfere significantly with the binding of sperm to eggs *in vitro* (Table IV). These results suggest that ZP3 possesses the receptor activity responsible for the binding of sperm to zonae pellucidae of unfertilized mouse eggs; fertilization apparently results in modification of ZP3 such that it can no longer serve as a receptor for sperm. Consistent with the observation that ZP3 is synthesized throughout oocyte growth (51), we find that sperm can bind to growing oocytes and that, when sperm are exposed to solubilized zonae pellucidae isolated from growing oocytes, they no longer bind to unfertilized eggs to the same extent as untreated sperm.

DISTRIBUTION OF NEWLY SYNTHESIZED PROTEINS IN FULLY GROWN MOUSE OOCYTES

It is now well documented from studies of oogenesis in nonmammalian animal species, that the oocyte's GV serves as the storage site for certain macromolecules to be utilized during early embryogenesis (2). It has been shown that, although most proteins are taken up into the GV, only specific proteins are selectively sequestered there such that they are highly concentrated in the GV as compared to the cytoplasm

TABLE V
Intracellular Distribution of Newly Synthesized Proteins in
Fully Grown Mouse Oocytes

	% in germinal vesicle[a]	% in cytoplasm
Total oocyte protein	2.5	97.5
Tubulin ($\alpha + \beta$ subunits)	1.0	99.0
Ribosomal proteins	65	35
Histone-H4	45	55

[a] Distribution following a 5-hour labeling period with [^{35}S]methionine.

of the oocyte (53–55). Since GVs can be isolated individually from fully grown mouse oocytes (56), we have been able to examine the distribution of newly synthesized proteins between the mammalian oocyte's GV and cytoplasm (see footnote on p. 129). The results of these experiments are summarized in Table V and demonstrate the highly selective nature of the mouse oocyte's GV as a storage site for particular proteins. It is apparent that newly synthesized histone-H4 and ribosomal proteins are highly concentrated in the GV (about 100-fold compared to cytoplasm), whereas, tubulin, although present in the GV at a level expected for free diffusion, is not accumulated in the oocyte's GV. In other experiments (56) we identified a protein (germinal vesicle-associated protein, GVAP) that is at least 100 times more concentrated in the GV than in the cytoplasm of the oocyte. Furthermore, the synthesis and phosphorylation of GVAP are apparently terminated at a time which coincides with GV breakdown during meiotic maturation. GVAP appears to be an example of a protein that is selectively sequestered in the oocyte's GV during oogenesis and whose synthesis and modification are dependent upon the presence of an intact GV.

COMPARISON OF GENE EXPRESSION DURING OOGENESIS AND EARLY EMBRYOGENESIS IN THE MOUSE

In order to compare gene expression during mammalian oogenesis with that during early embryogenesis, we have extended our measurements of overall and specific protein synthesis to the fertilized mouse egg (one-cell embryo) and eight-cell embryo. Such measurements have enabled us to begin to assess the contribution of the mammalian egg to preimplantation development.

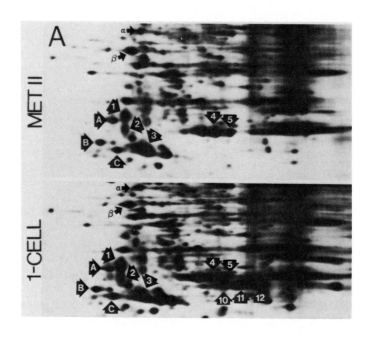

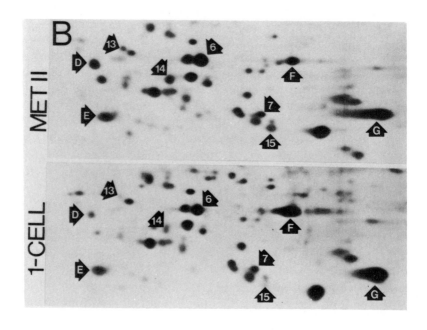

COMPARISON OF OVERALL PROTEIN SYNTHESIS

High-resolution two-dimensional gel electrophoresis revealed that meiotic maturation of mouse oocytes is associated with numerous changes in the pattern of protein synthesis (37,40). To ascertain whether or not fertilization of mouse eggs is accompanied by alterations in the pattern of protein synthesis similar experiments were performed on one-cell and eight-cell embryos (28). As seen in Fig. 10, fertilization of mouse ova is *not* characterized by radical changes in the overall pattern of proteins synthesized; a similar conclusion has been drawn by other investigators as well (57–59). The majority of polypeptides synthesized by mature, unfertilized mouse eggs are also made in one-cell embryos. However, some changes in protein synthesis are associated with fertilization; for example, polypeptides 10–12 (Fig. 10A) show an increased relative rate of synthesis following fertilization, whereas, polypeptides 13–15 (Fig. 10B) show a decreased relative rate of synthesis. Of particular interest is the finding that certain proteins, whose synthesis is detected for the first time during meiotic maturation of the oocyte, continue to be synthesized in the one-cell embryo; polypeptides 1–7 (Fig. 10A and B) are examples of the latter phenomenon.

Whereas, electrophoretic patterns of proteins synthesized in one and eight-cell embryos are very similar to those of unfertilized eggs, overall there is a significant increase in the absolute rate of protein synthesis following fertilization of the egg. The absolute rates of protein synthesis in unfertilized mouse eggs, one-cell embryos, and eight cell embryos are 33.0, 45.1, and 51.2 pg/hour per egg or embryo, respectively; at the same time, the size of the intracellular methionine pool increases from 74 (unfertilized egg) to 222 (eight-cell embryo) fmole/egg or embryo (Table VI). Therefore, fertilization is accompanied by a 40% increase in the absolute rate of protein synthesis, whereas, between the one-cell and eight-cell compacted embryo stages the rate of protein synthesis increases only about another 14%.

Fig. 10. High-resolution two-dimensional gel electrophoresis of [^{35}S]methionine-labeled proteins synthesized in unfertilized mouse eggs (met II) and fertilized mouse eggs (one-cell) as described by Schultz *et al.* (28). Polypeptides common to both met II eggs and one-cell embryos are denoted by arrowheads and serve as reference points to facilitate comparative analysis of the fluorograms. Two regions of the fluorograms, A and B, are shown.

TABLE VI

Absolute Rates of Protein Synthesis and Sizes of Methionine Pool during Early Embryogenesis in the Mouse

Stage of development	Pool size (avg. ± SD) fmoles Met/egg or embryo	Absolute rate (avg. ± SD) pg/hour per egg or embryo
Unfertilized egg	74 ± 12	33.0 ± 2.2
One-cell embryo	137 ± 8	45.1 ± 5.5
Eight-cell embryo	222 ± 18	51.2 ± 3.3

COMPARISON OF SPECIFIC PROTEIN SYNTHESIS

Tubulin, Lactate Dehydrogenase, Histone-H4. The absolute rates of synthesis of tubulin (28) and histone-H4 (see footnote on p. 129) increase during early embryogenesis as compared to the unfertilized egg. Fertilization is accompanied by a 60% increase in the rate of tubulin synthesis, from 0.36 to 0.60 pg/hour per egg or embryo, respectively; as development progresses to the eight-cell stage, the absolute rate increases to 0.66 pg/hour per embryo (the β-tubulin subunit continues to be synthesized at a greater rate than the α subunit). Similarly, histone-H4 synthesis, which is 0.04% of total protein synthesis in unfertilized eggs, represents more than 0.1% of total protein synthesis in eight-cell embryos (Table VII). On the other hand, LDH synthesis decreases slightly following fertilization and remains fairly constant as less than 0.1% of total protein synthesis during early embryogenesis (see footnote on p. 129); in fact, the rate of synthesis of

TABLE VII

Relative Rates of Synthesis of Specific Proteins during Early Embryogenesis in the Mouse

Stages of development	% of total protein synthesis					
	Tubulin	LDH "Heart"	"Muscle"	Histone-H4	Ribosomal proteins	Zona pellucida proteins
Unfertilized egg	1.1	<0.1	<0.1	0.04	1.1	<0.1
One-cell embryo	1.3	<0.1	<0.05	—	—	<0.1
Eight-cell embryo	1.3	<0.1	<0.05	>0.1	8.1	<0.1

heart-type LDH resembles that of the "muscle-type" enzyme in the early embryo (Table VII).

Ribosomal and Zona Pellucida Proteins. The eight-cell compacted mouse embryo synthesizes ribosomal proteins at a much greater rate than the unfertilized egg (30). The individual proteins are synthesized at different absolute rates, ranging from 26.4 to 99.7 fg/hour per embryo or, on a molar basis, 6.9 to 29.4 × 10^{-19} moles/hour per embryo. These rates represent from 0.052 to 0.195% of the rate of total protein synthesis in the embryo. A comparison of the rates of synthesis of these ribosomal proteins in eight-cell embryos and in unfertilized eggs, reveals as much as a 58-fold increase in some cases during early embryogenesis. Overall synthesis of ribosomal proteins accounts for at least 8.1% of total protein synthesis in the eight-cell embryo; a value considerably higher than the 1.1% determined for the unfertilized mouse egg (Table VII). This result is significantly different than that reported for the amphibian, where ribosomal protein synthesis accounts for less than 0.05% of total protein synthesis during early cleavage (48). While the rate of ribosomal protein synthesis in the mouse increases dramatically following fertilization, synthesis of zona pellucida proteins continues to be undetectable during early embryogenesis (Table VII).

SUMMARY AND DISCUSSION

In nonmammalian animal species, fertilization of eggs generally results in a many-fold increase in the rate of protein synthesis as early cleavage proceeds, and this occurs without an increase in ribosomal- or messenger-RNA synthesis (2,60–63). The precise mechanisms responsible for the progressive increases in rates of protein synthesis are complex (64,65), but the increase is largely attributable to the sudden availability of translatable messenger RNAs that had heretofore been stored in an untranslatable form in the egg (2,66,67). Despite substantial increases in rates of protein synthesis during early embryogenesis in nonmammalian animal species, large changes in the types of polypeptide chains synthesized are not seen until late in development when the embryo consists of tens-of-thousands of cells (68,69).

We have found that the absolute rate of protein synthesis undergoes a modest increase (55%), as compared to the unfertilized egg, during the first three cleavage divisions of mouse embryos. However, the rate of protein synthesis in the eight-cell embryo is only about 20% greater than that in the fully grown oocyte and, on a per cell basis, actually declines about sevenfold (Fig. 11). Furthermore, as in nonmammalian animal species (68,69), the types of polypeptide chains synthesized in the eight-cell mouse embryo do not differ greatly from those synthesized in the unfertilized egg (28,57–59). Therefore, at a time in mouse development when certain structural genes, some contributed by the paternal genome, are first expressed (70–74), the overall rate and pattern of protein synthesis remains remarkably like that of the unfertilized egg. It is tempting to suggest from these and other (75,76) observations that at least the first three cleavage divisions of mouse embryos (taking about 2.5 days) are supported by distributing the macromolecular stores of the unfertilized egg among the blastomeres of the early embryo. Only at later embryonic stages, when cellular differentiation into trophectoderm and inner cell mass occur, would reliance on relatively new gene expression (76–78) become paramount for the continued progress of mouse development. Certain of the ear-

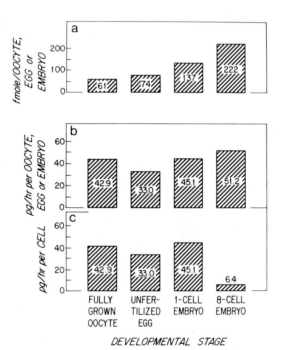

Fig. 11. Summary of measurements of sizes of the endogenous free methionine pool and absolute rates of total protein synthesis during oogenesis and early embryogenesis in the mouse.

lier changes in gene expression, identified at the protein level, many, in fact, be ascribed to posttranscriptional control of messenger RNAs contributed by the unfertilized egg (see footnote on p. 129) (79).

In addition to contributing a store of messenger RNA to the early embryo, the unfertilized mouse egg apparently provides certain proteins, which accumulate in large amounts during oocyte growth. As we have pointed out (24), some of these proteins may not be synthesized by the growing oocyte itself, but may be taken up into the oocyte by endocytosis; analogous to yolk accumulation in several nonmammalian animal species. While it has been suggested from morphological observations that mammalian oocytes contain a yolk component (80), there is no clear biochemical evidence to either support or refute this suggestion. However, the presence of a mammalian yolk could resolve a paradox. For, while the absolute rate of protein synthesis increases and the rate of degradation of newly synthesized protein does not change significantly during early embryogenesis in the mouse (see footnote on p. 129) (28,81), the protein content of the mouse embryo actually decreases substantially (82). Degradation of a yolk component during early embryogenesis could account for these findings and for the dramatic rise in the size of the endogenous methionine pool (28).

It is clear from results presented here that growing mouse oocytes synthesize and accumulate some proteins in large amounts for use during early embryogenesis. In fact, synthesis of certain of these proteins occurs at drastically reduced rates in the early embryo as compared to the oocyte; LDH (see footnote on p. 129) (20,83,84) and zona pellucida proteins, (see footnote on p. 129) (51) are examples of such a situation (Fig. 12). While as much as 300 pg of LDH (see footnote on p. 129) and 4.5 ng of zona pellucida proteins accumulate during oocyte growth, less than 3 pg of either type of protein is synthesized during the first three cleavage divisions of mouse embryos. The synthesis of LDH is drastically reduced as the fully grown oocyte is transformed into an unfertilized egg, while synthesis of zona pellucida proteins (including the "sperm receptor," ZP3) is nearly undetectable by the time the oocyte has achieved full growth (see footnote on p. 129) (51) (Fig. 12).

In contrast to the above, certain other proteins are synthesized in large amounts by growing mouse oocytes, but continue to be synthesized at similar or even greater rates during early embryogenesis; tubulin (28) and ribosomal proteins (30) are examples of such a situation (Fig. 12). As in a variety of nonmammalian animal species (85–88), tu-

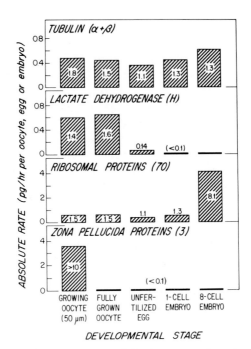

Fig. 12. Summary of measurements of absolute rates of synthesis of specific proteins during oogenesis and early embryogenesis in the mouse.

bulin is one of the major proteins synthesized by growing and fully grown mouse oocytes, unfertilized eggs, and early embryos. While tubulin synthesis in sea urchin embryos is apparently carried out using "stored" messenger RNA present in the unfertilized egg (89), it is not clear to what extent maternal tubulin messenger RNA directs tubulin synthesis during early embryogenesis in the mouse. On the other hand, it is clear that the early mouse embryo contains a large pool of tubulin inherited directly from the unfertilized egg.

Like tubulin, ribosomal protein synthesis represents a major fraction of total protein synthesis in mouse oocytes and eggs, and, taken into consideration with other evidence on ribosomal-RNA synthesis in the mouse (90,91), suggests that the unfertilized mouse egg, like eggs from nonmammalian animal species (2,92,93), contains a store of ribosomes for use during early embryogenesis. However, unlike tubulin, the absolute rate of synthesis of ribosomal proteins increases more than 11-fold as the mouse embryo reaches the eight-cell stage (Fig. 12). Consequently, on a per cell basis, the rate of ribosomal protein synthesis in the eight-cell embryo is comparable to that found in the fully grown oocyte; on a per cell basis, tubulin synthesis decreases about eight-fold. The latter observations are at least consistent with a situation in which tubulin is synthesized on maternally derived RNA templates and ribosomal proteins on newly transcribed templates in the eight-cell embryo; obviously, this interpretation is not unique. The absolute rate of RNA synthesis increases about 10-fold as the mouse embryo progresses from the one to eight-cell stage (94) and the bulk of this newly synthesized RNA is ribosomal (95–97). It is likely that the greater than 11-fold increase in the rate of synthesis of ribosomal proteins during this period of oogenesis is directly related to an increased rate of ribosomal-RNA synthesis (98). While the ovulated egg probably contains some 200 pg of ribosomal protein, presumably in intact ribosomes, the 8-cell embryo is synthesizing another 100 pg every 24 hours. This strongly suggests that, at least by the eight-cell stage, new ribosomes are being assembled in order to keep pace with the increasing rate of total protein synthesis.

Overall, the experimental evidence summarized here emphasizes, at the molecular level, the idea that, even in the mammal, "embryogenesis really begins during oogenesis" (1). Growth of mouse oocytes results in the accumulation of a large macromolecular store to be used during early embryogenesis, in the acquisition of the ability to resume meiosis, and in the accumulation of sperm receptors in readiness for fertilization. In addition, transformation of the fully grown oocyte into an unfertilized egg ("meiotic maturation"), the final stage of oogenesis, is accompanied by changes in gene expression which are maintained in the early embryo and, presumably, are necessary for the successful progress of early development. It seems likely that future studies will reveal additional examples of ways in which the progress of early mammalian embryogenesis depends upon the reserve of developmental potential present in the mature egg.

ACKNOWLEDGMENTS

The research of the authors described here was supported in part by grants awarded to P. M. Wassarman by the National Institutes of Health, the National Science Foundation, and the Rockefeller Foundation. R. M. Schultz was a postdoctoral fellow of the Rockefeller Foundation, M. J. LaMarca was supported in part by the William F. Milton Fund, Harvard University, and J. D. Bleil and S. M. Cascio were predoctoral trainees supported by a National Research Service Award in Cell and Developmental Biology.

REFERENCES

1. Wilson E. B. (1925) "The Cell in Development and Heredity," 3rd ed. Macmillan, New York.
2. Davidson, E. (1976) "Gene Activity in Early Development," 2nd ed. Academic Press, New York.
3. Brambell, F. W. R. (1956) *In* "Marshall's Physiology of Reproduction" (A. S. Parkes, ed.), 3rd ed., Vol. 1, Part 1, pp. 397–542. Longmans, Green, New York.
4. Franchi, L. L., Mandl, A. M., and Zuckerman, S. (1962) *In* "The Ovary" (S. Zuckerman, ed.), Vol. 1, pp. 1–88. Academic Press, New York.
5. "Webster's New Collegiate Dictionary" (1956) G. and C. Merriam Co., Springfield, Illinois.
6. Biggers, J. D., and Schuetz, A. W. (1972) *In* "Oogenesis" (J. D. Biggers and A. W. Schuetz, eds.), pp. 1–3. University Park Press, Baltimore, Maryland.
7. Baker, T. G. (1972) *In* "Reproduction in Mammals" (C. R. Austin and R. V. Short, eds.), Vol. 1, pp. 1–13. Cambridge Univ. Press, London and New York.
8. Hardisty, M. W. (1978) *In* "The Vertebrate Ovary" (R. E. Jones, ed.), pp. 1–45. Plenum, New York.
9. Gondos, B. (1978) *In* "The Vertebrate Ovary" (R. E. Jones, ed.), pp. 83–120, Plenum, New York.
10. Krarup, T., Pedersen, T., and Faber, M. (1969) *Nature (London)* **224**, 187–188.
11. Peters, H., Byskov, A. G., Lintern-Moore, S., Faber, M., and Andersen, M. (1973) *J. Reprod. Fertil.* **35**, 139–141.
12. Pedersen, T., and Peters, H. (1968) *J. Reprod. Fertil.* **17**, 555–557.
13. Brambell, F. W. R. (1928) *Proc. Soc. London, Ser. B* **103**, 258–271.
14. Pedersen, T. (1969) *Acta Endocrinol. (Copenhagen)* **62**, 117–132.
15. Pedersen, T. (1972) *In* "Oogenesis" (J. D. Biggers and A. W. Schuetz, eds.), pp. 361–376. University Park Press, Baltimore, Maryland.
16. Tsafriri, A. (1978) *In* "The Vertebrate Ovary" (R. E. Jones, ed.), pp. 409–442. Plenum, New York.
17. Wassarman, P. M., and Josefowicz, W. J. (1978) *J. Mrophol.* **156**, 209–236.
18. Wassarman, P. M., and Fujiwara, K. (1978) *J. Cell Sci.* **29**, 171–188.
19. Cross, P. C., and Brinster, R. L. (1970) *Biol. Reprod.* **3**, 298–307.
20. Mangia, F., and Epstein, C. J. (1975) *Dev. Biol.* **45**, 211–220.
21. Sorensen, R. A., and Wassarman, P. M. (1976) *Dev. Biol.* **50**, 531–536.
22. Eppig, J. J. (1977) *J. Exp. Zool.* **198**, 375–382.
23. Eppig, J. J. (1977) *Dev. Biol.* **60**, 371–388.
24. Schultz, R. M., Letourneau, G. E., and Wassarman, P. M. (1979) *Dev. Biol.* **73**, 120–133.
25. Regier, J. C., and Kafatos, F. C. (1971) *J. Biol. Chem.* **246**, 6480–6488.
26. Ecker, R. E. (1972) *In* "Biology and Radiobiology of Anucleate Systems" (S. Bonotto, R. Goutier, R. Kirchmann, and J. R. Maisin, eds.), Vol. 1, pp. 165–179. Academic Press, New York.
27. Schultz, R. M., LaMarca, M. J., and Wassarman, P. M. (1978) *Proc. Natl. Acad. Sci. U.S.A.* **75**, 4160–4164.
28. Schultz, R. M., Letourneau, G. E., and Wassarman, P. M. (1979) *Dev. Biol.* **68**, 341–359.
29. O'Farrell, P. H. (1975) *J. Biol. Chem.* **250**, 4007–4021.
30. LaMarca, M. J., and Wassarman, P. M. (1979) *Dev. Biol.* **73**, 103–119.
31. Schultz, R. M., and Wassarman, P. M. (1977) *J. Cell Sci.* **24**, 167–194.

32. Wallace, R. A. (1978) *In* "The Vertebrate Ovary" (R. E. Jones, ed.), pp. 469–502. Plenum, New York.
33. Glass, L. E. (1961) *Dev. Biol.* **3**, 797–804.
34. Glass, L. E. (1966) *Fertil. Steril.* **17**, 226–233.
35. Glass, L. E., and Cons, J. M. (1968) *Anat. Rec.* **162**, 139–156.
36. Smith, L. D. (1975) *In* "Biochemistry of Animal Development" (R. Weber, ed.), Vol. 3, pp. 1–46. Academic Press, New York.
37. Schultz, R. M., and Wassarman, P. M. (1977) *Proc. Natl. Acad. Sci. U.S.A.* **74**, 538–541.
38. Wassarman, P. M., Josefowicz, W. J., and Letourneau, G. E. (1976) *J. Cell Sci.* **22**, 531–545.
39. Schultz, R. M., Letourneau, G. E., and Wassarman, P. M. (1978) *J. Cell Sci.* **30**, 251–264.
40. Wassarman, P. M., Schultz, R. M., Letourneau, G. E., LaMarca, M. J., Josefowicz, W. J., and Bleil, J. D. (1978) *In* "Ovarian Follicular and Corpus Luteum Function" (C. P. Channing, J. Marsh, and W. D. Sadler, eds.), pp. 251–268. Plenum, New York.
41. Smith, L. D., and Ecker, R. E. (1969) *Dev. Biol.* **19**, 281–309.
42. Shih, R. J., O'Connor, C. M., Keem, K., and Smith, L. D. (1978) *Dev. Biol.* **66**, 172–182.
43. Wassarman, P. M., and Letourneau, G. E. (1976) *Nature (London)* **361**, 73–74.
44. Woodland, H. R., and Adamson, E. D. (1977) *Dev. Biol.* **57**, 118–135.
45. Adamson, E. D., and Woodland, H. R. (1977) *Dev. Biol.* **57**, 136–149.
46. Hoffman, W. L., and Ilan, J. (1977) *Biochim. Biophys. Acta* **474**, 411–424.
47. Wool, I. G., and Stoffler, G. (1974) *In* "Ribosomes" (M. Nomura, A. Tissieres, and P. Lengyel, eds.), pp. 417–460. Cold Spring Harbor Lab., Cold Spring Harbor, New York.
48. Hallberg, R. L., and Smith, D. C. (1975) *Dev. Biol.* **42**, 40–52.
49. Rodman, T. C., and Bachvarova, R. (1976) *J. Cell Biol.* **70**, 251–257.
50. Bleil, J. D., and Wassarman, P. M. (1980) *Dev. Biol.* **76**, 185–202.
51. Bleil, J. D., and Wassarman, P. M. (1980) *Proc. Natl. Acad. Sci. U.S.A.* **77**, 1029–1033.
52. Bleil, J. D., and Wassarman, P. M. (1980) *Cell* **20**, 873–882.
53. Bonner, W. M. (1975) *J. Cell Biol.* **64**, 421–430.
54. Bonner, W. M. (1975) *J. Cell Biol.* **64**, 431–437.
55. DeRobertis, E. M., Longthorne, R. F., and Gurdon, J. B. (1978) *Nature (London)* **272**, 254–256.
56. Wassarman, P. M., Schultz, R. M., and Letourneau, G. E. (1979) *Dev. Biol.* **69**, 94–107.
57. Van Blerkom, J., and Manes, C. (1977) *In* "Concepts in Mammalian Embryogenesis" (M. I. Sherman, ed.), pp. 37–94. MIT Press, Cambridge, Massachusetts.
58. Levinson, J., Goodfellow, P., Vadeboncoeur, M., and McDevitt, H. O. (1978) *Proc. Natl. Acad. Sci. U.S.A.* **75**, 3332–3336.
59. Cullen, B., Emigholz, K., and Monahan, J. (1980) *Dev. Biol.* **76**, 215–221.
60. Epel. D. (1967) *Proc. Natl. Acad. Sci. U.S.A.* **57**, 899–906.
61. Regier, J. C., and Kafatos, F. C. (1977) *Dev. Biol.* **57**, 270–283.
62. Kaumeyer, J. F., Jenkins, N. A., and Raff, R. A. (1978) *Dev. Biol.* **63**, 266–278.
63. Jenkins, N. A., Kaumeyer, J. F., Young, E. M., and Raff, R. A. (1978) *Dev. Biol.* **63**, 279–298.
64. Brandis, J. W., and Raff, R. A. (1979) *Nature (London)* **278**, 467–469.

65. Hille, M. B., and Albers, A. A. (1979) *Nature (London)* **278**, 469–471.
66. Humphreys, T. (1971) *Dev. Biol.* **26**, 201–208.
67. Woodland, H. R. (1974) *Dev. Biol.* **40**, 90–101.
68. Brandhorst, B. P. (1976) *Dev. Biol.* **52**, 310–317.
69. Ballentine, J. E. M., Woodland, H. R., and Sturgess, E. A. (1979) *J. Embryol. Exp. Morphol.* **51**, 137–153.
70. Brinster, R. L. (1973) *Biochem. Genet.* **9**, 187–191.
71. Chapman, V., Whitten, W., and Ruddle, F. (1971) *Dev. Biol.* **26**, 153–158.
72. Epstein, C. J. (1972) *Science* **175**, 1467–1468.
73. Krco, C. J., and Goldberg, E. H. (1976) *Science* **193**, 1134–1135.
74. Wudl, L., and Chapman, V. (1976) *Dev. Biol.* **48**, 104–109.
75. Sherman, M. I. (1979) *Annu. Rev. Biochem.* **48**, 443–470.
76. Johnson, M. H., Handyside, A. H., and Braude, P. R. (1977) *In* "Development in Mammals" (M. H. Johnson, ed.), Vol. 2, pp. 67–97. North-Holland Biomedical Press, Amsterdam.
77. Van Blerkom, J., Barton, S. C., and Johnson, M. H. (1976) *Nature (London)* **259**, 319–321.
78. Handyside, A. H., and Johnson, M. H. (1978) *J. Embryol. Exp. Morphol.* **44**, 191–199.
79. Braude, P., Pelham, H., Flach, G., and Lobatto, R. (1979) *Nature (London)* **282**, 102–105.
80. Szollosi, D. (1972) *In* "Oogenesis" (J. D. Biggers and A. W. Schuetz, eds.), pp. 47–64. University Park Press, Baltimore, Maryland.
81. Brinster, R. L., Wiebold, J. L., and Brunner, S., (1976) *Dev. Biol.* **51**, 215–224.
82. Brinster, R. L. (1967) *J. Reprod. Fertil.* **13**, 413–420.
83. Brinster, R. L. (1965) *Biochim. Biophys. Acta* **110**, 439–441.
84. Mangia, F., Erickson, R. P., and Epstein, C. J. (1976) *Dev. Biol.* **54**, 146–150.
85. Pestell, R. Q. W. (1975) *Biochem. J.* **145**, 527–534.
86. Miller, J. H., and Epel, D. (1973) *Dev. Biol.* **32**, 331–344.
87. Raff, R. A., and Kaumeyer, J. D. (1973) *Dev. Biol.* **32**, 309–320.
88. Raff, R. A., Brandis, J. W., Green, L. H., Kaumeyer, J. D., and Raff, E. C. (1975) *Ann. N. Y. Acad. Sci.* **253**, 304–317.
89. Raff, R. A., Coholt, H. V., Selvig, S. E., and Gross, P. R. (1972) *Nature (London)* **235**, 211–214.
90. Jahn, C. L., Baran, M. M., and Bachvarova, R. (1976) *J. Exp. Zool.* **197**, 161–172.
91. Bachvarova, R., and DeLeon, V. (1977) *Dev. Biol.* **58**, 248–254.
92. Brown, D. D., and Gurdon, J. B. (1964) *Proc. Natl. Acad. Sci. U.S.A.* **51**, 139–146.
93. Brown, D. D., and Dawid, I. (1968) *Science* **160**, 272–280.
94. Clegg, K. B., and Pikó, L. (1977) *Dev. Biol.* **58**, 76–95.
95. Ellem, K., and Gwatkin, R. (1968) *Dev. Biol.* **18**, 311–330.
96. Woodland, H. R., and Graham, C. F. (1969) *Nature (London)* **221**, 327–332.
97. Pikó, L. (1970) *Dev. Biol.* **21**, 257–279.
98. Warner, J. R. (1974) *In* "Ribosomes" (M. Nomura, A. Tissieres, and P. Lengyel, eds.), pp. 461–488. Cold Spring Harbor Lab., Cold Spring Harbor, New York.

Association of Nucleoprotein Transitions with Chromatin Changes during Rat Spermatogenesis

MARVIN L. MEISTRICH, PATRICIA K. TROSTLE,
AND WILLIAM A. BROCK

Department of Experimental Radiotherapy
The University of Texas System Cancer Center
M. D. Anderson Hospital and Tumor Institute
Houston, Texas

INTRODUCTION

Spermatogenesis in mammals involves an extensive series of morphological changes that have been most elegantly described in rodents (1). An outline of the process (Fig. 1) shows the three major divisions of spermatogenesis, the spermatogonial, the spermatocyte, and the spermatid phases. Throughout this entire process, dramatic changes in chromatin structure and function occur. In this discussion we shall focus on the morphological and biochemical events during meiotic prophase in the primary spermatocyte and during elongation and condensation of the spermatid nucleus. Although our experimental material is primarily from the rat, we shall also use data obtained with the mouse, since spermatogenesis is similar in these two species (2).

CHROMATIN CHANGES DURING SPERMATOGENESIS

The spermatogonial cells undergo several mitotic cycles with accompanying S phase DNA synthesis. The final S phase occurs during the preleptotene stage, after which the cells enter the meiotic pro-

BIOREGULATORS OF REPRODUCTION
Copyright © 1981 by Academic Press, Inc.
All rights of reproduction in any form reserved.
ISBN 0-12-379980-5

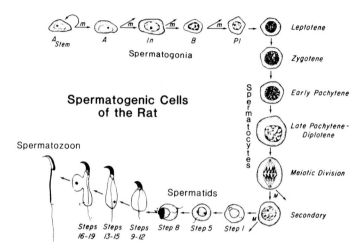

Fig. 1. Outline of spermatogenesis in the rat. Mitotic and meiotic cells are indicated by m and M, respectively. Drawings modified from Leblond and Clermont (1).

phase, which in the rat lasts 16 days (3). The first part of prophase, the leptotene stage, is characterized by the appearance of single chromosomes condensed along axial filaments (4). During the zygotene stage, synaptonemal complexes are formed and the homologous chromosomes pair along these structures. The synaptonemal complex is a protease-sensitive structure, but its specific biochemical composition and function is currently unknown. Pachytene is the longest portion of the meiotic prophase. This stage is characterized by the complete pairing of homologous chromosomes along the synaptonemal complexes and high levels of protein and RNA synthesis; a peak of RNA synthesis occurs during mid-pachytene (5). Genetic recombination most likely occurs during pachytene. Diplotene is marked by the separation of the paired homologs followed by diakinesis, during which chromosome condensation proceeds (4).

The morphological and functional changes described above do not provide a method for studying alterations in the structure of the bulk of the chromatin. One approach to investigating chromatin structure involves cytochemical techniques that quantitate staining with fluorescent probes by flow cytometry (6). In Fig. 2, flow cytometric profiles of acriflavin–Feulgen stained spermatocyte nuclei of the mouse are presented (7). The peak at 1c corresponds to round spermatids (haploid DNA content) and can be used to normalize the data. The primary spermatocytes (leptotene through diakinesis) have 4c (tetraploid) DNA content, but take up less stain than predicted by the hap-

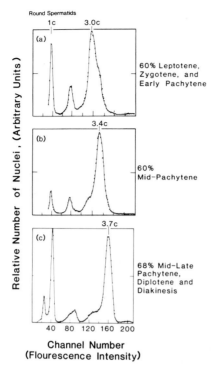

Fig. 2. Flow cytometric determination of fluorescence intensity frequency distributions of acriflavine-stained mouse testis nuclei. Nuclei were prepared from purified populations of cells separated by velocity sedimentation. In the cases of the early primary spermatocytes and mid-pachytene spermatocytes, the nuclei were further purified by velocity sedimentation separation. Nuclei were then fixed in 10% buffered formalin, subjected to hydrolysis in 4 N HCl, and stained with acriflavine. Preparations were enriched in (a) early primary spermatocytes, (b) mid-pachytene spermatocytes, and (c) late pachytene spermatocytes. The values of (c) given above the peaks indicate the apparent DNA contents in multiples of the mouse haploid DNA content, assuming stochiometric staining. Redrawn from Meistrich *et al.* (7).

loid peak. The amount of staining, which increases with differentiation from the leptotene to the late pachytene, is a result of changes in chromatin structure. This must be the case since it has been shown that only a minute amount of DNA synthesis occurs during the meiotic prophase (8–10). Thus, either the chromosomal protein composition or the state of condensation of the nucleoprotein matrix could be responsible for the changes in staining. In either case, cytochemical analysis of chromatin within nuclei by flow cytometry is a valuable technique for probing changes in chromatin structure during spermatogenesis.

The first part of spermiogenesis (i.e., spermatid development) is quiescent relative to changes in chromatin structure, but the second half of this stage is marked by the transition of the nucleus from a round structure with diffuse chromatin (1) to a highly compact and resistant mass (11). This transition is associated with a disappearance of the beaded fiber chromatin structure, replacement by smooth fibers, and, finally, condensation to a form so highly compact that individual fibers are no longer visible (12). At the same time, all detectable transcription of the spermatid genome ceases (5,12).

Changes in chromatin composition and configuration during these same stages has been monitored cytochemically. Decreased staining of spermatid DNA during spermiogenesis had been previously described using quantitative absorption microspectrophotometry (13). The same phenomenon can be measured more easily by flow cytom-

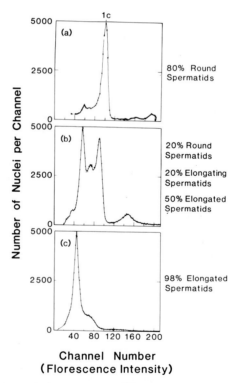

Fig. 3. Flow cytometric determination of fluorescence intensity frequency distributions of acriflavine-stained mouse spermatid nuclei. Fractions obtained by velocity sedimentation of cells were enriched in (a) round spermatids, (b) elongating spermatids, or (c) elongated spermatids. Redrawn from Meistrich *et al.* (7).

etry (7). A 30% decrease in the uptake of stain by mouse spermatid DNA occurs coincident with nuclear condensation and elongation (Fig. 3). The relationship of these changes to nuclear protein changes will be discussed later.

BASIC CHROMOSOMAL PROTEINS OF SPERMATOGENIC CELLS

Determination of the protein composition of the chromatin during spermatogenesis is essential for understanding the molecular mechanisms involved in this differentiation process. Previous work has shown that more dramatic changes occur in the basic (acid-soluble) proteins during spermatogenesis than in the acid-insoluble proteins (14,15). In addition, the basic proteins are the main structural proteins of chromatin. Therefore, we have focused our studies on these proteins.

In most somatic tissues, the basic chromosomal proteins consist of five classes of histones and four HMG proteins. A limited degree of heterogeneity occurs within the somatic histones, as shown in Table I

TABLE I
Histone Variants in Somatic and Spermatogenic Cells

| Histone | Somatic cells[a] | Germ cells | |
		Rat[b]	Mouse[c]
H1	H1a, H1b, H1c, H1d, H1c, H1°	TH1[d] {H1a, H1t	H1.S
H2A	H2A.1, H2A.2, M1, M2 (X2)[e]	X2, X9	H2A.S
H2B	H2B.1, H2B.2	TH2B	H2B.S
H3	H3.1, H3.2, H3.3	?	H3.S
H4	H4 (no variants)	(no variants)	

[a] Data from Franklin and Zweidler (16), Seyedin and Kistler (17), Panyim and Chalkley (18), and Zweidler (19).

[b] Data from Branson et al. (20), Shires et al. (21,22), Seyedin and Kistler (23), Levinger et al. (24), Trostle et al. (25), and Brock et al. (26).

[c] Data from Zweidler (27).

[d] The electrophoretic band on acid urea gels, originally designated X1 (20) or TH1 (21,26), has been resolved on SDS gels into two proteins (24). One of these proteins H1a appears to be identical to a somatic histone subfraction (17), while H1t is testis-specific (23). We shall refer to TH1 as the protein band on acid–urea gels, although we are aware that it contains two proteins, H1a and H1t.

[e] M2 (19) appears to be similar in electrophoretic mobility to the protein X2 found in the testis (20,25).

(16–27). In addition to the somatic histones, it has been shown that the testis contains unique histone variants in the mouse and the rat. Partial sequences of the mouse testis histones (27) and amino acid compositions of two rat testis histones (22,23) have been obtained. The testis histones H1t and TH2B in the rat and H2A.S, H2B.S, and H3.S in the mouse (Table I) are similar to their somatic counterparts but show significant differences in primary sequences. The protein X9 appears to be a variant of H2A that is localized to the germ cells of the rat testis (25); purification and analysis of this protein are currently in progress. Although the protein H1a, a variant of H1, is found in low amounts in some somatic tissues, it is prominent in testes containing predominantly germinal cells (17,23). Likewise, a band designated X2 (20), which also appears to be a variant of H2A (25), is found in low amounts in somatic tissues but is highly enriched in the germinal cells. By combinations of electrophoresis on acid–urea gels (28), sodium dodecyl sulfate (SDS) gels (29), or Triton-acid-urea gels (30), all of these proteins can be easily resolved.

In addition to histone variants, the rat testis nuclei contains five acid-soluble proteins (Table II) (14,31–35) that appear to be specific to the germinal cells (33). One protein, S1, is the major basic nuclear protein of epididymal spermatozoa, the so called "protamine" (36). The other four proteins, TP, TP2, TP3, and TP4, are found only in the testis, not in spermatozoa (32). These are all low-molecular weight basic proteins that are rich in arginine, lysine, and, with the exception of TP, cysteine.

TABLE II

Characteristics of Low Molecular Weight Basic Spermatidal Proteins from Rat Testis

Major amino acid composition (%)	TP[a]	TP2[b]	TP3[b]	TP4[c]	S1[d]
Arginine	20	14	24	22	60
Lysine	18	10	2	8	4
Serine	15	14	10	13	8
Glutam(ic,ine)	0	5	11	7	0
Proline	2	12	3	7	0
Cysteine	0	4	3	6	17
N-terminus	Ser	ND	ND	Val	Ala
Molecular weight	6219	11,200	≈10,000	≈20,000	7184

[a] Kistler *et al.* (31).
[b] Grimes *et al.* (32).
[c] Platz *et al.* (14) and Meistrich *et al.* (33,34).
[d] Kistler *et al.* (35).

CELL SEPARATION METHODS

In order to study the role of these proteins in chromatin structure of spermatogenic cells, it is first necessary to localize their distribution and synthesis to specific stages of spermatogenesis. This type of analysis is difficult because the adult mammalian testis contains germ cells at all stages of differentiation as well as nongerminal cells. Three approaches can be taken to study the individual cell populations in the testis. These are *in situ* histochemistry (37) or autoradiography (37,38), biochemical analysis of homogenates of testes with altered cellular composition (39,40), and cell and nuclear separation (14,26,32) followed by biochemical analysis.

We have altered cellular composition of the testis in two ways. In one technique we have used ionizing radiation (2 doses of 1300 rads) followed by a waiting time of at least 46 days so that the testis will become completely devoid at all germinal cells (14). This procedure produces a testis containing only somatic cells. In another approach we have used testes from immature rats that are going through the first wave of spermatogenesis (41). For example, at 8, 12, 16, and 20 days postpartum the most advanced germinal cells present are primitive type A spermatogonia, intermediate spermatogonia, very early pachytene spermatocytes, and spermatocytes in the meiotic divisions, respectively. However, there is great heterogeneity among the tubules in the most advanced cell type present. Furthermore, cells in less advanced stages constitute a large percentage of the cells in these immature animals. Even at 16 days of age, the somatic cells are more abundant than the germ cells.

A more effective method for analysis of proteins associated with specific stages is to separate cells or nuclei into purified populations of the different developmental stages that are present in the testis. We find that bulk separations based on the physical properties of the cells or nuclei are most suitable for rapid separation of large numbers of nuclei. The parameters we have chosen are the sedimentation rate under a gravitational or centrifugal field, the density, and the differential resistance to physical disruption by ultrasound (11,32,42). Sonication is a specific method for the preparation of late spermatids, while the other parameters can be used for a variety of cells and nuclei. Since sedimentation rate separates cells primarily on their differences in size (42) the separation obtained by this method differs from that obtained by equilibrium density centrifugation. In order to obtain highly purified cells or nuclei, it is often necessary to combine two different types of separation steps sequentially. The characteristics of the indi-

TABLE III
Methods for Separation of Testicular Cells and Nuclei

Principle		Cell separation	Nuclear separation
Velocity sedimentation	Method	Elutriator (43)	Staput (unit gravity) (44)
	Gradient	None	2–10% sucrose
	Max. cell no.	3×10^9	5×10^8 nuclei
	Time required	30 minutes	4–16 hours
Equilibrium density centrifugation	Gradient	22–36% Percoll (45)	57–67% Metrizamide (32)
	Max. cell no.	4×10^8	10^8 nuclei
	Time required	20 minutes	20 minutes

vidual steps are shown in Table III (32,43–45). The purities of cells and/or nuclei obtained by these methods are shown in Table IV. Cell types other than those shown have been difficult to obtain in high purity from adult rats. For example, nuclei or early elongating spermatids, steps 9–12, in the rat appear to be very fragile and are lost during nuclear isolation; this has also been shown to be true in the ram (46). Partial purification of cells at the early stages of spermatogenesis (spermatogonia throught leptotene spermatocytes) from immature mice or rats by the "staput" method of unit gravity sedimentation has been reported (47,48). We are currently investigating the use of elutriation and density centrifugation for further purification of large numbers of these cells.

TABLE IV
Cell or Nuclear Stages Obtained in High Purity

Cell or nuclear stage	Purity %	Number obtained per experiment	Methods (references)
Primary spermatocytes (mid-pachytene–diplotene)	99	3×10^7	Elutriation of cells Percoll density separation of cells (45)
Round spermatids (steps 1–8)	95	8×10^7	Elutriation of cells Staput separation of nuclei (26)
	91	10^8	Elutriation of cells Percoll density separation of cells (45)
Elongated spermatids (steps 13–15)	95	2×10^8	Elutriation of cells Sonication (32)
Elongated spermatids (steps 16–19)	99	10^8	Sonication Metrizamide density separation of nuclei (32)

HISTONES OF THE MEIOTIC PROPHASE

The distribution and synthesis of histones in meiotic cells was studied using purified populations of spermatocyte nuclei. The nuclear preparations contained 99% mid-pachytene through diakinesis nuclei and were obtained by a combination of cell separation methods (45). Gel electrophoresis patterns of histones from these nuclei indicate that H2B is almost completely replaced by TH2B and that the H1's consist almost exclusively of TH1, i.e., H1a and/or H1t (25). It is noteworthy that the somatic forms of these proteins are not completely replaced. The major somatic form of H3 is also largely replaced by a variant which may or may not be testis-specific. The H2A's show H2A.1 as the predominant band, with a low amount of H2A.2, and the presence of appreciable amounts of the supposed H2A variants, X2 and X9 (Table V). Purified round spermatids show distribution of histones almost identical to the spermatocytes. The synthesis of the proteins described above during the pachytene stage has been demonstrated by *in vivo* labeling with intratesticular injection of [^{3}H]arginine and [^{3}H]lysine 90 minutes prior to sacrifice. The histones were

TABLE V
Histone Changes during Spermatogonial and Spermatocyte Stages of the Rat[a]

Histone class	Variant	Changes	Synthesis
H1	b,c,d,e	Low in germ cells	—
	a,t	Present in spermatogonia (a) First appears in spermatocytes (t)	Spermatogonia or early spermatocytes, and pachytene
H2A	.2	Low in germ cells	Spermatogonia and pachytene
	.1	—	Spermatogonia and pachytene
	X2	Present in spermatogonia Decreases at later stages	Spermatogonia and pachytene
	X9	First appears in spermatocytes	Pachytene
H2B	H2B	Decreases in spermatocytes	Spermatogonia
	TH2B	First appears in spermatocytes	Pachytene and earlier spermatocytes
H3	.2	Decreases in spermatocytes	?
	.1	Increases in spermatocytes	?
H4	No variants	—	Mostly spermatogonia Low in pachytene

[a] Data taken from Seyedin and Kistler (23), Trostle *et al.* (25), Brock *et al.* (26), Meistrich *et al.* (45), Mills *et al.* (39), and Grimes *et al.* (40).

extracted from purified cells or nuclei, separated by electrophoresis (25,26). The results show that all classes of histones, with the possible exception of the H3's, are synthesized in the pachytene–diakinesis stage. The amounts of somatic H2B and somatic H1 (variants b, c, d, and e) are too low to determine whether synthesis occurs.

Testis-specific histones are synthesized during the pachytene stage, but the question of how much of the testis histone synthesis occurs prior to the pachytene stage remains. This question has been examined by three methods: gel electrophoresis of histones from immature rat testes (23,25,39,40), the effect of hydroxyurea on S-phase-coupled DNA and histone synthesis (26), and by partial purification of spermatogonia and early primary spermatocytes from rat testis (26).

Polyacrylamide gel electrophoresis of histones extracted from heavily irradiated rat testes shows the absence of X2, X9, TH1 (H1a plus H1t), and TH2B and low levels of a band migrating as H3.1. Therefore, these proteins are most likely localized to the germ cells. Studies of histones extracted from immature rat testes show that TH2B, X9, H1t, and possibly the H3.1 band first increase at 20 days of age (23,25,39,40). This age corresponds to the time of formation of appreciable numbers of primary spermatocytes and the progression of some cells to the meiotic metaphase. X2 and H1a are already detected at high levels in immature rats younger than 20 days, suggesting that they are present in spermatogonia (23,25,39,40).

Hydroxyurea inhibition of synthesis of histones in 20-day-old rats was used to determine which histones are coupled to DNA synthesis and hence synthesized during the spermatogonial (and preleptotene spermatocyte) stages (26). Under conditions at which 98% of the DNA synthesis is inhibited, the inhibitions of TH2B (7%), TH1 (14%), and H1 (19%) are not significant. On the other hand, significant inhibition of X2 (33%), H3 (51%), H2B (35%), H2A (30%), and H4 (78%) occur. Thus, we conclude that while X2 and the core somatic histones are synthesized prior to the meiotic prophase, little or no TH2B, TH1, and surprisingly, H1 are synthesized prior to the meiotic prophase and in conjunction with DNA replication.

By separation of adult rat testis cells, we have obtained an enriched fraction containing 72% spermatogonia and early primary spermatocytes (through early pachytene), with the major contaminant being round spermatids, which do not synthesize histones (26). In the cells of this fraction the synthesis of TH1 and TH2B is very high and synthesis of H1, X2, and H4 also occurs.

The results presented above are consistent with the following model (Table V): H1a and X2 are synthesized in the spermatogonia and probably reach their maximum levels in these cells. H1t, X9,

TH2B, and possibly an H3 variant are absent from the spermatogonia, but are synthesized starting at the beginning of the meiotic prophase. The synthesis of these proteins as well as most of the somatic histones continues up to the late pachytene stage.

POSSIBLE ROLES OF HISTONE TRANSITIONS DURING MEIOSIS

Even with the limited information we have on histone changes during meiosis, it may still be useful to speculate on the possible roles, if any, of these histone variants. Although the synthesis of H1t, X9, and TH2B continues throughout the meiotic prophase, sufficient levels of them may have been synthesized prior to pachytene to allow the attachment of the chromatin to the lateral elements of the synaptonemal complex and thus permit chromosome pairing. The continued synthesis and accumulation of these proteins during the pachytene stage might be necessary before genetic recombination can proceed. It is possible that the histone transitions play a role in the reprogramming of the genome for expression of testis-specific genes that may be associated with the high levels of pachytene RNA synthesis (5,12,49). Another possible role for these proteins could be in the mechanics of the meiotic (reductional) divisions; in this case, these proteins would most likely be important in the first meiotic division, since it is distinguished from mitosis by unique chromosomal events.

Histone changes may be related to the decrease in chromatin condensation as the cells pass from leptotene to late pachytene (Fig. 2). The continued synthesis of histones and the replacement of somatic histones with testis-specific histones occurs during this time. However, chromatin condensation and decondensation does occur without histone replacement during mitosis. In this case, post-translation histone modification has been proposed as a mechanism for chromatin condensation and decondensation (50). But it is possible that chromatin decondensation in the primary spermatocyte is a result of somatic histones being replaced by testis-specific histones.

REPLACEMENT OF HISTONES DURING SPERMIOGENESIS

Round spermatids contain the same histone complement as the late pachytene spermatocytes and synthesize negligible amounts of acid-soluble basic proteins (25,26,32). In the mouse it has been shown (37,38) by autoradiographic methods that there are only very low levels of basic protein synthesis until late step 12 (corresponding to step 14 in the rat). Then a burst of basic protein synthesis occurs, simultaneously with the most dramatic point of chromatin condensation. Neither the synthesis nor the presence of the low molecular weight basic proteins characteristic of elongated spermatids can be detected in rat round spermatids (25,26,32). Only one piece of evidence exists to the contrary: immunochemical detection of the mouse sperm protein (protamine) has been reported in round spermatids (51). The transition in the elongated spermatids (steps 13–19 in the rat) is striking; they completely lack histones but instead contain primarily five basic proteins (32–34,52).

Experiments with separated cells have been performed to determine which of these proteins are associated with specific stages of spermatid development. Purified spermatid nuclei in steps 13–15 of development contain almost exclusively TP, TP2, and TP4 (32–34,52). These same cells are actively engaged in the synthesis of these proteins (32,52). TP3 and S1 are absent in steps 13–15. TP, TP2, and probably TP4 are turned over within about 4 days of their synthesis (32). Purified step 16–19 spermatids contain only S1 and a small amount of TP3. Only S1 is retained in epididymal sperm (32,36). These data demonstrate a sequential synthesis, replacement, and turnover of basic nuclear proteins during spermatid maturation.

POSSIBLE ROLES OF SPERMATIDAL BASIC PROTEINS

The change in the chromatin ultrastructure from a nucleosomal type structure to a smooth fiber (12) occurs at about the same time as the histones are replaced by the TP proteins. These events are obviously correlated, since at least some of the core histones are required for nucleosomal structure. The relationship between histone replacement and cessation of RNA synthesis does not seem to be tightly correlated. The level of RNA synthesis declines between steps 1 and 8 of spermiogenesis (12) prior to the replacement of histones. However, DNA covered with the TP proteins may not permit transcription, and the loss of nearly all of the nonbasic proteins from the chromatin by step 13 (14) eliminates RNA polymerases and other proteins necessary for transcription. Thus, although the cessation of RNA synthesis may be controlled by a different mechanism, the replacement of other proteins by the TP's would act to keep the genome inactive.

A role for the TP proteins in nuclear elongation, which begins at step 9 of spermiogenesis, may be postulated. Since we are unable to isolate nuclei of step 9–12 spermatids, we cannot determine whether the nucleoprotein changes have already begun. However, autoradiographic studies of arginine and lysine incorporation in the mouse testes (37,38) indicate that spermatidal basic protein synthesis does not begin until after the nucleus has elongated. Thus, the initial stages of nuclear elongation appear to be independent of the spermatidal basic proteins and are probably controlled by cytoplasmic structures such as the manchette (53). It is still possible that the later stages of shaping of the sperm head may be regulated by the nuclear proteins. The spermatid nucleus assumes the species-specific shape of the sperm head by step 12 in the mouse or step 14 in the rat (1,2). Hence, only the proteins TP, TP2 and TP4, and not TP3 or S1, could have a role in nuclear shaping.

Nuclear condensation, however, begins slightly after nuclear elongation, and it is very likely that the TP proteins play a major role in this process. It appears that by step 15 of rat spermiogenesis [and correspondingly by step 13 of the mouse (38)] the chromatin is highly, but not completely, condensed. Thus the replacement of histones by TP, TP2, and TP4 could be responsible for a large measure of nuclear condensation, but the final replacement of these proteins by S1 and TP3 is needed for the complete condensation observed after step 16.

Chromatin structure, as probed by the accessibility of DNA to certain dyes or enzymes, changes during this period. The fluorescence of acriflavin-Feulgen stained nuclei decreases (Fig. 3) with spermatid elongation and condensation (7), but it has not yet been possible to observe by flow cytometry a second transition in stainability, corresponding to the shift from nuclei containing TP, TP2, and TP4 to those containing S1 and TP3. On the other hand, staining of sonication-resistant nuclei with hematoxylin reveals populations of darkly stained nuclei that correspond to steps 13–15 and of lightly stained ones that correspond to steps 16–19 (33). Thus, the cytochemical staining of the nucleic acid is altered as the protein transitions take place.

The susceptibility of DNA to cleavage by DNases has also proved to be an important probe of chromatin structure. For example, it has revealed the structure of nucleosomes in histone-containing chromatin. The DNA of rat elongated spermatids becomes resistant to the combined action of trypsin and DNase starting at step 16 when replacement of TP, TP2, and TP4 by S1 and TP3 has taken place (11). In the ram, resistance of the DNA to digestion by DNase alone occurs at about the same stage (49,54).

A role for the basic spermatidal proteins in chromatin condensation during spermiogenesis is quite likely. Their high content of basic residues allows for more effective neutralization of the DNA charge and would allow the DNA strands to be closely packed. The high cysteine content of these proteins could promote further compaction by cross-linking proteins on adjacent DNA strands.

CONCLUSION

In this chapter we have shown several associations, summarized in Fig. 4, between the alterations in basic protein composition and changes in chromatin structure and function during spermatogenesis. We have presented several hypotheses of how the different transitions might be causally related. It could, however, prove difficult to test the validity of these hypotheses. First of all, it will be necessary to elucidate the arrangement of these new proteins within the chromatin. Then, these proteins must be altered to determine how their changes

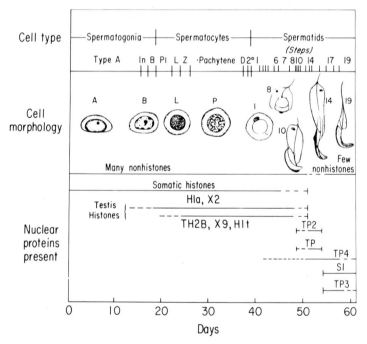

Fig. 4. Outline of the nucleoproteins present during the various stages of spermatogenesis correlated with the cell morphology and kinetics of spermatogenesis. Redrawn from Meistrich *et al.* (33).

affect chromatin structure. A direct but very difficult method would be to specifically prevent their synthesis *in vivo* and then determine the resulting modifications on chromatin structure. Alternatively, reconstitution experiments, involving addition of specific proteins to DNA *in vitro* could help determine how these proteins affect chromatin structure. The role of protein modification, such as formation of disulfide bonds, phosphorylation, or acetylation could also be studied *in vitro*. In conclusion, we believe that characterization of the association of nucleoprotein transitions with specific chromatin changes will provide the basis for the elucidation of the roles of these proteins.

ACKNOWLEDGMENTS

We thank Drs. Sidney Grimes, Robert Platz, Lubomir Hnilica, and Barton Gledhill for their collaboration on much of the work presented here. This work has been supported in part by grant No. 80-05508 from the National Science Foundation.

REFERENCES

1. Leblond, C. P., and Clermont, Y. (1952) *Ann. N. Y. Acad. Sci.* **55**, 548–573.
2. Oakberg, E. F. (1956) *Am. J. Anat.* **99**, 391–413.
3. Clermont, Y., and Harvey, S. C. (1965) *Endocrinology* **76**, 80–89.
4. Comings, D. E., and Okada, T. A. (1974) *Adv. Cell Mol. Biol.* **2**, 309–384.
5. Soderstrom, K. O., and Parvinen, M. (1976) *Mol. Cell. Endocrinol.* **5**, 181–200.
6. Darzynkiewicz, Z. (1979) *In* "Flow Cytometry and Sorting" (M. R. Melamed, P. F. Mullaney, and M. L. Mendelsohn, eds.), pp. 285–316. Wiley, New York.
7. Meistrich, M. L., Lake, S., Steinmetz, L. L., and Gledhill, B. L. (1978) *Mutat. Res.* **49**, 383–396.
8. Hotta, Y., Ito, M., and Stern, H. (1966) *Proc. Natl. Acad. Sci. U.S.A.* **56**, 1184–1191.
9. Meistrich, M., Reid, B. O., and Barcellona, W. J. (1975) *J. Cell Biol.* **64**, 211–222.
10. Soderstrom, K. O. and Parvinen, M. (1976) *Hereditas* **82**, 25–28.
11. Meistrich, M. L., Reid, B. O., and Barcellona, W. J. (1976) *Exp. Cell Res.* **99**, 72–78.
12. Kierszenbaum, A. R., and Tres, L. L. (1975) *J. Cell Biol.* **65**, 258–270.
13. Gledhill, B. L., Gledhill, M. P., Rigler, R., and Ringertz, N. R. (1966) *Exp. Cell Res.* **41**, 652–665.
14. Platz, R. D., Grimes, S. R., Meistrich, M. L., and Hnilica, L. S. (1975) *J. Biol. Chem.* **250**, 5791–5800.
15. Mills, N. C., and Means, A. R. (1977) *Biol. Reprod.* **17**, 769–779.
16. Franklin, S. G., and Zweidler. A. (1977) *Nature (London)* **266**, 273–275.
17. Seyedin, S. M., and Kistler, W. S. (1979) *Biochemistry* **18**, 1376–1379.
18. Panyim, S., and Chalkley, R. (1969) *Biochemistry* **8**, 3972–3979.
19. Zweidler, A. (1976) *In* "Organization and Expression of Chromosomes" (V. G. Allfrey *et al.*, eds.), pp. 187–196. Dahlem Konferenzen, Berlin.
20. Branson, R. E., Grimes, S. R., Yonuschot, G., and Irvin, J. L. (1975) *Arch. Biochem. Biophys.* **168**, 403–412.

21. Shires, A., Carpenter, M. P., and Chalkley, R. (1975) *Proc. Natl. Acad. Sci. U.S.A.* **72**, 2714–2718.
22. Shires, A., Carpenter, M. P., and Chalkley, R. (1976) *J. Biol. Chem.* **251**, 4155–4158.
23. Seyedin, S. M., and Kistler, W. S. (1980) *J. Biol. Chem.* **255**, 5949–5954.
24. Levinger, L. F., Carter, C. W., Kumaroo, K. K., and Irvin, J. L. (1978) *J. Biol. Chem.* **253**, 5232–5234.
25. Trostle, P. K., Brock, W. A., and Meistrich, M. L. (1979) *J. Cell Biol.* **83**, 229a.
26. Brock, W. A., Trostle, P. K., and Meistrich, M. L. (1980) *Proc. Natl. Acad. Sci. U.S.A.* **77**, 371–375.
27. Zweidler, A. (1981) *In* "Gene Families of Collagen and Other Structural Proteins" (D. J. Prockop and P. C. Champe eds.). Elsevier/North-Holland Publ., Amsterdam (in press).
28. Panyim, S., and Chalkley, R. (1969) *Arch. Biochem. Biophys.* **130**, 337–346.
29. Laemmli, U. K. (1970) *Nature (London)* **227**, 680–685.
30. Zweidler, A. (1978) *Methods Cell Biol.* **17**, 223–233.
31. Kistler, W. S., Noyes, D., Hsu, R., and Henrikson, J. L. (1975) *J. Biol. Chem.* **250**, 1847–1853.
32. Grimes, S. R., Meistrich, M. L., Platz, R. D., and Hnilica, L. S. (1977) *Exp. Cell Res.* **110**, 31–39.
33. Meistrich, M. L., Brock, W. A., Grimes, S. R., Platz, R. D., and Hnilica, L. S. (1978) *Fed. Proc., Fed. Am. Soc. Exp. Biol.* **37**, 2522–2525.
34. Meistrich, M. L., Bucci, L. R., Brock, W. A., Trostle, P. K., Platz, R. D., Grimes, S. R., and Burleigh, B. D. (1980) *Fed. Proc., Fed. Am. Soc. Exp. Biol.* **39**, 1884.
35. Kistler, W. S., Kein, P. S., and Heinrikson, R. L. (1976) *Biochim. Biophys. Acta* **47**, 752–757.
36. Kistler, W. S., Geroch, M. E., and Williams-Ashman, H. G. (1973) *J. Biol. Chem.* **248**, 4532–4543.
37. Monesi, V. (1965) *Exp. Cell Res.* **39**, 197–224.
38. Mayer, J. F., and Zirkin, B. R. (1979) *J. Cell Biol.* **81**, 403–410.
39. Mills, N. C., Van, N. T., and Means, A. R. (1977) *Biol. Reprod.* **17**, 760–768.
40. Grimes, S. R., Chae, C. B., and Irvin, J. L. (1975) *Biochem. Biophys. Res. Commun.* **64**, 911–917.
41. Clermont, Y., and Perey, B. (1957) *Am. J. Anat.* **100**, 241–267.
42. Meistrich, M. L. (1977) *Methods Cell Biol.* **15**, 15–54.
43. Grabske, R. J., Lake, S., Gledhill, B. L., and Meistrich, M. L. (1975) *J. Cell. Physiol.* **86**, 177–190.
44. Meistrich, M. L., and Eng, V. W. S. (1972) *Exp. Cell Res.* **70**, 237–242.
45. Meistrich, M. L., Longtin, J. L., and Brock, W. A. (1979) *J. Cell Biol.* **83**, 226a.
46. Loir, M., and Courtens, J. L. (1979) *J. Ultrastruct. Res.* **67**, 309–324.
47. Bellve, A. R., Cavicchia, J. R., Millette, C. F., O'Brien, D. A., Bhatnagar, Y. M., and Dym, M. (1977) *J. Cell Biol.* **74**, 68–85.
48. Davis, J. C., and Scheutz, A. R. (1975) *Exp. Cell Res.* **91**, 79–86.
49. Meistrich, M. L., Trostle, P. K., Frapart, M. L., and Erickson, R. P. (1977) *Dev. Biol.* **60**, 428–441.
50. Gurley, L. R., Walters, R. A., and Tobey, R. A. (1974) *J. Cell Biol.* **60**, 356–364.
51. Rodman, T. C., Litwin, S. D., Romani, M., and Vidali, G. (1980) *J. Cell Biol.* **80**, 605–620.
52. Grimes, S. R., Platz, R. D., Meistrich, M. L., and Hnilica, L. S. (1975) *Biochem. Biophys. Res. Commun.* **67**, 182–189.
53. Fawcett, D. W., Anderson, W. A., and Phillips, D. M. (1971) *Dev. Biol.* **26**, 220–251.
54. Loir, M., and Lanneau, M. (1978) *Exp. Cell Res.* **115**, 231–243.

Interspecific Fertilization

EDWINA RUDAK

MRC Reproductive Biology Unit
Centre for Reproductive Biology
Edinburgh, Scotland

Under natural conditions, interspecies matings are normally prevented by the ecological and behavioral barriers which exist between individuals of different species. There are a few well-known examples of crosses which can produce viable interspecific hybrids: the lion and the tiger, the horse and the donkey, but these are the rare cases where development of the hybrid embryo actually results in live-born offspring. Artificial insemination has shown that several other combinations of heterologous sperm and eggs can result in fertilization *in vivo*, for example, the rabbit and the hare (1), the mink and the ferret (2), but embryonic development is retarded and offspring are never produced. There is evidence which demonstrates that reciprocal crosses frequently vary in the efficiency with which fertilization is effected; ferret eggs are readily fertilized by mink sperm, yet mink eggs are never fertilized by ferret sperm (2). This difference in fertilization efficiency in reciprocal crosses has been attributed to the lack of survival of heterologous sperm in a foreign reproductive tract, the sperm of some species being more sensitive to the adverse anatomical and physiological barriers than others (3). This subject has been reviewed in detail by Chang and Hancock (4).

The use of *in vitro* fertilization techniques has facilitated many more detailed studies of the homologies which exist between the sperm and eggs of different species. It is now known that the zona pellucida of the mammalian oocyte is the major barrier to inter-specific fertilization (5). Insemination of zona-intact eggs with capacitated or uncapacitated heterologous spermatozoa *in vitro*, results in varying degress of sperm binding to the zona, depending on the species, but never, in fertilization (6). In one unusual instance, human sperm were found in the perivitelline space of gibbon follicular oocytes, but none of the sperm had fused with the vitelline membrane or had been incorporated into the egg cytoplasm (6). However, when the zona pellu-

167

cida is manually or enzymatically removed from mammalian oocytes, the vitelline membrane of the eggs of different species show marked variation in their affinities for foreign sperm. Yanagimachi (7) was the first to demonstrate penetration of zona-free eggs of one species, the golden hamster, (*Mesocricetus auratus*) by the sperm of another species, the guinea pig. It has also been shown that zona-free rat eggs can be penetrated by mouse sperm (8), zona-free rabbit eggs can be penetrated by mouse and rat sperm (9), while zona-free hamster eggs can be penetrated by the sperm of all species that have been tested to date: rat, mouse (8,9), guinea pig (7,10), human (11), boar (12), rabbit, and deer mouse (13).

Although interspecific fertilization studied *in vitro* is an interesting biological phenomenon in itself, in this chapter I will concentrate on the way in which human fertility research has been profoundly affected by the discovery that capacitated human spermatozoa will penetrate the zona-free eggs of a nonhuman species, the hamster (11). First, I will describe how a zona-free hamster egg technique has been used to evaluate the fertilizing capacity of human spermatozoa with a view to predicting the fertility of an individual and second, how the technique has been used to visualize human sperm chromosomes so that they can be analyzed with the same precision as the chromosomes of somatic cells.

ASSESSMENT OF THE FERTILIZING CAPACITY OF HUMAN SPERMATOZOA

Among infertile couples, male reproductive dysfunction accounts for at least 50% of the cases of suspected infertility and may occur at a frequency as high as 10% in the general population (14). In spite of its prevalence, an accurate diagnosis is only possible for those individuals who show some clinically identifiable organic anomaly, which only accounts for about 25% of the cases.

The mystery surrounding the aetiology of male infertility is almost certainly attributable to the lack of a clinical test which will directly and accurately predict the fertility of an individual with sufficient precision. Conventional methods of assessing fertility rely on seminal characteristics like sperm count, density, motility, and morphology but it is universally recognized that all these parameters are only very indirect indices of fertilizing capacity and are not necessarily always informative (14–17).

The first attempt to devise a more direct, biological assay to evaluate the fertilizing capacity of human sperm was made by Overstreet and Hembree (18). In their study, they recovered follicular oocytes from human cadaver ovaries, incubated them with sperm from fertile and suspected infertile donors, then examined the eggs for signs of sperm penetration through the zona pellucida. They found that the sperm from 69% of their suspected infertile donors had the ability to penetrate the zonae of cadaver oocytes, and the penetration rate (12.9%) was lower than that observed with sperm from fertile donors (46.4%). It is known that the human zona pellucida is a highly resilient structure, which will retain its specificity and most of its chemical and physical characteristics even after storage for long periods in concentrated salt solutions (19). It is, therefore, likely that sperm penetration through the zona of nonviable cadaver oocytes *in vitro* is an accurate reflection of the sperms ability to penetrate the zona of a human egg *in vivo*, but unfortunately, this system does not evaluate the ability of the sperm to actually effect fertilization by penetrating the vitellus, and decondensing to form a male pronucleus.

In 1976, Yanagimachi *et al.* (11) demonstrated that capacitated human sperm would penetrate zona-free hamster eggs, accompanied by decondensation of the sperm chromatin and pronucleus formation, and they suggested that hamster eggs might be an acceptable substitute for human eggs to assess the fertilizing capacity of human sperm. Since then, there have been three reports using Yanagimachi's technique to try to differentiate fertile and infertile donors on the basis of the ability of their sperm to penetrate zona-free hamster eggs (20–22). The results of a study which we are presently carrying out in Edinburgh (23) to evaluate the fertilizing capacity of patients attending an infertility clinic, correlates closely with those of Rogers *et al.* (22). In order to assess the clinical application of the zona-free hamster egg penetration test, we have investigated the relationship between fertility status, semen analysis and penetration rates using the data obtained from a total of 74 semen samples from a group of 60 males.

THE ZONA-FREE HAMSTER EGG PENETRATION TEST

The technique we use to assess the fertilizing capacity of human sperm is a modification of that described by Yanagimachi *et al.* (11) and Rogers *et al.* (22), the main differences being in the composition of the medium and the duration of the sperm preincubation period. The medium used throughout all procedures was a modified Krebs-Ringers salt solution, originally formulated by Biggers *et al.* (24), hereafter referred to as BWW. The composition of our BWW stock solution

TABLE I
Chemical Composition of Stock BWW Medium

Substance	g/liter
NaCl	5.540
KCl	0.356
$CaCl_2 \cdot 2H_2O$	0.250
KH_2PO_4	0.162
$MgSO_4 \cdot 7H_2O$	0.294
Phenol red (0.5%)	1.0 ml

is shown in Table I. The stock solution was stored at 4°C. Immediately before use, to 100 ml of BWW stock were added 210 mg $NaHCO_3$, 100 mg glucose, 3 mg sodium pyruvate, 2.0 ml 1 M Hepes buffer, pH 7.2–7.4, 1.0 ml of penicillin and streptomycin solution (10,000 IU, 10,000 μg), 370 μl of sodium lactate (60% syrup), and 300 mg of human serum albumin (fraction V). For sperm preincubation, a high-albumin BWW was prepared by dissolving 150 mg of human serum albumin (fraction V) in 10 ml. of complete BWW (final albumin concentration = 18 mg/ml).

Patients. In our study semen samples were obtained from men who were either (i) of proven fertility (N = 8), (ii) clinically diagnosed as infertile (N = 6), (iii) men from infertile couples whose wives show evidence of infertility (N = 14), or (iv) men from infertile couples with infertility of unknown aetiology (N = 32).

Sperm Processing. The semen sample to be tested was obtained by masturbation and collected into a sterile plastic jar. The semen was allowed to liquify either at room temperature or at 37°C, for 30 minutes to 2 hours, then diluted with about 8.0 ml BWW. The sperm were pelleted by centrifugation at 600 g for 6 minutes, then washed twice more in fresh medium. The final cell pellet was resuspended in high albumin BWW to give a concentration of 1×10^7 sperm/ml. The sperm were incubated in a 1.0 ml volume in sterile plastic tubes with caps, at 37°C in an atmosphere of 5% CO_2 in air, for 6 hours. This preincubation period is necessary for sperm capacitation (11). Barros *et al.* (21) using a medium (TMPA) of slightly different chemical composition allow only 1 hour for sperm capacitation, while Rogers *et al.* (22) allow 18–20 hours.

Egg Collection. Adult, female golden hamsters (*Mesocricetus auratus*) 8–10 weeks old were induced to superovulate by intraperitoneal injection of 25 IU pregnant mares' serum gonadotrophin on day 1 (the day of post-oestrous discharge) of their oestrous cycle, followed by an intraperitoneal injection of 25 IU human chorionic gonadotrophin on day 3). Seventeen–eighteen hours after HCG administration the animals were killed, their oviducts dissected out and the cumulus mass containing the eggs was obtained by tearing the wall of the ampulla with a needle. The cumulus cells were dissociated from the eggs in 0.1% hyaluronidase in BWW, the eggs washed twice in medium, then the zonae were digested away in 0.1% trypsin in BWW (Fig. 1). Approximately 40–60 eggs can be obtained from each superovulated hamster. The zona-free eggs were washed twice in BWW and were ready for insemination at the end of the 6 hours sperm preincubation period.

Insemination. Twenty-microliter volumes of the preincubated sperm suspension were placed in sterile plastic culture dishes, six drops per dish, and covered with mineral oil pre-warmed to 37°C. Eight–twelve zona-free eggs were placed in each 20 μl drop of sperm suspension, and the dishes were incubated at 37°C in 5% CO_2 in air for 3 hours. Approximately 40–60 eggs were inseminated for each semen sample tested.

Evaluation of Penetration. After 3 hours of incubation of eggs with sperm, the eggs were removed from the dish, washed in BWW, and transferred in a small volume of medium to the centre of four wax

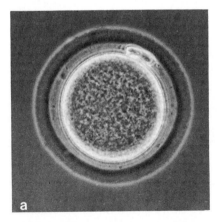 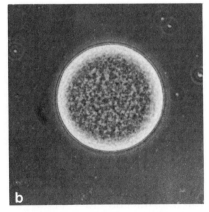

Fig. 1.   (a) An oocyte recovered from a superovulated female hamster 17 hours after HCG administration. The cumulus cells have been dispersed in 0.1% hyaluronidase. (b) A zona-free hamster egg. The zona-has been digested away in 0.1% trypsin.

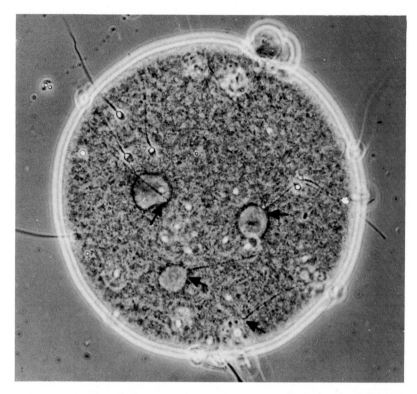

Fig. 2. A zona-free hamster egg which has been incubated with preincubated human sperm for 3 hours. The egg has been compressed slightly between a slide and coverslip and is viewed in phase contrast. Four sperm have penetrated the egg (arrows). Swollen sperm heads appear as large, clear areas associated with a sperm tail.

spots on a slide. A coverslip was placed over the wax spots and compressed gradually until swollen sperm heads could be seen within the egg cytoplasm. The positive assay for sperm penetration is a swollen sperm head with an attached or closely associated sperm tail. Figure 2 shows a zona-free hamster egg which has been penetrated by four human spermatozoa. Swollen sperm heads are easily identified as clear areas associated with a sperm tail.

RESULTS

The results obtained in our study are compared to those of Rogers *et al.* (22) in Tables II–VI. Table II shows the results obtained for males of proven fertility. The results of both studies are remarkably similar,

TABLE II
Penetration Rates of Males of Proven Fertility[a]

	Count ($\times 10^6$/ml)	Motile before preincubation (%)	Motile after preincubation (%)	Penetration rate (%)
Average				
Honolulu	114	63	—	56.3
Edinburgh	180	68	54	54.2
Range				
Honolulu	22–203	40–90	—	14–100
Edinburgh	26–340	37–83	14–79	19–100

[a] Honolulu study, number of patients (N_p) = Number of samples (N_s) = 21; Edinburgh study, $N_p = 8$, $N_s = 17$.

the average penetration rate of fertile males being around 54–56%, with a wide range of penetration values between 14% and 100%. The results we obtained for males who were clinically diagnosed as being infertile, either because of oligospermia, marked sperm agglutination, or because of the presence of a varicocoel, are shown in Table III. Their average count and percent motility are considerably lower than those of the fertile population, and their average penetration rate was 1.8%, with a range of 0–5.2%. Table IV shows the results obtained for men whose wives were diagnosed as showing evidence of infertility. Although of unproven fertility, the results obtained for these men were almost identical to the average values and ranges of the proven fertile population. In the study of Rogers et al. (22) all men of couples attending an infertility clinic whose wives had either previously been pregnant or showed no evidence of infertility, had penetration rates in the range 0–10% with an average of 2.6% (Table V). These patients were not further categorized to show the proportion who had abnormal semen analysis, although the values given for the range in sperm count and percent motile certainly indicates that those at the lower

TABLE III
Penetration Rates of Clinically Infertile Males[a]

	Count ($\times 10^6$/ml)	Motile in semen (%)	Motile after incubation (%)	Penetration rate (%)
Average	56	43	22	1.8
Range	15–136	18–74	8–39	0–5.2

[a] $N_p = N_s = 6$ (Edinburgh study).

TABLE IV
Penetration Rates of Males from Infertile Couples with
Wife Showing Evidence of Infertility[a]

	Count ($\times 10^6$/ml)	Motile before preincubation (%)	Motile after preincubation (%)	Penetration rate (%)
Average				
Honolulu	122	58	—	57.2
Edinburgh	135	64	52	52.1
Range				
Honolulu	42–309	45–85	—	22.5–100
Edinburgh	19–268	52–72	35–65	11.6–98

[a] Honolulu study $N_p = N_s = 10$; Edinburgh study $N_p = 14$, $N_s = 16$.

end of the scales would be classified as potentially infertile on semen analysis alone. Table VI shows the results which we have obtained for a group of 32 males from couples who have been investigated extensively at an infertility clinic, yet have infertility of unknown etiology. We have divided this group into those who score greater than 10%, and those who score less than 10% in the sperm penetration test. Semen analysis values for all men fall within the clinically accepted normal range. Of the 32 men investigated, 20 (62.5%) had penetration values of less than 10% within the range 0–10% with an average of 3.9%. The remaining 12 patients had penetration values in the range 11–93%, with an average of 37.9%. Although the average penetration value obtained for men who scored more than 10% in the penetration test (37.9%) is less than that for the population of proven fertile men (54.2%), the values for both populations as a whole are not statistically significantly different. Table VII shows the penetration rates of a male of proven fertility who was tested on six separate occasions. For this

TABLE V
Penetration Rates of Males from Infertile Couples Where Wives Either
Show no Evidence of Infertility or Have Previously Been Pregnant[a,b]

	Count ($\times 10^6$/ml)	Motile before preincubation (%)	Penetration rate (%)
Average	50	47	2.6
Range	4–330	10–90	0–10

[a] $N_p = N_s = 30$.
[b] From Rogers et al. (22).

TABLE VI
Penetration Rates of Males from Couples with Infertility of Unknown Etiology
(N = 32) (Edinburgh Study)

	Penetration rate > 10% (N_p = 12, N_s = 14)			
	Count ($\times 10^6$/ml)	Motile before preincubation (%)	Motile after preincubation (%)	Penetration rate (%)
Average	152	61	46	37.9
Range	33–314	43–72	30–58	10–93
	Penetration rate < 10% (N_p = 20, N_s = 21)			
	Count ($\times 10^6$/ml)	Motile in semen (%)	Motile after preincubation (%)	Penetration rate (%)
Average	141	57	36	3.9
Range	23–400	33–77	11–65	0–9.6

individual, the average penetration rate was 60.5 ± 11.8% (standard deviation).

DISCUSSION

The data presented here from the results of two comparable studies using the zona-free hamster egg penetration test clearly demonstrate that the test is a highly repeatable, sensitive indicator of fertility status. The sperm of fertile males penetrate zona-free hamster eggs with

TABLE VII
Penetration Rates of a Male of Proven Fertility Tested on Six Separate Occasions
(Edinburgh study)

Test	Count ($\times 10^6$/ml)	Motile before preincubation (%)	Motile after preincubation (%)	Penetration rate (%)
1	126	58	65	58.6
2	70	73	79	67.0
3	192	57	52	50.0
4	—	—	—	77.4
5	—	—	—	67.6
6	—	—	—	42.1
				$\bar{x}$ = 60.5%

greater efficiency (14–100%) than do sperm from clinically infertile men (0–5.2%). In the study of Rogers *et al.* (22) the males of couples attending an infertility clinic fell into two categories: either their wife showed evidence of infertility and their sperm showed penetration rates almost identical to those of fertile men, or their wife showed no signs of infertility and their sperm showed low values (0–10%) in the hamster egg penetration test, these values being outside and below the fertile populations' range. Rogers *et al.*, therefore, suggest that using this assay for sperm fertilizing ability, men whose sperm penetrate hamster eggs with a frequency of less than 10% are potentially infertile. Our results appear to support this conclusion. In our study, the range of penetration rates of fertile men (19–100%) were clearly distinct from those of clinically infertile men (0–5.2%), although the number of infertile patients studied was very small ($N = 6$). Among our group of 32 males from couples with infertility of unknown etiology, almost two-thirds (62.5%) had penetration values of less than 10% which is well below the range for proven fertile men in our population. It is, therefore, likely that the reason for their infertility lies in some lesion in their spermatozoa which is not reflected in the sperm number, density, count, morphology, or motility, yet which severely restricts the sperm's fertilizing ability.

Binor *et al.*(25) have evaluated several of the parameters that contribute to sperm penetration into zona-free hamster eggs and suggest that the penetrating ability of a constant constant concentration of motile sperm ($> 6 \times 10^5$ motile sperm/ml) should be tested for each specimen. While it is generally acknowledged that only motile spermatozoa have the ability to effect fertilization, alteration of the sperm concentration in the test system to compensate for the number of motile spermatozoa will artificially alter the intrinsic nature of a particular ejaculate, and the results may not reflect the true fertilizing potential of the semen sample. In addition, the high concentration of dead sperm in those semen samples with a low percentage motility may adversely affect sperm penetration despite the adjustment of the motile sperm concentration to a constant value. Techniques to separate the motile sperm from the nonmotile fraction (26) could, to some extent, overcome this problem.

The 2-hour (22) or 3-hour (23) insemination period, after which the eggs are scored, appears to give a clear distinction between the penetration rates of fertile and potentially infertile specimens. In our experience, for specimens with low to average penetration values ($< 50\%$), each penetrated egg usually contains only one swollen sperm head. As the penetration rate increases up to the maximum of 100%, more than one sperm can be found within each egg, due to the absence of a vitelline block to polyspermy in fresh zona-free hamster eggs (25). The degree of polyspermy is directly related to the penetration rate, those specimens which score 93–100% penetration having up to 15 sperm in each egg. Zona-free hamster eggs are maximally penetrated after 5 hours of incubation with capacitated sperm and the decline in penetration after this time is related to egg aging (25). Thus, when insemination times of longer than 3 hours are used, it may be necessary to quantitate the number of sperm incorporated per egg (25) which would serve to differentiate between specimens with maximum penetration values.

There is obviously great potential in the use of the zona-free hamster egg penetration test in conjunction with routine semen analysis to identify those cases of infertility which are the result of a functional deficiency in the spermatozoa which restricts their fertilizing ability. Although further studies are necessary to determine whether very low (< 10%) penetration rates are unequivocally a reflection of infertility or sterility, there is at least some good evidence that we may now be able to begin to explain some of the cases of hitherto undiagnosed idiopathic infertility.

CHROMOSOME ANALYSIS OF HUMAN SPERMATOZOA

There is increasing evidence from the study of the chromosome constitutions of clinically recognizable pregnancies, including both live-born babies and spontaneous abortions, which suggests that chromosomal errors occurring during gametogenesis may be the most important single factor contributing to both a real and apparent failure to conceive, and to the production of conceptuses which abort spontaneously in the first few weeks of pregnancy. At the present time, very little is known regarding the relative contributions of chromosomally abnormal male and female gametes in the production of aneuploud human embryos. Estimates of the frequency of chromosome abnormalities occurring during gametogenesis have been obtained indirectly by looking at the chromosomes of those conceptuses that survive long enough to be clinically recognized as a pregnancy. These include both live-born babies, among which 1 in 200 have a chromosome aberration (27) and spontaneous abortions, which represent at least 15% of all recognized conceptions, and where the frequency of chromosome abnormalities is 1 in 2, a hundred-fold higher than in the live-born population (28). A recent study (E. M. Williamson and J. F. Miller, unpublished) using β-HCG measurement to detect early pregnancies has shown that 32% of conceptions are lost before the first missed menstrual period. Within the remaining 68% clinically recognized pregnancies, 10% aborted spontaneously and 58% resulted in live births. It is, therefore, apparent that almost one-third of all human conceptions are lost very early in gestation, a remarkably high incidence of reproductive loss which, unfortunately cannot be investigated further if the embryos are unavailable for analysis. There is obviously a need to determine the contribution made by both sperm and egg in the generation of chromosomally abnormal embryos. The ideal method of analyzing the chromosome constitution of human gametes would be to fertilize human eggs with human sperm *in vitro* and to karyotype the resulting zygotes, but this approach is highly impractical and has many associated ethical considerations. There have been some attempts to analyze the chromosomes of follicular oocytes recovered from ovarian tissue (29), but such oocytes have undergone neither first nor second meiotic division *in vivo*, and it is known that nondisjunction frequently occurs at these stages in the human female (30–33). Even if follicular oocytes are matured by culture *in vitro*, any anomalies seen as a result of the first meiotic division could have been experimentally induced and would not be a true reflection of what might occur *in vivo*. It would appear that as far as the human female gamete is concerned, chromosome analysis is very difficult because it relies wholly on the surgical recovery and fertilization *in vitro* of a mature preovulatory oocyte.

Fortunately, human sperm are much more readily obtainable than human oocytes, and consequently there have been many attempts to bypass the need for the cytoplasm of a mature human oocyte to reactivate the sperm nucleus, decondense the chromatin and make chromosome analysis possible. Sperm have been fused with cultured somatic cells, using fusiogenic agents such as lysolecithin, polyethylene glycol, and Sendai virus (34–39), but the number of heterokaryons produced is very small, and none have gone through a subsequent cell division.

Fixed smears of whole sperm have been stained using cytological staining procedures more usually applied to somatic cell chromosomes (40–50). Certain chromosome regions such as the long arm of the Y and the heterochromatic regions of chromosomes 1 and 9 are presumed to be represented in appropriately stained sperm nuclei as differentially staining spots. Estimates of 1–2% for the nondisjunction frequency of these chromosomes have been obtained by counting the number of stained spots per nucleus, which would imply a staggering 40% level of aneuploidy in a population of sperm from a normal male. Such an estimate was found to be biased by the cytological analysis used (49,50).

The landmark paper by Yanagimachi and colleagues (11) made it possible to investigate whether the hamster egg might be an acceptable substitute for the human oocyte in reactivating the human sperm nucleus (51). It was found that the zona-free hamster egg was the ideal reactivating vehicle for human sperm; it obviously contains those oocyte-specific factors which are thought to be essential for the decondensation of the tightly packed sperm chromatin necessary for the resumption of DNA synthesis and subsequent development of the zygote. A technique was, therefore, developed whereby zona-free hamster eggs which had been penetrated by human spermatozoa could be cultured *in vitro* until the sperm chromosomes condensed and could be analyzed directly (51).

TECHNIQUE FOR ANALYSIS OF HUMAN SPERM CHROMOSOMES

The author's technique for the analysis of human sperm chromosomes is essentially an extension of "The Zona-Free Hamster Egg Penetration Test"; the methods for processing the sperm, collecting zona-free hamster eggs and insemination being almost identical to those described previously. Zona-free hamster eggs were incubated for 3 hours with capacitated (5- to 7-hour preincubation) human spermatozoa at a concentration of $2–3 \times 10^7$ sperm/ml. After this time, most of the eggs had been penetrated by one or more sperm. The eggs were washed free of sperm and reincubated in a fresh 200 μl droplet of BWW, or F10 containing 15% fetal calf serum, under mineral oil for 12–13 hours. To arrest the chromosomes at metaphase of the first cleavage division, colcemid at a final concentration of 0.5 μg/ml was added to the medium containing the eggs, and the dishes incubated for a further 6–7 hours. The eggs were hypotonically treated with 1% sodium citrate solution for 10–15 minutes, then fixed in Carnoy's 3:1 fixative and air-dried onto slides according to the method described by Tarkowski (52).

Fixed preparations were either stained with an Atebrin/quinacrine mustard solution and subsequently stained with lactic aceto–orcein, or C-banded to differentiate the heterochromatic regions of the chromo-

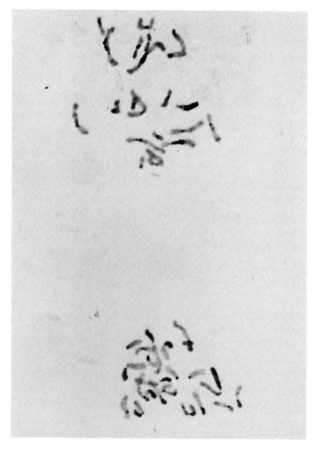

Fig. 3. C-banded hamster (bottom) and human (top) haploid chromosome comple-ments, in a colcemid-treated zona-free hamster egg fixed 22 hours after insemination with human sperm. The penetrating sperm has a 23,Y chromosome constitution.

somes. This technique gives preparations of human sperm chromo-somes which are usually of excellent quality and which can be ana-lyzed as easily as the chromosomes of somatic cells. Figure 3 shows a C-banded preparation of the chromosomes of the male (human) and female (hamster) pronuclei within a colcemid-treated hamster egg. The hamster chromosomes are easily distinguishable from those of the human by their C-banding pattern. Figure 4 shows the chromo-some complement of a sperm with a 23,Y chromosome constitution. The chromosomes appear very long and decondensed with distinct

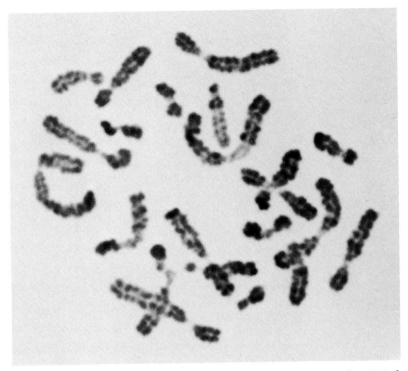

Fig. 4. An Orcein-stained haploid chromosome set from a sperm with a 23,Y chromosome constitution. Note the elongated heterochromatic regions of chromosomes 1, 9, 16, and the Y. [from Rudak *et al.* (51).]

spiralization of each chromatid. The heterochromatic regions of chromosomes 1, 9, 16, and the Y are the most decondensed chromosome regions. Figure 5 shows a C-banded preparation of a 23,Y complement of sperm chromosomes.

The results of chromosome analysis of 88 human spermatozoa from four different males, all of whom had penetration rates within the range of fertile males is shown in Table VIII. Of the 70 sperm analyzed from donor B345, only 3 were aneuploid, giving an aneuploidy frequency of 4.3%. In view of the lack of detectable autosomal monosomies in man, it is interesting to note that if either of the sperm nullisomic for a G or an F chromosome had fertilized a human egg, a monosomic conceptus would have resulted. More 23,X sperm than 23,Y sperm have been identified, but the deviation from a 1:1 ratio is not statistically significant.

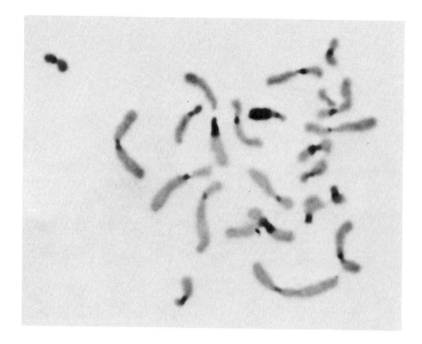

Fig. 5. A C-banded haploid chromosome set from a sperm with a 23,Y chromosome constitution. [from Rudak *et al.* (51).]

TABLE VIII
Chromosome Analysis of Human Spermatozoa

Analysis	B345	B402	B399	B398
Normal				
23,X	37	5	2	2
23,Y	30	6	2	1
Abnormal				
22,X,-G	1	—	—	—
22,X,-F	1	—	—	—
24,X,+mar,+ace	1	—	—	—
Total	70	11	4	3
Aneuploidy	4.3%	—	—	—

Using this technique, it should now be possible to assess the level of aneuploidy in any sample of sperm which will penetrate zona-free hamster eggs. This will allow us to gain a much better understanding of the contribution made by chromosome errors occurring during male gametogenesis to infertility and reproductive failure in man.

OTHER APPLICATIONS OF THE ZONA-FREE HAMSTER EGG TECHNIQUE

At the present time there have been investigations into the effects of seminal plasma (53), and heterologous antisperm antibodies (54) on the ability of human sperm to penetrate zona-free hamster eggs. The use of cryopreserved zona-free hamster ova in the evaluation of the fertilizing capacity of human sperm has also been described (55). Recently, we have investigated the relationship between antisperm antibody titer in serum assessed by the techniques of sperm agglutination (56–58) and immobilization (59), and the dilution of antiserum which effectively inhibits sperm penetration *in vitro* (60). Using both heterologous (rabbit) and homologous antisperm antisera of known titer, we have found that there is no significant inhibition of sperm penetration at the antiserum dilutions which gave positive titres in sperm agglutination or immobilization tests. It is, therefore, possible that the clinical tests of agglutination and immobilization are too sensitive to accurately diagnose cases of immune infertility, a hypothesis which is supported by the observation that there is no significant difference in the pregnancy rates between infertile couples showing positive or negative results with the immobilization test (61).

There are many other aspects of human sperm function which can be examined in detail now a suitable technique is available. Future developments can be expected to include studies on the following:

1. The effectiveness of male contraceptives, particularly in those cases where the use of anti-androgens (62,63) or steroids (64) does not suppress sperm production completely.
2. The effect of cryopreservation on the fertilizing ability and the chromosome constitution of human sperm. This type of study would have direct clinical relevance to centers involved in AID. It has been reported that reduced numbers of blastocysts were recovered from rabbits inseminated with rabbit sperm stored at $-196°C$, and the frequency of chromosome abnormalities increased with increasing storage time (65).

3. The screening of semen donors used by AID clinics, to determine their penetration rates.
4. Examination of the sperm chromosomes of (a) men exposed to occupational and therapeutic mutagens, carcinogens and X-irradiation, (b) men whose wives have had multiple spontaneous abortions, and (c) men whose wives have had a trisomic conceptus and it is known that the extra chromosome is of paternal origin.

Within the next decade we can expect considerable progress to be made in the diagnosis of infertility if the zona-free hamster egg penetration test is unequivocally found to be a reliable indicator of fertility status. This is the only technique available at the present time for the study of human sperm function and their chromosome constitution, and the simplicity and directness of the technique holds great potential for future research.

REFERENCES

1. Chang, M. C., Marston, J. H., and Hunt, D. (1964)*J. Exp. Zool.* **155**, 437–466.
2. Chang, M. C. (1968) *J. Exp. Zool.* **168**, 49–60.
3. Chang, M. C., and Bedford, J. M. (1962) *Int. Congr. Anim. Reprod., 4th, 1961* Vol. 2, pp. 367–370.
4. Chang, M. C., and Hancock, J. L. (1967) *In* "Comparative Aspects of Reproductive Failure" (K. Benirshke, ed.), pp. 206–217, Springer-Verlag, Berlin and New York.
5. Yanagimachi, R., (1977) *In* "Immunobiology of Gametes" (M. Edidin and M. H. Johnson, eds.), p. 255. Cambridge Univ. Press, London and New York.
6. Bedford, J. M. (1977) *Anat. Rec.* **188**, 477–488..
7. Yanagimachi, R. (1972) *J. Reprod. Fertil.* **28**, 477–480.
8. Hanada, A., and Chang, M. C. (1972) *Biol. Reprod.* **6**, 300–309.
9. Hanada, A., and Chang, M. C. (1976) *J. Reprod. Fertil.* **46**, 239–241.
10. Barros, C., Berrios, M., and Herrera, E. (1973) *J. Reprod. Fertil.* **34**, 547–549.
11. Yanagimachi, R., Yanagimachi, H., and Rogers, B. J. (1976) *Biol. Reprod.* **15**, 471–476.
12. Imai, H., Niwa, K., and Iritani, A. (1977)*J. Reprod. Fertil.* **51**, 495–497.
13. Hanada, A., and Chang, M. C. (1978) *J. Exp. Zool.* **203**, 277–286.
14. Hembree, W. C., Fang, J. F., and Jagiello, G. (1977) *In* "The Testis in Normal and Infertile Men" (P. Troen and H. R. Nankin, eds.), pp. 25–29. Raven, New York.
15. Smith, K. D., Rodriguez-Rigau, L. J., and Steinberger, E. (1977) *Fertil. Steril.* **28**, 1314–1319.
16. Zukerman, Z., Rodriguez-Rigau, L. J., Smith, K. D., and Steinberger, E. (1977) *Fertil. Steril.* **28**, 1310–1313.
17. David, G., Jouannet, P., Martin-Boyce, A., Spirm, A., and Schwartz, D. (1979) *Fertil. Steril.* **31**, 453–455 (1979).
18. Overstreet, J. W., and Hembree, W. D. (1976) *Fertil. Steril.* **27**, 815–831.
19. Yanagimachi, R., Lopata, A., Odom, C. B., Bronson, R. A., Mahi, C. A., and Nicolson, G. L. (1979) *Fertil. Steril.* **31**, 562–574.

20. Barros, C., Gonzalez, J., Herrera, E., and Bustos-Obregon, E. (1978) *Contraception* **17**, 87–91.
21. Barros, C., Gonzalez, J., Herrera, E., and Bustos-Obregon, E. (1979) *Andrologia* **11**, 197–210.
22. Rogers, B. J., Van Campen, H., Ueno, M., Lambert, H., Bronson, R., and Hale, R. (1979) *Fertil. Steril.* **32**, 664–670.
23. Aitken, R. J., Rudak, E., Newman, F., Templeton, A., Djahanbakhch, O., Mortimer, D., and Richardson, D. W. (1980). In preparation..
24. Biggers, J. D., Whitten, W. K., and Whittingham, D. G. (1971) *In* "Methods in Mammalian Embryology" (J. C. Daniel, ed.), p. 86, Freeman, San Francisco, California.
25. Binor, Z., Sokoloski, J. E., and Wolf, D. P. (1980) *Fertil. Steril.* **33**, 321–327.
26. Hellema, H. W. J., and Rumke, P. (1978) *Clin. Exp. Immunol.* **31**, 1–11.
27. Jacobs, P. A. (1977) *Am. J. Epidemiol.* **105**, 180–191.
28. Hassold, T. J., Matsuyama, A., Newlands, I. M., Matsuura, J. S., Jacobs, P. A., Manuel, B., and Tsuei, J. (1978) *Ann. Hum. Genet.* **41**, 443–454.
29. Jagiello, G., Karnicki, J., and Ryan, R. J. (1968) *Lancet* **1**, 178–180.
30. Hassold, T. J., and Matsuyama, A. (1979) *Hum. Genet.* **46**, 285–294.
31. Magenis, R. E., Overton, K. M., Chamberlin, J., Brady, T., and Louvrien, E. (1977) *Hum. Genet.* **37**, 7–16.
32. Mikkelsen, M., Hallberg, A., and Poulsen, H. (1976) *Hum. Genet.* **32**, 17–21.
33. Niikawa, N., Merotto, E., and Kajii, T. (1977) *Hum. Genet.* **40**, 73–78.
34. Sawicki, W., and Koprowski, H. (1971) *Exp. Cell Res.* **66**, 145–151.
35. Phillips, S. G., and Phillips, D. M. (1974) *J. Cell Biol.* **63**, 269a.
36. Bendich, A., Borenfreund, E., and Sternberg, S. S. (1974) *Science* **183**, 857–859.
37. Elsevier, S. M., and Ruddle, F. H. (1976) *Chromosoma* **56**, 227–241.
38. Johnson, R. T., Rao, P. N., and Hughes, H. D. (1970) *J. Cell. Physiol.* **76**, 151–158.
39. Gledhill, B. L., Sawicki, W., Croce, C. M., and Koprowski, H. (1972) *Exp. Cell Res.* **73**, 33–40.
40. Pearson, P. L., and Bobrow, M. J. (1970) *J. Reprod. Fertil.* **22**, 177–179.
41. Barlow, P., and Vosa, C. G. (1970) *Nature (London)* **226**, 961–962.
42. Sumner, A. T., Robinson, J. A., and Evans, H. J. (1971) *Nature (London), New Biol.* **229**, 231–233.
43. Pawlowitski, I. H., and Pearson, P. L. (1972) *Hum. Genet.* **16**, 119–122.
44. Beatty, R. A. (1975) *Biol. J. Linn. Soc.* **7**, Suppl. 1, 291–299.
45. Roberts, A. M., and Goodall, H. (1976) *Nature (London)* **262**, 493–494.
46. Schwinger, E., Ites, J., and Korte, B. (1976) *Hum. Genet.* **34**, 265–270.
47. Geraedts, J. P. M., and Pearson, P. L. (1973) *Bull. Eur. Soc. Hum. Genet.* pp. 24–31.
48. Evans, H. J. (1971) *In* "The Genetics of the Spermatozoon" (R. A. Beatty and S. Gluecksohn-Waelsh, eds.), pp. 144–159. Bogtrykkeriet Forum, Copenhagen.
49. Beatty, R. A. (1977) *Cytogenet. Cell Genet.* **18**, 33–49.
50. Sumner, A. T., and Robinson, J. A. (1976) *J. Reprod. Fertil.* **48**, 9–15.
51. Rudak, E., Jacobs, P. A., and Yanagimachi, R. (1978) *Nature (London)* **274**, 911–913.
52. Tarkowski, A. K. (1966) *Cytogenetics* **5**, 394–400.
53. Kanwar, K. C., Yanagimachi, R., and Lopata, A. (1979) *Fertil. Steril.* **31**, 321–327.
54. Menge, A. C., and Black, C. S. (1979) *Fertil. Steril.* **32**, 214–218.
55. Fleming, A. D., and Yanagimachi, R. (1979) *Biol. Reprod.* **20**, Suppl. 1, 41A (abstr.).
56. Franklin, R. R., and Dukes, C. D. (1964) *Am. J. Obstet. Gynecol.* **89**, 6–9.
57. Kibrick, S., Belding, D. L., and Merrill, B. (1952) *Fertil. Steril.* **3**, 430–438.
58. Friberg, J. (1974) *Acta Obstet. Gynecol. Scand., Suppl.* **36**, 31–38.
59. Isojima, S., Li, T. S., and Ashitaka, Y. (1968) *Am. J. Obstet. Gynecol.* **101**, 667–683 (1968).

60. Dor, J., Rudak, E., and Aitken, R. J. (1980) In preparation.
61. Jones, W. R. (1974) *In: Karolinska Symp. Res. Methods Reprod. Endocrinol., 7th Symposium.*
62. Koch, U. J., Lorenz, F., Danehl, K., Ericsson, R., Hasan, S. H., Keyserlingk, D. V., Lubke, K., Mehring, M., Rommler, A., Schwartz, U., and Hammerstein, J. (1976) *Contraception* **14,** 117–137.
63. Roy, S., Chatterjee, S., Prasad, M. R. N., Poddar, A. K., and Pandey, D. C. (1976) *Contraception* **14,** 403–420.
64. Paulsen, C. A., and Leonard, J. M. (1976) *In* "Regulatory Mechanisms of Male Reproductive Physiology" (C. H. Spilman, T. J. Lobl, and K. T. Kirton, eds.), pp. 197–208. Exerpta Med. Found., Amsterdam.
65. Robson, K. E., and Shaver, E. L. (1979) *Biol. Reprod.* **20,** 516–522.

Meiosis, Synaptonemal Complex, and Cytogenetic Analysis

MONTROSE J. MOSES

Department of Anatomy
Duke University Medical Center
Durham, North Carolina

INTRODUCTION

MEIOSIS

The term meiosis is derived from the Greek verb "meioun": to make smaller; to reduce. The principal purpose of meiosis is to effect chromosome reduction, by which "the diploid or so-called 'somatic' number must be reduced by half to the haploid or gametic. . . . Reduction results from a regrouping of the chromosomes of the diploid group and their segregation into two single or haploid groups corresponding in a general way to those that originally came together in the egg" (1). At the time of Wilson's writing, "the main facts (seemed) well established," but "many intricate and difficult questions of detail . . . are still matters of controversy." Many, if not most, of these questions remain unsettled today.

Three central events characterize meiosis: pairing, crossing over, and distribution (separation) of parental chromosomes. Pairing (two-by-two association) may be regarded as a general property of chromosomes, most often restricted to homologs, but not infrequently expressed by nonhomologous chromosomes and chromosomal regions. Though pairing is usually thought of as a meiotic phenomenon, it is also expressed to various extents in somatic chromosomes (the polytene "bivalent" of dipteran salivary glands and other tissues is the most familiar, if extreme, example). In meiosis, pairing in some form is an absolute, though not sufficient, requirement for equal segregation of maternal and paternal chromosomes, and their distribution to daughter gametocytes.

BIOREGULATORS OF REPRODUCTION

SYNAPSIS AND THE SYNAPTONEMAL COMPLEX*

Synapsis is a special form of pairing in which chromosomes are closely apposed, so intimately that the bivalent thus formed often appears as a single structure. The usual form of synapsis between maternal and paternal homologs is a precise and regular association in which homologous regions are placed in as close register as cytological criteria are able to define.

Chromosomes that synapse are most often of common ancestry and hence are "alike" in certain fundamental ways, but in what respects, to what extents, and by what means such common properties lead to their meeting, their recognition and intimate, restricted, two-by-two association, are presently central, unanswered questions.

The regular concomitant of synapsis in meiotic cells is the synaptonemal complex (SC). It comprises the proteinaceous axes of the two paired homologous chromosomes (lateral elements), connected together by fine protein transverse filaments, and lying in parallel with a central element that marks a pairing line. At the time of synapsis (zygotene) (Fig. 1), as exemplified in mammalian spermatocytes (for review see Moses, 2), the homologous axes, which have formed as unpaired filaments originating from the telomeric attachments to the inner face of the nuclear envelope, move together and, with the central material, assemble into the regularly spaced, tripartite SC, generally from the ends toward the kinetochores. The latter are represented by dense differentiations of the lateral elements. Sometimes the SCs initiate interstitially. When the SC has completely formed as a continuous structure, it persists as the axis of the bivalent throughout pachytene. With the onset of separation of the axes (desynapsis) at diplotene, the SC either disassembles (e.g., hamster: Moses, 3; human: Moses et al., 4; Lemur: Moses et al., 5) or, during diplotene, separates again into individual axes (mouse: Moses, 2; Solari, 6; Tres, 7) which may remain temporarily joined together in localized places by residual segments of SC, thought to represent sites were crossing over has occurred (6). The axes subsequently attenuate and disassemble. The organized SC is thus a transient structure, though until the nature, source and fate of its component proteins are known, it cannot be said whether or not its constituents are persistent parts of the nucleus. The heteromorphic axes of the X and Y chromosomes also synapse for part of their lengths (an exception being the Egyptian sand rat, in which the X and Y axes do not form an SC and associate only by their ends toward the close of pachytene: Solari and Ashley, 8). Desynapsis may occur at any time during pachytene, usually preco-

---

* Four detailed reviews on the SC are available that provide a supplementary background for the present paper (22–25).

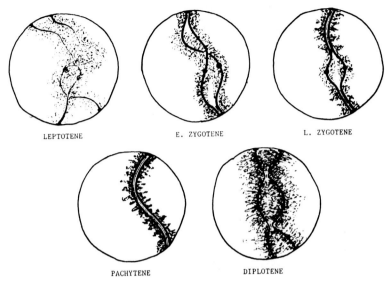

LEPTOTENE   E. ZYGOTENE   L. ZYGOTENE

PACHYTENE   DIPLOTENE

Fig. 1. Schematic diagram of autosomal synapsis and desynapsis in meiosis based on studies of spread preparations from five mammals. The essential structural components are shown: nuclear envelope, axial elements (chromosome axes), SC (with lateral and central elements), chromatin extending from the lateral (axial) elements, kinetochores on lateral (axial) elements, terminal plaques by which axial and lateral elements are anchored to the inner face of the nuclear envelope, and nuclear envelope. (From Moses (2), with permission of Academic Press).

ciously, depending on species: shortly after maximum synapsis in early pachytene (mouse: Moses, 2; Tres, 7; Solari, 9; Moses *et al.*, 10), at mid-pachytene (human: Moses *et al.*, 4; Solari, 11) or late pachytene (Chinese hamster: Moses, 12; Armenian hamster: Solari, 13). Although the timing of XY synapsis and desynapsis is characteristically out of phase with the autosomes, the evidence is overwhelming that in both autosomes and sex chromosomes, synapsis and SC formation may be taken as synonomous. Moreover, while the SC is undoubtedly the structural device maintaining the close apposition of the paired chromosomes that characterizes the synaptic state, the lateral elements each join two sister chromatids into a single structural unit.

IMPORTANCE OF SYNAPSIS

Synapsis (and hence the SC) is an essential, though not sufficient prerequisite for crossing over. Synapsis that leads to crossing over is most usefully termed "effective" (14,15). It provides for a complex of biochemical events during which recombination of homologous DNA segments occurs (15).

The cytological consequence of reciprocal crossing over is chiasma formation, and it is generally accepted that chiasmata are essential to proper chromosome distribution at the reduction division. In the absence of effective synapsis, no chiasmata form. In instances where this is a regular condition (e.g., *Drosophila* male), operation of a second "distributive pairing" mechanism has been proposed (16).

Failure of, or errors in, pairing, crossing over or distribution can have profound effects on the genetic makeup of the gametes produced, and hence on the reproductive effectiveness of the individual. Chromosomal rearrangements constitute an important source of such errors, certainly in humans where such abnormalities are found in a significant fraction (4–10%) of subfertile males (e.g., Kjessler, 17). The problem may be underestimated as rearrangements affecting small chromosome segments, or occurring more frequently in germ cells than in somatic cells, may not be detectable in somatic cells with conventional cytological methods of chromosome analysis.

Because of the drive for homologous, two-by-two pairing, the synaptic period of meiosis (pachytene) is particularly revealing of structural differences between homologs. One of the foundations of modern cytogenetics is McClintock's remarkable series of demonstrations in the early 1930s of the characteristic synaptic figures formed by structural chromosome heterozygotes during pachytene in maize, and their genetic correlates (18). The elegance of these studies was in part due to the unusually suitable characteristics of maize pachytene chromosomes for cytological study, unmatched in most other organisms. The 10 bivalents of the microsporocyte, amenable to rapid whole mount preparations for light microscopy, are long, compact filaments, distinct, easily stained and individually recognizable, ideal for the construction of meiotic karyotypes. In sharp contradistinction are the meiocytes of mammals in which the bivalents at pachytene are often difficult to separate and identify, and thus do not lend themselves well to pachytene analysis (but see Luciani *et al.*, 19; Pathak *et al.*, 20; Jagiello and Fang, 21).

THE SC AS A PARADIGM OF THE BIVALENT

SC COMPLEMENTS

As methods for visualizing entire complements of SCs have evolved, it has become evident that the pairing behavior of the homologs in forming bivalents is accurately reflected in the formation of the

SC (e.g., Moses, 2). Thus, serial section reconstruction and surface microspreading methods provide full complements of complete SCs for viewing and analyzing synaptic behavior. In addition to the formation of the SC at zygotene and its separation into two axes at diplotene as discussed above, two other lines of evidence demonstrate that the SCs, or more precisely the axes that are the lateral elements, provide quantitative as well as qualitative representations of the chromosomes in synapsis: (a) SC karyotypes are reproducible and agree with established mitotic and meiotic karyotypes and (b) the SC analyses of known chromosomal rearrangements correspond with the expectations from established cytological and genetic methods. As one consequence of such validation, it is now possible through the SC to detect and map chromosomal abnormalities that lead to synaptic heteromorphisms at pachytene.

With the first SC karyotypes by three-dimensional serial section reconstruction (6,7) the potential of SC analysis for determining meiotic karyotype became apparent (e.g., Moens, 28). While this method has the advantage of preserving three-dimensional relationships both inter- and intracellularly, it is exacting and slow, and does not lend itself to the examination of large numbers of cells.

MICROSPREADING: A SIMPLE, DIRECT, AND VERSATILE APPROACH

Visualization of full SC complements in essentially two-dimensional whole mount preparation of meiocytes derives from the principle of spreading cells on a surface, usually an aqueous–air interface (e.g., Comings and Okada, 29; Solari, 30; Moses and Solari, 31; Counce and Meyer, 32). The first SC karyotypes using this approach were obtained from mammalian spermatocytes by an adaptation of Counce and Meyers' (32) procedure (3,4), which has since been applied to a number of organisms.

In this method, surface spreading ruptures cells, disperses cytoplasm, and distributes undisrupted meiocyte nuclei over the surface, from which they are transferred to electron microscope grids or microscope slides. They are then briefly fixed in formaldehyde, rinsed in a surface wetting agent and air-dried, at which point the nuclei become flattened. The SCs may be observed immediately in the light microscope by phase optics (3), or, after staining with ethanolic phosphotungstic acid (PTA), in the electron microscope (Fig. 2) (33). Because of their greater density and staining capacity, the SCs stand out in contrast to the pale background of chromatin in which they are embedded. Alternatively, the slides may be stained with silver (34,35) and

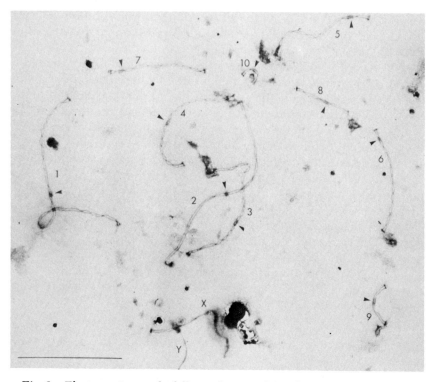

Fig. 2. Electron micrograph: full complement of SCs from a surface spread spermatocyte of the Chinese hamster (phosphotungstic acid stain). Autosomal SCs are numbered according to rank and length as measured from one nuclear envelope attachment plaque to the other. Differentiation of the XY pair indicates the stage to be mid to late pachytene. Kinetochores (arrowheads) distinguish long and short arms for measurement. Magnification bar = 10 μm. From Moses *et al.* (33), with permission of *Chromosoma*.

examined in the light microscope by ordinary bright field optics (Fig. 3), or, if the slide has been first coated with a plastic film, the film may be removed, a number of grids placed on it, and the silver stained or PTA stained nuclei observed in the electron microscope (Fig. 4). The latter modifications have greatly increased the speed and practicality of the method. For example, in our hands, it is possible to process a small, conservative, testicular biopsy in less than 1 hour, and to produce in this time a number of slides and scores of grids for staining and study. Selection with the light microscope of material for EM study reduces the use of the EM. Moreover, certain kinds of information can be simply obtained by correlated light microscopic analysis

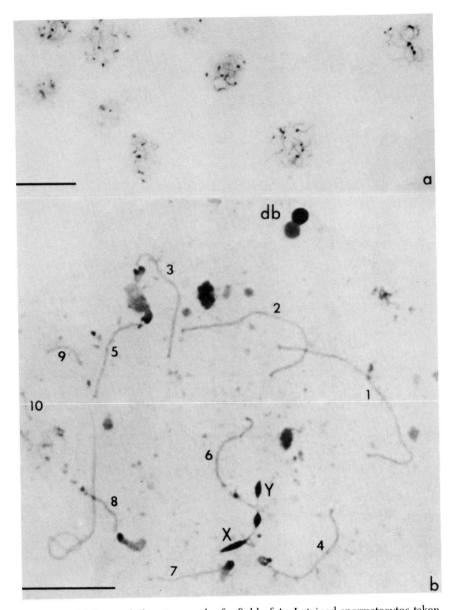

Fig. 3. (a) Survey light micrograph of a field of Ag-I stained spermatocytes taken with a 10 X, N.A. 0.25 objective. Six pachytene nuclei with recognizable SCs and nucleoli are visible. Bar = 50 μm. (b) Light micrograph of an Ag-AS stained mid-pachytene spermatocyte. The ten autosomal SCs are numbered according to their ranked lengths. The unpaired axes of the X and Y chromosomes show characteristic thickenings. Comet-shaped nucleoli are associated by their dense heads to five SCs: Nos. 3, 4, 5, 7, and 8. Other silver stained bodies are scattered throughout the nucleus; a double dense body, with moieties that stain differentially, is indicated (db). The filamentous structure at lower left is an unrelated segment of sperm tail. Bar = 10 μm. From Dresser and Moses (35), with permission of *Chromosoma*.

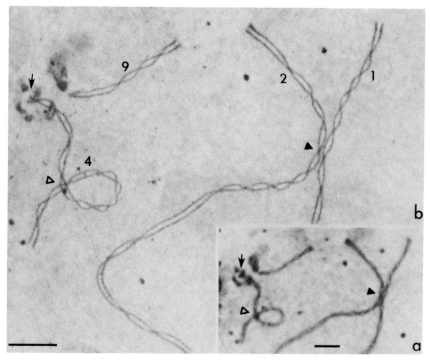

Fig. 4. (a) Light micrograph of four SCs from a full complement illustrating difficulties of interpretation, due to limits of resolution, which are easily clarified in (b), an electron micrograph of the same SCs. It cannot be decided from (a) whether the loop in SC No. 4 (hollow arrowhead) is the result of an inversion or of a fold-over of the SC; from (b) it is seen to be the latter. Because of clustered nucleolar material at the upper end of SC No. 4, the termination of the SC is not evident in (a), whereas it is evident in (b) (small arrows). SC Nos. 1 and 2 appear to cross in (a) and might be interpreted as a translocation (solid arrowhead); in (b) it is clear that neither is the case and that they merely lie closely adjacent to each other. Bars = 2 μm. From Dresser and Moses (35), with permission of *Chromosoma*.

from large numbers of nuclei on a few slides. Modification of Miller's microcentrifugation technique (36) provides another means of spreading SC complements over a specimen carrier. Such preparations are useful for visualizing the relationship of chromatin fibrils and the SC (e.g., Kierszenbaum and Tres, 37; Rattner *et al.*, 38), but are less efficient and of limited value for SC analysis.

QUANTITATION: KARYOTYPING

Following the demonstration that SC karyotypes (e.g., Fig. 5), based on SC relative length and arm ratios, could be derived from micro-

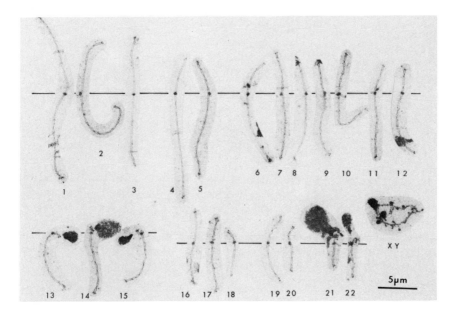

Fig. 5. Human (male) SC karyotype, based on relative length, arm ratio·and presence of nucleoli (SCs Nos. 13, 14, 15, 21, and 22). The XY is synapsed via a length of SC; the unpaired axes show thickenings and excrescences (electron micrographs, phosphotungstic acid stain). Magnification bar = 10 μm. Illustration kindly provided by Dr. A. J. Solari.

spread preparations (3,4,39) quantitative study of Chinese hamster spermatocytes showed the validity of the method (33). In particular, relative lengths and arm ratios were shown to be essentially constant parameters by which SCs could be identified. Such conditions could not hold if there were significant distortions, such as SC stretching, in the preparations due to spreading or flattening. Moreover, the autosomal SC karyotype was shown to correspond closely with its mitotic counterpart. Relative lengths as well as arm ratios are virtually equivalent in SCs and mitotic chromosomes throughout the autosomal complement (Fig. 6). The relationship is so regular that the small but significant deviations from this overall equivalency that have been observed in certain chromosomes (e.g., human chromosomes no. 1, 16, 17 and 19; Solari, 11) must be attributable to biological differences in their organization at meiosis and mitosis. The dependability of SC karyotyping in microspread preparations is further borne out in human spermatocytes (Fig. 5), where the karyotype established by serial section reconstructions (40) and that by microspreading (11) have been shown to be equivalent (Fig. 7).

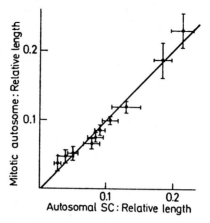

Fig. 6. Relationship between autosomal SC relative length and mitotic autosome relative length in the Chinese hamster. The data indicate an overall 1:1 proportionality. From Moses *et al.* (33), with permission of *Chromosoma*.

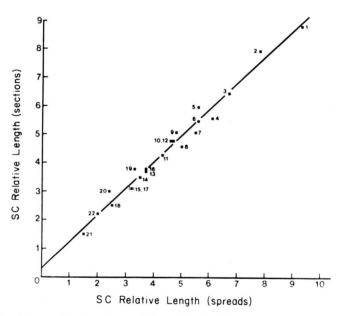

Fig. 7. Relationship between SC relative lengths from 22 spread human pachytene spermatocytes in spread preparations (11) and 22 serially sectioned pachytene spermatocytes (40). From data in Solari (11).

QUANTITATION: CHROMOSOMAL REARRANGEMENTS

A study of known chromosomal rearrangements in the mouse was undertaken in order to investigate the extent to which they could be characterized by SC analysis in microspread preparations (41). Three reciprocal translocations (10), a tandem duplication (42), and two paracentric inversions (43) have been analyzed in heterozygous males. In all cases, mitotic chromosome banding and genetic data characterizing the sizes and positions of the rearrangements were available for comparison. The SC configurations observed corresponded exactly with those expected from cytogenetic theory (Figs. 8 and 9) (10,44), and reasonable agreement was found between the SC and mitotic banding data (Table I). The closeness of the agreement was variable, but consistent for any given rearrangement. Thus, the breakpoints by SC analysis for inversion *In-1* (involving chromosome no. 1) correspond almost exactly with those by banding analysis, whereas in *In-5* (involving chromosome no. 2), the positions of the breakpoints are different by as much as 7% of the chromosome length. Such small but regular discrepancies indicate the capability of the SC method to detect either a systematic error in the banding estimate, or a regular, regional length difference between the mitotic and meiotic chromosome. Such a comparison has not hitherto been feasible with conventional preparations. Not only do such results establish confidence in the SC analyses, but they indicate their usefulness in detecting and characterizing chromosomal abnormalities as well as for providing the basis for genetic mapping of meiotic chromosomes.

The method has rapidly found application to the study of cytogenetic irregularities in mammals, such as tetraploidy (45), Robertsonian translocation (*Lemur:* Moses *et al.,* 5), trisomy (46), pericentric inversions (sand rat: T. Ashley, M. J. Moses, and A. J. Solari, unpublished; mouse: M. T. Davisson *et al.,* (57), and unusual XY pairing behavior (sand rat: Solari and Ashley, 8; Ashley and Moses, 47).

NEW INSIGHTS INTO SYNAPSIS

SYNAPTIC ADJUSTMENT

From the above studies of chromosomal rearrangements, originally aimed at validating the spreading/SC analysis methods, have also come new insights into the events of meiotic prophase, particularly of synapsis and desynapsis.

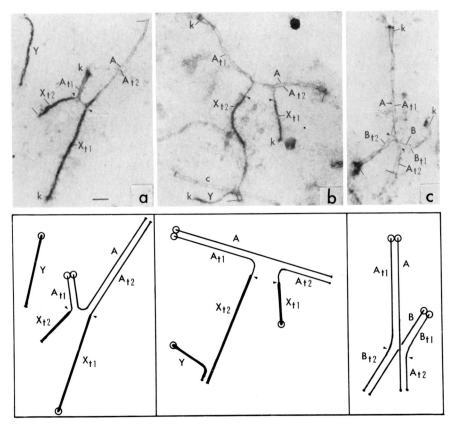

Fig. 8. (a) (b) (c) Above: electron micrographs of spread pachytene pairing figures from three different translocations in the mouse. Below: schematic diagrams, drawn to scale. Symbols: A, nontranslocated autosomal (axis); A_{t1} and A_{t2}, axes of translocated axis of second autosome; B_{t1} and B_{t2}, axes of translocated portions of second autosome; X_{t1} and X_{t2}, translocated portions of X axis; c, indifferent autosomal SC; k, kinetochore, Y, Y axis; (−), distal attachment plaque; arrowheads, translocation breakpoints. Scale bar = 1 μm. (a) T(X;7)6Rl (or R6). Translocation trivalent. In the smaller translocation product, $A_{t1} X_{t2}$, the distal (X_{t2}) segment is shorter than the full pairing region (compare with length of the Y, which is unpaired. (b) T(X;7)2Rl. Translocation quadrivalent. In the long translocation product $A_{t1} X_{t2}$, the X_{t2} portion consists of the distal ¾ of the X. The X and Y are terminally paired by a short segment of SC. (c) T(10;18)12Rl (or R12). Translocation quadrivalent. The dense granule in the proximal third of one SC is identified as a recombination nodule. From Moses *et al.* (10). Bar = 1 μm.

The most striking observation has been that of "synaptic adjustment", a phenomenon first observed to occur regularly in a tandem duplication and two inversions in the mouse (41). In these rearrangements, the loops formed as a consequence of homosynapsis at zygo-

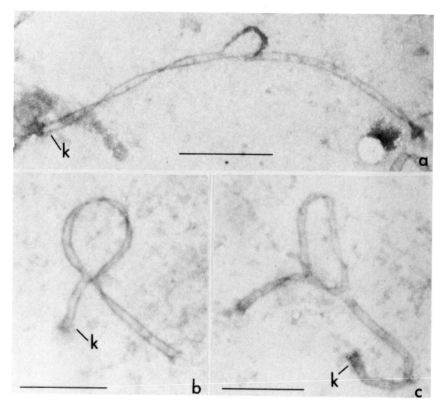

Fig. 9. SC pairing figures for heterozygous rearrangements in the mouse. (a) Tandem duplication. The buckled-out axis represents the unpaired portion of the duplication (10). (From Moses, 44, with permission of Raven Press.) (b) Paracentric inversion in chromosome 1, [In(1)1Rk]. (c) Paracentric inversion in chromosome 2 [In(2)5Rk]. In both cases typical inversion loops are formed and the breakpoints are definable. ((b) and (c) are from a collaborative study with T. H. Roderick and M. T. Davisson.) k = Kinetochore. Bar = 2 μm.

tene in the heteromorphic bivalent resynapse by late pachytene to form simple, nonhomologously synapsed SCs that are indistinguishable from the normals. In the duplication (48), the loop is reduced by shortening of the long axis (lateral element of the SC) to equality with the normal short axis. During this process of equalization (Fig. 10), which may sometimes begin while the nucleus is still in late zygotene, synapsed regions of the SC flanking the ends of the loop undergo limited desynapsis. When resynapsis occurs, because of the unequal shortening of the two axes, the resulting SC contains regions of nonhomologously synapsed axes. In the case of the inversions, the loops are

TABLE I
Chromosomal Rearrangements in the Mouse: Comparison of SC and Banding Analyses

Rearrangement	Chromosome number	SC analysis Chromosome involved (%)	SC Breakpoints Proximal	SC Breakpoints Distal	Banding analysis Chromosome involved (%)	Banding Breakpoints Proximal	Banding Breakpoints Distal	References
Translocations								(10)
T(X;7)6Rl	X	—	0.71	—	—	0.81	—	
	7	—	0.22	—	—	0.27	—	
T(X;7)2Rl	X	—	0.28	—	—	0.22	—	(10)
	7	—	0.60	—	—	0.66	—	
T(10;18)12Rl	10	—	0.79	—	—	0.78	—	(10)
	28	—	0.49	—	—	0.50	—	
Duplication	7	22	0.50	0.72	24	0.48	0.71	(42)
Inversions								(43)
In(1)1Rk	1	46	0.20	0.65	56	0.16	0.73	
In(2)5Rk	2	44	0.42	0.86	42	0.43	0.85	(43)

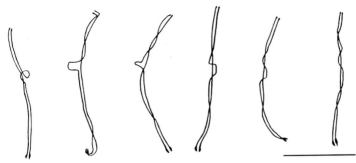

Fig. 10.   Tracings of SCs from duplication-bearing bivalents in surface microspread spermatocytes progressing from early pachytene (left), where the buckle in the long axis, produced by homologous synapsis flanking the duplicated region, is longest, to late pachytene (right), where no evidence of the buckle remains. During pachytene, the long axis shortens to equal the short, normal axis, and nonhomologous synapsis occurs, producing a normal SC indistinguishable except by length from its neighbors. Bar = 6 μm. From Moses (44), with permission of Raven Press.

reduced during pachytene (Fig. 11), presumably by progressive, localized switching of pairing partners at the base of the loop. As a consequence, homosynapsed axis pairs are transformed into heterosynapsed ones in the inversion segment, to form a homomorphic SC. In duplication and inversions alike, intermediate stages of this adjustment are observed in early pachytene: the transformation evidently

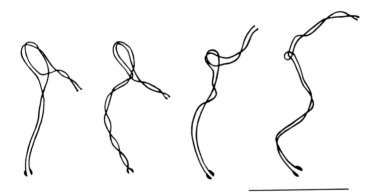

Fig. 11.   Tracings of SCs from inversion-bearing bivalents [In(2)5Rk]. At early pachytene (left), the homologously paired inversion loop is longest. As synaptic adjustment progresses during pachytene, the loop decreases in length with nonhomologously synapsed SCs flanking it. Only normal appearing SCs without loops are seen at the latest stage of pachytene (not shown). Bar = 5 μm. From Moses (44), with permission of Raven Press.

occurs in all SCs heteromorphic for the rearrangements and is completed by late pachytene.

The last point has been verified in silver-stained preparations where five distinct pachytene stages, defined in the EM by XY morphology and extent of pairing, nucleolar morphology, and prominence of the kinetochore and heterochromatic knobs, are recognizable by light microscopy (Poorman and Moses, cited by Moses, 44; Fig. 12) (49). In addition, it is also possible to classify early- and late-zygotene and diplotene stages. From the frequency of different stages, as scored in large numbers of nuclei, the relative duration of each substage in mouse pachytene may be determined. The first four pachytene substages occupy the first half of pachytene, while the fifth takes up the last half. Inversion loops, which can be seen in the LM, are never found at the fifth stage in the several hundred nuclei that have been examined, indicating that synaptic adjustment of the inversion is completed in all nuclei during the first half of pachytene.

The phenomenon of synaptic adjustment raises a number of new and interesting points concerning synapsis and crossing over. Duplication buckles and inversion loops are present in virtually all nuclei at early pachytene, and while incomplete (delayed) synapsis may occa-

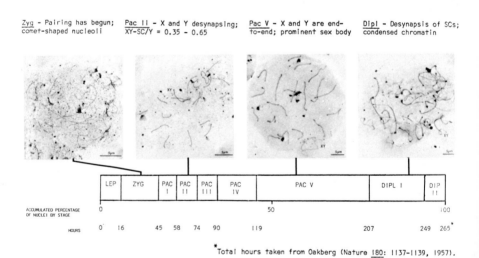

Fig. 12.   Staging schedule of meiotic prophase in the mouse. Using criteria established by electron microscopy but analyzable by light microscopy, nine meiotic prophase stages are definable (four LM examples with criteria are shown). The relative frequencies of the stages were determined in a sample of 1000 nuclei. Their duration in hours has been calculated (49). From Moses (44), with permission of Raven Press.

sionally be evident, no instances of nonhomologous synapsis have been observed, apart from some early stages of synaptic adjustment. These observations imply that at zygotene, synapsis occurs exclusively between homologous regions. In fact, it may be inferred that synapsis depends upon homology at this stage. This is borne out, for example, by the variations in mapped positions of the ends of the duplication buckle in a population of early pachytene nuclei (42).

TWO PAIRING PHASES: HOMOSYNAPSIS AND HETEROSYNAPSIS

Assuming that the buckle in the axis carrying the duplication is formed at the point where synapsis proceeding from one end meets that from the opposite end, the observed range of loop positions is attributable to the precocity of synapsis from one direction or the other. If there were no restriction of synapsis to homologous regions, precocious synapsis in one direction could very well overrun the region of homology. However, this does not happen; it is observed that the limits of the loop are always within those expected if SC formation only occurs between homologous regions, and ceases when nonhomology due to the repeated segment is encountered. It follows that here homology is a requirement for synapsis, and that nonhomologous synapsis is thus forbidden. The same conclusion is reached from the study of inversion loops at early pachytene before synaptic adjustment has begun. The loops occupy a fixed position, determined by the inversion breakpoints. To form a loop, there must be at least three synaptic initiation sites, all of which recognize homology: one on either side of the inversion, and one within it. Without control and with synapsis proceeding from so many sites, a significant variation in loop position would be expected to result from synapsis overrunning homologous regions. That this does not occur indicates that synapsis is restricted, as in the duplication, to homologous regions.

On the other hand, as the duplication buckle and inversion loops are resolved, as discussed above, to form a simple SC containing heterosynapsed regions, the requirement for homology is evidently lost and synapsis occurs irrespective of homology. This implies two synaptic phases: one at zygotene, regulated by homology, and a subsequent one at mid-pachytene, independent of it. A similar conclusion was reached by Rasmussen (50) from the conversion of trivalents at early pachytene in triploid *Bombyx* oocytes to homosynapsed and heterosynapsed bivalents at later pachytene. Evidently, in normal diploid meiosis, homosynapsis is stable throughout pachytene and the heterosynapsed phase is not expressed. It is conceivable that if the heterosynaptic phase provides a mechanism for pairing chromosomes and facilitating disjunction, it may be related to the "distributive pairing" phenomenon proposed by Grell (16), and could account for the numerous reports of SC formation between nonhomologous chromosomes (e.g., Menzel and Price, 51; Ting, 52; Gillies, 53).

The earliest reports of rearrangement configurations at pachytene recognized the coexistence of homosynapsed, nonsynapsed, and heterosynapsed bivalents. These were generally interpreted as alternative synaptic modes in the expression of the drive for two-by-two pairing (e.g., McClintock, 54). However, the observations on mouse rearrangements indicate that the states are sequential, and raise the possibility that they may also be so in maize and other forms. Thus the presence of homosynapsed and heterosynapsed bivalents simultaneously in the same preparation could be attributed to a lack of synchrony in synaptic adjustment, underscoring the need for observations at different substages of pachytene.

The nature of the instability leading to the elimination of duplication buckles and inversion loops and the replacement of homosynapsed segments by heterosynapsed ones is not known. Whatever the cause, it does not affect reciprocal translocations in the same way. Translocation quadrivalents are present throughout pachytene, although some shifting of the apparent breakpoints has been observed (unpublished observations). One of the consequences of synaptic adjustment could be to prevent crossing over within the rearrangement. However, the fact that crossing over does occur within the duplication (55) and the inversions (56) indicates that some crossing over must take place in the first half of pachytene, before or during adjustment. That crossing over is reduced in the rearrangements suggests the latter timing. Surprisingly, crossovers do not prevent adjustment, although the topological complications of adjustment of an inversion containing a crossover would seem to be great.

PROSPECTS

Clearly, much is yet to be learned about the processes of meiotic synapsis and crossing over. SC analysis has already provided new leads and promises more. At the same time, the approach constitutes a new way of detecting and characterizing a variety of irregularities in meiotic chromosomes and their pairing behavior that could be associated with reproductive effectiveness. Accessible to investigation by the techniques discussed are irregularities in karyotype, chromosomal rearrangements, pairing anomalies, the timetable of meiotic prophase, the sex pair (including XY synapsis, end-to-end association at late pachytene, relative lengths, differentiations of the axes, and association with autosomes), nucleolus expression, and the presence and localization of structures related to crossing over. It seems likely that these capabilities have promising clinical as well as research applications.

ACKNOWLEDGMENT

The author's work described herein has been supported at various times by the National Science Foundation and the National Institutes of Health, U. S. P. H. S.

REFERENCES

1. Wilson, E. B. (1925) "The Cell in Development and Heredity," 3rd ed. Macmillan, New York.
2. Moses, M. J. (1977) *ICN-UCLA Symp. Mol. Cell. Biol.* **7**, 101–125.
3. Moses, M. J. (1977) *Chromosoma* **60**, 99–125.
4. Moses, M. J., Counce, S. J., and Paulson, D. F. (1975) *Science* **187**, 363–365.
5. Moses, M. J., Karatsis, P. A., and Hamilton, A. E. (1979) *Chromosoma* **70**, 141–160.
6. Solari, A. J. (1970) *Chromosoma* **31**, 217–230.
7. Tres, L. L. (1977) *J. Cell Sci.* **25**, 1–15.
8. Solari, A. J., and Ashley, T. (1977) *Chromosoma* **62**, 319–336.
9. Solari, A. J. (1970) *Chromosoma* **29**, 217–236.
10. Moses, M. J., Russell, L. B., and Cacheiro, N. L. (1977) *Science* **196**, 892–894.
11. Solari, A. J. (1980) *Chromosoma* **81**, 315–337.
12. Moses, M. J. (1977) *Chromosoma* **60**, 127–137.
13. Solari, A. J. (1974) *Chromosoma* **48**, 89–106.
14. Pritchard, R. H. (1960) *Genet. Res.* **1**, 1–24.
15. Stern, H., and Hotta, Y. (1978) *Annu. Rev. Plant Physiol.* **29**, 415–436.
16. Grell, R. F. (1962) *Proc. Natl. Acad. Sci. U. S. A.* **48**, 165–172.
17. Kjessler, B. (1974) *In* "Male Fertility and Sterility" (R. E. Mancini and L. Martini, eds.), pp. 231–247. Academic Press, New York.
18. McClintock, B. (1931) *Mo. Agric. Exp. Stn., Bull.* **163**, 1–30.
19. Luciani, J. M., Morazzani, M.-R., and Stahl, A. (1975) *Chromosoma* **52**, 275–282.
20. Pathak, S., Hsu, T. C., and Markvong, A. (1976) *Cytogenet. Cell Genet.* **17**, 1–8.
21. Jagiello, G., and Fang, J.-S. (1980) *Chromosoma* **77**, 113–121.
22. Moses, M. J. (1968) *Annu. Rev. Genet.* **2**, 363–412.
23. Westergaard, M., and von Wettstein, D. (1972) *Annu. Rev. Genet.* **6**, 71–110.
24. Gillies, C. B. (1975) *Annu. Rev. Genet.* **9**, 91–109.
25. Moens, P. B. (1978) *Annu. Rev. Genet.* **12**, 433–450.
26. Gillies, C. B. (1972) *Chromosoma* **36**, 119–130.
27. Gillies, C. B. (1973) *Chromosoma* **43**, 145–176.
28. Moens, P. B. (1973) *Cold Spring Harbor Symp. Quant. Biol.* **38**, 99–107.

29. Comings, D. E., and Okada, T. A. (1970) *Chromosoma* **30**, 269–286.
30. Solari, A. J. (1972) *Chromosoma* **39**, 237–263.
31. Moses, M. J., and Solari, A. J. (1976) *J. Ultrastruct. Res.* **54**, 109–114.
32. Counce, S. J., and Meyer, G. F. (1973) *Chromosoma* **76**, 1–22.
33. Moses, M. J., Slatton, G., Gambling, T., and Starmer, C. F. (1977) *Chromosoma* **60**, 345–375.
34. Dresser, M. E., and Moses, M. J. (1979) *Exp. Cell Res.* **121**, 416–419.
35. Dresser, M. E., and Moses, M. J. (1980) *Chromosoma* **76**, 1–22.
36. Miller, O. L., and Beatty, B. R. (1969) *Science* **164**, 955–957.
37. Kierszenbaum, A. L., and Tres, L. L. (1974) *J. Cell Biol.* **63**, 923–925.
38. Rattner, J. B., Goldsmith, M., and Hamkalo, B. A. (1980) *Chromosoma* **79**, 215–224.
39. Moses, M. J., and Counce, S. J. (1974) *In* "Symposium on Mechanisms in Recombination" (R. F. Grell, ed.), pp. 385–390. Plenum, New York.
40. Holm, P. B., and Rasmussen, S. W. (1977) *Carlsberg Res. Commun.* **42**, 283–323.
41. Moses, M. J. (1977) *Chromosomes Today* **6**, 71–82.
42. Poorman, P. A., Moses, M. J., Russell, L. B., Publ., and Cacheiro, N. L. A. (1981) *Chromosoma* **81**, 507–508.
43. Poorman, P. A., Moses, M. J., Davisson, M. T., and Roderick, T. H. (1981). Submitted.
44. Moses, M. J. (1981) *In* "Animal Models in Human Reproduction" (M. Serio, ed.). Raven, New York pp. 169–190.
45. Solari, A. J., and Moses, M. J. (1977) *Exp. Cell Res.* **108**, 464–467.
46. de Boer, P., and Branje, H. E. B. (1979) *Chromosoma* **73**, 369–379.
47. Ashley, T., and Moses, M. J. (1980) *Chromosoma* **78**, 203–210.
48. Moses, M. J., and Poorman, P. A. (1981) *Chromosoma* **81**, 519–535.
49. Oakberg, E. F. (1957) *Nature (London)* **180**, 1137–1139.
50. Rasmussen, S. W. (1977) *Carlsberg Res. Commun.* **42**, 163–197.
51. Menzel, M. Y., and Price, J. M. (1966) *Am. J. Bot.* **53**, 1079–1986.
52. Ting, Y. C. (1973) *Cytologia (Firenze)* **38**, 497–500.
53. Gillies, C. B. (1974) *Chromosoma* **48**, 441–453.
54. McClintock, B. (1933) *Z. Zellforsch. Mikrosk. Anat.* **19**, 192–237.
55. Russell, L. B., Russell, W. L., Cacheiro, N. L. B., Vaughan, C. M., Popp, R. A., and Jacobson, K. B. (1975) *Genetics* **80**, s71.
56. Roderick, T. H., and Hawes, N. L. (1974) *Genetics* **76**, 109–117.
57. Davisson, M. T., Poorman, P. A., Roderick, T. H., and Moses, M. J. *Cytogenet. Cell Genet.* (in press).

The Structural and Functional Cycle of Sertoli Cells in Culture

A. L. KIERSZENBAUM AND LAURA L. TRES

Department of Anatomy
and The Laboratories for Reproductive Biology
School of Medicine
University of North Carolina,
Chapel Hill, North Carolina

INTRODUCTION

Sertoli cells maintain dynamic and complex relationships with germinal cells in the mammalian seminiferous tubule that are both spatial and functional in nature. As germinal cells proliferate and differentiate in the sexually mature animal, the Sertoli cells, a unique, nonproliferating population of the seminiferous epithelium, provide mechanical support and play a significant role in mediating the flow of substances between the extratubular space and the lumen of the seminiferous tubule. Because the association between germinal cells and Sertoli cells varies characteristically along the length of the seminiferous tubule, it is possible to assume that the nonmitotic Sertoli cell population responds via a cyclic function to support spermatogenic events (1).

Sertoli cell functional cycle may depend on the hormonal signals originating in the hypothalamic–pituitary axis (FSH, LH), testis (testosterone), and possible intratubular signals generated by cell components of the mitotic, meiotic, and spermiogenic compartments to each of which the Sertoli cell is closely associated (Fig. 1). It is also possible to envisage that each cell association can be regarded as the functional *domain* of a cycling Sertoli cell traversing alternative responsive and non responsive phases of its function (Fig. 2) required for initiation, maintenance, and completion of spermatogenesis.

One of the first indications of a possible cyclic function of Sertoli

207

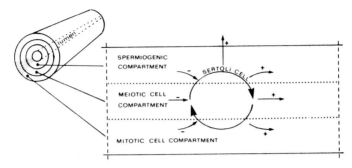

Fig. 1. Diagrammatic representation of a segment of a seminiferous tubule. The seminiferous epithelium is represented by three compartments: the *mitotic cell compartment* close to the tubular wall, defined by the continuous production of spermatogonia as a result of successive mitotic cell divisions; *the meiotic cell compartment,* formed by primary and secondary spermatocytes involved in the exchange of genetic information between homologous chromosomes and final reduction of the genetic material to a haploid state; and the *spermiogenic cell compartment* composed of differentiating spermatids undergoing acrosome and flagellum formation and replacement of somatic histones by protamines. A nondividing Sertoli cell establishes functional and spatial links among the three cell compartments. The functional cycle of a Sertoli cell (represented by clockwise arrows) is assumed to interregulate the metabolic activities of distinct segments of the seminiferous epithelium. Positive (+) and negative (−) feedback signals are indicated in the diagram.

cells was provided by autoradiographic studies showing (i) variable structural and cytoplasmic [³H]uridine and [³H]amino acid labeling patterns of mouse Sertoli cells (1,2) within adjacent areas of the seminiferous epithelium which may reflect differential metabolic activities and (ii) the persistence of long-lived [³H]uridine labeled RNA species in spermatocyte nuclei contrasting with a fast turn-over of

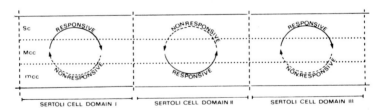

Fig. 2. A somatic cell–germinal cell association in a given segment of the seminiferous epithelium determines a *Sertoli cell domain.* Each domain differs from adjacent Sertoli cell domains (Roman numerals) as the phase of the Sertoli cell functional cycle changes with respect to the needs of a different germinal cell association and its hormonal responsiveness. A certain degree of coordination is anticipated between neighboring Sertoli cell domains to maintain a synchronous function. mcc, Mitotic cell compartment; Mcc, meiotic cell compartment; Sc, spermiogenic compartment.

[³H]uridine labeled RNAs in Sertoli cells detected at the same pulse labeling time (1,3). In addition, it was shown (4) that the occurrence of lipid droplets within Sertoli cells exhibited cyclic variations with the stages of the rat spermatogenic cycle. This finding was interpreted to reflect variations in the synthetic mechanisms of Sertoli cells participating in the production of a feedback signal controlling FSH levels. More recently, biochemical studies (5) have demonstrated variation of the secretion of androgen-binding protein (ABP), a specific secretory product of Sertoli cells (6), binding of FSH, and FSH-stimulated release of cyclic AMP (cAMP) in different stages of rat spermatogenesis.

Variation of ABP immunoreactivity in rat Sertoli cells within different seminiferous tubules and even along adjacent regions of the same seminiferous tubule have been demonstrated by immunoperoxidase cytochemistry (7). These data lend support to the assumption that Sertoli cells in vivo display a cyclic activity which may be dependent on extratesticular signals.

An approach for the study of Sertoli cell cyclic activities under manageable conditions is the use of an in vitro system. The development of techniques for the isolation and culture of Sertoli cells (8–10) has facilitated the study of Sertoli cell structure and function and the assessment of several hormone-dependent processes in vitro. In this chapter we review (i) the isolation and cell culture procedure of mouse and rat Sertoli cells, (ii) the use of a specific antiserum against ABP to identify Sertoli cells in culture and determine their proliferative potential in vitro, and (iii) the temporal sequence of Sertoli cell shape changes after experimental elevation of intracellular cAMP. The results of these studies show that Sertoli cells in vitro can proliferate while still maintaining a nonsynchronous ABP secretory function and hormonal responsiveness.

ISOLATION AND CULTURE OF SERTOLI CELLS

Primary cultures of Sertoli cells together with the use of ABP as a biological marker, provide a valuable experimental system for the study of physiological responses of Sertoli cells in vitro. Kodani and Kodani (11) were among the first to report a procedure for the isolation and culture of Sertoli cells. Previous and latter work, focusing on the culture of germinal cells, pointed out the growth and/or proliferative potential of Sertoli cells in culture (12, rat; 13,14, rabbit; 15, guinea pig; 16, rat; 17, Chinese hamster). However, the lack of a marker for the characterization of cultured Sertoli cells and the finding of mitotic

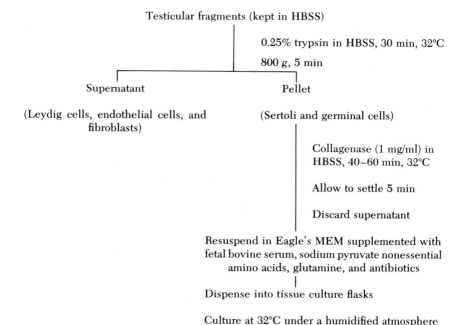

Testicular fragments (kept in HBSS)

0.25% trypsin in HBSS, 30 min, 32°C

800 g, 5 min

Supernatant   Pellet

(Leydig cells, endothelial cells, and   (Sertoli and germinal cells)
fibroblasts)

Collagenase (1 mg/ml) in
HBSS, 40–60 min, 32°C

Allow to settle 5 min

Discard supernatant

Resuspend in Eagle's MEM supplemented with
fetal bovine serum, sodium pyruvate nonessential
amino acids, glutamine, and antibiotics

Dispense into tissue culture flasks

Culture at 32°C under a humidified atmosphere
of 95% air and 5% CO_2

Fig. 3. Outline of the isolation and culture procedure of mammalian Sertoli cells. HBSS, Hanks Balanced Salt Solution. MEM, Minimum essential medium.

activity in the cultures, assumed to represent cell contaminants, hampered further development and use of the Sertoli cell *in vitro* system.

The cell isolation and culture procedure used in our laboratory is based on the method of Dorrington and Fritz (8) with slight modifications (Fig. 3). The effects of trypsin and collagenase treatments used for the dissociation of mouse testicular material are illustrated in Figs. 4–7. Figure 4 depicts the action of trypsin (0.25%) alone for 30 minutes. A cleavage space between the seminiferous epithelium and the seminiferous tubular wall is readily apparent. When the action of trypsin is followed by collagenase treatment (1 mg/ml) for 30 minutes only, an incomplete detachment of the tubular wall can be seen (Fig.

Fig. 4. Effect of a 30-minute trypsin digestion treatment on mouse testicular fragments. The arrowhead points to the seminiferous tubular wall separated by a cleavage space from the seminiferous epithelium composed of Sertoli cells, spermatogonia, and meiotic prophase spermatocytes (12-day-old mouse).

Fig. 5. Post-trypsin collagenase treatment for 30 minutes. The tubular wall components are detaching from the epithelial cells (arrowhead) but are not completely removed at this digestion time (12-day-old mouse).

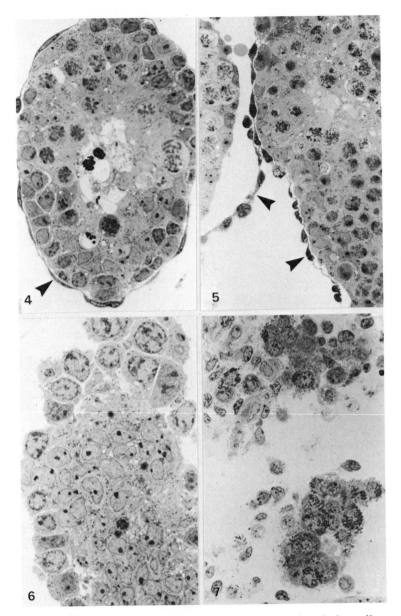

Fig. 6. Post-trypsin collagenase treatment for 45 minutes. The tubular wall components are totally removed. The digested specimens consists of clusters of seminiferous epithelial cells free of nonepithelial cell contaminants. The germinal cells at the periphery of the cluster are loose. The central portion of the cluster contains Sertoli cells (12-day-old mouse).

Fig. 7. Cells observed in the supernatant of the post-trypsin sample. Groups of Leydig cells displaying osmiophilic cytoplasmic lipid droplets and other intertubular cell components can be identified.

5). If the post-trypsin collagenase digestion is increased to 60 minutes, then clusters of seminiferous epithelial cells free of tubular wall components and consisting of Sertoli cells and germinal cells can be obtained (Fig. 6). After low-speed centrifugation of the trypsinized sample, the supernatant contains clusters of Leydig cells, endothelial cells and other nonepithelial cell components of the intertubular space (Fig. 7). Similar results can be obtained with rat testicular specimens.

The tissue culture medium consists of Eagle's minimum essential medium supplemented with nonessential amino acids (0.1 mM), sodium pyruvate (1 mM), glutamine (final concentration 4 mM), 10% fetal bovine serum, and antibiotics (penicillin 100 U/ml and streptomycin 100 μg/ml). More recently, we used a chemically defined, serum-free medium which contains insulin, 5 μg/ml, transferrin, 5 μg/ml, epidermal growth factor, 3 ng/ml, somatomedin C, 1 ng/ml, growth hormone, 6.5 μU/ml, retinoic acid, 10 μM, testosterone 0.1 μM, and FSH, 1 μg/ml. Using this serum-free medium, we demonstrated that FSH caused the accumulation of at least seven polypeptides in the culture medium of cultured Sertoli cells isolated from 10-day-old rats that were not detectable in the medium of nonstimulated control Sertoli cells. FSH also enhanced the accumulation of at least four polypeptides in the medium of Sertoli cells isolated from 20-day-old rats. For these studies we used two-dimensional polyacrylamide gel electrophoresis to resolve [^{35}S]methionine- and [^{3}H]fucose-labeled proteins (18).

After plating, the aggregates of seminiferous epithelial cells attach to the substrate leaving germinal cells either in suspension or trapped among Sertoli cells. Germinal cells are later removed by the phagocytic activity of Sertoli cells. The attached cell aggregates establish very rapidly a colony-like growth defined by the putative epithelial cell cluster in the center of the colony and the outgrowing Sertoli cells at the periphery (Fig. 8). When the tissue culture medium, consisting of Eagle's minimum essential medium and fetal bovine serum, is sup-

---

Fig. 8. Rat Sertoli cell culture in the presence of Eagle's minimum essential medium supplemented with fetal bovine serum after 48 hours of culture. The colony-like organization is characterized by the explanted cell cluster in the center surrounded by epithelial-like Sertoli cells spreading out from the explant.

Fig. 9. Autoradiogram of cultured rat Sertoli cells maintained for 24 hours in a culture medium supplemented with [^{3}H]thymidine (0.01 μCi/ml). The arrowheads indicate a few of the many peripherally located Sertoli cells displaying silver grains over the nuclei.

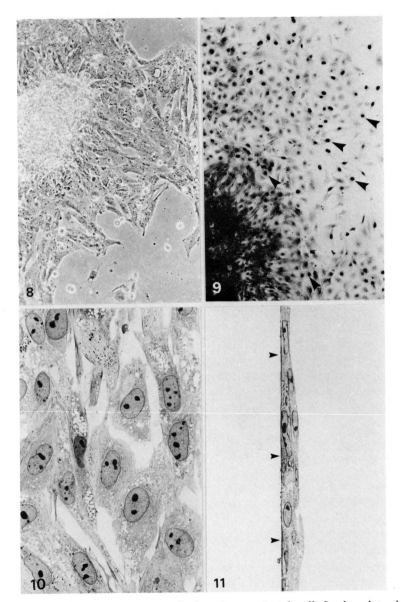

Fig. 10. Light microscopic view of cultured mouse Sertoli cells fixed in glutaralde-hyde–osmium tetroxide and embedded in an epoxy resin. The specimen has been sec-tioned through a plane parallel to the substrate. This *in situ* fixation procedure allows the visualization of the topographic relationship among Sertoli cells *in vitro*.

Fig. 11. Light microscopic view of cultured mouse Sertoli cells sectioned per-pendicularly to the substrate face (arrowheads). Sertoli cells overlap in the culture form-ing three distinct layers of cells.

plemented with [³H]thymidine (0.05 µCi/ml) for 24 hours, the peripherally located Sertoli cells display a conspicuous nuclear labeling in autoradiograms which contrasts with the absence of radioactivity in Sertoli cells forming part of the center of the colony (Fig. 9). [³H]thymidine nuclear labeling coincides with an increase in Sertoli cell number and mitotic figures. These observations demonstrate that Sertoli cells *in vitro* have the ability to synthesize DNA and divide by mitosis when released from the constraints of the seminiferous epithelium.

When the monolayer cultures are fixed *in situ* with glutaraldehyde and osmium tetroxide, embedded in an epoxy resin and sectioned through a plane parallel (Fig. 10) or perpendicular to the substrate (Fig. 11), one can distinguish Sertoli cells with a typical epithelial-like pattern maintaining monolayer growth characteristics. The Sertoli cells remain associated with each other through cytoplasmic processes and broad cytoplasmic regions (Figs. 10–12). A transmission electron microscopic study of cultured Sertoli cells demonstrates that these cells display an epithelial-like pattern defined by the presence of junctional specializations between adjacent cells, irregularly outlined nuclei, lipid droplets (also observed in light microscopic preparations, Fig. 13), a well-developed Golgi apparatus which suggests glycosylation and other organelles usually related to the mechanism of protein synthesis and cytoplasmic transport (Fig. 12).

THE LOCALIZATION OF ABP IN PROLIFERATING RAT SERTOLI CELLS IN CULTURE

Direct biochemical evidence for ABP secretion by Sertoli cells in the presence of FSH, testosterone and Bt₂cAMP was provided by primary cultures of rat Sertoli cells (19–21). We have recently demonstrated immunoperoxidase and immunofluorescent patterns of ABP in cultured Sertoli cells from 20- to 22-day-old rats and determined by radioimmunoassay the secretion into the tissue culture medium of this biological marker of Sertoli cell function (22).

Sertoli cells cultured in the presence of Eagle's minimum essential medium supplemented with fetal bovine serum or with FSH in the absence of fetal bovine serum displayed ABP immunoreactive granules of variable diameter in the cytoplasm (Figs. 14 and 15). ABP was not detected in all Sertoli cells especially in those undergoing mitosis (Fig. 16).

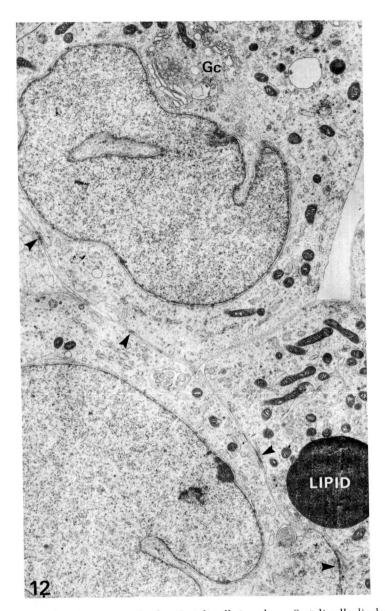

Fig. 12.   Electron micrograph of rat Sertoli cells in culture. Sertoli cells display an epithelial-like arrangement stabilized by junctional specializations (arrowheads). The irregular outline of Sertoli cell nuclei, a lipid droplet, and a well-developed Golgi complex (Gc) are characteristic features of these cells in culture.

While it is generally assumed that Sertoli cells remain in a pro-longed interphase in the adult testis, there are conflicting reports re-garding the proliferative capacity of these cells in culture. It has been suggested that Sertoli cells can be either maintained (19,23) or prolif-erate in tissue culture (11,17,24). Therefore, we decided to combine ABP immunocytochemistry with autoradiography to determine in ABP-immunoreactive cells their ability to synthesize DNA (22). Re-sults from these studies demonstrated that (i) in primary cultures, ABP was detected in approximately 30–35% of the [³H]thymidine-labeled cells after a pulse of 18 hours; (ii) subcultured Sertoli cells labeled with [³H]thymidine for 48 hours and prepared from ABP immunocyto-chemistry 48 hours later show an increase in cell number (from 2×10^3 cells/coverslip at the time of plating to 6×10^3 cells/coverslip 96 hours later). 90–95% of these Sertoli cells displayed silver grains on nuclei and 30% of the [³H]thymidine-labeled cells demonstrated ABP in the cytoplasm (Fig. 17). Because Sertoli cells lacking ABP im-munoreactivity still displayed lipid droplets in their cytoplasm and a colony-like, epithelial-like growth pattern, we assumed that under the culture conditions used for these experiments the ABP gene is not ex-pressed throughout the whole cell cycle or that, because of limitations of the light microscope, all the ABP-containing Sertoli cells may not have been detected (22).

These experiments demonstrated that despite the low potential of postpuberal Sertoli cells to replicate DNA *in vivo* (25), Sertoli cells *in vitro* can maintain their capacity to produce ABP while retaining their capability to undergo DNA synthesis and mitotic cell division. In ad-dition, these experiments lent support to the assumption that prolifer-ating cells in primary cultures of Sertoli cells are indeed Sertoli cells and not proliferating nonepithelial cell contaminants.

Fig. 13. Rat Sertoli cells cultured on glass coverslips, fixed in 1% osmium tetroxide, and counterstained with 1% toluidine blue. The brown cytoplasmic bodies adjacent to Sertoli cell nuclei are lipid droplets, a characteristic product of Sertoli cells (see color plate).

Fig. 14. ABP immunoperoxidase staining (brown stained granules) of cultured Ser-toli cells from a 22-day-old rat (working dilution of rabbit anti-ABP serum, 1 : 1000). The arrowheads indicate clear spaces corresponding to unstained lipid droplets. For techni-cal details of the immunocytochemical procedure, see (22) (see color plate).

Fig. 15. ABP immunofluorescent staining of cultured Sertoli cells from a 22-day-old rat. ABP-containing granules are scattered throughout the cytoplasm (anti-ABP serum, 1 : 45). See (22) for further technical details (see color plate).

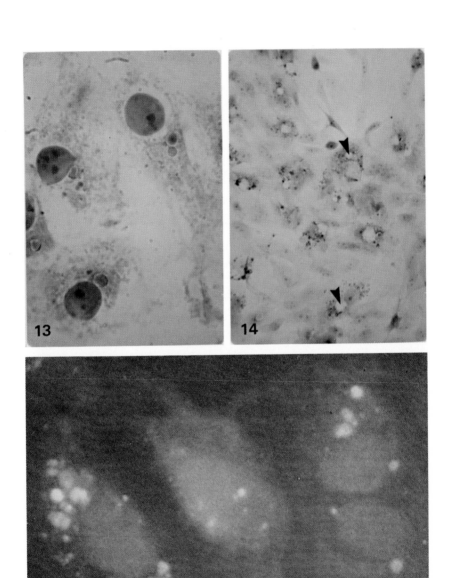

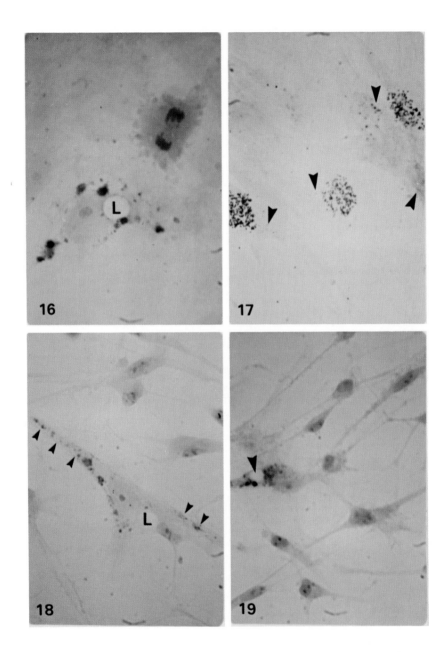

HORMONAL AND CYCLIC NUCLEOTIDE RESPONSIVENESS OF SERTOLI CELLS IN CULTURE

It has been reported that cultured Sertoli cells exposed to FSH or Bt$_2$cAMP for 24 hours or more change their characteristic flat, epithelial-like cell shape into a stellate or spindle-like shape (26–28). We have used ABP (22) and cAMP immunocytochemistry (29) and time-lapse cinematography (30) to determine (i) the distribution of ABP and cAMP in control and morphologically altered Sertoli cells after treatment with FSH, Bt$_2$cAMP, 3-isobutyl-L-methylxanthine (MIX) (an inhibitor of cyclic nucleotide phosphodiesterase which increases intracellular levels of cAMP), and a combination of FSH-MIX and (ii) the time course of the induction and recovery of Sertoli cell shape changes during and after treatment with FSH and cyclic nucleotide analogs.

We have observed striking cell shape changes within 30–120 minutes when FSH and pharmacological agents were added to cultures of rat Sertoli cells kept in Eagle's minimum essential medium without serum 24 hours prior to the experiments (29). As Sertoli cells changed their shape, ABP-immunoreactive granules were preferentially localized along the cell processes (Fig. 18). ABP immunoreactivity was present in Sertoli cells at intermediate stages of cell shape change (Fig. 19). A considerable number of Sertoli cells were morphologically affected by the hormonal and pharmacological treatments but others remained unchanged. Because ABP immunocytochemistry provides a clear basis for distinguishing both morphologically changed and unchanged Sertoli cells in the cultures, we concluded

---

Fig. 16. ABP immunoperoxidase staining of cultured Sertoli cells. ABP immunoreactive granules can be observed in the cytoplasm of a Sertoli cell with a lipid droplet (L) but not in a mitotic dividing Sertoli cell (see color plate).

Fig. 17. ABP immunoperoxidase staining combined with autoradiography of [^{3}H]thymidine-labeled Sertoli cells. The arrowheads point to immunoreactive ABP in the cytoplasm of cells displaying silver grains over the nuclei (see color plate).

Fig. 18. Sertoli cells in culture exposed to FSH for 120 minutes. ABP immunoreactive granules can be detected along the cell edges and in the cytoplasmic processes. Note the absence of ABP in the morphologically altered rat Sertoli cells present in this field. L, Lipid droplet. Immunoperoxidase (see color plate).

Fig. 19. Sertoli cells in culture treated with MIX for 30 minutes. Most of the cells exhibit a stellate configuration, and they are joined by cell processes which maintain cell-to-cell contacts. A single cell, which has not completed its shape transformation, contains a lipid droplet (arrowhead) and ABP-stained granules in the cytoplasm. Immunoperoxidase (see color plate).

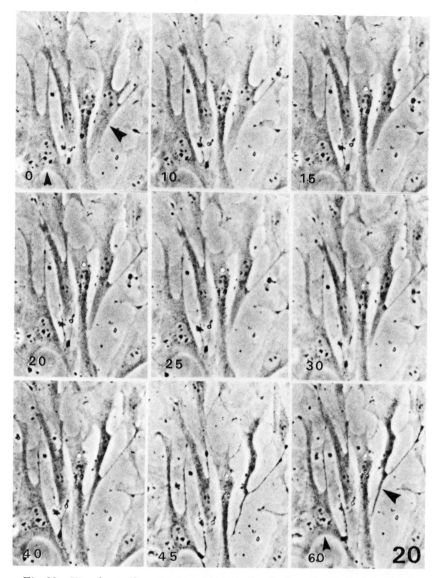

Fig. 20. Time-lapse phase contrast micrographs of cultured rat Sertoli cells during exposure to FSH (10 μg/ml) plus MIX (0.5 mM) for 60 minutes. The time in minutes is given in each print. The arrowheads indicate Sertoli cells at time zero and the same contracted cells 60 minutes after treatment. Note differences in the magnitude of cell shape responses in Sertoli cells present in this field. (From Spruill *et al.*, 29.)

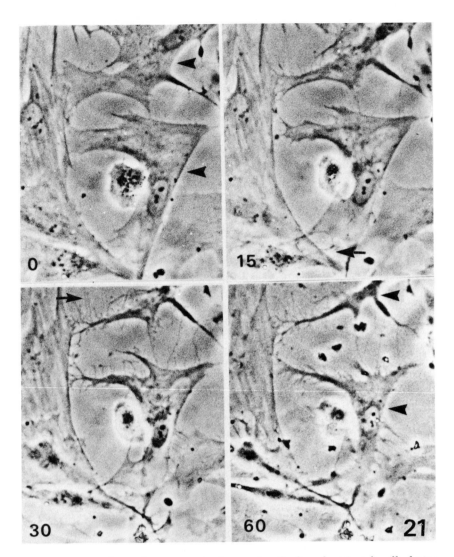

Fig. 21. Time lapse phase contrast micrographs of cultured rat Sertoli cells during exposure to Bt$_2$cAMP (0.5 mM) for 60 minutes. The time in minutes is given in each print. The arrowheads indicate Sertoli cells at time zero and 60 minutes after treatment. The arrow (15 minutes) points to a thin cytoplasmic process which connects a morphologically altered Sertoli cell with an adjacent cell (compared to Figs. 25 and 26). (From Spruill *et al.*, 29.)

that the variation in the percentage of cell affected by the shape changes cannot be attributed to nonresponsive cell contaminants (22).

Time-lapse studies of Sertoli cells exposed to FSH-MIX (Fig. 20) (29) and Bt₂cAMP (Fig. 21) for 60 minutes showed that subpopulations of Sertoli cells were either morphologically responsive or nonresponsive. Furthermore, the time course of the development and recovery of cell shape changes were biological agent-dependent. For instance, while a 120-minute exposure to FSH induced shape changes in 37% of the cells, MIX, Bt₂cAMP, and FSH-MIX effected shape changes in 75% of the cells. The morphological conversion induced by MIX, Bt₂cAMP (Fig. 22), and FSH-MIX (Fig. 23) persisted as long as these biological agents were present in the medium. The removal of these simulating agents from the tissue culture medium determined the reversion of stellate Sertoli cells to a flat morphology observed in control cells within 22–24 hours (29). However, a different recovery rate was observed in FSH-treated Sertoli cells as compared to FSH-MIX treated cells (Fig. 23). Sertoli cells stimulated with FSH alone showed a *transient* cell shape change whether or not FSH was present in the medium. Sertoli cells stimulated continuously with FSH began to return progressively to a flat morphology after 6 hours of exposure to the

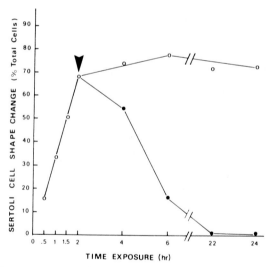

Fig. 22. Time exposure to Bt₂cAMP. —○—, Bt₂cAMP (0.5 m*M*) present continuously in the medium. —●—, Bt₂cAMP removed from the medium after 2 hours of treatment (arrowhead). Note the persistence of Sertoli cell shape changes when Bt₂cAMP is continuously present in the medium. (From Spruill *et al.*, 29.)

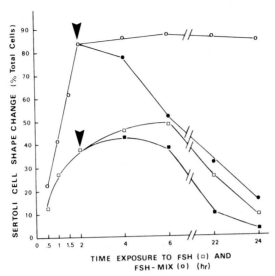

Fig. 23. Comparison of FSH and FSH-MIX effects on Sertoli cell shape. Whether FSH is continuously present (—□—) or not (—■—) in the culture medium, Sertoli cell shape changes are transient. A different results emerges from FSH-MIX treatment (—○—), MIX overrides FSH effects. The removal of FSH-MIX results in progressive cell shape recovery (—●—). The arrowheads indicate time of FSH and FSH-MIX removal from the medium. (From Spruill *et al.*, 29.)

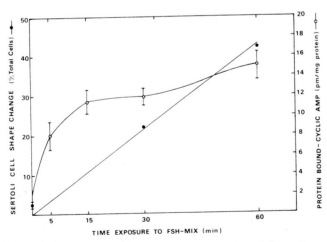

Fig. 24. Correlation of the early development of Sertoli cell shape changes and the level of protein bound cAMP during exposure to FSH-MIX. The appearance of Sertoli cell shape changes is preceded by an increase in protein bound cAMP. (From Spruill *et al.*, 29.)

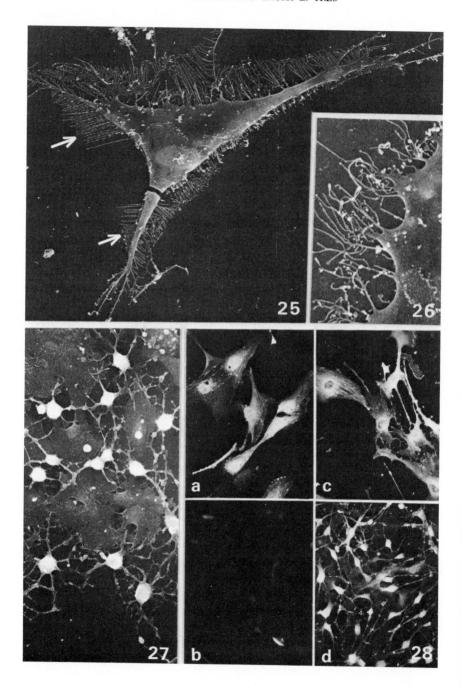

gonadotropin and 4 hours after FSH removal from the medium (Fig. 23).

Time-lapse cinematographic experiments have shown that the replacement of FSH-containing medium after 4 hours of exposure to Sertoli cells with fresh medium containing FSH, results in a rapid recovery of morphologically altered cells and progressive induction of morphological changes of previously unresponsive Sertoli cells (Kierszenbaum and Tres, unpublished observation). The implications of these observations merit further study.

Scanning electron microscopy provided a detailed view of the process of Sertoli cell morphological alterations. After exposure to MIX or Bt$_2$cAMP for 15–30 minutes, Sertoli cells contracted and assumed a nearly triangular shape (Fig. 25). The cell edges displayed projecting cytoplasmic processes of uniform diameter (Fig. 26) with uniform length or short-to-long gradient patterns (Fig. 25). As time progressed, some Sertoli cells exhibited a spherical shape with multiple cytoplasmic process projecting from the cell. These processes organized an irregular network by maintaining multiple contact points with similar processes of morphologically altered and nonaltered Sertoli cells (Fig. 27).

FSH and cyclic nucleotide analogs induced an increase in the content of protein bound cAMP which preceded the changes in Sertoli cell morphology (Fig. 24). Because Bromo cyclic GMP, an analog of cGMP, was unable to generate the stellate morphology in Sertoli cells, we concluded that a surge of cAMP triggers a still undefined mechanism by which Sertoli cells modify their shape in coincidence with a progressive depletion of cytoplasmic secretory granules (29).

Fig. 25. Scanning electron micrograph of a Sertoli cell stimulated with MIX for 30 minutes. Cytoplasmic projections of variable length but uniform diameter can be observed. The arrows point to short-to-long gradient arrangements of the cell processes. [From (29).]

Fig. 26. Scanning electron micrograph showing the branching pattern of Sertoli cell cytoplasmic projections 30 minutes after MIX treatment.

Fig. 27. Scanning electron micrograph of Sertoli cells treated with MIX for 60 minutes. Cells adopt a spherical shape and the cell processes organize an irregular network. Morphological changes in some cells contrast with other unaffected Sertoli cells present in the same field.

Fig. 28. Immunocytochemical localization of cAMP in Sertoli cells. The distribution of immunoreactive cAMP is shown in control Sertoli cells (a). Fluorescence is abolished after solid absorption of the anti-cAMP serum (b). The distribution of cAMP in Sertoli cells is illustrated after FSH-MIX treatment for 30 minutes (c) and 120 minutes (d) (From 29.)

A methodology developed for the immunocytochemical study of cyclic nucleotides (31) was used to study qualitative changes in the distribution of cAMP in cultured rat Sertoli cells after FSH and cyclic nucleotide analog treatment. Because protein bound cAMP is most likely the physiological active form, this immunocytochemical technique presumably detects part of the functionally active cyclic nucleotide. Figure 28a illustrates the distribution of cAMP in control Sertoli cells. cAMP immunoreactivity was observed in the perinuclear region of Sertoli cell cytoplasm and in association with cytoskeletal components (stress fibers). 30 minutes after incubation with FSH-MIX, some Sertoli cells changed their shape and cAMP fluorescence was enhanced around the nuclear region of morphologically altered cells (Fig. 28c) in coincidence with an increase in the levels of protein bound cAMP (Fig. 24). After 60–120 minutes, whereas a high proportion of FSH-MIX treated Sertoli cells underwent rounding and exhibited a stellate morphology (Fig. 28d), other morphologically nonresponsive cells displayed a cAMP immunoreactive pattern which could not be distinguished from that observed before exposure to FSH-MIX. Similar cAMP fluorescence was observed in Sertoli cells exposed to MIX alone (not shown).

CONCLUDING REMARKS

In this chapter we briefly review evidence supporting (i) the capacity of Sertoli cells to proliferate *in vitro* while preserving their ABP immunoreactivity, (ii) the time course of hormonal and cyclic nucleotide responsiveness, (iii) the biological agent dependency of the induction and recovery of Sertoli cell shape changes, and (iv) the existence of a heterogeneous population of Sertoli cells which exhibits both differential ABP immunoreactivity and morphological responsiveness. We also review experimental data obtained *in vivo* supporting the cyclic activity of Sertoli cells. These are (i) the reversible Sertoli cell activation represented by increases and decreases of RNA and protein synthesis detected both by different structural patterns and by [³H]uridine and [³H]amino acid labeling patterns in these cells (1,2,32), (ii) the cyclic variation of lipid content in rat Sertoli cells (4), (iii) the observation that variation in Sertoli cell ABP secretion, FSH binding, and FSH-stimulated secretion of cAMP correlates with particular associations of germinal cells to which Sertoli cells are spatially related within discrete segments of the seminiferous tubule (5), and (iv) the fluctuation in the content of immunoreactive ABP in Sertoli cells within the same seminiferous tubule (7).

These *in vivo* and *in vitro* observations provide further support to the hypothesis of a cyclic nature of Sertoli cell function that may be related to the existence of morphologically distinct cell types and cell associations within the seminiferous epithelium (32).

Two aspects of this review require further discussion. These are (i) the functional significance of Sertoli cell contractile properties and (ii) the possible mechanism which triggers Sertoli cell contraction.

Immunofluorescence light microscopic studies using antibodies to purified constitutive proteins of cytoskeletal components have been used to demonstrate the accumulation and distribution of microtubules and microfilaments in the cytoplasm of Sertoli cells [α-actinin (33), actin (28,33,34), tubulin (28), vimentin (35)]. Actin immunoreactive filaments in cultured Sertoli cells changed their distribution pattern after FSH treatment (28). These components of the mechanochemical system, generally designated as cytoskeletal filaments, establish and maintain the cytoarchitecture of Sertoli cells as these cells interact with different cell members of the mitotic, meiotic and spermiogenic compartments (Fig. 1) perhaps by facilitating the progression of differentiating germinal cells from one compartment to another and, finally, by allowing the release of mature spermatids into the seminiferous tubular lumen (spermiation). A similar driving mechanism based on the dynamic properties of the mechanochemical system could be involved in the inter and trans-sertolian flow of substances from the intertubular space towards germinal cells and the tubular lumen as well as in the intracellular vectorial transport of Sertoli cell products (2), including ABP (Fig. 29).

The role of phosphorylation–dephosphorylation in the short-term regulation of microfilament function is relevant to observations from our laboratory of cAMP immunoreactivity (29; Fig. 28) associated with stress fibers and the increase of protein bound cAMP preceding Sertoli cell shape changes (29; Fig. 24). It is generally accepted that the major cell receptors for cyclic nucleotides are the cyclic nucleotide-dependent protein kinases composed of regulatory (R) and catlytic (C) subunits. The C subunit is inactive when bound to the R subunit and becomes free to phosphorylate protein substrates only after its dissociation from the R subunit. The dissociation of the C subunit follows binding of cyclic nucleotides by the R subunit (see review by Glass and Krebs, 36). The activity of the C subunit in its dissociated state can be inhibited by the protein kinase inhibitor (37). It has been shown that FSH stimulates the *de novo* synthesis of protein kinase in-

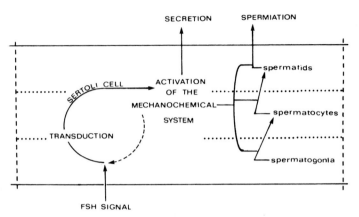

Fig. 29. Diagram representing the role of the mechanochemical system composed of microfilaments (thick, intermediate, and thin) and microtubules in the Sertoli cell. A FSH signal triggers a cascade of biochemical and structural events. When the FSH signal is transduced through a cyclic nucleotide-mediated mechanism, the mechanochemical system is either activated or integrated. As a result, proteins can be secreted into the lumen of the seminiferous tubule (or tissue culture medium) and germinal cells translocate from one cell compartment to another. Sertoli cell physiological responses may depend on a conditioning phase of its cycle and/or the differentiation stages of the germinal cells associated with the Sertoli cell in a given domain.

hibitor in Sertoli cells (38). Therefore, two control points exist for protein kinase activity: the activation of the C subunit upon cAMP binding to the R subunit and the direct inhibition by the protein kinase inhibitor. In addition, calmodulin, and intracellular receptor for calcium, regulates various cellular activities in the form of a Ca^{2+}–calmodulin complex (39). These activities include cyclic nucleotide metabolism, the function of the mechanochemical system and the Ca^{2+}-dependent protein kinases. The Ca^{2+}–calmodulin and cAMP-dependent mechanisms interact with each other through either cooperative or antagonistic regulation of protein phosphorylation (40). Since both the Ca^{2+}–calmodulin and cAMP systems are active and hormonally regulated in Sertoli cells (28), it is possible to consider the mechanochemical system as the site of dual or antagonistic regulation mediating the induction and recovery of Sertoli cell shape changes in culture and *in vivo.* Thus, the secretion of ABP and other proteins (18) into the lumen of the seminiferous tubule and the tissue culture medium, the displacement of differentiating spermatogonia, spermatocytes, and spermatids toward the lumen and final spermiation may all be regulated in part by forces generated by contractile cytoplasmic proteins under the control of a FSH–cyclic nucleotide-mediated mechanism.

ACKNOWLEDGMENTS

We gratefully acknowledge the collaboration of Frank S. French, Peter Petrusz, Alton L. Steiner, Robert M. DePhilip, W. Austin Spruill, and Michael G. White during the course of this work. This work was supported by a Public Health Service Research Grant HD11884.

REFERENCES

1. Kierszenbaum, A. L. (1974) *Biol. Reprod.* **11**, 365–376.
2. Kierszenbaum, A. L. (1977) *In* "The Testis in Normal and Infertile Men" (P. Troen and H. R. Nankin, eds.), pp. 125–136. Raven, New York.
3. Kierszenbaum, A. L., and Tres, L. L. (1974) *J. Cell Biol.* **60**, 39–53.
4. Kerr, J. B., and De Kretser, D. M. (1975) *J. Reprod. Fertil.* **43**, 1–8.
5. Parvinen, M., Hansson, V., and Ritzen, M. (1980) *In* "Testicular Development, Structure and Function" (E. Steinberger and A. Steinberger, eds.), pp. 425–435. Raven, New York.
6. French, F. S., and Ritzen, E. M. (1973) *Endocrinology* **93**, 88–95.
7. Petrusz, P., Lea, O. A., Feldman, M., and French, F. S. (1981). *In* Reproductive Processes and Contraception (K. W. McKerns, ed.), Plenum, New York (in press).
8. Dorrington, J. H., and Fritz, I. B. (1975) *Endocrinology* **96**, 879–889.
9. Steinberger, A., Heindel, J. J., Lindsey, J. N., Elkington, J. S. H., Sanborn, B. M., and Steinberger, E. (1975) *Endocr. Res. Commun.* **2**, 261–272.
10. Welsh, M. J., and Wiebe, J. P. (1975) *Endocrinology* **96**, 618–624.
11. Kodani, M., and Kodani, K. (1966) *Proc. Natl. Acad. Sci. U. S. A.* **56**, 1200–1206.
12. Dux, C. (1939–1940) *Arch. Anat. Microsc. Morphol. Exp.* **35**, 391–413.
13. Michailow, W. (1937) *Z. Zellforsch. Mikrosk. Anat.* **26**, 174–179.
14. Mendelsohn, W. (1938) *Anat. Rec.* **69**, 355–359.
15. Jordan, R. T., Katsh, S., and de Stackelburg, N. (1961) *Nature (London)* **192**, 1053–1055.
16. Vilar, O., Steinberger, A., and Steinberger, E. (1967) *Z. Zellforsch. Mikrosk. Anat.* **78**, 221–233.
17. Ellingson, D. J., and Yao, K. T. S. (1970) *J. Cell Sci.* **6**, 195–205.
18. DePhilip, R. M., Tres, L. L., and Kierszenbaum, A. L. (1980) *J. Cell Biol.* **87**, 149a.
19. Steinberger, A., Walther, J., Heindel, J. J., Sanborn, B. M., Tsai, Y.-H., and Steinberger, E. (1979) *In Vitro* **15**, 23–31.
20. Fritz, I. B., Rommerts, F. G., Louis, B. G., and Dorrington, J. H. (1976) *J. Reprod. Fertil.* **46**, 17–24.
21. Louis, B. G., and Fritz, I. B. (1977). *Mol. Cell. Endocrinol.* **7**, 9–16.
22. Kierszenbaum, A. L., Feldman, M., Lea, O., Spruill, W. A., Tres, L. L., Petrusz, P., and French, F. S. (1980) *Proc. Natl. Acad. Sci. U. S. A.* **77**, 5322–5326.
23. Welch, J. P., Mitchell, R. B., and Davis, J. C. (1979) *Biol. Reprod.* **21**, 69–74.
24. Griswold, M. D., Mably, E. R., and Fritz, I. B. (1976) *Mol. Cell. Endocrinol.* **4**, 139–149.
25. Nagy, F. (1972) *J. Reprod. Fertil.* **28**, 389–395.
26. Tung, P. S., Dorrington, J. H., and Fritz, I. B. (1975) *Proc. Natl. Acad. Sci. U. S. A.* **72**, 1838–1842.
27. Hutson, J. C. (1978) *Am. J. Anat.* **151**, 55–69.

28. Welsh, M. J., Van Sickle, M., and Means, A. R. (1980) *In* "Testicular Development, Structure and Function" (A. Steinberger and E. Steinberger, eds.), pp. 89–98. Raven, New York.

29. Spruill, W. A., White, M. G., Steiner, A. L., Tres, L. L., and Kierszenbaum, A. L. (1981) *Exp. Cell Res.* (to be published).

30. White, M. G., Spruill, W. A., Tres, L. L., and Kierszenbaum, A. L. (1980) *J. Cell Biol.* **87**, 148a.

31. Spruill, W. A., and Steiner, A. L. (1979) *Adv. Cyclic Nucleotide Res.* **10**, 169–186.

32. Tres, L. L., and Kierszenbaum, A. L. (1975) *In* "Hormonal Regulation of Spermatogenesis" (F. S. French, V. Hansson, E. M. Ritzen, and S. N. Nayfeh, eds.), pp. 455–478. Plenum, New York.

33. Franke, W. W., Grund, C., Fink, A., Weber, K., Jockusch, B. M., Zentgraf, H., and Osborn, M. (1978) *Biol. Cell.* **31**, 7–21.

34. Toyama, Y. (1976) *Anat. Rec.* **186**, 477–492.

35. Franke, W. W., Grund, C., and Schmid, E. (1979) *Eur. J. Cell Biol.* **19**, 269–275.

36. Glass, D. B., and Krebs E. G. (1980) *Annu. Rev. Pharmacol. Toxicol.* **20**, 363–388.

37. Walsh, D. A., Perkins, J. P., and Krebs, E. G. (1968) *J. Biol. Chem.* **243**, 3763–3774.

38. Tash, J. S., Dedman, J. R., and Means, A. R. (1979) *J. Biol. Chem.* **254**, 1241–1247.

39. Cheung, W. Y. (1980) *Science* **207**, 19–27.

40. Conti, M. A., and Adelstein, R. S. (1980) *Fed. Proc., Fed. Am. Soc. Exp. Biol.* **39**, 1569–1573.

Meiotic Chromosomes of Mouse Spermatocytes: Identification of Bivalents, Lampbrush Organization, and Transcription Activities*

LAURA L. TRES AND A. L. KIERSZENBAUM

*Department of Anatomy and
the Laboratories for Reproductive Biology, The School of Medicine
University of North Carolina,
Chapel Hill, North Carolina*

INTRODUCTION

Mouse spermatocyte nuclei contain autosomal and sexual bivalents each held together by a tripartite structure named the synaptonemal complex. As meiotic chromosomes pair during meiotic prophase, molecular events leading to genetic recombination (crossing-over) correlate with a transcriptional process which generates distinct classes of RNA molecules at various chromosomal segments. Thus, while genes coding for ribosomal RNA (rRNA) molecules are distributed on the paracentromeric region (terminal or basal knob, Fig. 1) of autosomal bivalents, gene activity responsible for heterogeneous nuclear RNA (HnRNA) molecules takes place along the "lampbrush" segment of autosomal bivalents (Fig. 1). A characteristic feature of male meiotic prophase (mouse, human) transcriptional activity is that the synthesis of rRNA precedes HnRNA transcription. A maximal production of rRNA occurs during leptotene–zygotene, preceding HrRNA which is at a peak at middle pachytene (Fig. 2). While autosomal bivalents dis-

---

* Dedicated to Dr. H. Stanley Bennett, whose scientific principles and ideals greatly influenced our generation of scientists.

BIOREGULATORS OF REPRODUCTION

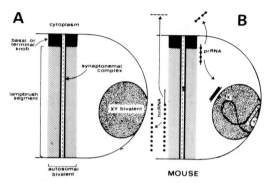

Fig. 1. (A) Diagram and nomenclature of a mouse spermatocyte nucleus displaying an autosomal bivalent with a synaptonemal complex attached to the nuclear envelope. The condensed chromatin mass close to the nuclear envelope represents the XY bivalent. (B) Preribosomal RNA (prRNA) molecules transcribed at the basal knob region of an autosomal bivalent and HnRNA molecules synthesized along the lampbrush segment of autosomal bivalents are shown in this diagram. The arrows indicate the possible pathways and fate of prRNA and HnRNA molecules (from Kierszenbaum and Tres, 21).

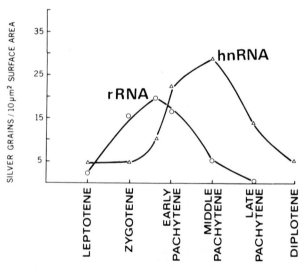

Fig. 2. Autoradiographic data of [³H]uridine labeling experiments showing that rRNA (—○—) synthesis precedes the synthesis of HnRNA (—△—) during meiotic prophase (modified from Tres, 42).

play a conspicuous transcriptional activity, the XY pair remains almost transcriptionally inactive (17,35).

A detailed analysis of the mode of pairing and disjunction of autosomal and sexual bivalents as well as the study of the structure of chromatin fibers of the lampbrush chromosomal segment, either free or associated with nascent transcripts, can be carried out using a whole-mount electron microscopic technique. This technique provides an adequate display of bivalents of a large number of spermatocytes and facilitates the morphological analysis of transcription occurring at distinct stages of meiotic prophase.

In this chapter, we review the criteria for the identification of meiotic prophase stages of mouse spermatocytes in whole-mount electron microscopic preparations and examine the characteristics of the transcriptional activity of HnRNA during pachytene and diplotene. A clear distinction of the meiotic prophase stage-dependency of HnRNA synthesis is relevant to (i) the post-transcriptional processing of primary HnRNA into specific mRNA molecules presumably required for meiotic and postmeiotic translational activities, (ii) the understanding of the mechanism which regulates the activation of transcription at specific stages of meiotic prophase, and (iii) the configuration of the lampbrush chromosomal loops and their transcripts.

PREPARATIVE PROCEDURES FOR THE ELECTRON AND LIGHT MICROSCOPIC VISUALIZATION OF MEIOTIC CHROMOSOMES

A whole-mount electron microscopic technique based on the method of Miller and co-workers (32,33) and adapted for mammalian and insect testes in our laboratory (18–20, 43) has provided a satisfactory display of synaptonemal complexes, chromatin fibers, and associated ribonucleoprotein (RNP) fibers representing nascent and newly synthesized transcripts. Figure 3 illustrates the technical procedure for the preparation of spermatocytes nuclear contents for electron microscopy. Different aspects of this procedure have been described in our previous papers and a comprehensive and detailed description is presented here.

Mouse testes are removed under ether anesthesia. The tunica albuginea is dissected out and the seminiferous tubules are cut into segments 2–3 mm in length and suspended in either phosphate-buffered saline (pH 7.2) or 0.05 M Tris–hydrochloride buffer (pH 7.4) containing 0.15 M NaCl. Testicular cells are then dissociated from the tu-

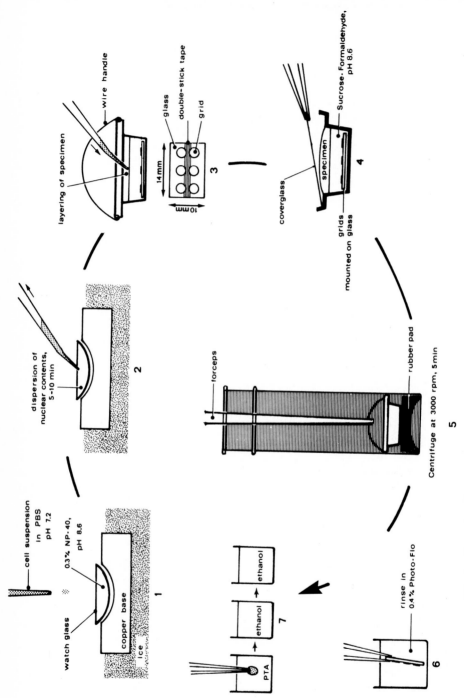

Fig. 3. Procedure for the preparation of testicular specimens for whole-mount electron microscopy.

bules by shearing forces produced by repeated aspirations and ejections with a 1 ml syringe. The cell suspension is then transferred to centrifuge tubes and centrifuged at 1000 rpm for 4 minutes in a refrigerated centrifuge (4°C). The pellet is resuspended in fresh buffer with a Pasteur pipette and either strained through a stainless steel mesh with openings 0.5 mm in diameter to trap nondissociated seminiferous tubular pieces or used without straining for the preparation of electron or light microscope samples. The following steps are used for electron microscopic preparations:

Step 1 (Fig. 3): About 0.1 ml of the testicular cell suspension (50 cells/μl) is transferred with a Pasteur pipette to 0.5 ml of a 0.3% solution of the detergent Nonidet P-40 (NP-40, BDH Chemicals Ltd., Poole, England). The pH of the NP-40 aqueous solution is adjusted to 8.6 titrating with stock of 0.1 M borate buffer (pH 9.0). The NP-40 solution is kept in a watch glass placed on shallow recess in a thick copper plate maintained on crushed ice. For dispersal of nuclear contents of maturing spermatids and spermatozoa we use the detergent Joy (Procter and Gamble, Cincinnati, Ohio) instead of NP-40 (19,20).

Step 2 (Fig. 3): After allowing the testicular cells to disperse for 5–10 minutes in ice cold NP-40 solution, 0.5 ml of the solution containing the dispersed nuclear contents is transferred with a micropipette (Lang-Levy type, 500 μl) into a plastic trough. The plastic trough is a modification of a plastic block molding cup with a specimen chamber of 16 × 12 × 5 mm (Sorvall, Newton, Connecticut, Cat. no. 45460) as shown in Fig. 3.

Step 3 (Fig. 3): The plastic trough contains: At the bottom of the plastic trough, a piece of microscope slide glass (10 × 14 mm) with six electron microscope carbon-coated copper grids (300-mesh) attached to a narrow strip of double-stick tape. The carbon-coated grids are made hydrophilic by immersing them in ethanol 95% for 1 minute (29). The attached grids are then covered by filling the trough with 0.5 ml of a solution of 0.1 M sucrose with 10% formaldehyde (pH 8.6).

Step 4 (Fig. 3): The dispersed nuclear contents containing meiotic chromosomes are layered on the sucrose–formaldehyde cushion and the specimen chamber is sealed with a round glass coverslip 25 mm in diameter.

Step 5 (Fig. 3): The plastic trough is then placed with forceps on the inverted flat surface of a rubber tube cushion in a centrifuge bucket and spun at 3000 rpm for 5 minutes at 4°C.

Step 6 (Fig. 3): The piece of glass containing nuclear contents collected on the carbon-coated surface of the copper grids is removed from the trough, rinsed in a 0.4% Photo-flo (Kodak) solution in distilled water for a few seconds and air-dried.

Step 7 (Fig. 3): Electron microscope grids are detached from the tape with forceps and stained individually in a freshly prepared 1% phosphotungstic acid solution in ethanol 95% (PTA, pH 2.5 unadjusted), rinsed in 95% ethanol twice, and air-dried. The grids on the glass can also be rotary-shadowed with platinum–palladium in a vacuum evaporator.

Using the same basic principles of the above described technique, preparations of meiotic chromosomes stained with silver nitrate (8) can be made for light microscopic examination. After dispersal of nuclear contents (step 2), two drops of the sample is gently deposited with a Pasteur pipette on a large drop of sucrose–formaldehyde solution placed on a microscope slide and let to sediment for 10 minutes in a moist chamber with formaldehyde vapors. The preparations are then dried at 45°C for 1 hour. After rinsing with water, the slides are air-dried. Then, a few drops of a freshly prepared 50% aqueous solution of silver nitrate is placed on the microscope slide surface containing the sample and covered with a glass coverslip. The preparation is incubated at 45°C overnight or at 60°C for 1 hour in a moist chamber and then rinsed with water.

Westergaard and von Wettstein (51) have shown with the electron microscope that silver grain precipitates are specifically deposited in both lateral elements of the synaptonemal complex. Similar observations have been recently documented by Dresser and Moses (7). Therefore, the dense rods of variable length observed in silver impregnated spreads of mouse spermatocytes (Figs. 10–12) correspond to synaptonemal complexes.

THE VISUALIZATION OF AUTOSOMAL AND SEXUAL BIVALENTS IN WHOLE-MOUNT ELECTRON MICROSCOPIC PREPARATIONS

The identification of meiotic prophase stages in whole-mount preparations is based on (i) the mode of pairing and disjunction of homologous chromosomes (43), (ii) the association of nucleoli to putative autosomal sites (17,18,21,43), (iii) the length of the XY pairing segment (43), (iv) the morphology of the chromosomal axial cores and core free endings (43,45), and (v) the amount of RNP, representing HnRNA complexed to proteins, present in the complete chromosomal complement (47).

While autosomal bivalents display in whole-mount preparations a complete pairing between homologs of the same length, the X and Y chromosomes can be identified as two side by side associated chromosomes of unequal length. The pairing segment of the sexual bivalent is restricted to one end and is much shorter than either the X or Y chromosomes (43). During zygotene (Fig. 4), autosomal bivalents display an asynchronous chromosomal pairing. Some of the homologous chromosomes display a complete synaptonemal complex whereas others display short stretches of synaptonemal complex. The presence of a

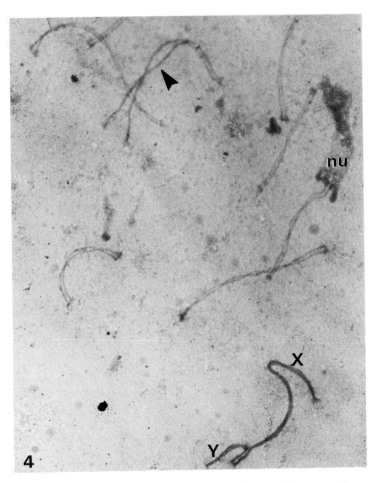

Fig. 4. Late zygotene mouse spermatocyte observed in a whole-mount electron microscopic preparation. A nucleolus (*nu*) is attached to the basal knob region of an autosome. X and Y chromosomes display a pairing segment. The arrowhead points to an autosomal bivalent with less complete synapsis than others (from Tres, 43).

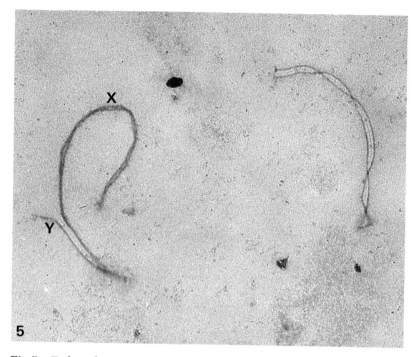

Fig. 5. Early pachytene mouse spermatocyte. Whereas the XY bivalent is extensively paired, an autosome is totally paired (from Tres, 45).

nucleolus still attached to an autosomal bivalent indicates chromo-somal synapsis and not disjunction as at diplotene (compare Figs. 4 and 12b). At diplotene, nucleoli are not longer observed associated with autosomal bivalents (17).

During pachytene, autosomal bivalents remain associated side by side along their entire length. However, the XY bivalent displays variations in both the extent of pairing and in the conformation of the axial chromosomal cores (43). Thus, during late zygotene–early pachytene, X and Y chromosomes pair side by side along most of the length of the Y chromosome (43, and Fig. 5). Figure 6 is a schematic representation of a mouse XY bivalent at late zygotene–early pachy-tene. According to Darlington (5) and Koller and Darlington (23), a paired segment (with a synaptonemal complex in the middle (40) bears *partially sex-linked genes*. The "differential segments," repre-sented by the unpaired X and Y chromosomal regions contain *totally sex-linked genes*. In both mouse (43) and hamster (45) sex bivalents, a small terminal segment of the Y chromosome (the differential segment) does not participate in pairing and is displaced from the X chromosomal core. Koller and Darlington (23) have proposed that each sex chromosome contains a homologous segment by which they pair and form chiasmata during meiotic prophase. Formation of chiasmata implies that genes located in the pairing segment can be exchanged between X and Y chromosomes whereas genes in the unpaired regions of the sex chromosomes cannot be exchanged. The mode of pairing of the sexual bivalent and the possibility that the differential segment of the Y chromosome contains sex-linked genes are relevant to the location and function of the histocompatibility-Y (H-Y) locus in human Y chromosomes (24). It has been suggested that the Y-terminal segment (paracentromeric region) diverging from the X chromosomal core may represent a mechanism for preserving from crossing-over the sex-linked nature of the H-Y locus (45). In fact, whole-mount electron and light microscopic studies of "sex reversed" (*Sxr*), XY carrier male mice (44,49) have shown a short synaptonemal complex between the complete Y chromosome and a fragment of a Y presumably associated to an autosome (Fig. 11C, ps², and Tres and Lewis, 49). The length of the autosomal bivalent carrying the associated Y fragment is within the length range of chromosomes 15, 16, and 17. Since mouse chromosomes 12, 15, 16, 18, and 19 have a nucleolar organizing function (12) and no nucleolus is associated with the autosome carrying the associated Y fragment (Fig. 11B), it may be possible that chromosome 17 contains the associated Y fragment. The finding of a complete Y and a Y fragment associated to an autosome lends support to the possibil-

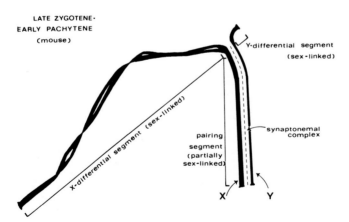

Fig. 6.   Schematic representation and nomenclature of an extensively paired XY bivalent according to Koller and Darlington (23) (from Tres, 45).

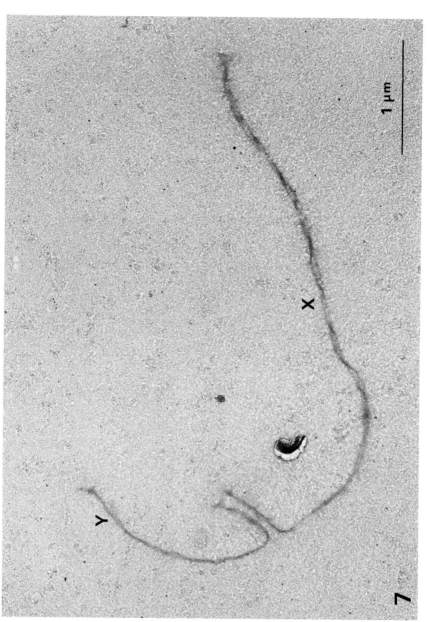

Fig. 7. The XY bivalent during middle pachytene. Mouse spermatocyte.

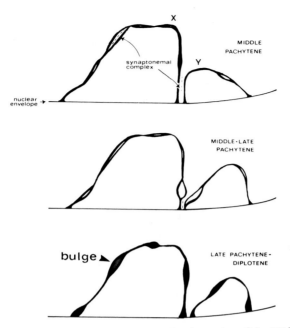

Fig. 8. Structural patterns observed during the disjuntion of the XY bivalent. Note the structural modifications of the axial chromosomal cores (from Tres, 45).

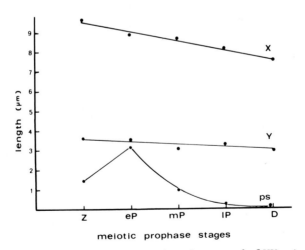

Fig. 9. Lengths of X and Y chromosomal axial cores and of XY paired segments. Note the progressive reduction in axial length during meiotic prophase. The length of the pairing segment (ps) approaches the length of the Y chromosomal core (see Fig. 5) at early pachytene and decreases thereafter (see Figs. 7–8) (from Tres, 43). Z, Zygotene; eP, early pachytene; mP, middle pachytene; lP, late pachytene; D, diplotene.

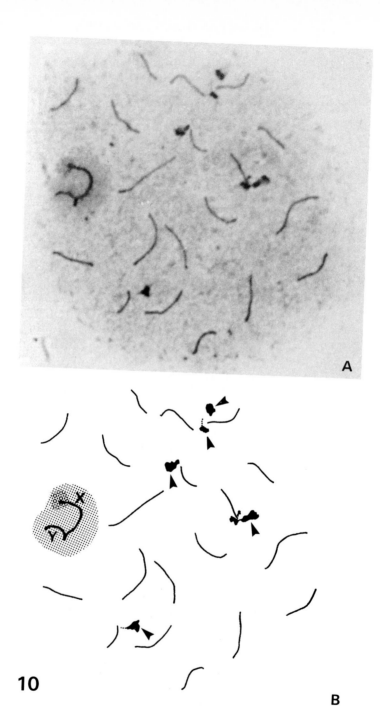

10

ity that in *Sxr*,XY carrier male mice, a duplicated structural gene of the paracentromeric region of the Y chromosome specifies increased production of H-Y antigen (1,39). For more details on the H-Y locus and sexual differentiation see Wachtel's chapter in this volume.

As pachytene spermatocytes progress in their differentiation, the synaptonemal complex region between X and Y chromosomes shortens (Figs. 7–9). At late pachytene–early diplotene, the sexual bivalent maintains either (i) a very short side by side pairing region, (ii) an end-to-end association (Fig. 12a), or (iii) X and Y chromosomal cores are separated from each other but surrounded by a mass of condensed chromatin (Fig. 12b). As the pairing region between X and Y chromosomes decreases in length until disappearing at diplotene, each of the unpaired chromosomal axial cores increases in thickness, splits lengthwise into two major fascicles first (Fig. 7) [forming a short synaptonemal complex in between (Kierszenbaum and Tres, 18)] and then adopting a multistranded ribbon-like configuration. Finally, at diplotene, the sex chromosomal axial cores display at variable intervals outward expansions or "bulges" (Fig. 12B). The free endings of the autosomal synaptonemal complexes increase in density as a result of the formation of deltoid expansions (Fig. 12B). Autosomal bivalents disjoin asynchronously adopting elliptic, circular and "Y"-shaped configurations (Fig. 12a). Some of the autosomal bivalents remain associated at terminally deltoid expanded segments by both side-by-side and end-to-end associations (Fig. 12A). The end-to-end association is found predominantly at the basal knob region of disjoining bivalents (Fig. 12B).

THE VISUALIZATION OF TRANSCRIPTION ACTIVITY IN LAMPBRUSH CHROMOSOMES DURING MALE MEIOTIC PROPHASE IN THE MOUSE

In the preceding section it was emphasized that the identification of male meiotic prophase stages in whole-mount preparations can be accomplished by the recognition of the mode of pairing of bivalents and

---

Fig. 10. Silver-stained preparation. Pachytene spermatocyte. (A)The dense rods of variable length represent the synaptonemal complex portion of the bivalents. The XY bivalent can be identified as a condensed chromatin structure displaying a conspicuously condensed chromatin region at the free ending of the X chromosome (paracentromeric region). Five nucleolar masses (arrowheads in B) can be seen associated with at least four autosomal bivalents.

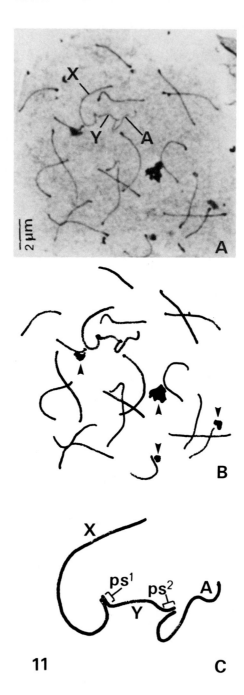

the structure of axial chromosomal cores and core endings. The same morphological criteria can be used for the study of RNA transcriptive patterns within a single spermatocyte genome in a distinct meiotic prophase stage.

Although the lampbrush organization of autosomal bivalents is well displayed in whole-mount electron microscopic preparations, it is rather difficult to visualize the organizational level at the synaptonemal complex region obscured by overlapping chromatin fibers.

Previous studies have shown that the timing of DNA (41), RNA (17,19,35), and arginine-rich protein synthesis (19,34) during meiotic and postmeiotic stages of spermatogenesis is well defined and characteristic (Fig. 13). In mouse and human spermatocytes, various regions of autosomal bivalents transcribe RNA at different rates during consecutive meiotic prophase stages. rRNA synthesis takes place near the paracentromeric region of certain autosomes (Fig. 4) whereas HnRNA synthesis occurs along the chromatin loops of lampbrush chromosomal segments. The nucleolar organizing process in human (42) and mouse (17,21) spermatocytes has been described in detail.

During meiotic prophase, the XY bivalent displays a uniform and continuous chromatin condensation state which contrasts with fluctuations in chromatin condensation of the autosomal bivalents. During pachytene, autosomes display a lampbrush pattern defined by chromatin loops extending radially from the synaptonemal complex region (Fig. 14).

The structure and function of lampbrush chromosomes in invertebrates and vertebrates has been extensively studied (for a review, see Davidson, 6). Lampbrush chromosomes are generally considered as (i) diplotene meiotic prophase structures containing a 4C genome, (ii) they are frequently observed in oocytes, (iii) the lampbrush-like appearance arises from projecting chromatin loops of considerable length originated in chromomeres irregularly spaced along the chromosomal axis, (iv) most of the length of individual chromatin loops are transcribed, and (v) each loop contains one or more transcription units. However, lampbrush chromosomes can also be observed in somatic cell nuclei [green algea *Acetabularia mediterranea* (38)] and

---

Fig. 11. (A) Silver stained preparation of a pachytene spermatocyte of a *Sxr*, XY carrier male mouse. X and Y chromosomes display a short-paired segment [ps¹ in (C)]. An autosome (A) with an associated Y segment is paired with the free end of a complete Y [ps² in (C)]. Autosomal bivalents with associated nucleoli are indicated with arrowheads in (B). Measurements in μm: X, 4.89; Y, 1.70; A, 3.25.

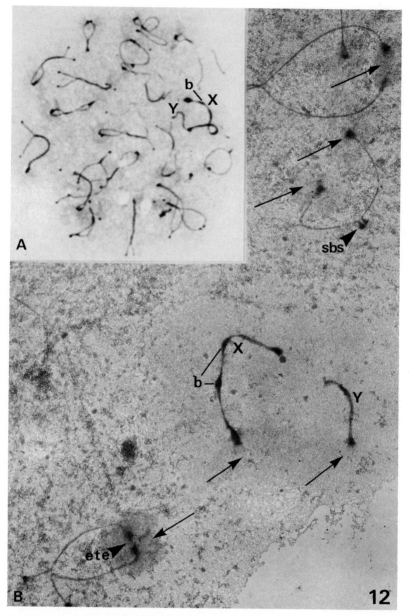

Fig. 12. Mouse spermatocyte. Diplotene. (A) Silver stained preparation (light microscopy). (B) Whole-mount electron microscopic preparation. The XY pair can be seen at this meiotic prophase stage either associated end to end (A) or separated from each other (B). The characteristic chromosomal axial core bulges (b) of the XY pair are well

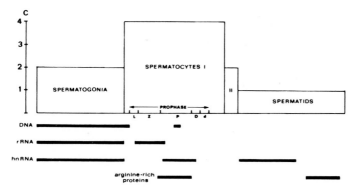

Fig. 13. Synthesis of DNA, RNA (rRNA and hnRNA), and arginine-rich proteins during premeiotic, meiotic, and postmeiotic stages of spermatogenesis. L, leptotene; Z, zygotene; P, pachytene; D, diplotene and d, diakinesis. (From Kierszenbaum and Tres, 21). C values indicate the genome size of germinal cells during spermatogenesis.

spermatocytes (11,13,17,35,36). Therefore, lampbrush chromosomes are not restricted to female meiotic prophase cells.

The lampbrush-like organization of autosomes of mouse spermatocytes was recognized in light microscopic preparations (35) and confirmed later by whole-mount electron microscopic techniques (18,46). Mammalian lampbrush chromosomes differ from amphibian (32,38) and insects (13; c.f. in Davidson, 6) lampbrush chromosomes in the length of the chromosomal loops and the arrangement of nascent transcripts. In addition, mouse spermatocyte lampbrush chromosomes are best displayed in preparations of pachytene spermatocytes whereas lampbrush chromosomes in amphibian oocytes are observed at diplotene (cf. Davidson, 6).

Figure 14 illustrates two autosomal bivalents of a pachytene spermatocyte displaying a lampbrush organization. The lateral chromatin loops projecting from synaptonemal complex regions display multiple and randomly distributed fibrilar aggregates which correspond to HnRNA complexed with proteins. At high magnification, the chromatin loops possess the basic structural features of eukaryotic chromatin (Fig. 15). Single chromatin loops of transcriptionally inactive chromatin appear as a periodic array of spherical units, the nucleosomes,

---

displayed in (A) and (B). Autosomal bivalents exhibit end to end (ete) or side by side (sbs) associations. End-to-end associations are generally observed at the basal knob region (paracentromeric heterochromatin). The axial core of autosomes and sex chromosomes show deltoid expansions at their free endings. Arrows indicate the basal knob region of autosomes and sex chromosomes (Fig. 12B from Tres, 45).

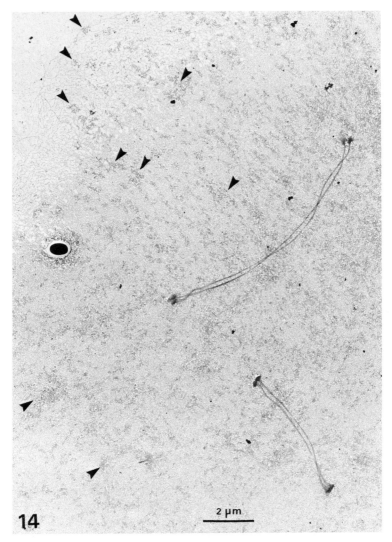

Fig. 14. Autosomal bivalents of a mouse spermatocyte at pachytene. Arrowheads indicate ribonucleoprotein aggregates representing HnRNA–protein complexes associated with chromatin fibers looping out from the synaptonemal complex region.

measuring 8–10 nm in diameter and linked by internucleosomal DNA, 10–70 base pairs in length. Each nucleosome consists of about 140 base pairs of DNA wrapped around a protein core of eight histones, one pair of each H2A, H2B, H3, and H4 (for reviews on chromatin structure, see Kornberg, 25; Lilley and Pardon, 27). The chromatin loops measure about 6–12 μm in length. These length values are smaller than those observed in *Triturus* oocytes (50–200 μm in length) (3). Transcriptionally active chromatin loops displaying nascent transcripts coexist with nontranscribing loops in the same bivalent (Fig. 16). Transcripts consist of both RNA polymerase particles (30 nm in diameter) attached to chromatin and nascent RNP fibrils of variable length distributed at random points along the chromatin axis forming altogether a *transcription complex*. RNP representing HnRNA transcripts have a chain-like organization since they are composed of particles of 13–20 nm in diameter linked by thiner segments of variable length (15–25 nm) (18,46). Evidence supporting the assumption that these RNP chains attached to the loops of autosomal bivalents of mouse spermatocytes correspond to newly transcribed HnRNA molecules was presented elsewhere (18).

Although less frequent and generally spaced along spermatocyte genome segments, it is possible to find nascent HnRNA molecules organized as *transcription units* (Fig. 17) with a RNA polymerase packaging ratio of about 12 polymerases/μm. A transcriptional unit defines a segment of chromatin limited by initiation and termination sites identified in the preparations by a short (initiation)-to-long (termination) gradient of nascent transcripts. Most likely, a transcription unit reflects the activity of a single gene. The RNP fibrils or chains displayed in Fig. 17 are highly coiled and show at random points the characteristic particles 13–20 nm in diameter. Because of the coiled nature of the HnRNA transcripts which persists throughout the transcription unit and in single transcription complexes (Fig. 16), it is difficult to determine the frequency of particles per unit length. A repeat of particles along nascent HnRNA transcripts as described in mouse spermatocytes (18) has also been reported in lampbrush chromosomes of amphibian oocytes (31) and *Drosophila* spermatocytes (37), rat hepatocytes (10) and *Drosophila* embryos (2). Supporting the particular nature of HnRNA transcripts, biochemical studies have shown particles consisting of HnRNA sequences complexed with basic proteins of 30,000–45,000 molecular weight (22).

When one compares the transcriptional activities of amphibian and mouse lampbrush chromosomes, several features become relevant. In amphibian oocytes, the chromosomal loops are densely covered by numerous lateral RNP fibrils in a gradient length array (transcription unit). The length of a single transcription unit may be equivalent to the total length of the chromosomal loop (cf. in Davidson, 6) or several transcription units are arranged in a serial array on one loop (38).

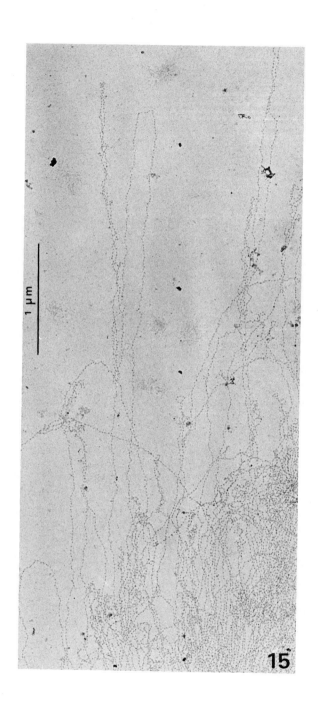

Most transcription units in *Xenopus laevis* measure about 2–10 μm in length (38). In mouse spermatocytes, transcription units are remarkably smaller [about 1.12 μm (Fig. 5 in Kierszenbaum and Tres, 19) and 1.35 μm (Fig. 17)]. Transcription units occur singly rather than in tandem arrays, and the distance between adjacent transcription complexes is highly variable (Fig. 16).

We have reported that, in mouse spermatocytes, both transcriptionally active and inactive chromatin fibers exhibit a nucleosomal configuration (19) consistent with the first level of coiling of chromatin into a jointed flexible chain. We also demonstrated that nucleosomes gradually disappear during late spermiogenesis as arginine-rich protamine replaces somatic histones. The absence of repeating nucleosomes in chromatin of spermatids and spermatozoa has been reported in the trout (15), house-cricket (30), and mouse (4). The presence of dense protein aggregates among smooth chromatin fibers (mouse, cricket; Kierszenbaum and Tres, 19,20) and the existence of irregularly spaced nucleosomal-like globular structures (about 13 nm in diameter) in bull, man, and trout spermatozoa (9) have been also described. The nature of these protein arrangements and their functional implications is presently unknown.

Nucleosomes have been described to be absent in transcriptionally active chromatin of amphibian oocyte lampbrush chromosomes (*Xenopus laevis, Triturus alpestris, Triturus cristatus* (38). It has been reported that, in maturing oocytes undergoing regression of the lampbrush loops and decrease of transcriptive activity, smooth chromatin fibers return to a beaded appearance (38). These findings do not coincide with our observations in mouse spermatocytes and spermatids showing that the nucleosomal configuration is associated with transcriptive activity (19). In fact, a recent study has shown that lampbrush chromosomes of *Xenopus laevis* oocytes display a beaded, nucleosomal structure wherever the transcriptive loop can be visualized (14). Several experimental results lend support to the possibility that the nucleosomal configuration of chromatin is not lost during transcription. For instance, it has been shown the recovery of DNA fragments of identical size (200 base pairs) to DNA fragments derived from transcriptionally active chromatin after micrococcal nuclease treatment (26). In addition, somatic histones have been localized along transcribing chromatin axes using electron microscope immunocytochem-

Fig. 15.   Chromatin loops of an autosomal bivalent (pachytene spermatocyte) displaying a periodic linear array of beads or nucleosomes.

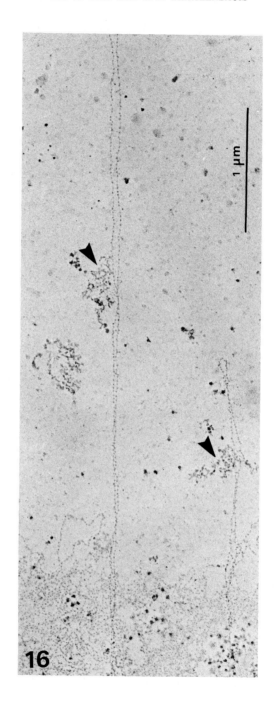

istry (28). Therefore, it is not clear whether the reported absence of nucleosomes in transcriptionally active chromatin loops of amphibian lampbrush chromosomes is related to (i) the considerable length of the transcription units with a high density of RNA polymerase molecules attached to the template, (ii) the transient dissociation of the heterotypic octamer by RNA polymerase which obscures the nucleosomal repeat, or (iii) an artifact of the procedure used to spread cell genomes.

As mouse pachytene spermatocytes differentiate into diplotene, the incorporation of [³H]uridine is reduced in diplotene spermatocytes (17), thus suggesting that the transcription activity is decreasing as meiotic bivalents disjoin. However, when diplotene spermatocytes are displayed in whole-mount electron microscope preparations, it is possible to visualize dense and widely dispersed aggregates of RNP fibrils associated with the chromatin fibers of the autosomal bivalents (Fig. 18). These dense aggregates are not seen in the chromatin mass of the sexual bivalent known to remain transcriptionally inactive (Fig. 12). Chromatin fibers of the XY pair are beaded but organized in a high level of folding (47). Although a satisfactory explanation for the presence of RNP aggregates in diplotene spermatocytes showing a decline in [³H]uridine labeling is lacking, it is possible to suggest that the RNP aggregates corresponding to HnRNA molecules remaining either free in the nucleoplasm or attached to chromatin fibers, reflect a restriction in the processing of mRNA. This conclusion is based on the observation that [³H]uridine cytoplasmic labeling of diplotene spermatocytes is very low (17) thus reflecting a reduced cytoplasmic transfer of newly synthesized RNA molecules. In addition, autoradiographic experiments have shown the presence of persistent, long-lived [³H]uridine-labeled RNA species in pachytene spermatocyte nuclei, which contrast with the rapid turnover of RNA species in Sertoli cells after a pulse labeling for 8–12 days (16,46, and Fig. 19). We interpreted this finding to indicate that Sertoli cells and spermatocytes, including pachytene and diplotene spermatocytes, differ from each other in the post-transcriptional processing. Whether the persistence of RNA molecules in pachytene and diplotene spermatocytes represents selective gene expression or selective restriction in the transport of transcripts to fulfill a specific nuclear function are aspects which require further study.

Fig. 16. Chromatin loops of an autosomal bivalent (pachytene spermatocyte) showing HnRNA–protein fibrilar complexes associated with a nucleosomal chromatin type. Free ribonucleoprotein fibrils are also observed.

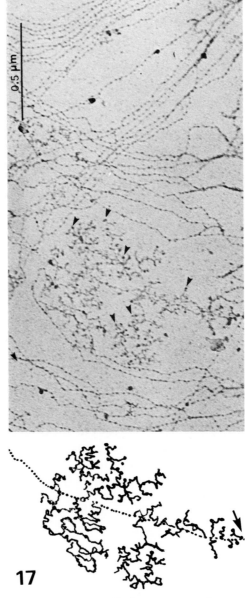

Fig. 17. Nascent HnRNA–protein fibrils are organized into a transcription unit. The arrowheads indicate discrete particles along the highly tangled fibrils. The arrow in the tracing of the transcription unit indicates the initiation site of the unit. Pachytene spermatocyte.

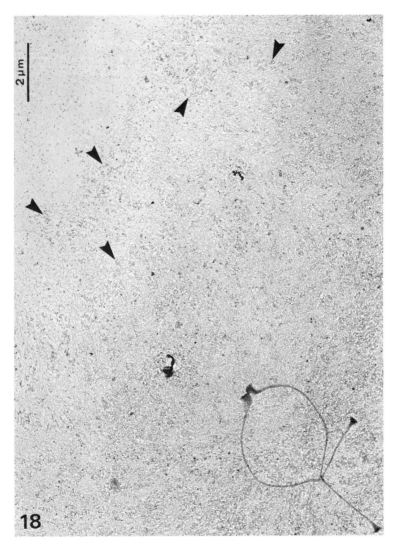

Fig. 18. A disjoining autosomal bivalent of a diplotene spermatocyte shows chromatin loops associated with HnRNA–protein complexes (arrowheads).

CONCLUDING REMARKS

In this chapter we review work of our laboratory showing (i) that specific meiotic prophase stages can be identified in whole-mount light and electron microscopic preparations, (ii) the visualization of

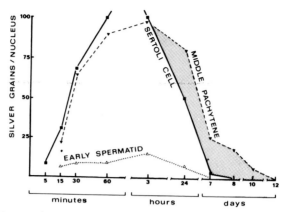

Fig. 19. RNA synthetic activities studies in autoradiograms of Sertoli cells, middle pachytene spermatocytes, and early spermatids (mouse testis). A single dose of [^{3}H]uridine was injected under the testicular albuginea of several mice which were sacrificed at the indicated time intervals. The gray area shows that there is a difference in the turnover of [^{3}H]uridine-labeled species between Sertoli cells and germinal cells (from Tres and Kierszenbaum, 46).

lampbrush chromosomes in pachytene spermatocytes, (iii) the persistence of nucleosomes in transcriptionally active chromatin, and (iv) the organization of nascent HnRNA transcripts into RNP fibrils consisting of 20-nm particles linked by thin fibrils of variable length.

One aspect of considerable interest is the transcriptional activity of autosomal bivalents contrasting with the persistent gene inactivation of the XY bivalent. Whereas autosomal bivalents are engaged in rRNA synthetic activities during early meiotic prophase stages (late leptotene–zygotene), HnRNA synthesis occurs in later stages (pachytene). While rRNA transcription involves the activation of ribosomal DNA cistrons clustered in the paracentromeric region of at least four autosomal bivalents, HnRNA is produced in the lampbrush segment of all autosomal bivalents. The temporal and spatial activation of rRNA and HnRNA genes throughout meiotic prophase, the distinct inactivity of the sexual bivalent, and the slow turnover of meiotic prophase transcripts suggest that a mechanism operates for programming the stage dependency of gene expression during male meiosis. We have suggested that the Sertoli cell may play a significant role in the coordination of spermatogenic events (46). The advent of tissue culture techniques for the study of Sertoli cell function (Kierszenbaum and Tres, this volume) may shed light on the bioregulation of spermatogenesis.

ACKNOWLEDGMENTS

We acknowledge the support of a grant from the Rockefeller Foundation given to the Laboratories for Reproductive Biology, the University of North Carolina at Chapel Hill. This work was supported in part by grants from the Population Council, World Health Organization, and Public Health Service Research Grant HD11884.

REFERENCES

1. Bennett, D., Mathieson, B. J., Scheid, M., Yanagisawa, K., Boyse, E. A., Wachtel, S., and Cattanach, B. M. (1975) *Nature (London)* **265**, 255–257.
2. Beyer, A. L., Miller, O. A., Jr., and McKnight, S. L. (1980) *Cell* **20**, 75–84.
3. Callan, H. G. (1963) *Int. Rev. Cytol.* **15**, 1–34.
4. Cech, T., Potter, D., and Pardue, M. L. (1977) *Biochemistry* **16**, 5313–5321.
5. Darlington, C. D. (1931) *Biol. Rev. Cambridge Philos. Soc.* **6**, 221–264.
6. Davidson, E. H. (1976) "Gene Activity in Early Development." Academic Press, New York.
7. Dresser, M. E., and Moses, M. J. (1979) *Exp. Cell Res.* **21**, 416–419.
8. Fletcher, J. M. (1979) *Chromosoma* **72**, 241–248.
9. Gusse, M., and Chevaillier, P. (1980) *J. Cell Biol.* **87**, 280–284.
10. Harper, F., and Puvion-Dutilleul, F. (1979) *J. Cell Sci.* **40**, 181–192.
11. Henderson, A. S., (1971) *Chromosoma* **35**, 28–40.
12. Henderson, A. S., Eicher, E. M., Yu, M. T., and Atwood, K. C. (1976) *Cytogenet. Cell Genet.* **17**, 307–316.
13. Hennig, W., Meyer, G. F., Hennig, I., and Leoncini, O. (1974) *Cold Spring Harbor Symp. Quant. Biol.* **38**, 673–683.
14. Hill, R. S. (1979) *J. Cell Sci.* **40**, 145–169.
15. Honda, B. M., Baillie, D. L., and Candido, E. P. M. (1975) *J. Biol. Chem.* **250**, 4643–4647.
16. Kierszenbaum, A. L. (1974) *Biol. Reprod.* **11**, 365–376.
17. Kierszenbaum, A. L., and Tres, L. L. (1974) *J. Cell Biol.* **60**, 39–53.
18. Kierszenbaum, A. L., and Tres, L. L. (1974) *J. Cell Biol.* **63**, 923–935.
19. Kierszenbaum, A. L., and Tres, L. L. (1975) *J. Cell Biol.* **65**, 258–270.
20. Kierszenbaum, A. L., and Tres, L. L. (1978) *J. Cell Sci.* **33**, 265–283.
21. Kierszenbaum, A. L., and Tres, L. L. (1978) *Fed. Proc., Fed. Am. Soc. Exp. Biol.* **37**, 2512–2516.
22. Kinninburgh, A., and Martin, T. E. (1976) *Proc.Natl.Acad.Sci. U.S.A.* **73**, 2725–2729.
23. Koller, P. C., and Darlington, C. D. (1934) *J. Genet.* **24**, 159–173.
24. Koo, G. C., Wachtel, S. S., Krupen-Brown, K., Mittl, L. R., Breg, W. R., Genel, M., Rosenthal, I. M., Borgaonkar, D. S., Miller, D. A., Tantravahi, R., Schreck, R. R., Erlanger, B. F., and Miller, O. J. (1977) *Science* **198**, 940–942.
25. Kornberg, R. D. (1977) *Annu. Rev. Biochem.* **46**, 931–954.
26. Lacy, E., and Axel, R. (1975) *Proc.Natl.Acad.Sci. U.S.A.* **72**, 3978–3982.
27. Lilley, D. M. J., and Pardon, J. F. (1979) *Annu.Rev.Genet.* **13**, 197–233.
28. McKnight, S. L., Bustin, M., and Miller, O. L., Jr. (1978) *Cold Spring Harbor Symp. Quant. Biol.* **42**, 741–754.

29. McKnight, S. L., and Miller, O. L., Jr. (1976) *Cell* **8**, 305–319.
30. McMaster-Kaye, R., and Kaye, J. S. (1980) *Chromosoma* **77**, 41–56.
31. Malcolm, D. M., and Sommerville, J. (1974) *Chromosoma* **48**, 137–158.
32. Miller, O. L., Jr., and Bakken, A. H. (1972) *Acta Endocrinol. (Copenhagen)*, Suppl. **168**, 155–177.
33. Miller, O. L., Jr., and Beatty, B. R. (1969) *Science* **164**, 955–957.
34. Monesi, V. (1964) *Exp. Cell Res.* **36**, 683–688.
35. Monesi, V. (1965) *Chromosoma* **17**, 11–21.
36. Nebel, B. R., and Coulon, E. M. (1962) *Chromosoma* **13**, 358–364.
37. Oda, T., Nakamura, T., and Watanabe, S. (1977) *J. Electron Microsc.* **26**, 203–207.
38. Scheer, U., Spring, H., and Trendelenburg, M. F. (1979) *In* "The Cell Nucleus" (H. Busch, ed.), Vol. 3, pp. 3–47. Academic Press, New York.
39. Shapiro, M., and Erickson, R. P. (1981) Submitted for publication.
40. Solari, A. J., and Tres, L. L. (1970) *J. Cell Biol.* **45**, 43–53.
41. Stern, H., and Hotta, Y. (1980) *Mol. Cell Biochem.* **29**, 145–158.
42. Tres, L. L. (1975) *Chromosoma* **53**, 141–151.
43. Tres, L. L. (1977) *J. Cell Sci.* **25**, 1–15.
44. Tres, L. L. (1978) *J. Cell Biol.* **79** (Pt.2), 125a.
45. Tres, L. L. (1979) *Arch. Androl.* **2**, 101–108.
46. Tres, L. L., and Kierszenbaum, A. L. (1975) *In* "Hormonal Regulation of Spermatogenesis" (F. S. French, V. Hansson, E. M. Ritzén, and S. N. Nayfeh, eds.), pp.455–478. Plenum, New York.
47. Tres, L. L., and Kierszenbaum, A. L. (1976) *J. Cell Biol.* **70** (Pt.2), 228a.
48. Tres, L. L., and Kierszenbaum, A. L. (1977) *In* "The Testis in Normal and Infertile Men" (P. Troen and H. R. Nakin, eds.), pp. 9–23. Raven, New York.
49. Tres, L. L., and Lewis, S. E. (1981) Submitted for publication.
50. Wachtel, S. S. (1977) *Science* **198**, 797–799.
51. Westergaard, M., and von Wettstein, D. (1970) *C.R.Trav.Lab.Carlsberg* **37**, 239–268.

PART III

GONADOTROPINS

The Brain and Gonadotropin Secretion in the Primate

MICHEL FERIN

Institute for Reproductive Sciences
and
Departments of Physiology and Obstetrics and Gynecology
College of Physicians and Surgeons
Columbia University, New York, New York

INTRODUCTION

This chapter will review recent experimental evidence obtained in this laboratory as well as in other primate centers on the neuroendocrine control of gonadotropin secretion in the female rhesus monkey. This species was chosen as animal model for the pattern and time course of circulating gonadotropins and ovarian steroid hormones during its menstrual cycle (Fig. 1) are quite similar to those observed in the human (1).

ESTRADIOL, THE MAIN OVARIAN HORMONE FEEDBACK AND ITS SITE OF ACTION

17β-estradiol levels (the principal secretory product of the maturing follicle) increase slowly during the early and midfollicular phases of the menstrual cycle, then rise exponentially at the end of the follicular phase. This latter increase in the secretion of estradiol always preceeds the midcycle ovulatory gonadotropin surge (Fig. 1). There is considerable experimental evidence linking this estradiol rise to the midcycle gonadotropin surge. For instance, inactivation of circulating estradiol by antiestrogen antiserum blocks the midcycle rise in LH and FSH and renders the immunized monkey anovulatory (2); the stimulatory feedback effect of estradiol on gonadotropins (positive estrogen feedback loop) can be reinstituted in estrogen-immunized ani-

259

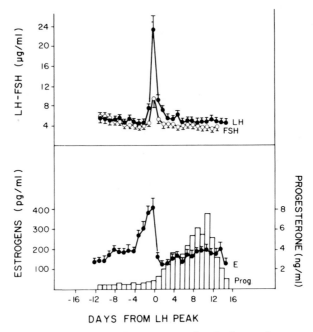

Fig. 1. LH, FSH, estrogens, and progesterone levels during the menstrual cycle of the rhesus monkey.

mals by the administration of a synthetic estrogen not recognized by antiestrogen antibodies; in normal monkeys as well, a surge in gonadotropins can be induced following an estradiol challenge during the early follicular phase, at a time of the cycle when spontaneous LH surges are not seen. In this particular experimental situation, the induced LH surge is not followed by ovulation, as follicular development has not yet reached a sufficient state of maturity; in the normal cycle, however, the linkage of the midcycle estradiol and gonadotropin surges insures that of follicular maturity and the hypophyseal signal for ovulation.

While estradiol can, under specific conditions exert a clear-cut stimulatory effect on LH and FSH release, at most times this hormone has an inhibitory action on gonadotropin secretion (negative estrogen feedback loop). In the absence of this hormone, such as after ovariectomy, there is a large persistent increase in gonadotropin levels. These are easily suppressed following the administration of estradiol (3). During most of the menstrual cycle, therefore, the main role of estradiol is to keep gonadotropin secretion in check and at a low level.

Progesterone, another ovarian product, is secreted in significant amounts only after the LH surge. Maximal levels are seen midway through the luteal phase (Fig. 1). Under certain circumstances, progesterone may synergize with estradiol to suppress gonadotropin secretion (4). Progesterone has also been shown to inhibit the estradiol-induced gonadotropin surge, when administered at an appropriate time before the estrogen challenge (4); it may thereby prevent the occurence of spontaneous gonadotropin surges during the luteal phase. Under other specific conditions, progesterone has been speculated to modulate the absolute amounts of gonadotropins released during the midcycle surge (5). Estradiol, however, remains the principal ovarian feedback hormone affecting gonadotropin secretion.

The site at which estradiol exerts its feedback action on gonadotropin secretion has been controversial for a number of years. It has been

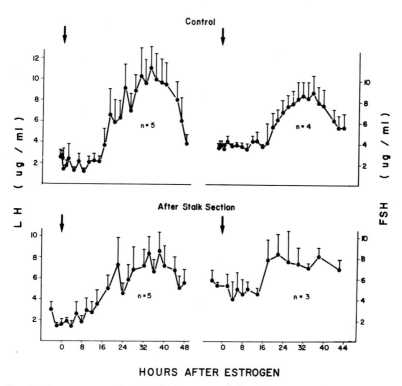

Fig. 2. A comparison of LH and FSH surges following an estradiol challenge in female rhesus monkeys before and 1 day after pituitary stalk section indicates that estradiol can exert its positive feedback effect directly at the pituitary level. [Reproduced with permission from *Endocrinology* (7).]

known that not only the hypothalamus but also the anterior pituitary possess specific receptors binding estradiol (6); however because of the close anatomical relationship between the hypothalamus and the pituitary, *in vivo* experiments to differentiate direct pituitary effects from those relayed through the hypothalamus were difficult to design. In the rhesus monkey, experimental evidence now indicates that the principal positive feedback site for estradiol does reside within the anterior pituitary gland. We have studied this aspect in monkeys in which the pituitary gland has been acutely isolated from direct hypothalamic influences by pituitary stalk section. A comparison of the effects of an estradiol challenge test performed prior to the surgery and within the first day following pituitary stalk section reveals similar LH and FSH responses (Fig. 2) and clearly indicates that estradiol can exert its positive feedback effect directly on the gonadotrope (7).

GONADOTROPIN-RELEASING HORMONE (GnRH): ITS ROLE IN GONADOTROPIN SECRETION

The fact that identical gonadotropin surges can be observed following an estrogen challenge in intact and acutely pituitary stalk sectioned monkeys indicates that a surge of GnRH is not prerequisite to the occurrence of a normal gonadotropin surge in the monkey. Indeed, in the operated animals, the estrogen challenge had been given after stalk section and after a barrier had been installed to isolate the pituitary gland. In the rat, a GnRH surge clearly preceeds the proestrus LH surge (8), but its existence in the monkey remains to be fully characterized.

Does GnRH then not play a role in the control of gonadotropin secretion in the monkey? On the contrary, recent experiments clearly indicate that this decapeptide is essential to maintain adequate tonic gonadotropin synthesis and release. By immunocytochemistry, GnRH has been localized to various areas of the brain and the pituitary gland of the rhesus monkey (9). The two main sites at which it is concentrated include the anterior hypothalamic preoptic area, with fibers extending to the organum vasculosum laminae terminalis, and the arcuate nucleus within the medial basal hypothalamus, with axons directed toward the median eminence and the site of origin of the long portal vessels which irrigate the anterior pituitary gland. As far as gonadotropin secretion is concerned, the main GnRH site appears to be the arcuate nucleus, as lesions of this area in the monkey (10) result in a rapid decrease in the circulating levels of both gonadotropins. Similar gonadotropin decreases are observed after immunization with anti-GnRH antibodies (11). Stalk sectioned monkeys cease rapidly to secrete gonadotropins, lack specific pituitary staining for LH or FSH within 2–3 weeks after surgery (12) and become anestrogenic and amenorrheic (13).

Since GnRH appears to play a crucial role in gonadotropin synthesis and release, one should be able to restore LH and FSH secretion in stalk sectioned monkeys following GnRH therapy. Our first attempts

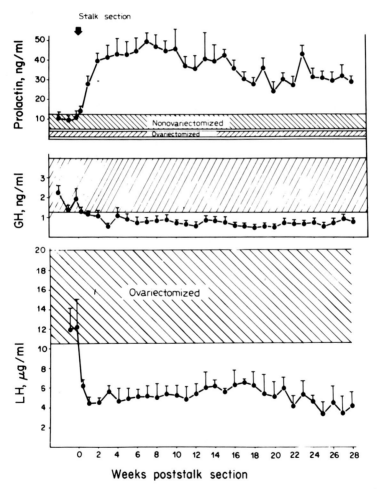

Fig. 3. Prolactin, GH, and LH levels following pituitary stalk section in rhesus monkeys.

using continuous infusions of the decapeptide for periods of 8 days
were unsuccessful; after an initial short-lived increase, gonadotropins
quickly returned to their postsurgical undetectable levels. The possibility that this absence of response was related to necrosis of the isolated pituitary was investigated. However, this appears unlikely since
necrotic areas did not exceed 20% of the pituitary gland (13) (the small
degree of necrosis following stalk section in our animals, in comparison to other studies, may be related to the different surgical approach),
and since the isolated glands were perfectly capable of secreting increasing amounts of prolactin (12) (a result of the reversal of the central inhibitory influences on the lactotrope) (Fig. 3.). Rather, this may

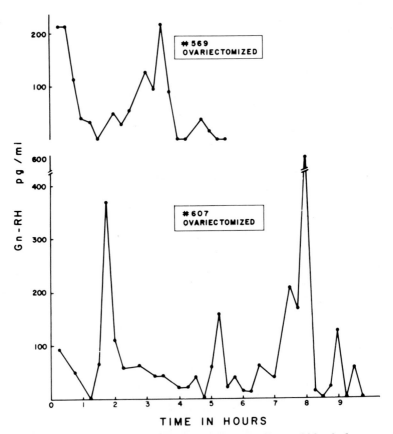

Fig. 4.   GnRH levels in hypothalamo-hypophyseal stalk portal blood of two ovariectomized rhesus monkeys. Each point represent a 15-minute collection period. [Repro-
duced with permission from *Endocrinology* (16).]

have been related to changes induced at the pituitary level (possibly on the GnRH receptor) by the chosen mode of administration of the peptide. And indeed, similar response patterns (significant but short-lived increases, and in some instances even suppression of LH and FSH) were observed following continuous GnRH infusions in intact monkeys (14).

In view of these unsuccessful attempts, a study was then undertaken in monkeys to evaluate the physiological pattern of GnRH secretion from the median eminence into the long portal vessels of the pituitary stalk and to the anterior pituitary. The first experiments were performed in ovariectomized monkeys, for it had been hypothesized that the intermittent release of LH observed in these animals was the result of pulsatile hypothalamic secretory activity (4). Our experiments confirmed this hypothesis, as determinations by radioimmunoassay of GnRH levels in hypothalamo-hypophyseal portal blood collected over periods of 6–12 hours indicated that the decapeptide is indeed not released in a continuous fashion but rather is secreted intermittently (Fig. 4) (15). When GnRH infusions, mimicking the physiological pulsatile mode of GnRH release, were instituted in stalk sectioned monkeys or in animals bearing arcuate lesions, gonadotropin secretion not only increased to reach presurgical levels but was maintained over long periods. A recent paper by Belchetz *et al.* (16) comparing the effects of continuous and pulsatile GnRH infusions vividly illustrates the primordial importance of pulsatile hypothalamic activity patterns. The neural factors which control these remain to be investigated. In this respect, it is worthwhile to note that most anterior pituitary hormones are released in a pulsatile mode.

GnRH–ESTRADIOL INTERRELATIONSHIPS AND THE MENSTRUAL CYCLE

Evidence presented above leads to the hypothesis that, in the female rhesus monkey, the positive feedback action of estradiol is exerted at the level of the anterior pituitary gland and that GnRH does not play a role in this regard, although this hypothalamic hormone is essential in maintaining the viability of the gonadotrope and, therefore, proper synthesis of gonadotropins. This hypothesis has been tested and confirmed in rhesus monkeys bearing arcuate lesions (17). Long-term unchanging but pulsatile GnRH infusions not only increased LH and FSH but were also followed by increasing estradiol secretion (indicating follicular maturation), LH and FSH surges (indi-

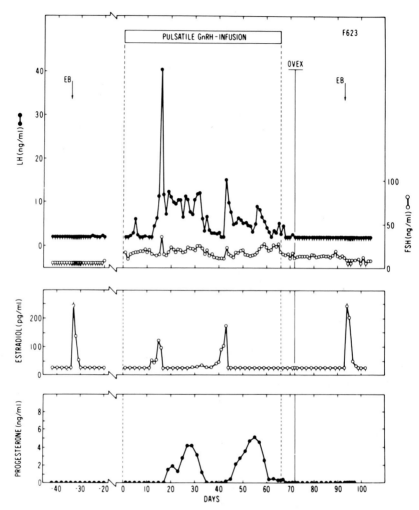

Fig. 5. Induction of menstrual cyclicity in a stalk sectioned monkey following the long-term pulsatile administration of GnRH.

cating a direct pituitary estradiol feedback in the absence of a GnRH surge), ovulation, a normal luteal phase, and menstruation. Several menstrual cycles, identical to normal ones, were induced. Similar results were obtained in GnRH-replaced stalk sectioned animals (see Fig. 5 for an illustrative example) in experiments in progress performed in collaboration with Dr. K. Knobil's laboratory in Pittsburgh.

HYPOTHALAMIC SITES AND GONADOTROPIN SECRETION

The recent observations that estradiol exerts a direct pituitary feedback action can now explain previous results obtained in the rhesus monkey following surgical isolation of the medial basal hypothalamus from the remainder of the brain. Indeed, complete medial basal hypothalamic disconnection (leaving the arcuate nucleus and its connections to the anterior pituitary intact) did not interfere with gonadotropin secretion and allowed continued uninterrupted menstrual cycles (18,19). At the time of the experimentation, the results were surprising since they contradicted those obtained in the rodent in which similar hypothalamic islands induced anovulation (20). They also refuted the classical theory of two hypothalamic centers controlling gonadotropin secretion: the first in the rostral hypothalamus involved with "cyclic" release of gonadotropin, and the second within the medial basal hypothalamus concerned with "tonic" gonadotropin secretion. That this concept would not hold in the primate had been suspected for we found it impossible to induce a gonadotropin surge by implanting or infusing estradiol into the rostral hypothalamus (W. P. Diefenback and M. Ferin, unpublished observations), a procedure which readily induces a LH surge in the rat (21).

Areas other than the medial basal hypothalamus may however still exert some modulatory influences on gonadotropin secretion in the monkey. This is indicated by results from experiments involving lesions in the anterior hypothalamus (22) or anterior hypothalamic disconnection (23). In these deafferentation experiments, in which fibers entering the medial basal hypothalamus were interrupted using a transorbital approach, we observed a disruption of gonadotropin release during the first few months after surgery. Such results, contrasting with those following complete hypothalamic disconnection, suggest that anterior hypothalamic afferents, originating either from the nuclei in this region, or "en passage" from other neural structures may act to modify the release of gonadotropins by the pituitary gland. However, long-term observation of these animals shows a resumption of normal gonadotropin secretion and of menstrual cyclicity and indicates that these modulatory influences are not essential for normal gonadotropin secretion. (Resumption of cyclicity could not be attributed to regeneration of fibers across the cut, for a barrier had been introduced within the cut.) Gonadotropin responses to estradiol challenges in these animals are illustrated in Fig. 6. The reasons for the discrepancies between the results of complete and anterior hypothalamic disconnection remain unknown. One hypothesis currently

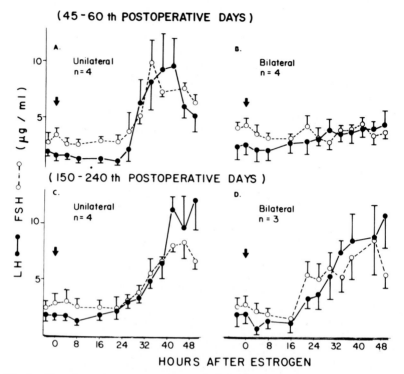

Fig. 6. Gonadotropin responses to estradiol challenge test given early and late following anterior hypothalamic disconnection. [Reproduced with permission of *Endocrinology* (23).]

being tested in our laboratories involves recently documented GnRH fiber pathways which appear to link the median eminence to the rostral region and which are situated in close juxtaposition to the optic chiasm. In view of the different surgical approach used in the anterior and complete hypothalamic disconnection experiments, it is indeed possible that such fibers may have remained intact in the latter animals.

ACKNOWLEDGMENTS

Support for these experiments was provided by the National Institutes of Health grants # HD0577 and HD 10873. The excellent secretarial assistance of Mrs. Kate Hildreth is also acknowledged.

REFERENCES

1. Vande Wiele, R. L., Bogumil, R. J., Dyrenfurth, I., Ferin, M., Jewelewicz, R., Warren, M., Mikhail, G., and Rizkallah, T. (1970) *Recent Prog. Horm Res.* **26**, 63–103.
2. Ferin, M., Dyrenfurth, I., Cowchock, S., Warren, M., and Vande Wiele, R. L. (1974) *Endocrinology* **94**, 765–776.
3. Karsch, F. J., Weick, R. J., Butler, W. R., Dierschke, D. J., Krey, L. C., Hotchkiss, J., Yamaji, T., and Knobil, E. (1973) *Endocrinology* **92**, 1740–1747.
4. Knobil, E. (1974) *Recent Prog. Horm. Res.* **30**, 1–46.
5. Chang, R. J., and Jaffe, R. B. (1978) *J. Clin. Endocrinol. Metab.* **47**, 119–125.
6. Pfaff, D. W., Gerlach, J. L., McEwen, B. S., Ferin, M., Carmel, P. W., and Zimmerman, E. A. (1976) *J. Comp. Neurol.* **170**, 279–293.
7. Ferin, M., Rosenblatt, H., Carmel, P. W., Antunes, J. L., and Vande Wiele, R. L. (1979) *Endocrinology* **104**, 50–52.
8. Sarkar, D. K., Chiappa, S. A., Fink, G., and Sherwood, N. M. (1976) *Nature (London)* **264**, 461–463.
9. Silverman, A. J., Antunes, J. L., Ferin, M., and Zimmerman, E. A. (1977) *Endocrinology* **101**, 134–142.
10. Nakai, Y., Plant, T. M., Hess, D. L., Keogh, E. J., and Knobil, E. (1978) *Endocrinology* **102**, 1008–1014.
11. McCormack, J. T., Plant, T. M., Hess, D. L., and Knobil, E. (1977) *Endocrinology* **100**, 663–667.
12. Antunes, J. L., Louis, K., Cogen, P., Zimmerman, E. A., and Ferin, M. (1980) *Neuroendocrinology* **30**, 76–82.
13. Vaughan, L., Carmel, P. W., Dyrenfurth, I., Frantz, A. G., Antunes, J. L., and Ferin, M. (1980) *Neuroendocrinology* **30**, 70–75.
14. Ferin, M., Bogumil, J., Drewes, J., Dyrenfurth, I., Jewelewicz, R., and Vande Wiele, R. L. (1978) *Acta Endocrinol. (Copenhagen)* **89**, 48–59.
15. Carmel, P. W., Araki, S., and Ferin, M. (1976) *Endocrinology* **99**, 243–248.
16. Belchetz, P. E., Plant, T. M., Nakai, Y., Keogh, E. G., and Knobil, E. (1978) *Science* **202**, 631–633.
17. Knobil, E., Plant, T. M., Wildt, L., Belchetz, P. E., and Marshall, G. (1980) *Science* **207**, 1371–1373.
18. Krey, L. C., Butler, W. R., and Knobil, E. (1975) *Endocrinology* **96**, 1073–1087.
19. Ferin, M., Antunes, J. L., Zimmerman, E. A., Dyrenfurth, I., Frantz, A. G., Robinson, A., and Carmel, P. W. (1977) *Endocrinology* **101**, 1611–1620.
20. Halasz, B., and Pupp, L. (1969) *In* "Frontiers in Neuroendocrinology" (W. F. Ganong and L. Martini, eds.), pp. 307–342. Oxford Univ. Press, London and New York.
21. Goodman, R. L. (1978) *Endocrinology* **102**, 151–159.
22. Norman, R. L., Resko, J. A., and Spies, A. G. (1976) *Endocrinology* **99**, 59–71.
23. Cogen, P. H., Antunes, J. L., Louis, K. M., Dyrenfurth, I., and Ferin, M. (1980) *Endocrinology* **107**, 677–683.

The Biosynthesis of Gonadotropin-Releasing Hormone

JAMES L. ROBERTS, BETH SCHACHTER, AND
MARIAN EVINGER

Center for Reproductive Sciences
and
Department of Biochemistry
Columbia University Health Sciences
New York, New York

INTRODUCTION

Gonadotropin-releasing hormone(GnRH) stimulates the release of the two anterior pituitary peptides, luteinizing hormone (LH) and follicle-stimulating hormone (FSH). GnRH, a peptide hormone, was originally isolated, sequenced, and synthesized by the groups of Schally and Guilleman (1–3). The primary sequence, established as pyro-Glu-His-Trp-Ser-Tyr-Gly-Leu-Arg-Pro-Gly-NH for porcine (4,5) and ovine (6,7) GnRH, appears to be biochemically and immunologically identical for numerous mammalian GnRHs, including rat, human, and bovine GnRH (1,8). The primary site of GnRH synthesis in the brain is the hypothalamus; subsequently, direct transport to the anterior pituitary occurs via the hypophysial portal vein (9,10).

Current concepts in the biosynthesis of peptide hormones suggest that although some small biologically active peptides, e.g., gramicydin, are synthesized enzymatically by nonribosomal machinery, GnRH is probably synthesized from a mRNA template as a precursor protein. Indeed, large molecular weight proteins have been identified which exhibit GnRH immunoactivity (11). Attempts to purify and characterize these "precursor" GnRH proteins have been severely hampered by the low concentration (~300 ng/g wet tissue) and the la-

BIOREGULATORS OF REPRODUCTION

bile nature of the protein. An alternative approach for identification of the precursor protein from which GnRH is derived is to isolate and sequence the mRNA that codes for it using recombinant DNA technology. Thus, by identifying the start and stop codons in the mRNA sequence, the complete primary amino acid sequence for the GnRH precursor can be determined. A similar strategy has already proven successful in determining the complete primary amino acid sequence of the corticotropin (ACTH)/endorphin precursor (12).

PRECURSOR HYPOTHESIS FOR SYNTHESIS OF SMALL PEPTIDE HORMONES

Many small peptide hormones have now been shown to be initially synthesized as larger precursor proteins. A partial list of these is given in Table I. Recent developments in the area of secretory protein biosynthesis have lead to the formulation of a hypothesis to explain why these small peptides are necessarily synthesized initially as larger proteins. This hypothesis states that a precursor hormone is necessary for the proper recognition of the peptide as a secretory protein and for the efficient sequestering of the peptide hormone in secretory granules.

As expected from their endocrine function, the peptide hormones can also be described as secretory proteins. These proteins are packaged into secretory granules to await the proper environmental stimuli necessary for their release into the bloodstream. The intracellular pathway of secreted proteins has been described in detail by Palade and colleagues using the pancreatic zymogen producing cell as a

TABLE I
Peptide Hormone Precursors
(No. of Amino Acids)

Name of hormone	Hormone	Precursor[a]	References
Insulin	51	81	(20)
Gastrin	12	~80	(20)
Glucagon	29	~100	(20)
ACTH/β-LPH	39/91	239	(12)
Parathyroid hormone	84	90	(21)
Leu- and Met-enkephlin	5/5	~400	(22)
Vasopressin	9	~180	(23)
Calcitonin	32	~160	(24)

[a] Does not include the 20–30 amino acids of the signal sequence.

model(13): the secretory proteins are synthesized on membrane-bound polyribosomes located on the rough endoplasmic reticulum (RER). The newly synthesized proteins are vectorially discharged into the cisternae of the RER and subsequently transferred to a smooth membrane organelle, the golgi apparatus. After passing through the golgi apparatus, the secretory proteins are packaged into secretory granules to await their exit from the cell. Such a biosynthetic scheme predicts that a secretory protein is present only within membrane organelles and not found free in the cellular cytosol. Indeed, subcellular fractionation studies on tumor cells producing either growth hormone (GH) or adrenocorticotropin (ACTH) showed that greater than 98% of the peptide hormone was located in the particulate fraction of the cell (14,15). How these proteins are sequestered exclusively into the membrane organelles of the cell has been a process that has only recently come to light.

The use of cell-free protein-synthesizing systems, in which there is little or no post-translational modification of the newly synthesized protein has permitted the characterization of the primary translation products for a variety of mRNAs. Interestingly, when mRNAs coding for secretory peptides were added to these systems to direct protein synthesis, the corresponding proteins synthesized were 20 to 30 amino acids larger than expected from their known structure (16). Further analysis showed that this extra peptide portion was located at the amino terminal of the protein and was highly hydrophobic in nature. Blobel and Dobberstein (17,18) hypothesized that this hydrophobic amino terminal extension of the secretory protein "signals" the cell that this protein is to be synthesized on the RER and that it may actually aid in the initial recognition of the nascent chain on the polysome by the cytoplasmic surface of the RER. Hence, the amino terminal extension, which is proteolytically removed once inside the cisternae of the RER, has been termed "the signal sequence." To date, all peptide hormones whose primary amino acid sequence has been investigated contain a signal sequence.

Another major reason for a precursor hormone mode of synthesis of the small peptide hormones deals with the efficiency of sequestering the newly synthesized secretory protein into the cytoplasmic membrane organelles. In order for the signal sequence to serve as the recognition unit for binding of the nascent protein chain on the polysome to the surface of the RER, it must be capable of interacting with that surface. Because the structure of the large ribosomal subunit appears to shield the growing nascent peptide chain, approximately 60–70 amino acids must be synthesized before the signal sequence is sufficiently exposed for interaction with the RER (19,20). For example, it is anticipated that if GnRH were initially synthesized with only a 25 amino acid signal sequence, synthesis of this small peptide hormone would be terminated before any of the protein emerged form the ribosome and would thus not be effectively sequestered. If this concept of small peptide hormone synthesis is valid, then one can predict that precursors to these hormones must be at least 70 amino acids in length. Indeed, all small peptide hormones whose biosynthesis has been extensively studied (Table I) (12, 20–24) are all synthesized initially as proteins of 100 amino acids and larger when the signal sequence is taken into account. Based on this argument and immunochemical data presented in the next section, it is reasonable to predict the presence of a precursor to GnRH.

IDENTIFICATION OF GnRH PRECURSORS

Two types of studies in the literature suggest the presence of precursors to GnRH. One, a purely immunological approach, relies on the variable cross-reactivity of GnRH with different antisera and the other, a more physical approach, attempts to size the GnRH precursor. Although both kinds of studies are indirect, when taken together in the context of the discussion in the preceeding section, there is little doubt that the precursor exists.

GnRH nerve fibers stain more intensely than GnRH-producing cell bodies (review, ref. 25). In fact, it was initially necessary to treat animals with colchicine to block axonal transport before intracellular localization of GnRH in the perikarya could be firmly established (26). One explanation of these results is that the hormone concentration in the axons is much greater than that in the perikarya. An alternative explanation, which is not mutually exclusive and is favored by this group and others (25), is that the GnRH antigenic determinants that are present in the cell body are primarily in the form of a prohormone that is subsequently processed to the mature peptide prior to or during axonal transport. If the prohormone were less immunoactive than the mature peptide, then the staining pattern which is observed would occur.

That the prohormone may be less immunoactive with certain antisera relative to the processed is a reasonable assumption. GnRH, with only 10 amino acids has very few possible antigenic sites; consequently, antisera generated to GnRH often require either the carboxy or amino terminus (both of which are modified) for recognition (25). In the prohormone, at least one, if not both, ends of the peptide must be involved in a peptide linkage to the remainder of the protein. Even if one terminus were exposed in the prohormone, it is not certain that it would be modified yet, i.e., either pyrolized or amidated, modifications often necessary for recognition by antisera raised to GnRH.

In the physical type of study, Millar and co-workers used denaturing gel filtration to show that there was high molecular weight GnRH immunoactivity (11). Using a Sephadex G-25 column for chromatography GnRH immunoactivity was identified in several different fractions corresponding to proteins with molecular weights as large as 10,000. The use of denaturing solvents before and during chromatography precludes the possibility that the high molecular weight forms of GnRH seen were merely aggregates of GnRH with other protein. In fact, trypsinization of these higher molecular weight forms of GnRH increased the amount of GnRH immunoactivity present in the sample. This observation is consistent with the concept that GnRH is present in a larger molecular weight form, since removal of protein which "hides" the GnRH sequence (trypsin does not cleave GnRH) may increase the accessability of this peptide to the specific antisera. Thus, there appears to be reasonable evidence in the literature to support the precursor protein mode of synthesis for GnRH.

IDENTIFICATION OF GnRH mRNA

Isolation and chemical characterization of the GnRH precursor protein will yield valuable information concerning how the GnRH peptide is synthesized. However, such a task may prove to be a very difficult task due to the small number of GnRH-producing cells in the expressing tissues and the inherent instability of a protein which is destined for extensive proteolytic degradation. An alternative route for determining the structure of the GnRH precursor protein would be to identify the sequence of the mRNA which codes for this protein. The use of recently developed recombinant DNA techniques makes this alternative an attractive one and has already been successfully used in determining the amino acid sequence of the ACTH/endorphin precursor.

Although the levels of GnRH precursor mRNA will be low, this approach should have the sensitivity required to identify this mRNA out of a mixture of hypothalamic mRNAs. Advances in recombinant DNA technology have made it possible to isolate mRNA transcripts representing less than 0.005% of the total cellular RNA, or approximately 0.25–0.5% of the mRNA, as evidenced by the cloning of the gastrin and interferon genes (27–29). Additionally, the use of defined sequence oligonucleotides as specific primers for reverse transcription has immensely improved the efficiency of isolation and cloning of one specific messenger RNA from a complex mixture of RNAs. For example, 10-, 12-, and 15-base oligodeoxynucleotides, were used as primers for synthesis of specific cDNAs for rat insulin, porcine gastrin, and human fibroblast interferon, respectively (27,29,30). Therefore, using a similar approach, we intend to develop specific oligonucleotides to aid in the isolation and identification of recombinant DNAs derived from the low abundance mRNA for GnRH.

Figure 1 outlines the scheme by which a synthetic oligonucleotide that recognizes the GnRH mRNA will be made. The relatively limited redundancy and natural frequency of mRNA codon selection observed for these four amino terminal amino acids (31–33) virtually insures that at least one of the oligonucleotides with the sequences 3' GTT-GTG-ACC-TC 5' and 3' GTT-GTG-ACC-AG 5' will specifically hybridize with GnRH mRNA. Because the amino terminal pyro-Glu residue results from cyclization of Gln (5,7), the cDNA should contain 5' TTG 3' or 5' CTG 3' as the appropriate conmplementary sequences for the Gln codon choices of 5' CAA 3' and 5' CAG 3'. Selection of T and G in the third codon positions of the synthetic sequences for Gln and His is, however, determined by the observation that dT:dG and dG:rU base mismatches do not have destabilizing effects on DNA: RNA hybrid formation (34). These 11-base synthetic oligonucleotides

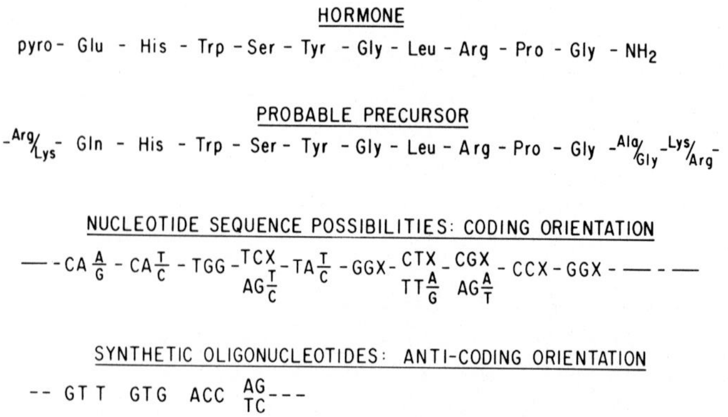

Fig. 1. Scheme for development of a GnRH specific DNA probe.

can be assembled by the phophotriester block synthesis approach (35).

The availability of the synthetic oligonucleotides provides several alternative approaches for isolation of the GnRH gene. These oligonucleotides may be utilized in three separate manners: (1) as a "primer" for reverse transcription of GnRH mRNA into cDNA from total cellular RNA, (2) as a "probe" to detect the presence of GnRH cDNA in a cDNA population which has been reverse transcribed from total cellular RNA using an oligodeoxythymidylate (oligo-dT) primer, and (3) as a specific probe for the full length sequence of the GnRH gene contained in a phage library of genomic DNA. Any one of these three methods should allow for the isolation of a DNA that codes for the GnRH precursor. Subsequent nucleic acid sequence analysis will allow the determination of the amino acid sequence of the precursor protein.

Knowledge of the primary amino acid sequence of the precursor to GnRH will be an invaluable asset in the study of the biosynthesis of this hormone. Antibodies can be raised against synthetic peptides from different regions of the precursor. Such antisera will be useful in delineating the biosynthetic scheme by which GnRH is produced and identifying sites of synthesis of the precursor itself.

REFERENCES

1. Schally, A. V., Arimura, A. V., and Kastin, A. J. (1973) *Science* **179**, 341–350.
2. Schally, A. V., Coy, D. H., and Meyers, C. A. (1978) *Annu. Rev. Biochem.* **47**, 89–128.
3. Saffran, M. (1979) *Hand. Physiol. Sect. 7: Endocrinol.* **4**, Part 2, 563–568.
4. Matsuo, H., Nair, R. M. G., Arimura, A. and Schally, A. V. (1971) *Biochem. Biophys. Res. Commun.* **43**, 1334–1339.
5. Schally, A. V., Arimura, A., Baba, Y., Nair, R. M. G., Matsuo, H., Redding, T. W., Debeljuk, L., and White, W. F. (1971) *Biochem. Biophys. Res. Commun.* **43**, 393–399.
6. Burgus, R., Butcher, M., Amoss, M., Ling, N., Monahan, M., Rivier, J., Fellows, R., Blackwell, R., Vale, W., and Guillemin, R. (1972) *Proc. Natl. Acad. Sci. U.S.A.* **69**, 278–282.
7. Amoss, M., Burgus, R., Blackwell, R., Vale, W., Fellows, R., and Guillemin, R. (1971) *Biochem. Biophys. Res. Commun.* **44**, 205–210.
8. King, J. A., and Millar, R. P. (1980) *Endocrinology* **106**, 707–716.
9. Wheaton, J. E., Krulich, L., and McCann, S. M. (1975) *Endocrinology* **97**, 30–38.
10. Krulich, L., Quijada, M., Wheaton, J. E., Illner, P., and McCann, S. M. (1977) *Fed. Proc.* **36**, 1953–1959.
11. Millar, R. P., Aehnelt, C., and Rossier, G. (1977) *Biochem. Biophys. Res. Commun.* **74**, 720–731.

12. Nakanishi, S., Inoue, A., Kita, T., Nakamura, M., Chang, A. C. Y., Cohen, S. N., and Numa, S. (1979) *Nature* **278**, 423–427.
13. Palade, G. (1975) *Science* **189**, 347–358.
14. Roberts, J. L., and Herbert, E. (1977) *Proc. Natl. Acad. Sci. U.S.A.* **74**, 4826–4830.
15. Bancroft, F. C. (1973) *Exp. Cell Res.* **79**, 275–278.
16. Devillers-Thiery, A., Kindt, I., Schelle, G., and Blobel, G. (1975) *Proc. Natl. Acad. Sci. U.S.A.* **72**, 6015–6020.
17. Blobel, G., and Dobberstein, B. (1975) *J. Cell Biol.* **67**, 835–851.
18. Blobel, G., and Dobberstein, B. (1975) *J. Cell Biol.* **67**, 852–862.
19. Blobel, G., and Sabatini, D. D. (1970) *J. Cell Biol.* **45**, 130–145.
20. Steiner, D. F., Kemmler, W., Tager, H. S., and Peterson, J. D. (1974) *Fed. Proc., Fed. Am. Soc. Exp. Biol.* **33**, 2105–2115.
21. Habener, J. F., and Potts, J. T., Jr. (1978) *N. Engl. J. Med.* **299**, 580–585.
22. Stern, A. S., Lewis, R. V., Kimura, S., Rossier, J., Gerber, L. D., Brink, L., Stein, S., and Undenfriend, S. (1979) *Proc. Natl. Acad. Sci. U.S.A.* **76**, 6680–6684.
23. Gainer, H., Sarne, Y., and Brownstein, M. J. (1977) *J. Cell Biol.* **73**, 366–381.
24. Amara, S. G., David, D. N., Rosenfeld, M. G., Roos, B. A., and Evans, R. M. (1980) *Proc. Natl. Acad. Sci. U.S.A.* **77**, 4444–4448.
25. Sternberger, L. A., and Hoffman, G. E. (1978) *Neuroendocrinology* **25**, 111–128.
26. Barry, J., and Dubois, M. P. (1973) *Endocrinology* **34**, 735–742.
27. Noyes, B. E., Mevarech, M., Stein, R., and Agarwal, K. L., (1979). *Proc. Natl. Acad. Sci. U.S.A.* **76**, 1770–1774.
28. Nagata, S., Taira, H., Hall, A., Hohnsrud, L., Streuli, M., Ecsodi, J., Boll, W., Cantell, K., and Weissman, C. (1980) *Nature (London)* **284**, 316–320.
29. Houghton, M., Stewart, A. G., Doel, S. M., Emtage, J. S., Eaton, M. A. W., Smith, J. C., Patel, T. P., Lewis, H. M., Porter, A. G., Birch, J. R., Cartwright, R., and Carey, N. H. (1980) *Nucleic Acids Res.* **8**, 1913–1931.
30. Chan, S. J., Noyes, B. E., Agarwal, K. L., and Steiner, D. F. (1979) *Proc. Natl. Acad. Sci. U.S.A.* **76**, 5036–5040.
31. Nakanishi, S., Inoue, A., Kita, T., Nakamura, M., Chang, A. C. Y., Cohen, S. N., and Numa, S. (1979) *Nature (London)* **278**, 423–427.
32. Seeburg, P. H., Shine, J., Martial, J. A., Baxter, J. D., and Goodman, N. H. (1977) *Nature (London)* **270**, 486–494.
33. Shine, J., Seeburg, P. H., Martial, J. A., Baxter, J. D., and Goodman, H. M. (1977) *Nature (London)* **270**, 494–499.
34. Gillam, S., Waterman, K., and Smith, M. (1975). *Nucleic Acids Res.* **2**, 625–634.
35. Crea, R., Kraszewski, A., Hirose, R., and Itakura, K. 1978) *Proc. Natl. Acad. Sci. U.S.A.* **75**, 5765–5769.

Structure of the Human Gonadotropin Genes

JOHN C. FIDDES† AND HOWARD M. GOODMAN

Howard Hughes Medical Institute Laboratory
Department of Biochemistry and Biophysics
University of California
San Francisco, California

INTRODUCTION

The gonadotropin hormones in the human and in several other species have been studied extensively. The amino acid sequences of the hormones have been established and a considerable amount is known about the physiological roles of the gonadotropins and about their mode of action. Very little, however, is known about the mRNA species which encode these hormones and nothing is known about the structural organization and expression of the corresponding genes.

The development of recombinant DNA technology in the past few years has enabled the structure of eukaryotic genes to be studied in considerably more detail than was possible before. To a large extent this approach has concentrated on the genes for the globins, immunoglobulins, and the chick egg white proteins though several polypeptide hormones such as growth hormone, insulin, and corticotropin have also been investigated.

The gonadotropins provide a particularly interesting group of hormones for this type of structural analysis since they represent a complex family of mammalian polypeptide hormones. All of the gonadotropins consist of noncovalently associated α- and β-subunits, which can be dissociated into the individual subunits by denaturing agents. These separated subunits lack biological activity but this can be regenerated by *in vitro* reassembly of the subunits.

All three gonadotropins, chorionic gonadotropin (CG), luteinizing hormone (LH), and follicle stimulating hormone (FSH), as well as the

† Present address: Cold Spring Harbor Laboratory P.O. Box 100, Cold Spring Harbor, New York, New York 11724.

BIOREGULATORS OF REPRODUCTION

TABLE I
Alignment of Amino Acid Sequences for the Common α Subunit and the Individual β Subunits of Human CG, LH, FSH, and TSH[a]

αhCG	Ala Pro Asp Val Gln Asp Cys Pro Glu Cys	Thr Leu Gln Glu Asn Pro Phe Phe Ser Gln	20
βhCG	Ser Lys Glu Pro Leu Arg Pro Arg Cys	Arg Pro Ile Asn Ala Thr Leu Ala Val Glu	19
βLH	Ser Arg Glu Pro Leu Arg Pro Trp Cys	His Pro Ile Asn Ala Ile Leu Ala Val Glu	19
βFSH		Asn Ser Cys Glu Leu Thr Asn Ile Thr Ile Ala Ile Glu	13
βTSH		Phe Cys Ile Pro Thr Glu Tyr Thr His His Ile Glu	12

αhCG	Pro		Gly Ala Pro		Cys	Met Gly Cys	Cys Phe	33
βhCG	Lys Glu Gly	Cys	Pro Val	Cys	Ile Thr Val Asn Thr Thr Ile	Cys Ala Gly Tyr	Cys Pro	39
βLH	Lys Glu Gly	Cys	Pro Val	Cys	Ile Thr Val Asn Thr Thr Ile	Cys Ala Gly Tyr	Cys Pro	39
βFSH	Lys Glu Glu	Cys	Arg Phe	Cys	Leu Thr Ile Asn Thr Thr Trp	Cys Ala Gly Tyr	Cys Tyr	33
βTSH	Arg Arg Glu	Cys	Ala Tyr	Cys	Leu Thr Ile Asn Thr Thr Trp	Cys Ala Gly Tyr	Cys Met	32

αhCG	Ser Arg Ala Tyr Pro Thr Pro Leu Arg Ser Lys Lys Thr Met Leu Val	Gln Lys	51
βhCG	Thr Met Thr Arg Val Leu Gln Gly Val Leu Pro Ala Leu Pro Gln Val	Val	Cys 57
βLH	Thr Met Arg Val Leu Gln Ala Val Leu Pro Pro Leu Pro Gln		Cys 55
βFSH	Thr Arg Asp Leu Val Tyr Lys Asp Pro Ala Arg Pro Lys Ile Gln Lys	Thr	Cys 51
βTSH	Thr Arg Asp Ile Asn Gly Lys Leu Phe Leu Pro Lys Tyr Ala Leu Ser Gln Asp	Val	Cys 52

αhCG	Asn Val Thr Ser Glu Ser Thr Cys Cys Val Ala Lys Ser Tyr Asn Arg Val Thr Val	Met 71
βhCG	Asn Tyr Arg Asp Val Arg Phe Glu Ser Ile Arg Leu Pro Gly	Cys	Pro Arg Gly Val	Asn 77
βLH	Thr Tyr Arg Asp Val Arg Phe Glu Ser Ile Arg Leu Pro Gly Cys Pro Arg Gly Val	Asp 71
βFSH	Thr Phe Lys Glu Leu Val Tyr Glu Thr Val Arg Val Pro Gly Cys Ala His His Ala	Asp 71
βTSH	Thr Tyr Arg Asp Phe Ile Tyr Arg Thr Val Glu Ile Pro Gly Cys Pro Leu His Val	Ala 72

280

αhCG	Gly	Gly	Phe	Lys	Val	Glu	Asn	His	Thr	Ala	Cys	His	Cys	Ser	Thr	Cys	Tyr	Tyr	His	Lys	91
βhCG	Pro	Val	Val	Ser	Tyr	Ala	Val	Ala	Leu	Ser	Cys	Gln	Cys	Ala	Leu	Cys	Arg	Arg	Ser	Thr	97
βLH	Pro	Val	Val	Ser	Phe	Pro	Val	Ala	Leu	Ser	Cys	Arg	Cys	Gly	Pro	Cys	Arg	Arg	Ser	Thr	95
βFSH	Ser	Leu	Tyr	Thr	Tyr	Pro	Val	Ala	Thr	Gln	Cys	His	Cys	Gly	Lys	Cys	Asp	Ser	Asp	Ser	91
βTSH	Pro	Tyr	Phe	Ser	Tyr	Pro	Val	Ala	Leu	Ser	Cys	Lys	Cys	Gly	Lys	Cys	Asx	Thr	Asx	Tyr	92

αhCG	Ser	92																		
βhCG	Thr	Asp	Cys	Gly	Gly	Pro	Lys	Asp	His	Pro	Leu	Thr	Cys	Asp	Asp	Pro	Arg	Phe	Gln	Asp	117
βLH	Ser	Asp	Cys	Gly	Gly	Pro	Lys	Asx	His	Pro	Leu	Thr	Cys	Asx	Glx	Pro	His	Lys	Ser	Gly	115
βFSH	Thr	Asp	Cys	Thr	Val	Arg	Gly	Leu	Gly	Pro	Ser	Tyr	Cys	Ser	Phe	Gly	Glu	Met	Lys	Gln	111
βTSH	Ser	Asx	Cys	Ile	His	Glu	Ala	Ile	Lys	Thr	Asn	Tyr	Cys	Thr	Lys	Pro	Gln	Lys	Ser	Tyr	112

βhCG	Ser	Ser	Ser	Lys	Ala	Pro	Pro	Pro	Ser	Leu	Pro	Ser	Pro	Ser	Arg	Leu	Pro	Gly	Pro	137
βFSH	Tyr	Pro	Thr	Ala	Leu	Ser	Tyr	118												

βhCG	Ser	Asp	Thr	Pro	Ile	Leu	Pro	Gln	145

a The amino acid sequence data is from 1–11. The proposal that α- and β-sequences are homologous was made initially by Pierce (12) from an examination of the sequences for bovine TSH. The alignment used here differs somewhat in the N terminal region from that proposed by Pierce. The locations of the conserved cysteine residues are indicated and the amino acids are numbered. The α chain is 92 amino acids long while the β chains for CG, LH, FSH, and TSH are 145, 115, 118, and 112 amino acids long, respectively. Deletions, shown as gaps, have been introduced to the sequences in order to maximise the homologies.

related glycoprotein hormone, thyroid stimulating hormone (TSH), share a common α subunit. The β subunits are unique to each hormone and confer the biological specificity. The amino acid sequences of the individual β subunits of hLH and hCG (h = human) show an 81% amino acid sequence homology while the homologies for the other pairs of β subunits range from about 30 to 40%. The alignment of the amino acid sequences of the human β subunits of CG, LH, FSH, and TSH is shown in Table I.

There is a complete conservation of the location of the 12 cysteine residues in all of the β subunits implying that these residues are important in determining the β subunit structure. The β subunit of hCG is unique in that it contains a C-terminal extension of about 30 amino acids which has no homologous counterpart in the other three hormones. A very limited degree of sequence homology can also be detected between the common α subunit and the various β subunits. In this case the locations of six of the cysteines are conserved. The alignment of the α subunit amino acid sequence with the various β subunit sequences is also given in Table I (1–12).

This chapter describes the isolation and characterization of the DNAs complementary to the α and β mRNAs for human chorionic gonadotropin. A more detailed account of this work has been presented in Fiddes and Goodman (13,14). In addition, preliminary data on the structure of the chromosomal gene for the common α subunit is presented here.

The cloned sequences for the gonadotropin genes will provide information concerning the structural organization of a group of related genes which have evolved from a common ancestor yet now show different patterns of tissue specific and developmentally regulated expression. In addition, the cloned DNA sequences will provide hybridization probes to quantitate the levels of synthesis of the gonadotropin mRNAs in both the pituitary and the placenta and in the various transformed cell lines, which express these genes.

IN VITRO TRANSLATION OF PLACENTAL mRNA

Human chorionic gonadotropin is synthesized in large amounts by first trimester placentas. The hormone can be detected immunologically in the urine several days after implantation of the fertilized ovum. Throughout the first trimester of pregnancy production of hCG increases steadily in proportion to the total amount of trophoblastic tissue. At the peak of production, about 10–12 weeks after conception, huge amounts of hCG are being secreted by the placenta with circu-

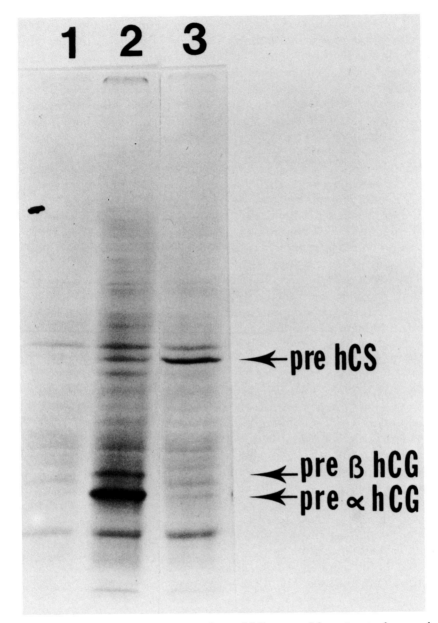

Fig. 1. Wheat germ translation products of full term and first trimester human placental RNA. The translation products, labeled with [³⁵S]methionine, were fractionated by electrophoresis on an SDS–15% polyacrylamide slab gel, and the dried gel was autoradiographed. Lane 1, endogenous wheat germ products; lane 2, first trimester placental RNA; lane 3, full term placental RNA. The proposed identifications of the products, as discussed in the text, are indicated.

lating plasma levels on the order of 1 μg/ml. At the end of the first trimester, the level of hCG synthesis declines considerably toward term.

The level in the placenta of mRNAs coding for both the α- and the
β-subunits of hCG can be demonstrated by *in vitro* translation of total
placental polyadenylated RNA. Total RNA was isolated from both first
trimester and full term human placentas by the guanidine thiocyanate
procedure (15) and the polyadenylated fraction was enriched by chromatography over an oligo (dT) cellulose column (16). The polyadenylated RNA was then translated *in vitro* by a wheat germ system with
[^{35}S]methionine and the resulting radioactively labeled proteins ana-
lysed by SDS polyacrylamide gel electrophoresis followed by autoradiography of the gel (Fig. 1).

Full term placental RNA (Fig. 1, lane 3) shows a major protein of
molecular weight 24,000 which has been identified previously (17,18)
as the precursor form of human chorionic somatomammotropin (hCS);
the major product synthesized by full term placentas.

The major proteins synethesized *in vitro* by first trimester RNA
(Fig. 1, lane 2) have estimated molecular weights of 13,000 and 16,000
and are only observed in trace quantities with full term RNA (lane 3).
These products are candidates for the precursor forms of the α- and
β-subunits of hCG, respectively. This identification was confirmed by
precipitating the *in vitro* translation products with an antibody
directed against the mature hCG. Both the 13,000 and 16,000 molecular weight products precipitated specifically (data not shown). The results from the *in vitro* translation also indicate that there is an abundance of α- over β-specific mRNA.

The data are consistent with that obtained by others. Landefeld *et
al.* (19) showed that the major translational product from first trimester
RNA had tryptic peptides in common with the native α subunit while
Daniels-McQueen *et al.* (20) and Chatterjee *et al.* (21) observed a
greater level of sythesis of the α- and β-subunits with first trimester
than with term mRNA.

The results from the *in vitro* translation of placental RNA, therefore,
confirm that first trimester human placental RNA is an enriched
source for the α- and β-specific mRNAs and is thus a suitable material
to use in attempts to clone these sequences.

RESTRICTION ENDONUCLEASE ANALYSIS OF
PLACENTAL cDNA

The first step in cloning α- and β-specific sequences from the placenta is to generate a complementary DNA (cDNA) copy of the pla-

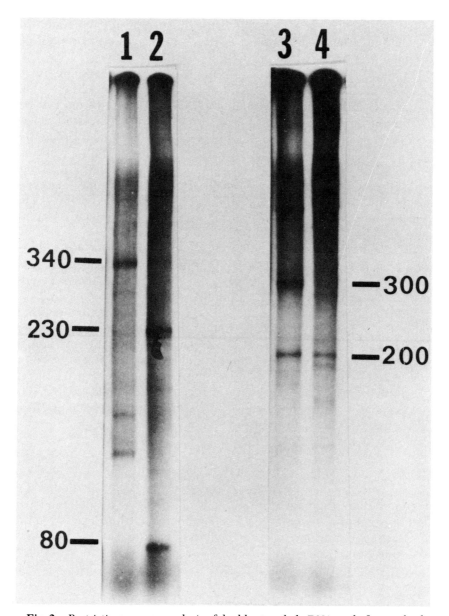

Fig. 2. Restriction enzyme analysis of double-stranded cDNA made from polyade-nylated RNA extracted from both full term and first trimester human placentas. The digestion products, labeled with ^{32}P, were fractionated by electrophoresis through a 5% polyacrylamide gel, and the dried gel was autoradiographed. Lane 1, *Alu*I digest of term placental cDNA; lane 2, *Alu*I digest of first trimester placental cDNA; lanes 3 and 4, as lanes 1 and 2 but with *Hpa*II. Sizes are in base pairs.

cental RNA. This is accomplished using the enzyme reverse transcriptase with synthetic oligo (dT) to prime synthesis from the poly (A) stretch at the 3' end of the mRNAs.

Dicrete restriction endonuclease fragments can be generated from heterogeneous cDNA if that cDNA contains a reasonably enriched species (17,22,23). Double-stranded cDNA synthesized from first trimester placental mRNA was digested with a variety of restriction endonucleases and the products were visualized by polyacrylamide gel electrophoresis. Prominent fragments were observed and were assumed to be generated from hCG cDNA. This assumption was supported by making a comparison of the restriction enzyme fragments observed with both first trimester and full term placental cDNAs. The restriction enzyme fragments considered to be hCG specific were not observed with term placental cDNA.

This type of analysis is illustrated in Fig. 2. First trimester and full term placental cDNA was digested with the restriction enzymes AluI and HpaII and the products were fractionated on a 5% polyacrylamide gel which was then dried and autoradiographed. With both enzymes a specific band pattern is observed which varies according to the source of the RNA used to synthesis the cDNA. For example, AluI generates a 340 base pair fragment from full term placental cDNA (Fig. 2, lane 1) while the same enzyme generates 230 and 80 base pair fragments from first trimester placental cDNA (Fig. 2, lane 2). These restriction enzyme fragments are assumed to be diagnostic of the major cDNA species present, which in the case of the first trimester placental cDNA is either the α- or the β-specific mRNAs or both.

CLONING OF THE cDNA FOR THE α SUBUNIT OF hCG

The strategy used for identifying potential hCG recombinants relied on screening several cDNA recombinants with restriction endonucleases to determine whether any had digestion patterns consistent with those observed in the total unfractioned cDNA.

First trimester placental cDNA, in the size range of 500–700 base pairs, was, therefore, cloned into the single HindIII site of the plasmid vector pBR322 via the addition of synthetic HindIII oligonucleotide linkers to the cDNA. Small scale DNA preparations were made from 22 such recombinants and were analyzed by restriction endonuclease digestion and polyacrylamide gel electrophoresis. One clone was identified as a potential hCG recombinant since it digested with PstI and XbaI to produce fragments similar to those observed with

```
                                                              -24
                                                              Met Asp Tyr
CAGTAACCGCCCTGAACACATCCTGCAAAAAGCCCAGAGAAAGGAGCGCC ATG GAT TAC
1                           30                            HhaI
     -20                                                  -10
Tyr Arg Lys Tyr Ala Ala Ile Phe Leu Val Thr Leu Ser Val Phe Leu
TAC AGA AAA TAT GCA GCT ATC TTT CTG GTC ACA TTG TCG GTG TTT CTG
60                    AluI                    90
                       1                                         10
His Val Leu His Ser Ala Pro Asp Val Gln Asp Cys Pro Glu Cys Thr
CAT GTT CTC CAT TCC GCT CCT GAT GTG CAG GAT TGC CCA GAA TGC ACG
110                         130
                                    20
Leu Gln Glu Asn Pro Phe Phe Ser Gln Pro Gly Ala Pro Ile Leu Gln
CTA CAG GAA AAC CCA TTC TTC TCC CAG CCG GGT GCC CCA ATA CTT CAG
    160                             HpaII      190
                30                                      40
Cys Met Gly Cys Cys Phe Ser Arg Ala Tyr Pro Thr Pro Leu Arg Ser
TGC ATG GGC TGC TGC TTC TCT AGA GCA TAT CCC ACT CCA CTA AGG TCC
                 220      XbaI                              250
                          50
Lys Lys Thr Met Leu Val Gln Lys Asn Val Thr Ser Glu Ser Thr Cys
AAG AAG ACG ATG TTG GTC CAA AAG AAC GTC ACC TCA GAG TCC ACT TGC
                                       280         HinfI
60                                              70
Cys Val Ala Lys Ser Tyr Asn Arg Val Thr Val Met Gly Gly Phe Lys
TGT GTA GCT AAA TCA TAT AAC AGG GTC ACA GTA ATG GGG GGT TTC AAA
    AluI                                      330
             80                                        90
Val Glu Asn His Thr Ala Cys His Cys Ser Thr Cys Tyr Tyr His Lys
GTG GAG AAC CAC ACG GCG TGC CAC TGC AGT ACT TGT TAT TAT CAC AAA
                 360                 PstI                  390
92
Ser OC
TCT TAA ATGTTTTACCAAGTGCTGTCTTGATGACTGCTGATTTTCTGGAATGGAAAATTAA
    400                             430

GTTGTTTAGTGTTTATGGCTTTGTGAGATAAAACTCTCCTTTTCCTTACCATACCACTTTGAC
    460                      AluI        590
ACGCTTCAAGGATATACTGCAGCTTTACTGCCTTCCTCCTTATCCTACAGTACAATCAGCAGT
         530       PstI                       560
                                        AluI
CTAGTTCTTTTCATTTGGAATGAATACAGCATTAAGCTT
         590                     HindIII
```

Fig. 3. Nucleotide sequence of the 621 base pair cloned cDNA fragment which codes for the α subunit of hCG. The amino acid sequence of the 92 residue long mature protein is shown as well as the 24 residue presequence deduced from the cDNA sequence. The nucleotides and amino acids are numbered. Restriction enzyme sites for PstI, HindIII, XbaI, HpaII, AluI, HinfI, and HhaI are marked.

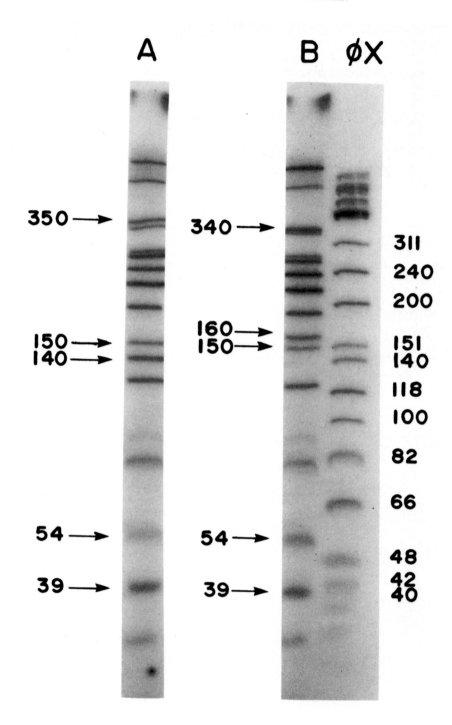

the total cDNA (data not shown). DNA sequence analysis confirmed that this cDNA coded for the α subunit of hCG.

The entire nucleotide sequence of this 621 bp cDNA fragment was then determined by the chain termination method (24) and is shown in Fig. 3. Single-stranded DNA templates were obtained by transferring both strands of the cDNA to the single-stranded phage vector M13-mp5 (25). The DNA sequence confirmed the amino sequence of the 92 amino acid long mature hormone (2) and predicted the amino acid sequence of a 24 amino acid presequence which had previously been only characterized partially (26). The 621 bp fragment contains 50 bases of 5'-untranslated sequence and 221 bases of 3'-untranslated sequence. This does not represent the entire 3'-untranslated region due to the existence of the HindIII site close to the end of the 3'-untranslated region.

CLONING OF THE cDNA FOR THE β SUBUNIT OF hCG

The results obtained with the in vitro translation of first trimester placental RNA implied that the mRNA coding for the β subunit of hCG is a less enriched species than that coding for the α subunit (see Fig. 1). A more direct approach correlating amino acid sequences with specific restriction enzyme targets was devised to identify βhCG recombinants.

Most restriction enzymes do not have recognition sites which are uniquely determined by certain amino acid pairs, but Sau96I is specific for glycine–proline dipeptides. Sau96I recognizes the sequence GGNCC (27) and since glycine is coded for by the four codons GGN and proline by the four codons CCN, every Gly-Pro dipeptide must be represented by a Sau96I site in the corresponding gene. Other groups of amino acids may also be coded for by sequences containing Sau96I sites since the sequence GGNCC may be translated in two other reading frames.

Since there are Gly-Pro dipeptides at positions 102 and 103 and po-

---

Fig. 4. Restriction enzyme analysis with Sau 96I of the two recombinants between pBR 322 and the cDNA for the β subunit of hCG. Following digestion of the plasmid DNA with Sau96I the fragments were labeled with ^{32}P using E.coli DNA polymerase, electrophoresed through a 5% polyacrylamide gel, and then autoradiographed. The sizes of the fragments (in base pairs), which correspond to the βhCG sequences in recombinants A and B, are indicated. The third lane is a HinfI digest of φχ174 RF DNA used as size markers.

sitions 136 and 137 in the β subunit of hCG, the corresponding gene must have Sau96I sites 102 base pairs apart. Within this 102 base pairs of DNA at amino acid positions 104–105 and 122–124 are the sequences Lys-Asp-His and Lys-Ala-Pro, respectively, which, with the appropriate codon choice, would also correspond to Sau96I sites. These restriction enzyme sites would result in the 102 base pair fragment being divided into pieces of 54 and 39 bp long.

Plasmid DNAs were isolated from 72 recombinants between pBR322 and first trimester placental cDNA and were digested with the enzyme Sau96I and fractionated on 5% polyacrylamide gels (see Fig. 4). Two plasmids were observed to have restriction enzyme fragments 54 and 39 bp long and were thus considered to be potential βhCG cDNA recombinants. These two recombinants appear to represent slightly different lengths of copying of the same mRNA. DNA sequence analysis was used to confirm the identity of these recombinants as containing βhCG cDNA sequences. Subsequently the complete DNA sequence for one of the recombinants, which is 579 bp long, was established by a combination of the chemical degradation method (28) and the modified chain termination method (29) and is presented in Fig. 5.

Like the α subunit recombinant this cDNA contains the coding sequence for the entire mature protein and the precursor sequence (see below). In addition, the βhCG recombinant has 25 bases of the 5'-untranslated region and 16 bases of the 3'-untranslated region preceding the poly (A) region.

ANALYSIS OF THE α AND β SUBUNITS OF hCG cDNA SEQUENCES

The isolation of individual recombinants containing α- and β-subunits of hCG sequences proves that the two proteins are coded for by separate mRNA. This finding agrees with the deduction of Daniels-McQueen et al. (20) who showed that the α- and β-translational activities for hCG sedimented at different positions on sucrose gradients. Similar observations have been made with mouse TSH by Kourides and Weintraub (3) and Vamvakopoulos and Kourides (31) who have purified mRNAs 620 and 560 bases long which code for the α- and β-subunits, respectively. The sizes of the cloned α- and β-subunits of hCG sequences agree well with the estimates made by Vamvakopoulos and Kourides for the mouse TSH subunits.

In the case of the α subunit a hydrophobic precursor sequence of 24

```
                                        -20
                                        Met  Glu  Met  Phe  Gln  Gly  Leu  Leu  Leu
AGACAAGGCAGGGGACGCACCAAGG               ATG  GAG  ATG  TTC  CAG  GGG  CTG  CTG  CTG
1                                       30
         -10                                                      1
Leu  Leu  Leu  Leu  Ser  Met  Gly  Gly  Thr  Trp  Ala  Ser  Lys  Glu  Pro  Leu
TTG  CTG  CTG  CTG  AGC  ATG  GGC  GGG  ACA  TGG  GCA  TCC  AAG  GAG  CCG  CTT
          60                                                 90
                    10                                                       20
Arg  Pro  Arg  Cys  Arg  Pro  Ile  Asn  Ala  Thr  Leu  Ala  Val  Glu  Lys  Glu
CGG  CCA  CGG  TGC  CGC  CCC  ATC  AAT  GCC  ACC  CTG  GCT  GTG  GAG  AAG  GAG
     HaeIII                      120
                                             30
Gly  Cys  Pro  Val  Cys  Ile  Thr  Val  Asn  Thr  Thr  Ile  Cys  Ala  Gly  Tyr
GGC  TGC  CCC  GTG  TGC  ATC  ACC  GTC  AAC  ACC  ACC  ATC  TGT  GCC  GGC  TAC
150                                                     180
               40                                            50
Cys  Pro  Thr  Met  Thr  Arg  Val  Leu  Gln  Gly  Val  Leu  Pro  Ala  Leu  Pro
TGC  CCC  ACC  ATG  ACC  CGC  GTG  CTG  CAG  GGG  GTC  CTG  CCG  GCC  CTG  CCT
               210                    PstI       Sau96I    HaeIII/Sau96I
                                           60
Gln  Val  Val  Cys  Asn  Tyr  Arg  Asp  Val  Arg  Phe  Glu  Ser  Ile  Arg  Leu
CAG  GTG  GTG  TGC  AAC  TAC  CGC  GAT  GTG  CGC  TTC  GAG  TCC  ATC  CGG  CTC
                                        270          TaqI/HinfI
70                                                  80
Pro  Gly  Cys  Pro  Arg  Gly  Val  Asn  Pro  Val  Val  Ser  Tyr  Ala  Val  Ala
CCT  GGC  TGC  CCG  CGC  GGC  GTG  AAC  CCC  GTG  GTC  TCC  TAC  GCC  GTG  GCT
          300                                               330
                    90                                                       100
Leu  Ser  Cys  Gln  Cys  Ala  Leu  Cys  Arg  Arg  Ser  Thr  Thr  Asp  Cys  Gly
CTC  AGC  TGT  CAA  TGT  GCA  CTC  TGC  CGC  CGC  AGC  ACC  ACT  GAC  TGC  GGG
     PvuII                 360
                                        110
Gly  Pro  Lys  Asp  His  Pro  Leu  Thr  Cys  Asp  Asp  Pro  Arg  Phe  Gln  Asp
GGT  CCC  AAG  GAC  CAC  CCC  TTG  ACC  TGT  GAT  GAC  CCC  CGC  TTC  CAG  GAC
Sau96I         Sau96I                            420                          Hin
          120                                               130
Ser  Ser  Ser  Ser  Lys  Ala  Pro  Pro  Pro  Ser  Leu  Pro  Ser  Pro  Ser  Arg
TCC  TCT  TCC  TCA  AAG  GCC  CCT  CCC  CCC  AGC  CTT  CCA  AGC  CCA  TCC  CGA
fI                  HaeIII/Sau96I                                     480      Hin
                              140                      145
Leu  Pro  Gly  Pro  Ser  Asp  Thr  Pro  Ile  Leu  Pro  Gln  OC
CTC  CCG  GGG  CCC  TCG  GAC  ACC  CCG  ATC  CTC  CCA  CAA  TAA  AGGCTTCTCAAT
fI/SmaI/Sau96I/HaeIII                   MboI                           530

CCGC[A]₄₀
539
```

Fig. 5. Nucleotide sequence of the 579 base pair cloned cDNA fragment which codes for the β subunit of hCG. The amino acid sequence of the 145 residue long mature protein is shown as well as the 20 residue presequence predicted from the cDNA sequence (see text). The nucleotides and amino acids are numbered. Restriction enzymes sites for *Pst* I, *Pvu* II, *Sau* 96I, *Taq* I, *Hae* III, *Hin* fI, *Mbo* I, and *Sma* I are marked.

amino acids can be predicted from the cDNA sequence. This sequence agrees with the preliminary data of Birken *et al.* (26) who have identified a 24 amino acid precursor sequence for the α subunit of hCG and have located the positions of the Ala, Phe, and Leu residues.

With the β subunit of hCG no such preliminary information is available but it is still possible to predict the nature of the amino acid presequence. If the nucleotide sequence preceding the serine codon at position 1 in βhCG is read in triplets toward the 5' end, potential ATG initiation codons are observed at positions -18 and -20 (see Fig. 5). No other ATG codons are observed between this position and the 5' and of the cloned cDNA in this or the other two reading frames. It has been proposed, on the basis of examining the 5'-untranslated sequences of 22 eukaryotic mRNA species, that the initiator methionine codon is the AUG located closest to the 5' end of the mRNA (32). The β subunit of hCG can thus be predicted to have a presequence 20 amino acids long, but the existence of a larger presequence (greater than 28 amino acids long) can not be definitely ruled out since there are no termination codons in phase in the part of the 5'-untranslated region which has been cloned. Characteristically the presequence of βhCG is hydrophobic with the somewhat unusual structure of seven consecutive leucines at position -8 to -14.

The base compositions of the cDNA sequences for the two hCG subunits and for four other human cDNAs are presented in Table II (13,14,22,33–35). In several cases there is a considerable bias towards a high G + C content. For example, the βhCG subunit has a much

TABLE II
Base Distribution, Coding, and Noncoding Regions
of Some Human cDNAs[a]

cDNA	Base			
	A	T	G	C
hαCG	165	180	124	152
hβCG	88	95	151	205
hGH	190	173	183	253
hCS	161	162	188	245
hInsulin	75	71	128	142
hβ-Globin	122	153	159	142

[a] The sources of the data and the abbreviations used in the table are as follows: human chorionic gonadotropin α- and β-subunits (αhCG, βhCG) (13,14); growth hormone (hGH) (33); chorionic somatomammotropin (hCS) (22); insulin (34) and β-globin (35).

TABLE III
Third Position Base Distribution in the Coding
Regions of Some Human cDNAs[a]

cDNA	Base			
	A	T	G	C
hαCG	25	28	29	35
hβCG	12	17	53	84
hGH	31	29	65	93
hCS	17	17	60	75
hInsulin	14	8	43	45
hβ-Globin	10	40	53	45

[a] See footnotes to Table II.

higher G + C content (G 28.0%, C 38.0%, A 16.3%, T 17.6%) than is observed in total DNA (G 19.5%, C 19.8%, A 30.9%, and T 29.6%). This bias is also noted in the human insulin and chorionic somato-mammotropin cDNAs but is not evident with the α subunit of hCG.

Table III shows the distribution in these same cDNA sequences of the bases present in the third position of the codons. Consistent with the high G + C content of βhCG there is a very considerable bias towards codons terminating in G or C. As expected this bias is also observed with the G + C rich human insulin and chorionic somato-mammotropin sequences but interestingly both human growth hormone and the α subunit of hCG which do not have the overal G + C bias still have a preponderance of codons ending in G or C.

EVOLUTION OF THE GENES FOR THE GONADOTROPINS

The β subunits of the three gonadotropins CG, LH, FSH, and the related hormone TSH all show amino acid sequence homologies (see Table I). Alignment of all four sequences shows that the twelve cysteine residues are completely conserved and that there is an additional conserved region, located at positions 34–38 in βhCG.

A much less pronounced homology between the α- and β-subunits of bovine TSH has also been proposed by Pierce (12), leading to the suggestion that all glycoprotein hormones genes evolved from a common ancestor which subsequently diverged to generate α- and β-sequences. This amino acid sequence homology can also be detected between α- and β-subunits of hCG and is presented in Fig. 6. The alignment can now also be extended to include the pre sequences.

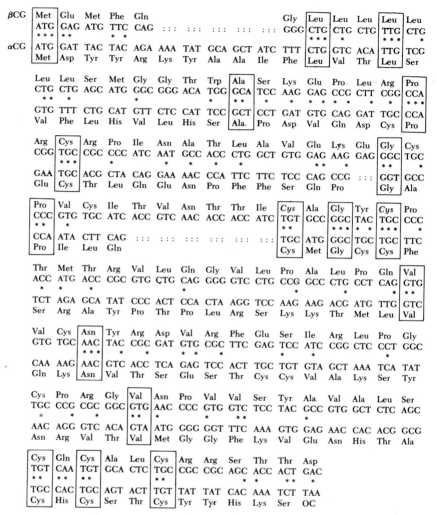

Fig. 6. Alignment of the amino acid and nucleotide sequences of the coding regions of the α (lower lines) and β (upper lines) subunits of hCG. In order to maximize the homologies one insertion of five codons, and two deletions of one and six codons have been proposed in the α sequence. The overall sequence homologies are 16.1 and 31.0% for the amino acids and nucleotides, respectively. These values do not take into account the deletions and insertions.

Overall the homology is very low (16% not including the deletions and insertions) but there is still a very noticeable conservation of the cysteine residues with 6 of the 12 being maintained between the α- and β-subunits.

Figure 6 shows the alignment of the coding nucleotide sequences for the α- and β-subunits of hCG based on the same alignment as used with the amino acid sequences in Table I. Overall the homology level is still very low (31%) but there are certain areas which are considerably more related, especially in the regions of the cysteine residues. The observed similarity between the sequences does not merely reflect a similar bias in base composition between the two species since the base composition of the αcDNA (G 20.0%, C 24.5%, A 26.6%, T 29.0%) is very different from that of the βcDNA (G 28.0%, C 38.0%, A 16.3%, T 17.6%).

The nucleotide sequence data, therefore, tend to confirm the proposal that the α- and β-genes are related and thus probably have evolved from a common ancestor, since the homology previously detected at the amino acid level is somewhat more apparent when the nucleotide sequences are considered. In this respect the glycoprotein hormone genes may be similar to the globin genes which are also assumed to have evolved from a common precursor into α genes and a family of several β-like genes.

READTHROUGH INTO THE 3′ UNTRANSLATED REGION OF THE GENE

The 3′-untranslated region of the βhCG mRNA is only 16 bases long and is thus remarkably short when compared with other eukaryotic mRNA species. For example, the 3′-untranslated region of the α subunit is greater than 221 bases long. The termination codon UAA is located in the sequence AAUAAA, which is found in the 3′-untranslated regions of all polyadenylated eukaryotic cellular mRNAs (36) at about 15–20 bases from the poly (A). The lack of this sequence in some non-polyadenylated plant viral mRNAs (37) lead to the proposal that the AAUAAA is involved in the process of polyadenylation (38). However, there is an exception to this as the genomic RNAs of several picornoviruses are polyadenylated but do not have the AAUAAA sequence (39). Thus it may be that the role of this sequence in the case of the cellular mRNAs is as a signal in the processing of a larger precursor mRNA molecule as well as polyadenylation. In βhCG mRNA this sequence therefore has a dual overlapping function as it codes for the last codon, CAA (gln), and for the terminator (UAA) in addition to the proposed regulatory function.

The alignment of the β subunit amino acid sequences shows that the β subunit of hCG has a C-terminal extension of about 30 amino acids which has no homologous counterpart in the other three gonado-tropins. Since the βhCG mRNA has such an unusually short 3'-un-translated region it can be proposed that the β subunit of hCG evolved from a common β subunit ancestor by some readthrough event so that the 3'-untranslated sequence became a coding region. This could have arisen by changes such as point or frame shift mutations or by an alteration of the splicing pattern of the precursor mRNA. Verification of this proposal will require sequence analysis of the genes for the other three β subunits to search for homologies between their 3'-un-translated regions and the C-terminal extension of βhCG.

A similar observation has also been made with the abnormal human α-hemoglobin Constant Spring which has a 31 amino acid C-terminal extension when compared to normal α-globin (40). Sequence analysis of normal human α-globin cDNA showed that the carboxy terminal amino acids of α-globin Constant Spring could be coded for by the 3'-untranslated region with a termination codon located in a similar posi-tion to that of βhCG (41).

ISOLATION OF THE GENE ENCODING THE COMMON α SUBUNIT

A complete structural analysis of the gonadotropin genes requires that the chromosomal sequences corresponding to the cDNAs are iso-lated. This is necessary to identify whether the genes contain inter-vening sequences and to establish whether any chromosomal linkage exists between the related gonadotropins. Isolation of the chromo-somal gene sequences is accomplished by using the cloned cDNA se-quences as hybridization probes.

The 621 base pair αhCG cDNA fragment was thus labeled with ^{32}P by nick translation and used as a hybridization probe to screen the li-brary of human DNA fragments cloned in the bacteriophage λ vector, Charon 4A. This library (a gift of T. Maniatis) was generated by clon-ing a partial *Hae*III and *Alu*I digest of human fetal liver DNA into the unique *Eco*RI site of λ Charon 4A. This was achieved by the addition of synthetic *Eco*RI oligonucleotide linkers to the partially digested DNA (42). A single isolate which hybridized consistently with the αhCG cDNA probe was detected and plaque purified (unpublished results of JCF and HMG).

This is illustrated in Fig. 7. Approximately 10^6 recombinant bac-teriophage from the library were plated on 25 large petri dishes and nitrocellulose filters were made from the plates. This resulted in the

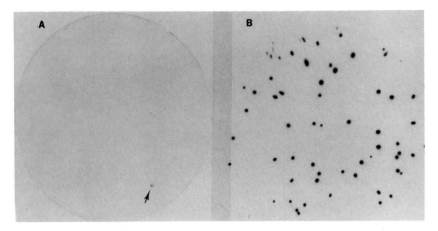

Fig. 7.   Purification of the recombinant between bacteriophage λ–charon 4A and the chromosomal sequences coding for the α subunit gene. Panel A shows the autoradiograph of a nitrocellulose filter obtained on the first round of plating the human genomic library. The hybridization spot corresponding to the phage plaque containing the α subunit DNA sequences is marked with an arrow. Panel B shows the autoradiograph obtained following purification of the phage identified in the first filter. The techniques involved are discussed in more detail in the text.

transfer of the free phage DNA present in the plaques from the plate to the filter thus forming a precise replica. The nitrocellulose filter was then baked to adhere the DNA irreversibly to the filter and bound DNA was then hybridized to the ^{32}P-labeled cDNA. Following hybridization the filter was washed and autoradiographed and the autoradiograph examined for spots which corresponded to areas of hybridization. Panel A of Fig. 7 shows the spot (marked with the arrow) corresponding to the single isolate of the αhCG chromosomal gene. The corresponding area of the petri dish was then removed and the phage carrying αhCG sequences purified by several additional rounds of plating and hybridization. Panel B shows an autoradiograph obtained from a filter made to the purified αhCG genomic recombinant. In this example every phage plaque hybridizes to the cDNA probe.

This recombinant contained three *Eco*RI fragments 3, 4, and 10 kb long of which only the 3 and 10 kb pieces hybridize to the cDNA. A detailed restriction map of this region of human DNA has been determined. The enzymes *Pst*I, *Xba*I, and *Hind*III were especially useful since they cut DNA relatively infrequently yet are known to have recognition sites in the αhCG cDNA and can be used to orient the restriction map of the gene with respect to that of the cDNA. The map was

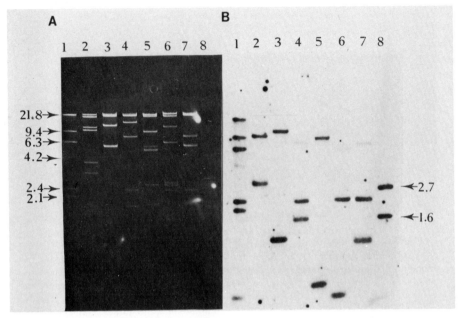

Fig. 8. Restriction enzyme and Southern transfer analysis of the αhCG gene sequences cloned in bacteriophage λ–charon 4A. Panel A shows the ethidium bromide staining pattern of various digests fractionated by electrophoresis through a 1% agarose gel. The restriction enzymes used are as follows; lane 2, EcoRI; lane 3, HindIII; lane 4, Xba I; lane 5, EcoRI and HindIII; lane 6, XbaI and EcoRI; lane 7, XbaI and HindIII. Lanes 1 and 8 contain marker fragments generated from the digestion of wild type bacteriophage λ DNA and φχ174 RF DNA with HindIII and MspI, respectively. Panel B shows the autoradiograph of the corresponding nitro cellulose filter hybridised to the ^{32}P-labeled αhCG probe. Lanes 1–8 in panel B correspond to the same lanes in panel A. The marker fragments, whose sizes are given kilobases are ^{32}P labeled.

determined by analyzing double restriction enzyme digests by the DNA transfer procedure of Southern (43) using both the full length αhCG cDNA and 5′- and 3′-terminal fragments as hybridization probes. The mapping was facilitated by subcloning the three EcoRI fragments into the plasmid pBR322.

The Southern DNA transfer method is illustrated in Fig. 8. DNA isolated from bacteriophage λ–αhCG recombinant was digested with several restriction endonucleases and the resulting fragments were fractionated by electrophoresis through an agarose gel. The gel was then stained with ethidium bromide and the fluorescing DNA bands photographed under an ultraviolet light (Fig. 8, panel A). The DNA fragments in the gel were then denatured and transferred to a nitrocellulose filter which was hybridized to ^{32}P-αhCG cDNA (in this case a fragment from the 3' end of the cDNA was used). Panel B of Fig. 8 shows the autoradiograph of the filter. A comparison of the staining pattern (panel A) and the hybridization pattern (panel B) shows which of the DNA fragments contain sequences which hybridize to the cloned cDNA. The restriction enzyme map obtained in this way is shown in Fig. 9.

A tentative structure of the αhCG gene was predicted from the correlation of the gene and cDNA restriction enzyme maps. The gene appeared to span a total of between 7 and 9.5 kb and to be split by three intervening sequences. This structure has been confirmed by DNA sequencing. The appropriate restriction enzyme fragments in the αhCG gene were labeled with polynucleotide kinase and (γ^{32}P) ATP and sequenced by the chemical and modified chain termination methods.

Two of the introns, B and C, were located as predicted in the coding region. Intron B, which is about 1.7 kb long, splits codon number 6 of the mature protein between the first and second nucleotide while the approximately 340 bp intron C separates codon 67 and 68. No introns are found in the presequence. The sequences at these intron–exon junctions show the expected homologies with other such sequences (44,45). No nucleotide sequence changes have so far been detected between the cDNA and gene despite the fact that they originated from different individuals.

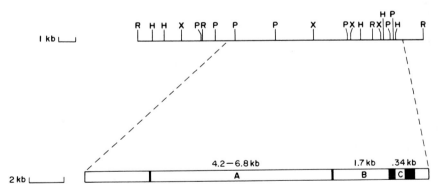

Fig. 9. Preliminary restriction endonuclease map of the cloned chromosomal gene coding for the common human α subunit. Sizes are in kilobases. The total length of the cloned fragment is 17 kb. The code for the restriction enzyme target sites is; R = *Eco*RI, H = *Hin*dIII, X = *Xba*I, P = *Pst* I. The exons are the shaded regions. Approximate sizes of the introns are given in kilobases. The precise location of the large intron (A) in the 5' untranslated region has not been established. The exon corresponding to the 5' end of the gene has been located within a 2.4 kb *Pst*I fragment and in this figure is located arbitrarily in the center of this fragment.

The precise location of intron A has not yet been established, though it is definitely found in the 5′-untranslated region. As a result of this intron the 5′ end of the gene is displaced a considerable distance from the coding region. At present, the size of the intron A is estimated to be between 4.2 and 6.8 kb long although the 5′ end of the intron has not yet been sequenced.

POLYMORPHISM OF THE SEQUENCES CODING FOR THE α SUBUNIT

Total human DNA has been digested with a variety of restriction endonucleases and analyzed by the transfer procedure of Southern using αhCG cDNA as the hybridization probe. No evidence has been obtained for the existence of more than a single gene for the α subunit though further experiments are required to substantiate this.

The situation is confused by the discovery of polymorphism in the hybridizing EcoRI restriction enzyme fragments. Three types of hybridization patterns have been identified in the approximately 20 individuals examined so far. The sizes of the fragments and their relative degrees of hybridization are shown in Table IV. Examples of the Southern transfers demonstrating these three types are shown in Fig. 10.

The nature of the observed polymorphism has not yet been adequately explained. The bulk of the hybridizing sequences in the cloned gene are located in the 3 kb/5 kb fragment (see footnote to Table IV) so it is particularly hard to explain the hybridization pattern of type III in which no hybridizing 5 kb fragment is observed. It

TABLE IV
EcoRI Fragments of Human DNA Which Hybridize to the αhCG cDNA[a]

	5kb	10kb
Type I	+	+
Type II	+ +	+
Type III	−	+

[a] The cloned α gene contains hybridizing fragments 3 and 10 kb long while those observed in the total genomic DNA are 5 and 10 kb long. This discrepancy results from the fact that the human DNA library was generated from a partial digestion with HaeIII and AluI and not with EcoRI. The 3 kb cloned fragment is thus considered to be a subfragment of the 5kb genomic fragment.

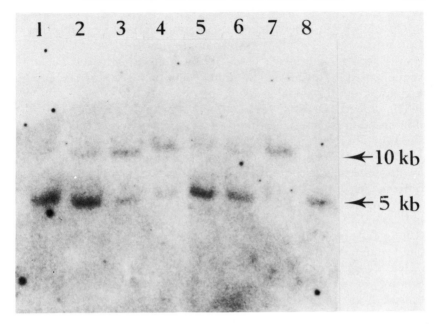

Fig. 10. Autoradiograph of a Southern transfer demonstrating the polymorphism of the *Eco* RI fragments which hybridise to the ³¹P-labeled αhCG cDNA probe. The sizes of the hybridising fragments are indicated in kilobases. The three types of patterns observed are identified in Table IV; lanes 1 and 2, type II; lanes 3 and 4, type I; lanes 5 and 6, type II; lane 7, type III; lane 8, type II.

would appear that the cloned gene corresponds to type II which has a greater intensity of hybridization to the 5 than the 10 kb piece. However, this interpretation could be erroneous if the polymorphism reflects the existence of multiple α-like genes. Further experiments are required to explain these observations.

CONCLUSIONS

Plasmid recombinants containing the cDNAs for both the α- and β-subunits of hCG have been isolated. The complete nucleotide sequences of these two cDNAs have been established. The amino acid sequences of the signal peptides of both subunits have been predicted from the nucleotide sequences and the amino acid sequence of the mature hormone has been confirmed. In addition the nucleotide sequences of the 5′- and 3′-untranslated regions of the two mRNAs coding for the individual subunits have been determined. Analysis of the βhCG cDNA sequences allowed the prediction to be made that the C-terminal extension of the β subunit arose by the loss of the termination codon of a shorter ancestral β-like gene. Finally, the nucleotide sequences show a limited amount of homology between the common α subunit and the variable β subunit.

The cloned cDNA for the α subunit has been used as a hybridization probe to isolate the chromosomal gene coding for the common α subunit. There is no indication of there being more than a single α gene but the situation is confused by the discovery that polymorphic forms of the α gene sequences exist in the human population. Restriction enzyme and DNA sequence analysis of the cloned α subunit gene show that it contains three intervening sequences and spans a total of between 7 and 9.5 kb. Two of the introns are located in the sequence coding for the mature protein while one is found in the 5'-untranslated region.

The structure of the chromosomal genes coding for the β subunits has not yet been investigated. We hope also to obtain cDNA recombinants from the pituitary which code for the β subunits of LH, FSH, and TSH and to use these along with the βhCG recombinant to investigate the chromosomal organization of this family of closely related sequences. In addition the cloned sequences for these genes will provide hybridization probes to use in the investigation of the synthesis of the gonadotropins in the pituitary and the placenta and in transformed cells. The possibility also exists of constructing recombinant plasmids which will permit the expression of these genes in *E.coli*.

ACKNOWLEDGMENTS

JCF was supported by a fellowship from the Anna Fuller Foundation. HMG is an investigator of the Howard Hughes Medical Institute. The work described here was supported by a grant (No. CA 14026) to HMG. We thank B. McCabe for typing the manuscript and S. Bock for preparation of the figures.

REFERENCES

1. Bellisario, R., Carlsen, R. B., and Bahl, O. P. (1973) *J. Biol. Chem.* **248**, 6796–6809.
2. Morgan, F. J., Birken, S., and Canfield, R. E. (1975) *J. Biol. Chem.* **250**, 5247–5258.
3. Sairam, M. R., Papkoff, H., and Li, C. H. (1972) *Biochem. Biophys. Res. Commun.* **48**, 530–537.
4. Inagami, T., Murakami, K., Puett, D., Stockell-Hartree, A., and Nureddin, A. (1971) *Biochem. J.* **126**, 441–442.

5. Shome, B., and Parlow, A. F. (1974) *J. Clin Endocrinol. Metab.* **39**, 169–202.
6. Rathman, P., and Saxena, B. B. (1975) *J. Biol. Chem.* **250**, 6735–6746.
7. Keutmann, H. T., and Williams, R. M. (1977) *J. Biol. Chem.* **252**, 5393–5397.
8. Birken, S., and Canfield, R. E. (1977) *J. Biol. Chem.* **252**, 5386–5392.
9. Saxena, B. B., and Rathman, P. (1976) *J. Biol. Chem.* **251**, 993–1005.
10. Sairam, R. M., and Li, C. H. (1973) *Biochem. Biophys. Res. Commun.* **54**, 426–431.
11. Shome, B., and Parlow, A. F. (1974) *J. Clin. Endocrinol. Metab.* **39**, 203–205.
12. Pierce, J. G., Liao, T. H., and Carlsen, R. B. (1973) *In* "Hormonal Proteins and Peptides" (C. H. Li, ed.), Vol. 1, pp. 27–92. Academic Press, New York.
13. Fiddes, J. C., and Goodman, H. M. (1979) *Nature (London)* **281**, 351–356.
14. Fiddes, J. C., and Goodman, H. M. (1980). *Nature (London)* **286**, 684–687.
15. Chirgwin, J. M., Przybyla, A. E., McDonald, R. J., and Rutter, W. J. (1979) *Biochemistry* **24**, 5294–5299.
16. Aviv, H., and Leder, P. (1972) *Proc. Natl. Acad. Sci. U.S.A.* **69**, 1408–1412.
17. Seeburg, P. H., Shine, J., Martial, J. A., Ullrich, A., Baxter, J. D., and Goodman, H. M. (1977) *Cell* **12**, 157–165.
18. Boime, I., McWilliams, D., Szczesna, E., and Camel, M. (1976) *J. Biol. Chem.* **251**, 820–825.
19. Landefield, T. D., McWilliams, D. R., and Boime, I. (1976) *Biochem. Biophys. Res. Commun.* **72**, 381–390.
20. Daniels-McQueen, S., McWilliams, D. R., Birken, S., Canfield, R., Landefeld, T., and Boime, I. (1978) *J. Biol. Chem.* **253**, 7109–7114.
21. Chatterjee, M., Baliga, S., and Munro, H. (1976) *J. Biol. Chem.* **251**, 2945–2951.
22. Shine, J., Seeburg, P. H., Martial, J. A., Baxter, J. D., and Goodman, H. M. (1977) *Nature (London)* **270**, 494–499.
23. Ullrich, A., Shine, J., Chirgwin, J., Pictet, R., Tischer, E., Rutter, W. J., and Goodman, H. M. (1977) *Science* **196**, 1313–1315.
24. Sanger, F., Nicklen, S., and Coulson, A. E. (1977) *Proc. Natl. Acad. Sci. U.S.A.* **74**, 5463–5467.
25. Gronenborn, B., and Messing, J. (1978) *Nature (London)* **272**, 375–377.
26. Birken, S., Fetherston, J., Desmond, J., Canfield, R., and Boime, I. (1978) *Biochem. Biophys. Res. Commun.* **85**, 1247–1253.
27. Sussenbach, J. S., Steenbergh, P. H., Rost, J. A., van Leeuwen, W. J., and van Embden, J. D. A. (1978) *Nucleic Acids Res.* **5**, 1153–1163.
28. Maxam, A. M., and Gilbert, W. (1977) *Proc. Natl. Acad. Sci. U.S.A.* **74**, 560–564.
29. Maat, J., and Smith, A. J. H. (1978) *Nucleic Acids Res.* **5**, 4537–4545.
30. Kourides, I. A., and Weintraub, B. D. (1979) *Proc. Natl. Acad. Sci. U.S.A.* **76**, 298–302.
31. Vamvakopoulous, N. C., and Kourides, I. A. (1979) *Proc. Natl. Acad. Sci. U.S.A.* **76**, 3809–3813.
32. Kozak, M. (1978) *Cell* **15**, 1109–1123.
33. Martial, J. A., Hallewell, R. A., Baxter, J. D., and Goodman, H. M. (1979) *Science* **205**, 602–607.
34. Bell, G. I., Swain, W. F., Pictet, R., Cordell, B., Goodman, H. M., and Rutter, W. J. (1979) *Nature (London)* **282**, 525–527.
35. Marotta, C. A., Wilson, J. T., Forget, B. G., and Weisman, S. M. (1977) *J. Biol. Chem.* **252**, 5040–5053.
36. Proudfoot, N. J., and Brownlee, G. G. (1976) *Nature (London)* **263**, 211–214.
37. Briand, J. P., Jonard, G., Guilley, H., Richards, K. D., and Hirth, L. (1977) *Eur. J. Biochem.* **72**, 453–463.

38. Porter, A. G., Merregaert, J., van Emmelo, J., and Fiers, W. (1978) *Eur. J. Biochem.* **87**, 551–561.
39. Porter, A. G., Fellner, P., Black, D. N., Rowlands, D. J., Harris, T. J. R., and Brown, F. (1978) *Nature (London)* **276**, 298–301.
40. Clegg, J. B., Weatherall, D. J., and Milner, P. F. (1971) *Nature (London)* **234**, 337–340).
41. Proudfoot, N. J., and Longley, J. I. (1976) *Cell* **9**, 733–746.
42. Lawn, R. M., Fritsch, E. F., Parker, R. C., Blake, G., and Maniatis, T. (1978) *Cell* **15**, 1157–1174.
43. Southern, E. M. (1975) *J. Mol. Biol.* **98**, 503–517.
44. Breathnach, R., Benoist, C., O'Hare, K., Gannon, F., and Chambon, P. (1978) *Proc. Natl. Acad. Sci. U.S.A.* **75**, 4853–4857.
45. Seif, I., Khoury, G., and Dhar, R. (1979) *Nucleic Acids Res.* **6**, 3387–3398.

Note added in proof: The precise location of the 5′ end of the α subunit gene has now been established. Intervening sequence A is 6.4 kb long and splits the 5′ untranslated region seven nucleotides before the ATG initiation codon. The α subunit gene therefore spans a total of 9.4 kb of human DNA. Detailed restriction enzyme analysis of total human DNA reveals that there is a single α subunit gene that codes for the α subunit of CG, LH, FSH, and TSH. This work is described in more detail in Fiddes, J. C., and Goodman, H. M., *Mol. Appl. Genet.* (in press), 1981.

Inhibition of Testicular and Ovarian Functions by LHRH Agonists

FERNAND LABRIE, ALAIN BÉLANGER,
CARL SEGUIN, LIONEL CUSAN,
GEORGES PELLETIER, FLEUR-ANGE LEFEBVRE,
PAUL A. KELLY, LOUISE FERLAND,
AND JERRY J. REEVES
Department of Molecular Endocrinology
Le Centre Hospitalier
de l'Université Laval
Quebec, Canada

ANDRÉ LEMAY
Laboratory of Reproductive Endocrinology
Hôspital St. François d'Assise
Quebec, Canada

JEAN-PIERRE RAYNAUD
Centre de Recherches Roussel-UCLAF, Romainville, France

INTRODUCTION

An exciting area of research in the past few years has been the control of hormone receptors by homologous hormones. Although the detailed mechanisms involved are not yet understood, the data obtained already show that the response of a tissue to a specific hormone is not only dependent upon the circulating level of this hormone but also on the level and activity of the tissue receptor for this hormone. The stud-

305

BIOREGULATORS OF REPRODUCTION
Copyright © 1981 by Academic Press, Inc.

ies performed during the last 5 years on the control of luteinizing hormone-releasing hormone (LHRH) action in the anterior pituitary gland and luteinizing hormone (LH) action in the testis and ovary provide the best documented example of autoregulation of hormone receptor levels and action.

The discovery of LHRH in 1971 (1) and the availability of a large series of potent LHRH agonists have permitted a rapid growth of our knowledge of the control of gonadotropin secretion in experimental animals and man. However, although the synthetic releasing hormones provided a potential new therapeutic approach to the treatment of human infertility (2,3), only limited success could be obtained, especially in men (4,5).

The difficulties in achieving therapeutical success in the treatment of human infertility are most likely related to the now well-documented "paradoxic" antifertility effects of treatment with these peptides in both male (6–22) and female (23–39) experimental animals. Moreover, recent data clearly indicate that treatment with LHRH agonists can also lead to inhibition of reproductive functions in the human. Treatment with LHRH agonists induces luteolysis and inhibits ovulation in normal women (37,40–48), while the same treatment decreases testicular steroidogenesis in men (21,22,49,50).

Although the precise mechanisms responsible for the antifertility action of LHRH agonists are not yet fully understood, at least part of these effects are probably mediated by the loss of gonadal receptors and desensitization secondary to LHRH agonist-induced endogenous LH release (6–8,32,33). The direct inhibitory effect of LHRH agonists at the gonadal level (26,37,38,51–56) could also play a role which remains to be assessed. Another site of the antifertility effects of LHRH agonists is the adenohypophysis where a decreased gonadotropin responsiveness to LHRH follows acute or chronic treatment with LHRH agonists in both men and experimental animals (10,14,49).

Since the data already obtained suggest the potential use of LHRH agonists as a new approach in both male and female contraception and also in the treatment of androgen-dependent pathologies such as cancer of the prostate as well as estrogen-dependent pathologies such as breast cancer and endometriosis, it becomes important to study in detail the mechanisms responsible for the paradoxical antifertility effects of LHRH agonists. Such knowledge should help to determine the doses and schedule of administration of the LHRH agonists, which could, according to the clinical needs, lead to stimulation or inhibition of reproductive functions.

INHIBITION OF TESTICULAR FUNCTIONS IN THE RAT BY TREATMENT WITH LHRH AGONISTS

INHIBITION OF TESTICULAR GONADOTROPIN RECEPTORS BY SHORT-TERM TREATMENT WITH LHRH AGONISTS

Following our first and unexpected finding that single injection or daily treatment for 1 week with a relatively large dose (1.8 μg) of the potent LHRH agonist [D-Leu⁶]LHRH-EA leads to a marked reduction of testicular and secondary sex organ weight, LH receptor levels and plasma testosterone concentration (6), the effect of lower and more physiological doses of the LHRH agonist was studied.

As illustrated in Fig. 1A, there is a significant loss (30%) of testicular LH receptors in animals treated with as little as 8 ng of the LHRH agonist while a maximal effect (80%) is observed at doses ranging from 40–200 ng. Interestingly, the desensitizing effect of the LHRH agonist is more apparent in animals injected once rather than three times a

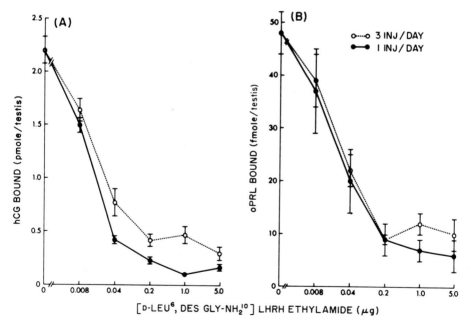

Fig. 1. Effect of increasing doses of [D-Leu⁶, des-Gly-NH₂¹⁰]LHRH-ethylamide injected once or 3 times a day for 7 days on testicular LH/hCG and prolactin receptor levels (7). (A) hCG bound (pmole/testis); (B) oPRL bound (fmole/testis).

day. Figure 1B shows that a similar inhibitory effect is seen on testicular prolactin receptor levels, a maximal effect being observed at 200 ng of the LHRH agonist. Since treatment with doses of 40 ng or higher of the LHRH agonist leads to a reduction of testis weight, it is important to mention that a similar inhibitory pattern is observed when LH and PRL receptor levels are expressed per gram of testis. It was also observed that plasma testosterone levels as well as testis and seminal vesicle weight are reduced after treatment with doses of 40 ng or higher of the LHRH agonist (7).

Since the LHRH agonist [D-Leu⁶]LHRH-EA is approximately 100 times more potent than LHRH and the fact that the natural decapeptide is used in many clinical studies for the treatment of oligospermia

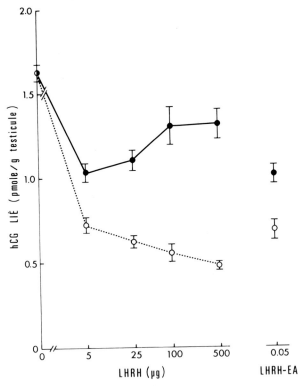

Fig. 2.   Effect of a single injection of increasing doses of native LHRH (5, 25, 100, or 500 μg) or [D-Ala⁶]LHRH-EA (0.05 μg) on binding of [¹²⁵I]hCG to testicular LH receptors in adult male rats. Determinations were made 2 (○) or 8 (●) days after administration of the peptide (8).

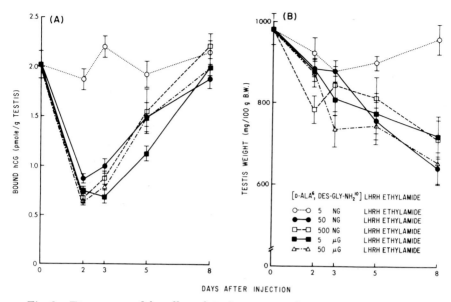

Fig. 3. Time course of the effect of single injection of increasing doses of [D-Ala⁶, des-Gly-NH₂¹⁰]LHRH-ethylamide on testicular [¹²⁵I]hCG binding and testis weight in adult male rats (57).

and male infertility, we next studied the effect of treatment with LHRH itself on testicular LH receptors and function in the rat (8).

Adult male Sprague-Dawley rats were injected s.c. with a single dose of 5, 25, 100, or 500 μg of LHRH or 0.05 μg of [D-Ala⁶]LHRH-EA (an analog approximately equipotent with [D-Leu⁶]LHRH-EA and the animals were killed 2 or 8 days later. It can be seen in Fig. 2 that single injection of 5 μg of LHRH or 0.05 μg of [D-Ala⁶]LHRH-EA leads to approximately the same inhibition of testicular LH receptor levels. It can also be noticed that the inhibitory effect is maximal at 2 days with a 50–75% recovery of LH receptor levels at 8 days. Treatment with LHRH or its agonist also leads to a 50–75% inhibition of plasma testosterone levels at 2 days with partial recovery at 8 days. In addition, a significant reduction of seminal vesicle weight is observed at 8 days with the LHRH agonist and at doses of LHRH of 100 μg or higher (8).

Before performing long-term studies of the effect of treatment with the LHRH agonist, we next investigated the time course of changes of LH receptor levels after single injection of increasing doses of [D-Ala⁶]LHRH-EA. While the 5 ng dose has no significant effect, a maximal inhibition of LH receptor levels is obtained at 2 and 3 days with as little as 50 ng of the peptide. Doses up to a 1000-fold higher (50 μg) do not show any increase in inhibitory activity (Fig. 3A). It can be seen in Fig. 3B that a progressive decrease of testis weight is obtained after single administration of doses of 50 ng or higher of the LHRH agonist.

INHIBITION OF TESTICULAR STEROIDOGENESIS (SHORT-TERM TREATMENT)

The above-mentioned studies show that treatment of adult male rats with LHRH or its agonistic analogs leads to a marked loss of testicular LH receptors accompanied by decreased testis, ventral prostate, and seminal vesicle weight as well as lowered plasma testosterone concentration (6–8,57). In order to analyze the steroidogenic pathway during desensitization induced by LHRH agonist treatment, we first examined the time course of the effect of daily administration of 1 μg of [D-Ala^6]LHRH-EA on testicular and plasma levels of steroid intermediates. Changes of testicular LH, prolactin, and FSH receptor levels have been correlated with changes of steroidogenesis. As can be seen on Fig. 4, the ratio of 17-OH-progesterone to progesterone decreases rapidly following LHRH agonist treatment, thus suggesting a rapid inhibition of 17-hydroxylase activity. The progressive and dramatic fall in testicular androstenedione and testosterone levels following treatment with the LHRH agonist is well illustrated in Fig. 5. An

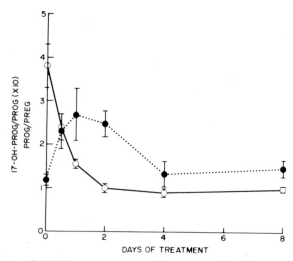

Fig. 4. Ratios of 17-OH-progesterone to progesterone (○) and progesterone to pregnenolone (●) testicular concentrations at different time intervals during treatment with the LHRH agonist [D-Ala^6, des-Gly-NH$_2$^{10}]LHRH-ethylamide (19).

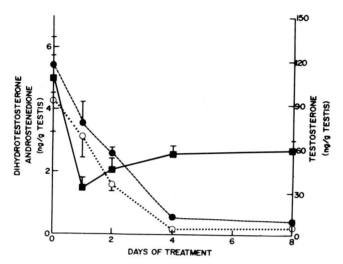

Fig. 5.   Time course of the effect of daily s.c. injection of 1 μg of [D-Ala[6], des-Gly-NH$_2$[10]]LHRH-ethylamide on testicular androstenedione (○), testosterone (●), and 5α-dihydrotestosterone (■) in adult rats (19).

approximately 25% inhibition of the concentration of these two steroids is already seen at 24 hours with a progressive decrease to 5–15% of control at 4 days. The inhibitory effect on 5α-dihydrotestosterone levels is however of much lower amplitude: the decrease to 30% of control observed at 1 day is followed by a slow increase reaching 50% of control values at 8 days.

Contrary to the marked changes observed in the androgen biosynthetic pathway after treatment with the LHRH agonist, except for the small increase of testicular estrone and 17β-estradiol levels seen 12 hours after the first injection of the peptide, no further change of estrogen levels is noticed up to 8 days of treatment. The 20-fold increase of the estrone to androstenedione ratio observed between days 2 and 4 after LHRH agonist treatment strongly suggests a corresponding increase of testicular aromatase activity.

The transformation of pregnenolone into testosterone can occur through two biosynthetic routes, the Δ^4 and Δ^5 pathways, in Leydig cells. The relative importance of the two pathways varies according to species but the Δ^4 pathway appears to be the main biosynthetic route in the adult male rat. As indicated by the ratio of 17-OH-progesterone to progesterone (Fig. 4), 17-hydroxylase activity is already significantly decreased 24 hours after the first injection of the LHRH agonist, at a time when no significant change of LH receptor levels could be observed. The apparent maximal inhibitory effect on 17-hydroxyl-ase activity is seen at 2 days when LH receptor levels are decreased to 30% of control. As indicated by the ratios of androstenedione to 17-OH-progesterone, decreased 17,20-desmolase activity is also measured at 24 hours, while a maximal inhibition is seen at 2 days. Parallel changes of testicular and plasma levels of progesterone and testosterone support the use of testicular levels of steroid intermediates as index of enzymatic activity.

Since our previous studies have indicated that inhibition of the testicular steroidogenic pathway is observed after 4 days of treatment with a relative high dose (1 μg) of the LHRH analog (Figs. 4 and 5), we next studied the effect of increasing doses of [D-Ala⁶]LHRH-EA administered daily for 9 days on testicular gonadotropin receptors as well as on steroid levels under basal conditions as well as after stimulation with oLH.

As previously observed with the LHRH agonist [D-Leu⁶]LHRH-EA, daily injection of increasing doses of [D-Ala⁶]LHRH-EA for 9 days induces a dose-dependent inhibition of testicular LH binding. While no significant effect is observed with the 1 and 5 ng doses, a 50% decrease in the number of LH receptors is found at the dose of 10 ng while a maximal inhibition at 5–10% of control ($P < .01$) is obtained after administration of the 50 or 250 ng doses. A progressive decrease of testicular prolactin receptor levels is also observed, a maximal effect ($P < .01$) being obtained with daily administration of 10 ng of the LHRH agonist.

As illustrated in Fig. 6A, the basal levels of testicular testosterone and androstenedione are not affected after administration of 1 or 5 ng of the agonistic analog while the 50 and 250 ng doses induce a marked decrease of the level of these androgens to 5–10% of control ($P < .01$). The 10 ng dose of the agonistic analog induces a 50% decrease of basal testicular testosterone levels while no significant effect is observed on androstenedione concentration. When the testicular testosterone and androstenedione responses to oLH are measured, a biphasic pattern is observed. At the lowest doses (1, 5, or 10 ng) of the agonistic analog, the androstenedione and testosterone responses to oLH are increased (Fig. 6B). A maximal stimulatory effect is observed at the 5 ng dose, the androstenedione and testosterone responses to oLH being increased from 452 ± 22 and 815 ± 40 to 745 ± 22 and 1511 ± 150 ng/g testis ($P < .01$), respectively. By contrast, an almost complete inhibition of the androgen response to oLH is seen in animals treated with the 50 or 250 ng doses of LHRH agonist ($P < .01$) (Fig. 6B). It should be mentioned that slightly increased androstene-

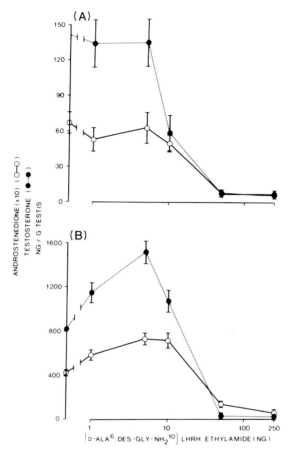

Fig. 6. Effect of treatment with increasing doses of [D-Ala⁶, des-Gly-NH₂¹⁰]LHRH-ethylamide injected once daily for 9 days on testicular androstenedione (○) and testosterone (●) concentrations. (A). Basal testicular levels. (B). Response to 10 μg of oLH kindly provided by Dr. M. R. Sairam (2 hours after injection) (19).

dione and testosterone responses to oLH are obtained in animals treated with the 10 ng dose of the agonistic analog when only 50% of LH receptors are present.

When the effect of treatment with increasing doses of the LHRH analog was measured on plasma steroid levels, no effect was observed on basal plasma progesterone concentration while plasma 17-OH-progesterone levels were 15–30% inhibited at the four highest doses of LHRH-A and plasma testosterone levels decreased progressively to 3% of control at the highest dose of LHRH-A used (from 6.6 ± 0.1 to

0.22 ± 0.01 ng/ml, $P < .01$). The increased response of testicular androgen levels to oLH observed after treatment with low doses of the LHRH agonist could also be measured in plasma. An increase of the plasma testosterone response to oLH from 25 ± 2 to 50 ± 10 ng/ml ($P < .01$) was observed at the 10 ng dose of LHRH-A. In analogy with the testicular steroid content, a marked inhibition of plasma testosterone levels was, however, observed after treatment with higher doses of the agonistic analog.

The present data clearly show that a marked inhibition of basal testicular and plasma testosterone concentrations, apparently due to a decrease of the enzymatic activities of 17-hydroxylase and 17,20-desmolase, is obtained after daily administration of the LHRH agonist at doses greater than 10 ng. It is of great interest that treatment with low doses of the LHRH agonist can lead to an increased steroidogenic response to oLH. In fact, after daily treatment with 1 or 5 ng of [D-Ala^6]LHRH-EA for 9 days, the testicular response of progesterone, 17-OH-progesterone, androstenedione, and testosterone is increased in the presence of unchanged testicular LH receptor levels. At the 10 ng dose of the LHRH agonist which leads to a 50% loss of LH receptors, a significant increase of the testicular androstenedione and testosterone as well as plasma testosterone responses to oLH is also observed. Such findings raise the interesting possibility that treatment with low doses of LHRH agonists could stimulate Leydig cell function while high doses could be inhibitory (9,57).

INHIBITION OF SPERMATOGENESIS (LONG-TERM TREATMENT)

Following the dramatic inhibitory effects of short-term treatment with LHRH and its agonists on testicular gonadotropin levels and steroidogenesis, we have studied the effect of long-term treatment with an LHRH agonist on the same parameters and on spermatogenesis.

Chronic administration of an LHRH agonist leads to a progressive decrease of testis, prostate, and seminal vesicle weight with a maximal inhibitory effect remaining up to at least 12 weeks, the longest time interval studied (14). This decreased weight of the accessory organs is accompanied by a progressive increase of both plasma LH and FSH levels.

Since the marked loss of testis weight following treatment with the LHRH agonist is likely due to some defect in spermatogenesis, it was important to investigate the cellular changes occurring in rat testis during chronic administration of [D-Ala^6]LHRH-EA. After 1 week of

treatment with the LHRH agonist (100 ng, twice a week), no striking
change can be observed in the histology of the testis except that a few
seminiferous tubules seem to present some regressive changes. However, from 2 to 8 weeks after the beginning of treatment, marked
changes can be seen. At 2 weeks, many tubules show degenerative
changes associated with disruption of cellular association. A few tubules still appear relatively normal and spermatozoa can be found in
large number in the epididymis. In most tubules, Sertoli cells appear
to contain vacuoles. This abnormality of Sertoli cells is present at all
time intervals studied after 2 weeks of treatment.

More dramatic changes are observed after 4 weeks of treatment, almost all tubules exhibiting signs of regression. In about 25% of tubules, the process of degeneration is so advanced that almost all germ
cells have disappeared leaving only the Sertoli cells (9). Only a few
spermatozoa can still be seen in the epididymis. At 8 weeks, all the
tubules show advanced degenerative changes. At all the time inter-

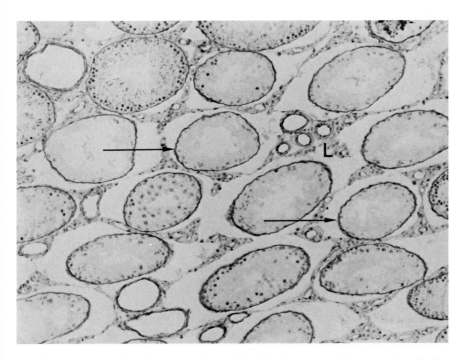

Fig. 7.   Section through a testis of a rat which had been treated for 4 weeks with the
LHRH analog. All the tubules are presenting degenerative changes. In some tubules
(→), all the germinal and Sertoli cells have completely disappeared. Leydig cells (L)
have a normal appearance.

vals studied, no morphological change can be observed in the Leydig cells. In fact, preliminary results obtained at the ultrastructural level indicate that Leydig cells retain their normal appearance after 1 to 4 weeks of administration of the LHRH agonist.

In a second series of experiments, where the same LHRH analog was administered at a higher dose (1 µg every second day instead of 100 ng, twice a week), the administration of the LHRH agonist for 4 weeks also induced degenerative changes in almost all seminiferous tubules. In about 20–30% of tubules, the process of degeneration is so advanced that almost all germinal and Sertoli cells have disappeared (Fig. 7). The Leydig cells do not show any significant morphological change. At this time interval, testis weight is decreased by approximately 40%.

REVERSIBILITY OF THE LOSS OF TESTICULAR GONADOTROPIN RECEPTORS, STEROIDOGENESIS, AND SPERMATOGENESIS

Four weeks after cessation of 1 month of LHRH-A treatment, the histology of the testis shows improvement. Whereas about 22% of tubules still have complete degenerative changes, many other tubules appear much less disrupted than immediately after the end of treatment. In several tubules, germ cells appear in the process of reorganization (Fig. 8) and some tubules are at advanced stages of spermatogenesis. Eight and sixteen (Fig. 9) weeks after the end of treatment, many more tubules show well-organized germinal cells and a normal appearance is even seen in some tubules. However, about 25% of tubules still remain completely degenerated at the longest time interval studied. It is of interest that in hypophysectomized rats, administration of the LHRH agonist for 10 or 30 days at the daily dose of 0.1 µg does not induce any morphological change different from those observed in hypophysectomized animals treated with the vehicle alone.

As illustrated in Fig. 10, testicular LH receptor levels which are reduced to 10% of control after 1 month of treatment with [D-Ala^6]LHRH-EA return to normal 1 month later. It can also be seen that the 35% loss of testicular prolactin receptors measured at the end of treatment with the LHRH analog completely disappears during the same recovery period (Fig. 10B). Both LH and prolactin receptor levels remain within normal values up to the last time interval studied (4 months after cessation of LHRH-A administration). The same pattern of recovery is observed when LH and prolactin receptors are expressed per testis.

Testis, ventral prostate, and seminal vesicle weights are 40, 30, and

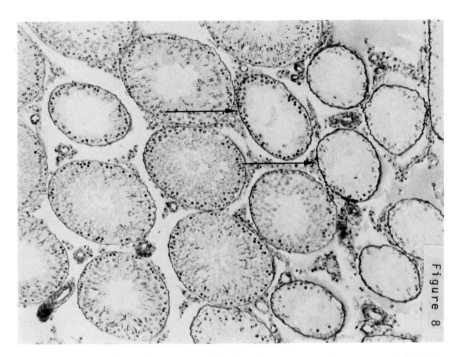

Figure 8

Fig. 8.   Section through a rat testis after 4 weeks of recuperation. Some tubules (→) are still almost completely degenerated whereas others show a reorganization of germ cells. × 175.

45% decreased, respectively, after 1 month of treatment with the LHRH analog (Fig. 11). Ventral prostate and seminal vesicle weights rapidly return to normal, the small differences (10–15%) observed 1 month after cessation of treatment being nonsignificant. Testis weight, however, returns more slowly toward normal values, incomplete recoveries at 77 ($P <$ .05), 78 ($P <$ .01), and 85% ($P <$ .05) of control being still found 1, 2, and 4 months after the end of treatment.

In agreement with the changes of ventral prostate and seminal vesicle weight (Fig. 11), it could be seen that testicular testosterone and dihydrotestosterone concentrations return to normal levels within 1 month after cessation of LHRH-A treatment. Parallel changes of plasma testosterone and dihydrotestosterone levels are observed.

The present data confirm our previous report which shows that the administration of an LHRH agonist to adult male rats leads to a marked inhibition of spermatogenesis (9) and indicates that this deleterious effect can be partially reversed within 1 or 2 months after cessation of treatment. Although almost all seminiferous tubules show

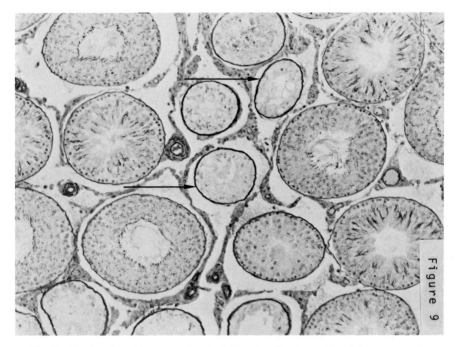

Figure 9

Fig. 9.   Section through a rat testis after 16 weeks of recuperation. A large proportion (60%) of tubules having a normal appearance can be observed. Some tubules (27, see arrows) are still completely regressed. ×175.

histological signs of damage after 4 weeks of treatment, normalization of the appearance of a large number of these tubules within 1 and 2 months indicates that they still contain elements capable of germ cell regeneration. However, even at 8 and 16 weeks after cessation of treatment, about 25% of tubules are still completely degenerated. The absence of recuperation of some tubules could be related to a complete disappearance of Sertoli cells which are considered as being the most resistant cellular elements in the seminiferous tubules.

The present data also show that the marked reduction in the concentration of testicular LH and prolactin receptors, the lowering of plasma testosterone and dihydrotestosterone concentration as well as the decrease in ventral prostate and seminal vesicle weight are reversible within 1 month after cessation of treatment of adult rats with the LHRH agonistic analog [D-Ala^6]LHRH-EA for the same time period.

Although the mechanisms by which the LHRH agonist can induce inhibition of spermatogenesis are still unknown, the partial reversal of the inhibitory effect observed in the present study raises the hope of

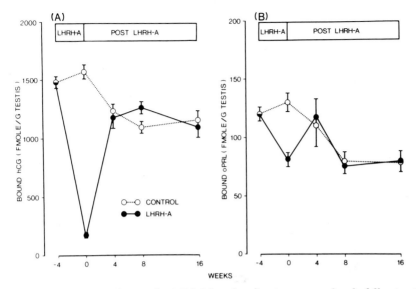

Fig. 10. Recovery of testicular LH/hCG and prolactin receptor levels following 1 month of treatment of adult rats with [D-Ala⁶, des-Gly-NH₂¹⁰]LHRH-ethylamide at a dose of 1 μg s.c. every second day.

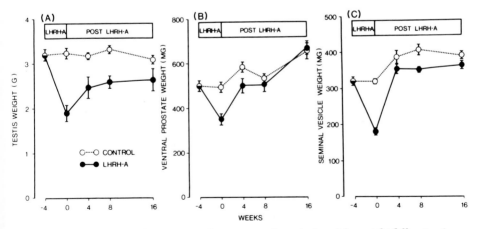

Fig. 11. Recovery of testis, ventral prostate, and seminal vesicle weight following 1 month of treatment of adult rats with [D-Ala⁶, des-Gly-NH₂¹⁰]LHRH-ethylamide at a dose of 1 μg s.c. every second day.

possible clinical use of such treatment as a contraceptive agent. Long-term studies (both treatment and recovery periods) are however required to support the clinical use of LHRH agonists as a reversible treatment for inhibition of spermatogenesis.

DIRECT ACTION OF LHRH AGONISTS AT THE TESTICULAR LEVEL

Since the antifertility effects of LHRH agonists are parallel to their LH-releasing activity (14), it has been suggested that endogenous LH release leading to a secondary loss of gonadal receptors and blockage of steroidogenesis is responsible for the antifertility effects observed after such treatment (6–8,57). However, the early observation by Rippel and Johnson (26) that administration of a potent LHRH agonist to hypophysectomized immature rats prevents the hCG-induced increase in ovarian weight already suggested a direct ovarian site of action of the peptide. More recently, a direct *in vivo* action of LHRH agonists has also been observed by other groups at both the ovarian (51,52,54,55,56,58) and testicular (21,22,53,59) levels. Moroever, LHRH agonists have been shown to inhibit steroidogenesis in granulosa and luteal cells in culture (51,52,58,60), thus providing strong support for the direct inhibitory action of these peptides on ovarian function in the rat.

Although LHRH and some of its agonistic analogs have been shown to have direct gonadal effects in hypophysectomized animals, pharmacological doses of the LH-releasing peptides have been used and no dose–response study has been performed. Comparison of the inhibitory effects of increasing doses of an LHRH agonist in intact and hypophysectomized animals should provide useful information about the relative importance of the pituitary and gonadal sites of action of the peptide for induction of antifertility effects. The present study compares the effects of increasing doses of an LHRH agonist on testicular and ovarian gonadotropin receptors and steroidogenesis in intact and hypophysectomized rats.

As illustrated in Fig. 12, the administration of 1 μg of [D-Ala^6, des-Gly-NH$_2$^{10}]LHRH-ethylamide, [D-Ala^6]LHRH-EA, 12 hours before hypophysectomy causes a 50% ($P < .01$) decrease of testicular LH receptor levels measured 48 hours after surgery. When administered immediately after hypophysectomy, the analog produces only a 20% ($P < .05$) loss of LH binding sites.

Since the previous data show that a relatively high dose of the LHRH agonist, [D-Ala^6]LHRH-EA, leads to a much greater loss of testicular LH receptors in intact than hypophysectomized animals, we

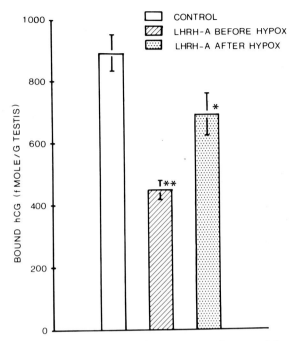

Fig. 12. Comparative effect of single injection of 1 μg of [D-Ala^6, des-Gly-NH$_2$^{10}]LHRH-ethylamide 12 hours before or immediately after hypophysectomy on testicular LH receptor levels in adult rats. The animals were sacrificed 2 days after surgery.

next investigated in more detail the effect of increasing doses of an LHRH agonist of comparable potency, [D-Ser(TBU)^6]LHRH-EA, on various parameters of gonadal function in intact and hypophysectomized rats.

As illustrated in Fig. 13, treatment of intact rats with the daily doses of 1 or 3 ng of [D-Ser(TBU)^6]LHRH-EA leads to a 35–50% stimulation of testicular LH receptor levels while the 10, 30, and 300 ng doses decrease LH receptors by 20, 65, and 90%, respectively. By contrast, in hypophysectomized animals, the 1 and 3 ng doses have no effect while the 10, 30, and 100 ng doses reduce LH receptor levels by only 20, 40, and 35% respectively.

Since treatment of adult male rats with LHRH agonists leads to an important blockage of the testicular steroidogenic pathway at the level of 17-hydroxylase and 17,20-desmolase activities (7,17,19), we next investigated a possible effect of similar treatment on the testicular steroidogenic pathway in the absence of the pituitary gland.

While testicular pregnenolone and 17-OH-pregnenolone levels are

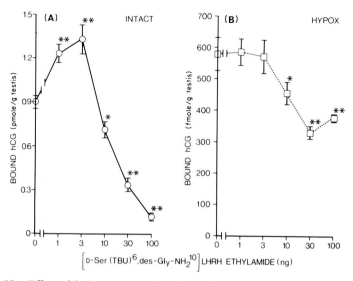

Fig. 13. Effect of daily treatment for 9 days of intact (A) or hypophysectomized (3 days earlier) (B) rats with increasing doses of [D-Ser(TBU)⁶, des-Gly-NH₂¹⁰]LHRH-ethylamide on testicular LH/hCG receptor levels. The animals were sacrificed 24 hours after the last injection of the LHRH agonist or vehicle alone (1% gelatin–0.9% NaCl).

not detectable in these animals, treatment with any dose (1 to 100 ng) of the LHRH agonist leads to an inhibition of testicular basal level of all steroids. Moreover, in contrast with the marked changes of the steroidogenic response to oLH observed in intact animals treated with the LHRH agonist (19), no or little effect of the same treatment can be seen in hypophysectomized animals (Fig. 14). In fact, only a slight (approximately 25%, $P < .05$) inhibition of the testosterone response is seen after treatment with the two highest doses of the LHRH agonist, while the 17-OH-progesterone response is increased and no significant change is seen on the response of the seven other steroids measured.

The present data show that single or repeated administration of LHRH agonists can lead to a loss of testicular LH receptors in the absence of the pituitary gland. However, the LH receptor loss observed in hypophysectomized rats is reduced compared to the effect seen in intact animals. These data extend previous observations obtained with high doses of LHRH agonists in hypophysectomized animals (53,59) and provide detailed information on the accompanying changes of steroidogenesis.

While treatment with LHRH agonists has been found to markedly decrease in the *in vitro* steroidogenic response to hCG in testes obtained from hypophysectomized animals treated concomitantly with FSH (59), the present data show little or no impairment of the *in vivo* steroidogenic response to oLH in animals not receiving FSH. Although different ages of the animals and doses of the LHRH agonists could play a role, it is possible that the LHRH agonists do not interfere directly with the enzymes of the steroidogenic pathway but inhibit the effect of LH possibily present at a low level in the FSH preparation used. This competition with LH action could be achieved through loss of LH receptors or possibly through LHRH receptor-mediated inhibition of adenylate cyclase activity in Leydig cells. We have in fact recently found that LHRH agonists can reverse the stimulatory effect of FSH on cyclic AMP accumulation in porcine granulosa cells *in vitro* (58).

While treatment of intact adult male rats leads to a loss of LH receptors accompanied by a marked blockage of the steroidogenic pathway at the level of 17-hydroxylase and 17,20-desmolase and a stimulation of 5α-reductase activities (17,19,21,22), the same treatment of hypo-

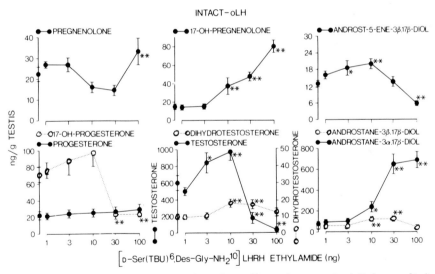

Fig. 14. Effect of daily treatment for 9 days of hypophysectomized (3 days earlier) adult rats with increasing doses of [D-Ser(TBU)^6, des-Gly-NH$_2$^{10}]LHRH-ethylamide on oLH-stimulated testicular levels of pregnenolone, 17-OH-pregnenolone, androst-5-ene-3α, 17β-diol, progesterone, 17-OH-progesterone, testosterone, 5α-dihydrotestosterone, androstane-3α, 17β-diol, and androstane-3β, 17α-diol. The animals were sacrificed 24 hours after the last injection of the LHRH agonist and 2 hours after the administration of 20 μg of oLH.

physectomized animals leads to a smaller loss of testicular LH receptors and a minimal or no effect on the steroidogenic pathway as measured by testicular steroid levels 2 hours after the administration of 10 μg of oLH. Such data suggest that endogenous LH release induced by the LHRH agonists is probably the main factor responsible for the loss of gonadotropin receptors, blockage of the steroidogenic pathway as well as inhibition of spermatogenesis after treatment of intact animals with LHRH agonists.

In order to gain a better understanding of the direct action of LHRH agonists at the testicular level, we have studied the characteristics of the LHRH receptors in this tissue. ^{125}I-labeled [D-Ser(TBU)^6]LHRH-EA binds to purified Leydig cells to a single class of high affinity sites at an apparent K_m of 0.2 nM. As illustrated in Fig. 14, unlabeled [D-Ser(TBU)^6]LHRH-EA, LHRH, and the weak agonist [Glu^1]LHRH displace the tracer at ED$_{50}$ values of 1.0, 5.6, and 45 nM, respectively. In the anterior pituitary gland, ED$_{50}$ values of 0.38, 48, and 170 nM are found. Although the relative affinity for the LHRH receptor in Leydig cells and anterior pituitary membranes should be studied with a much larger series of LHRH agonists and antagonists of different biological activity, the present data already indicate the presence of a specific LHRH receptors in Leydig cells. No binding of ^{125}I-labeled [D-Ser(TBU)^6]LHRH-EA is found in homogenates from seminiferous tubules or Sertoli cells.

Although the mechanisms involved remain to be assessed, it is quite likely that these gonadal receptors are involved in the direct inhibitory effects of LHRH agonists at the testicular level. The presence of specific LHRH receptors in testicular tissue raises the interesting question of a possible role of these receptors in the physiological control of gonadal function by a locally produced LHRH-like molecule.

INHIBITION OF OVARIAN FUNCTIONS IN THE RAT BY TREATMENT WITH LHRH AGONISTS

INHIBITION OF OVARIAN GONADOTROPIN RECEPTORS AND STEROIDOGENESIS (SHORT-TERM TREATMENT)

Following our observations of a loss of testicular LH receptors (6–8,57) and blockage of steroidogenesis (16,17,19) in male rats treated with LHRH agonists, it became of interest to investigate the possibility of a similar loss of ovarian gonadotropin receptors in female ani-

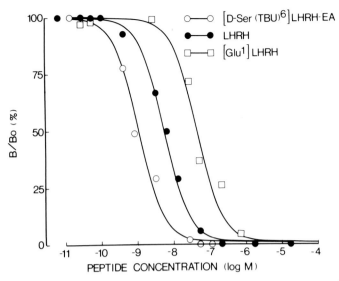

Fig. 15. Displacement of ¹²⁵I[D-Ser(TBU)⁶]LHRH-EA binding to isolated adult rat Leydig cells by increasing concentrations of unlabeled [D-Ser(TBU)⁶]LHRH-EA, LHRH, or [Glu¹]LHRH.

mals. Such a finding could offer an explanation for the antifertility effects of such treatment in rats and rabbits (23–31).

As illustrated in Fig. 16, LH and FSH ovarian receptors are at their lowest levels on estrus in intact 4-day cycling rats and increase progressively to a maximum on proestrus. A single injection of 25 μg of [D-Ala⁶, des-Gly-NH₂¹⁰]LHRH-ethylamide on the morning of diestrus I leads to a marked reduction of LH and FSH receptor levels as measured on diestrus II and proestrus. While the amount of LH receptors is still slightly below that of controls on the expected morning of estrus, the level of FSH receptors has reached values higher than control at that time.

Since we recently observed that a maximal inhibitory effect of [D-Leu⁶, des-Gly-NH₂¹⁰]LHRH-ethylamide on testicular LH receptor levels was obtained with a single injection of only 40 ng of the peptide in the intact male rat (7), we next examined the effect of increasing doses of the LHRH agonist on ovarian LH and FSH receptor levels measured on the morning of expected proestrus. A single injection of as little as 8 ng of the LHRH agonist on diestrus I leads to a significant reduction of ovarian LH receptors (30%, 32). A near-maximal inhibition (60%) of ovarian LH receptors is seen at the dose of

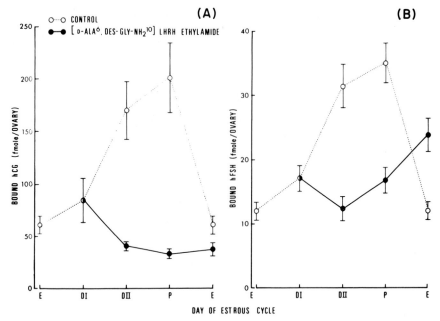

Fig. 16. Effect of a single injection of 25 μg of [D-Ala⁶, des-Gly-NH₂¹⁰]LHRH-ethyl-amide on ovarian LH/hCG (A) and FSH (B) receptor levels. Cycling female rats received injections on the morning of diestrus I and were killed 1, 2, or 3 days later (32).

40 ng, the inhibitory effect remaining of similar megnitude up to a dose of 25 μg.

The decrease of ovarian LH receptors is accompanied by a marked reduction of uterine wet weight, intrauterine fluid, and plasma progesterone concentration as measured on the morning of expected proestrus; serum LH and FSH levels remain unchanged (32).

The present data demonstrate that the single injection of relatively low doses of the LHRH agonist [D-Ala⁶, des-Gly-NH₂¹⁰]LHRH-ethyl-amide on the morning of diestrus I in 4-day cycling rats leads to a marked loss of ovarian LH receptors. This receptor loss is accompanied by a decreased plasma progesterone concentration and uterine weight as measured on the morning of expected proestrus.

Of the 10 rats that received injections on diestrus I of 160 ng of the peptide, only 7 ovulated. It thus appears that the maximal inhibitory effect on ovarian LH receptors occurs at a subovulatory dose of the LHRH analog. This observation might have relevance for a potential clinical application of the antifertility effects of LHRH and its agonists.

The same data show that the sensitivity of the ovarian LH receptors to the inhibitory effect of treatment with the LHRH agonists is very similar to that of the testicular LH receptors. In fact, we have observed that a maximal inhibitory effect on testicular LH receptors, plasma testosterone concentration, and testicular, ventral prostate, and seminal vesicle weight is achieved after single injection of 40 ng of an analog of similar potency, [D-Leu[6], des-Gly-NH$_2$[10]]LHRH-ethylamide (7).

A study of the effect of treatment with an LHRH agonist on ovarian gonadotropin receptors and serum steroid levels was then performed in pregnant rats (33). [D-Ala[6], des-Gly-NH$_2$[10]]LHRH-ethylamide (25 μg) or saline was injected subcutaneously three times daily for various lengths of time starting on day 7 of pregnancy. The last injection was given 12 hours before sacrifice with the exception of groups killed on day 18, which received the last injection on day 12. Uteri were examined for fetuses and implantation sites.

Although no apparent effect on fetuses could be seen 24 hours after the first injection of the analog, treatment from days 7 to 9 led to visible signs of resorption of all fetuses examined on day 10. Almost com-

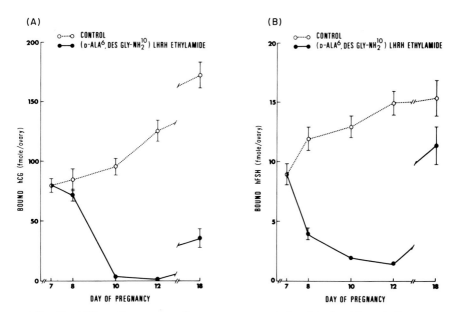

Fig. 17. Effect of treatment of pregnant rats with [D-Ala[6], des-Gly-NH$_2$[10]]LHRH-ethylamide on ovarian [^{125}I]hCG binding. The peptide was given at the dose of 25 μg, three times daily, starting on day 7 of pregnancy (33). (A) Bound hCG (fmole/ovary); (B) bound hFSH (fmole/ovary).

plete resorption was seen on day 12, and no sign of pregnancy was found on day 18 in animals treated from day 7 to 12.

As is illustrated in Fig. 17, treatment with the LHRH agonist leads to an almost complete loss of ovarian LH/hCG receptors measured on days 10, 12, and 18. The inhibitory effect of [D-Ala^6, des-Gly-NH$_2$^{10}]LHRH-ethylamide on the level of FSH receptors was already well established on day 8. Treatment with the LHRH agonist leads to a 45 to 60% reduction of plasma progesterone levels at all time intervals studied, whereas plasma LH levels are not affected at the times chosen (at least 12 hours after injection of the LHRH agonist (33).

The present data clearly demonstrate that the antifertility effects of [D-Ala^6, des-Gly-NH$_2$^{10}]LHRH-ethylamide are accompanied by a marked loss of LH/hCG and FSH receptors in ovarian tissue. Although LH is known to be essential for maintenance of pregnancy up to day 12 in the rat, the present findings show that increased gonadotropin secretion can have deleterious effects. The luteolytic action of treatment with [D-Ala^6, des-Gly-NH$_2$^{10}]LHRH-ethylamide is well illustrated by the 45 to 60% decrease in plasma progesterone levels in all treated groups.

DIRECT ACTION OF LHRH AGONISTS AT THE OVARIAN LEVEL

By analogy with the experiments performed in male animals, we have compared the efficiency of treatment to LHRH agonists to decrease ovarian LH receptors in intact and hypophysectomized female rats.

Figure 18 illustrates the comparative effect of a single injection of 1 μg of [D-Ala^6]LHRH-EA 12 hours before and immediately after hypophysectomy on the level of ovarian LH/hCG and FSH receptors. When injected before hypophysectomy, [D-Ala^6]LHRH-EA inhibits LH receptor levels by 65% while a 40% decrease is seen when the peptide is administered immediately after hypophysectomy. In the same groups, FSH receptors are decreased by 45 and 35%, respectively.

As illustrated in Fig. 19, the injection of 1, 3, or 10 ng of [D-Ser(TBU)^{6}LHRH-EA in intact rats has no significant effect on ovarian LH receptor levels while treatment with the 30 and 100 ng doses decreases LH receptor levels by 35 and 95% ($P < .01$), respectively. In hypophysectomized animals, a significant loss of ovarian LH receptors (30%, $P < .05$) is seen in animals treated with as little as 3 ng of the LHRH agonist. The daily 10, 30, 100 ng doses of the peptide decrease ovarian LH binding sites by 40, 82, and 94%, respectively.

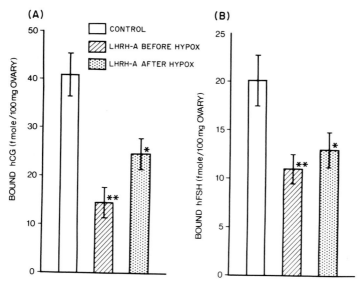

Fig. 18. Comparative effect of single injection of 1 μg of [D-Ala⁶, des-Gly-NH₂¹⁰]LHRH-ethylamide 12 hours before or immediately after hypophysectomy performed on diestrus I on ovarian LH and FSH receptors in adult rats. The animals were sacrificed 2 days after surgery. (A) Bound hCG (fmole/100 mg ovary); (B) bound hFSH (fmole/100 mg ovary).

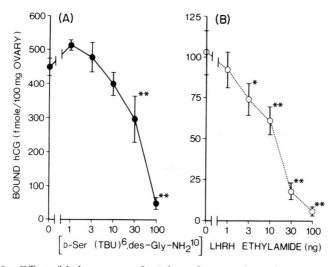

Fig. 19. Effect of daily treatment for 9 days of intact or hypophysectomized (3 days earlier) (HYPOX) rats with increasing doses of [D-Ser(TBU)⁶, des-Gly-NH₂¹⁰]LHRH-ethylamide on ovarian LH/hCG receptors. The animals were sacrificed 24 hours after the last injection of the peptide. (A) Intact; (B) hypox.

The experiments performed in male rats show that treatment with LHRH agonists leads to a much greater loss of testicular LH receptors in intact than hypophysectomized animals, thus indicating a major role of endogenous LH in gonadal desensitization. In the female rat, however, the similar potency of the LHRH agonist to induce a loss of ovarian LH receptors in intact and hypophysectomized animals suggests that the gonadal site of action may be more important.

The recent demonstration of specific uptake of a labeled LHRH agonist in the rat ovary (54) and the finding of high affinity LHRH binding sites in rat luteal cells and ovarian homogenate (60) support the findings of direct effects of LHRH agonists at the ovarian level.

In order to gain a better understanding of the action of LHRH analogs in the ovary, a large series of LHRH agonists and antagonists were used to study the specificity of the LHRH receptor in this tissue. The highly potent and stable LHRH agonist [D-Ser(TBU)^6]LHRH-EA was used as the iodinated tracer.

[D-Ser(TBU)^6]LHRH-EA and LHRH displace ^{125}I-labeled [D-Ser(TBU)^6]LHRH-EA at K_d values of 0.18 and 19 nM, respectively, in rat ovarian homogenate, while LHRH-EA has an intermediate value of 2.2 nM (61). It could also be seen that the superagonist [D-Leu^6]LHRH-EA has a high affinity while the weak LHRH agonists [Glu^1]LHRH and [D-Leu^2]LHRH displace the labeled tracer only at high concentrations. The ability of these peptides to inhibit binding of ^{125}I-labeled [D-Ser(TBU)^6]LHRH-EA to ovarian homogenates is similar to their activities in pituitary homogenates. Moreover, the order of potency of all the LHRH agonists to interact with the LHRH receptor in both pituitary and ovarian tissue correlates with their ability to stimulate LH release in rat anterior pituitary cells in primary culture (61).

It can be seen (61a) that the LHRH antagonists [Des-His^2, D-Phe^6]LHRH and [DpGlu^1, D-Phe^2, D-Trp^3, D-Phe^6]LHRH displace the iodinated ligand from both adenohypophyseal and ovarian homogenates at concentrations lower than LHRH itself while [D-Phe^2, D-Phe^3, D-Phe^6]LH-RH, [Des-His^2, D-Leu^6]LHRH, and [Des-His^2, D-Ala^6] are almost equipotent and [D-Phe^2, D-Phe^6, D-Trp^8]LHRH, [D-Phe^2, D-Phe^3, D-Phe^6, D-Leu^7]LHRH, and [des-His^2]LHRH are less potent than the natural hormone. As noticed previously for the LHRH agonists, the biological activity of all the antagonists corresponds well with their order of potency at the receptor sites in both tissues. The biologically inactive peptides, [D-pGlu^1, des-His^2]LHRH-EA, [des-His^2, Leu^3]LHRH-EA, H-Glu-His-OH, H-Glu-His-Trp-Ser-Tyr-OH, H-Glu-His-Trp-Ser-Trp-Gly-OH, H-Glu-His-Trp-Ser-Tyr-Gly-Leu-Arg-

OH, [His³]LHRH, oxytocin, and somatostatin were inactive in the receptor binding assay up to 10 μM.

The present data clearly demonstrate a close relationship between the binding activity of a large series of LHRH agonists and antagonists in the anterior pituitary gland and the ovary compared to their biological activity as modulators of LH release in anterior pituitary cells in culture. This information supports and extends recent findings (60,62).

The present demonstration of LHRH receptors having almost superimposable binding characteristics in the anterior pituitary and ovary indicates that the antifertility effects of LHRH and its agonists could partly be mediated by their action through ovarian LHRH receptors. The concentration of LHRH in the portal blood system of the rat has been reported as 150 pg/ml (63). This observation, combined with the fact that LHRH is diluted 500-fold between the portal circulation and the jugular vein (64) makes it unlikely that hypothalamic LHRH could have a physiological action on ovarian LHRH receptors. However, it would also be somewhat unexpected to have specific ovarian LHRH receptors which are not linked to a physiological function. Although the possibility of an action of hypothalamic LHRH at the ovarian level must be further investigated, the presence of specific ovarian LHRH receptors raises the possibility that LHRH secreted locally could be involved in the control of ovarian activity, a new area of investigation which should be of great biological interest.

INHIBITION OF TESTICULAR STEROIDOGENESIS IN MAN BY TREATMENT WITH AN LHRH AGONIST

The relative lack of success of LHRH and its agonistic analogs in the treatment of oligospermia and male infertility (4,5) might well be explained by the above-described findings of a loss of testicular LH and prolactin receptors accompanied by decreased testis, seminal vesicle, and ventral prostate weight following treatment of adult male rats with gonadotropin-releasing peptides. This loss of receptors is accompanied by decreased androgen biosynthesis and accumulation of pregnenolone and progesterone which suggest a blockage in the testicular steroidogenic pathway at the level of the 17-hydroxylase and 17,20-desmolase activities (17,19). It is thus of great interest to study the possibility of a similar inhibition of testicular steroidogenesis by treatment with LHRH agonists in man.

Since the potent LHRH agonist [D-Ser(TBU)⁶]LHRH-EA (Hoe 766)

(10,11) is active by the intranasal route (65), we have studied the effect of a single intranasal administration of 500 μg of this peptide on plasma levels of pregnenolone, 17-OH-pregnenolone, progesterone, 17-OH-pro-progesterone, androst-5-ene-3β, 17β-diol, testosterone, dihydrotestosterone, and 17β-estradiol during 7 consecutive days following treatment in six normal adult men (50).

Serum levels of all steroids were highest at 0800 hours and lowest at 2200 hours during the two control pretreatment days. Intranasal administration of 500 μg of [D-Ser(TBU)^6]LHRH-EA leads to a disturbance of this diurnal cyclicity and lowers serum steroid levels for the next 3 days. The concentrations of 17-OH-progesterone and testosterone are decreased to 40 and 50%, respectively of controls on day 3 following administration of the peptide. Normal cyclicity and serum steroid levels are observed on the 4th through 6th post-treatment days. The effect of treatment on the pattern of serum 17β-estradiol concentrations

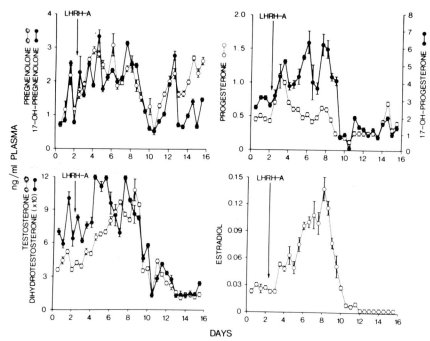

Fig. 20. Effect of daily intranasal administration of [D-Ser(TBU)^6]LHRH-EA on plasma levels of progesterone, 17 OH-Progesterone, testosterone, 5α-dihydrotestosterone, and 17β-estradiol in a patient suffering from cancer of the prostate.

is however completely different: no significant change is seen on the day of [D-Ser(TBU)^6]LHRH-EA treatment and a delayed increase (from 20–35 to 100–250 pg/ml in different subjects) is observed on the following day with a return to normal serum concentrations at later time intervals (50).

The present data clearly show that the administration of a potent LHRH agonist in normal men leads to inhibition of testicular steroidogenesis. The loss of diurnal cyclicity and decreased serum levels of testosterone and its precursors do in fact last for 3 days following a single intranasal administration of [D-Ser(TBU)^6]LHRH-EA. These data agree with the recent findings of an inhibition of serum testosterone levels in normal men treated s.c. daily for one week with 5 μg of the same LHRH analog (49) and in patients with cancer of the prostate treated with the same analogue by the intranasal route (Fig. 20).

LUTEOLYTIC AND ANTIOVULATORY ACTIVITY OF LHRH AGONISTS IN WOMEN

Following the observation of such potent antifertility effects of LHRH and its agonistic analogues in the rat and a better knowledge of the mechanism involved (down-regulation of ovarian gonadotropin receptor levels and function), we investigated the possibility of a similar luteolytic effect of treatment with gonadotropin-releasing peptides during the luteal phase in normal women. Such an approach could lead to a near-physiological method of control of the luteal phase length and time of appearance of menses. This chapter summarizes the results obtained after subcutaneous treatment with LHRH (40,41) and intranasal administration of [D-Ser(TBU)^6, des-Gly-NH$_2$^{10}]LHRH-ethylamide (42). Possible clinical applications of such treatment in the control of the menstrual cycle and fertility regulation in normal women are also discussed.

SUBCUTANEOUS LHRH TREATMENT

The administration of 250 μg of LHRH every 4 hours for five injections starting at 8 A.M. on 1 or 2 consecutive days beginning between days 1 and 9 following the LH surge shortened the luteal phase from 1 to 4 days in 16 of 17 treatment cycles (41). Figure 21 represents typical hormone profiles obtained in one woman treated for 1 day with five

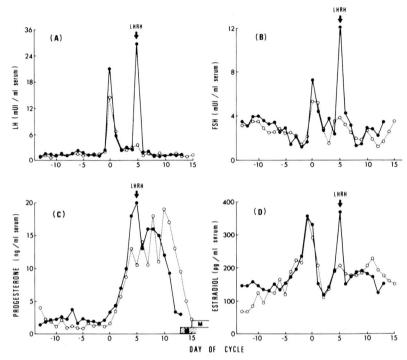

Fig. 21. Effect of five subcutaneous 250 μg doses of LHRH, given every 4 hours on day 5 after the LH surge, on serum LH (A), FSH (B), progesterone (C), and 17β-estradiol (D) and on time of menses in a normal woman (41).

doses of 250 μg of LHRH. When administered on day 5, LHRH injections caused a marked increase in serum LH and FSH levels. Five days later, serum progesterone levels started to decrease and menses appeared 2 days earlier than expected from the control cycle. A significant increase in the serum estradiol level was also noted on the day of LHRH treatment. Only one woman had no change in the length of her luteal phase after such treatment (17 treatment cycles). Two of three women whose luteal phases were shortened by only 1 day experienced unusual spotting from 3 and 5 days, respectively, before the beginning of their menses.

It could also be seen that there exists a tendency for better efficiency of treatment when LHRH is administered at a later stage of the luteal phase. In fact, in 10 cycles in which LHRH was administered between days 1 and 5, the mean shortening of the luteal phase was

1.4 ± 0.2 days as compared to 3.3 ± 0.2 days for the cycles when the neurohormone was injected between days 6 and 9 following the LH surge ($P < .01$). Serum progesterone levels were decreased to a greater extent when LHRH was administered after day 5 of the luteal phase. This appears to be analogous to the effect of LHRH treatment on the time of appearance of menses. In fact, in 10 cycles during which the women received injections between days 1 and 5, serum progesterone, on average, decreased to 71.2% ± 6.0% of control values whereas the mean serum progesterone levels were 43.9% ± 5.9% of control values after LHRH administration between days 6 and 9 ($P < .01$, six cycles).

In three women who received only two doses of 500 μg of LHRH or three doses of 250 μg of LHRH every 4 hours between days 2 and 5 after ovulation, the serum progesterone levels and the time of appearance of menses were unaffected, thus indicating that a greater number of LHRH injections are required to produce significant effects on corpus luteum function (40).

It should be mentioned that during the treatment cycle, some women reported a slight decrease in the amount and duration of their menses. LHRH treatment did not cause any noticeable side-effect. The immediate post-treatment cycle was apparently normal, and women usually experienced regular menstrual bleeding at the expected time.

INTRANASAL ADMINISTRATION OF [D-SER(TBU)⁶]LHRH-EA

Since the potent LHRH agonistic analog [D-Ser(TBU)⁶, des-Gly-NH₂¹⁰]LHRH-ethylamide (10) is active by the intranasal route, we have studied the effect of this peptide after intranasal administration during two successive menstrual cycles in six normal women. To facilitate the application of this treatment on a large scale in the general population, the intranasal route of administration would be much more acceptable than the subcutaneous, intramuscular, or intravenous route.

Figure 22 illustrates the typical patterns of serum LH, FSH, 17β-estradiol, and progesterone levels in one woman during six consecutive menstrual cycles: two control pre-treatment, two treatment, and two control post-treatment cycles. In this woman, the luteal phase was shortened by 2 days and 4 days in the first and second treatment cycles, when the LHRH analog was administered on days 8 and 6 after the LH peak, respectively. In the same treatment cycles, serum pro-

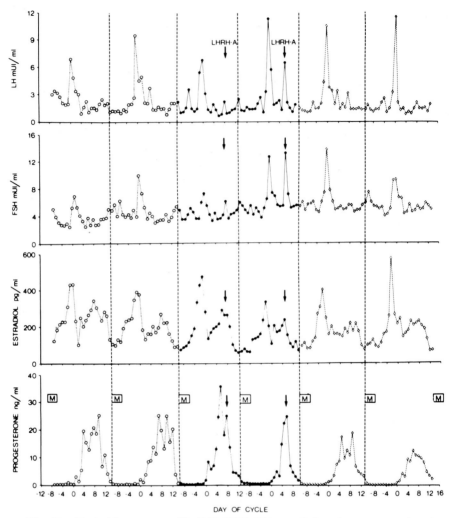

Fig. 22. Typical hormone profile (LH, FSH, 17β-estradiol, and progesterone) and response to the intranasal administration of 500 μg of [D-Ser(TBU)⁶, des-Gly-NH₂¹⁰] LHRH-ethylamide at 8 A.M. and 5 P.M. on days 8 and 6 after the LH peak during the third and fourth menstrual cycles, respectively. The luteal phase was shortened by 2 and 4 days in the corresponding cycle. M, Menstruation (42).

gesterone levels were reduced to 13% and 34% of control, respectively.

A summary of all data obtained in 6 women can be found in Fig. 23, which shows the combined hormone profile from the 12 pretreatment, treatment, and post-treatment cycles. The luteal phase was shortened

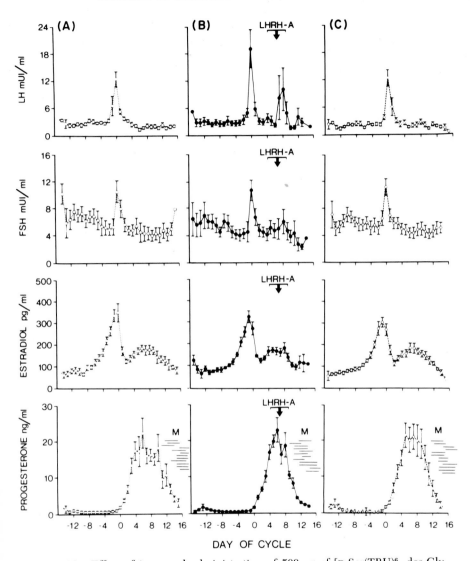

Fig. 23. Effect of intranasal administration of 500 μg of [D-Ser(TBU)⁶, des-Gly-NH₂¹⁰]LHRH-ethylamide in six women during two consecutive menstrual cycles. The LHRH analog was administered at 8 A.M. and 5 P.M. on 1 day between days 4 and 9 after the LH peak (day 0). The data are the average of 12 pretreatment (A), treatment (B), and post-treatment cycles (C). The length of the luteal phase was reduced from 13.6 ± 0.3 days to 10.9 ± 0.3 days (*P* < .01) by treatment with the LHRH analog with a return to 12.8 ± 0.3 days during the post-treatment cycles (*P* < .01, post-treatment versus treatment cycles). Serum progesterone levels were reduced to 61.3% of control by the same treatment (*P* < .01). M, Menstruation (42).

from 13.6 ± 0.3 days to 10.9 ± 0.3 days (mean shortening, 2.7 days; range, 0.5–4.5 days) while serum progesterone levels after the administration of [D-Ser(TBU)^6, des-Gly-NH$_2$^{10}]LHRH-ethylamide were reduced to 61.3% of control (range, 13–128%).

The present data support our previous observations obtained with LHRH (40,41) and clearly suggest that the intranasal administration of [D-Ser(TBU)^6, des-Gly-NH$_2$^{10}]LHRH-ethylamide has luteolytic effects in normal women. Although in some women, there were low levels of serum progesterone in the post-treatment cycles, recovery appeared to be complete when all 12 cycles were considered (97.3% ± 13.3%). This is also supported by the length of the luteal phase, which was normal during the post-treatment cycles (12.8 ± 0.3 days versus 13.6 ± 0.3 days). Similarly, the administration of 500 μg of LHRH on days 16 and 18 of the cycle in normal women led to an accelerated fall of plasma progesterone and early appearance of menses (45). In another study, the subcutaneous injection of 500 μg of another LHRH agonist, [D-Trp^6, des-GlyNH$_2$^{10}]LHRH-ethylamide, on two consecutive days in the luteal phase has been found to decrease serum progesterone levels within 2 days and to shorten the duration of the luteal phase by 2 to 4 days (44). Moreover, Koyama *et al.* (43) have observed that five daily injections of 100 μg of a less potent LHRH agonist, [des-Gly-NH$_2$^{10}]LHRH-ethylamide started within the first 5 days of the luteal phase suppressed plasma progesterone levels without affecting the length of the luteal phases (43).

Another promising new approach in female contraception is daily treatment with LHRH agonists. Daily intranasal administration of the LHRH agonist [D-Ser(TBU)^6]LHRH-EA inhibited ovulation in all except 2 of 89 treatment cycles in normal women (46,47). No secondary side-effects were noticed during the 3 to 6 months of trial except slight menstrual-like bleedings and normal ovulatory cycles returned rapidly upon cessation of treatment.

The above-mentioned studies clearly demonstrate a luteolytic action of LHRH and its agonists in normal women. Since progesterone secretion from the corpus luteum is essential for implantation and the maintenance of early pregnancy (66,67), it is hoped that LHRH agonists could be used as a new and near-physiological approach to contraception as inhibitors of ovulation or inducers of menses and as an alternative to the post-coital estrogenic pill.

The possibility of using potent LHRH agonists such as [D-Ser(TBU)^6, des-Gly-NH$_2$^{10}]LHRH-ethylamide by the intranasal route offers obvious advantages for easy routine application by the general population.

ACKNOWLEDGMENTS

This research was supported by grants from the Medical Research Council of Canada and the Conseil de la Recherche en Santé du Québec.

REFERENCES

1. Matsuo, H., Baba, Y., Nair, R. M. G., Arimura, A., and Schally, A. V. (1971) *Biochem. Biophys. Res. Commun.* **43**, 1334–1339.
2. Zarate, A., Canales, E., Schally, A. V., Ayala-Valdes, L., and Kastin, A. J. (1972) *Fertil. Steril.* **23**, 672–674.
3. Mortimer, C. H., McNeilly, A. S., Fisher, R. A., Murray, M. A. F., and Besser, G. M. (1974) *Br. Med. J.* **4**, 617–621.
4. Schwartzstein, L. (1976) *In* "Hypothalamus and Endocrine Functions" (F. Labrie, J. Meites, and G. Pelletier, eds.), pp. 73–91. Plenum, New York.
5. Krabbe, S., and Skakkeback, N. E. (1977) *Acta Paediatr. Scand.* **66**, 361–365.
6. Auclair, C., Kelly, P. A., Labrie, F., Coy, D. H., and Schally, A. V. (1977) *Biochem. Biophys. Res. Commun.* **76**, 855–862.
7. Auclair, C., Kelly, P. A., Coy, D. H., Schally, A. V., and Labrie, F. (1977) *Endocrinology* **101**, 1890–1893.
8. Auclair, C., Ferland, L., Cusan, L., Kelly, P. A., Labrie, F., Azadian-Boulanger, G., and Raynaud, J. P. (1978) *C. R. Hebd. Seances Acad. Sci., Ser. D*, 1305–1307.
9. Pelletier, G., Cusan, L., Auclair, C., Kelly, P. A., Désy, L., and Labrie, F. (1978) *Endocrinology* **103**, 641–643.
10. Sandow, J., von Rechenberg, W. V., König, W., Hahn, M., Jerzabek, G., and Fraser, H. (1978) *In* "Hypothalamic Hormones-Chemistry, Physiology and Clinical Applications" (D. Gupta and W. Voelter, eds.), pp. 307–325. Verlag Chemie, Weinheim.
11. Sandow, J., von Rechenberg, W., Jerzabek, G., and Stoll, W. (1978) *Fertil. Steril.* **30**, 205–211.
12. Tcholakian, R. K., De La Cruz, A., Chowdhury, M., Steinberger, A., Coy, D. H., and Schally, A. V. (1978) *Fertil. Steril.* **30**, 600–603.
13. Tcholakian, R. K., De La Cruz, A., Chowdhury, M., Schally, A. V., and Steinberger, A. (1978) *J. Reprod. Fertil.* **54**, 441–445.
14. Cusan, L., Auclair, C., Bélanger, A., Ferland, L., Kelly, P. A., Séguin, C., and Labrie, F. (1979) *Endocrinology* **104**, 1369–1376.
15. Catt, K. J., Baukal, A. J., Davies, T. F., and Dufau, M. L. (1979) *Endocrinology* **104**, 17–25.
16. Rivier, C., Rivier, J., and Vale, W. (1979) *Endocrinology* **105**, 1191–1201.
17. Bélanger, A., Auclair, C., Séguin, C., Kelly, P. A., and Labrie, F. (1979) *Mol. Cell. Endocrinol.* **13**, 47–53.
18. Sharpe, R. M., Fraser, H. M, and Sandow, J. (1979) *J. Endocrinol.* **80**, 249–257.
19. Bélanger, A., Auclair, C., Ferland, L., and Labrie, F. (1980) *J. Steroid Biochem.* **13**, 191–196.
20. Carmichael, R., Bélanger, A., Cusan, L., Séguin, C., Caron, S., and Labrie, F. (1980) *Steroids* **36**, 383–391.
21. Labrie, F., Bélanger, A., Cusan, L., Séguin, C., Pelletier, G., Kelly, P. A., Reeves, J. J., Lefebvre, F. A., Lemay, A., and Raynaud, J. P. (1980) *J. Andrology* **1**, 209–228.
22. Labrie, F., Bélanger, A., Pelletier, G., Séguin, C., Cusan, L., Kelly, P. A., Lemay, A.,

Auclair, C., and Raynaud, J. P. (1980b) *In* Regulation of Male Fertility" (G. R. Cunningham, W. B. Schell, and E. S. E. Hafez, eds.). Martinus Nyoff Publishers, The Hague, Netherlands (in press).

23. Banik, V. K., and Givner, M. L. (1975) *J. Reprod. Fertil.* **44**, 87–84.
24. Corbin, A., Beattie, C. W., Yardley, J., and Toell, T. J. (1976) *Endocr. Res. Commun.* **3**, 359–376.
25. Humphrey, R. R., Windsor, B. L., Bousley, F. G., and Edgren, R. A. (1976) *Contraception* **14**, 625–629.
26. Rippel, R. H., and Johnson, E. S. (1976) *Proc. Soc. Exp. Biol. Med.* **152**, 432–436.
27. Johnson, E. S., Gendrich, R. L., and White, W. F. (1976) *Fertil. Steril.* **27**, 853–860.
28. Hilliard, J., Pang, C. N., and Sawyer, C. H. (1976) *Fertil. Steril.* **27**, 421–425.
29. Humphrey, R. R., Windsor, B. L., Reel, J. R., and Edgren, R. A. (1977) *Biol. Reprod.* **16**, 614–621.
30. Beattie, C. W., and Corbin, A. (1977) *Biol. Reprod.* **16**, 333–339.
31. Sandow, J., von Rechenberg, W., and Jerzabek, G. (1977) *Acta Endocrinol. (Copenhagen)*, Suppl. **208**, 33.
32. Kledzik, G. S., Cusan, L., Auclair, C., Kelly, P. A., and Labrie, F. (1978a) *Fertil. Steril.* **30**, 348–353.
33. Kledzik, G. S., Cusan, L., Auclair, C., Kelly, P. A., and Labrie, F. (1978) *Fertil. Steril.* **29**, 560–567.
34. Ferland, L., Auclair, C., Labrie, F., Raynaud, J. P., and Azadian-Boulanger, G. (1978) *C. R. Hebd. Seances Acad. Sci., Ser. D* **286**, 1113–1116.
35. Rivier, C., Rivier, J., and Vale, W. (1978) *Endocrinology* **103**, 2299–2305.
36. Corbin, A., Beattie, C. W., Tracy, J., Jones, R., Foell, T. J., Yardley, J., and Rees, R. W. A. (1978) *Int. J. Fertil.* **23**, 81–92.
37. Labrie, F., Auclair, C., Cusan, L., Lemay, A., Bélanger, A., Kelly, P. A., Ferland, L., Klezik, G. S., Azadian-Boulanger, G., and Raynaud, J. P. (1979) *Adv. Exp. Biol. Med.* **112**, 687–693.
38. Labrie, F., Auclair, C., Lemay, A., Kledzik, G. S., Cusan, L., Kelly, P. A., Ferland, L., and Bélanger, A. (1979) *In* "Clinical Neuroendocrinology, A Pathophysiological Approach" (G. Tolis, F. Labrie, J. B. Martin, and F. Naftolin, eds.), pp. 115–128. Raven, New York.
39. Vilchez-Martinez, J. A., Pedroza, E., Arimura, A., and Schally, A. V. (1979) *Fertil. Steril.* **31**, 677–682.
40. Lemay, A., Labrie, F., Raynaud, J. P., and Azadian-Boulanger, G. (1978) *C. R. Hebd. Seances Acad. Sci.* **286**, 677–682.
41. Lemay, A., Labrie, F., Ferland, L., and Raynaud, J. P. (1979) *Fertil. Steril.* **31**, 29–34.
42. Lemay, A., Labrie, F., Béanger, A., and Raynaud, J. P. (1979) *Fertil. Steril.* **32**, 646–651.
43. Koyama, T., Ohkura, T., Humasaka, T., and Saito, M. (1978) *Fertil. Steril.* **30**, 549–552.
44. Casper, R. F., and Yen, S. S. C. (1979) *Science* **205**, 408–410.
45. Caldwell, B. W., Rotchell, Y. E., Pang, C. Y., Anderson, G. G., Kabre, N., N., and Behrman, H. R. (1980) *Am. J. Obstet. Gynecol.* **136**, 458–464.
46. Nillius, S. J., Bergquist, C., and Wide, L. (1980) *Contraception* **17**, 537–545.
47. Bergquist, C., Nillius, S. J., and Wide, L. (1979) *Lancet* **1**, 215–217.
48. Baumann, R., Kuhl, H., Taubert, H. D., and Sandow, J. (1980) *Contraception* **21**, 191–197.

49. Smith, R., Donald, R. A., Espiner, E. A., Stromach, S. G., and Edwards, I. A. (1979) *J. Clin. Endocrinol. Metab.* **48**, 167–170.
50. Bélanger, A., Lemay, A., Caron, S., and Labrie, F. (1980) *J. Steroid Biochem.* **13**, 123–126.
51. Hsueh, A. J. W., and Erickson, G. F. (1979) *Nature (London)* **281**, 66–67.
52. Hsueh, A. J. W., and Ling, N. C. (1979) *Life Sci.* **25**, 1223–1230.
53. Arimura, A., Serafini, P., Talbot, S., and Schally, A. V. (1979) *Biochem. Biophys. Res. Commun.* **90**, 697–693.
54. Mayar, M. Q., Tarnavsky, G. K., and Reeves, J. J. (1979) *Proc. Soc. Exp. Biol. Med.* **161**, 216–219.
55. MacDonald, G. J., and Beattie, C. W. (1979) *Life Sci.* **24**, 1103–1110.
56. Ying, S. Y., and Guillemin, R. (1979) *Nature (London)* **280**, 593–595.
57. Labrie, F., Auclair, C., Cusan, L., Kelly, P. A., Pelletier, G., and Ferland, L. (1978) *Int. J. Androl., Suppl.* **2**, 303–318.
58. Massicotte, J., Veilleux, R., Lavoie, M., and Labrie, F. (1980) *Biochem. Biophys. Res. Commun.* **94**, 1362–1366.
59. Hsueh, A. J. W., and Erickson, G. F. (1979b) *Nature (London)* **281**, 66–67.
60. Clayton, R. N., Harwood, J. P., and Catt, K. J. (1979) *Nature (London)* **282**, 90–92.
61. Reeves, J. J., Séguin, C., Lefebvre, F. A., Kelly, P. A., and Labrie, F. (1980) *Proc. Natl. Acad. Sci. U.S.A.* **77**, 5567–5571.
62. Conne, B. S., Aubert, M. L., and Sizonenko, P. C. (1979) *Biochem. Biophys. Res. Commun.* **90**, 1249–1256.
63. Eskay, R. L., Warberg, J., Mical, R. S., and Porter, J. C. (1975) *Endocrinology* **97**, 816–824.
64. Nett, T. M., Akbar, A. M., and Niswender, G. A. (1974) *Endocrinology* **94**, 713–718.
65. Wiegelmann, W., Solbach, H. G., Kley, H. K., Nieschlag, E., and Kruskemper, H. L. (1977) *Acta Endocrinol. (Copenhag)*, Suppl. **212**, 57.
66. Csapo, A. I., and Pulkinen, M. (1978) *Obstet. Gynecol. Surv.* **33**, 69–81.
67. Jones, G. S., and Madrigal-Castro, V. (1970) *Fertil. Steril.* **21**, 1–13.

TLCK-Binding Proteins in Freshly Harvested and Cultured Porcine Granulosa Cells

PATRICK J. McILROY, ANDREW R. LaBARBERA,[1]
AND ROBERT J. RYAN

Department of Cell Biology
Mayo Graduate School of Medicine
Rochester, Minnesota

INTRODUCTION*

Gonadotropic hormones stimulate various cell types in the gonads by binding to specific, plasma membrane receptors and activating adenylate cyclase on the inner surface of the membrane (1). During this process the cells being stimulated become desensitized (i.e., lose the ability of the adenylate cyclase to be restimulated by further hormone). In part, this is through the loss or down regulation of receptor (1). The mechanisms by which the hormone–receptor complex stimulates and desensitizes the adenylate cyclase enzyme are largely unknown.

Recently, work in this and other laboratories has implicated the possible involvement of proteinases in the phenomena. Proteinases are known to activate adenylate cyclase in cell membrane preparations

---

[1] Present address: Center for Endocrinology, Metabolism and Nutrition, Northwestern University Medical School, Chicago, Illinois 60611.

* The following abbreviations are used: TLCK, 7-amino-1-chloro-3-L-tosylamidoheptan-2-one ("tosyllysine chloromethylketone"); ^{125}I-labeled TLCK, 1-chloro-7-[3'(4"-hydroxy-3"[^{125}I]-iodophenyl)]propylamido-3-L-tosylamidoheptan-2-one; pFSH, porcine follicle stimulating hormone; hCG, human chorionic gonadotropin; cAMP, adenosine-3':5'-monophosphate; MEM, minimum essential medium; TCA, trichloroacetic acid; BSA, bovine serum albumin.

BIOREGULATORS OF REPRODUCTION

from a variety of tissues (2). Low molecular weight proteinase inhibitors not only block this stimulation of adenylate cyclase, but also block hormonal stimulation of the enzyme in rat ovary (3,4) and liver (4). Based on the above observations, a model for hormonal stimulation of adenylate cyclase was proposed in which membrane-bound proteinase(s) played a central role (3). The binding of hormone by receptor was proposed to activate a proteinase which in turn would activate adenylate cyclase and possibly destroy the receptor (3), or alternatively the binding of hormone by receptor could sensitize a bond to proteolytic cleavage and accomplish the same effects (5). Results of kinetic experiments suggested that the inhibitors were acting at two different sites, directly on the catalytic subunit and at another locus in the pathway for hormonal stimulation (4,5). The development of a method for preparing and isolating ^{125}I-labeled TLCK of high specific radioactivity (5) has provided a probe with which to examine the possible site(s) of action of these inhibitors.

The recent development of an *in vitro* model for the differentiation of FSH-responsive cells to LH/hCG-responsive cells has provided an intact cell system with which to investigate the mechanism of action of FSH and LH/hCG (6). FSH-responsive granulosa cells from porcine small follicles have been cultured as suspensions with FSH for 6 days. Under these conditions the cells showed signs of morphological luteinization as well as increased hCG binding, hCG-responsive adenylate cyclase activity, and hCG-responsive progesterone secretory capacity (6,7).

This chapter examines the hormone sensitivity of intact cells from porcine small follicles before and after 6 days of culture in the presence of pFSH, the effect of TLCK on the adenylate cyclase of the above cells, and the possible site(s) of action of the low molecular weight proteinase inhibitors.

MATERIALS AND METHODS

Highly purified hCG (CR 121) was obtained from Dr. Robert Canfield, Columbia University, New York, New York. pFSH was prepared by Dr. R. J. Whitley (8), Mayo Clinic, Rochester, Minnesota. TLCK, cAMP, and epinephrine were purchased from Sigma; MEM was obtained from Grand Island Biological Co.; Na^{125}I, carrier-free, was from Amersham; 3-(*p*-hydroxyphenyl)propionic acid, *N*-hydroxysuccinimidyl ester, and calf thymus DNA were from Cal Biochem; cholera toxin from Schwarz Mann; 2'-*O*-succinyladenosine-3':5'-monophosphate-L-tyrosyl methyl ester was from Boehringer Mannheim;

and goat anti-cAMP serum was from Research Products Inc. Other reagents were of the best grade available.

GRANULOSA CELLS

Granulosa cells were harvested from small (1–2 mm) follicles of ovaries from prepubertal pigs and used immediately (day 0 cells) or cultured for 6 days (day 6 cells) as suspensions in spinner flasks as described previously (6). For short-term incubations, day 0 or day 6 cultured granulosa cells were washed 3 times with MEM and resuspended in MEM previously equilibrated with humidified 5% CO_2–95% O_2. Cells were incubated in duplicate at 0° or 37° C for 10 minutes or 2 hours with additions as indicated.

cAMP DETERMINATIONS

For the quantitation of cAMP the incubated cells and medium were sonicated in cold 5% TCA, centrifuged and the TCA extracted from the supernatant with ether. After acylation as described by Harper and Brooker (9), the amount of cAMP in the supernatants was measured in triplicate by radioimmunoassay (10,11) using goat anti-cAMP serum.

^{125}I-LABELED TLCK

[125]I-labeled TLCK was prepared by coupling ^{125}I-Bolton-Hunter reagent (12) to the ε-amino group of TLCK (5) and isolating the product on a silica gel column.

SDS POLYACRYLAMIDE GEL ELECTROPHORESIS

Protein from cell incubations was solubilized and reduced with 2% SDS, 5% 2-mercaptoethanol, 10% glycerol, and 0.001% bromophenol blue in 30 mM Tris–HCl buffer, pH 7.4, incubated for 30 minutes at 37°C. The solubilized protein was applied to 10% polyacrylamide gels (0.5 × 9.0 cm) prepared in the presence of 0.1% SDS and run at 3 mA per gel (13). The gels were removed by rimming with H_2O and stained with Coomassie blue R-250 according to the procedure of Fairbanks *et al.* (14) or sliced into 1.0 mm slices with a Mickle gel slicer and counted for ^{125}I in a Packard Autogamma spectrometer. The standards routinely run were myosin, β-galactosidase, phosphorylase B, BSA, ovalbumin, carbonic anhydrase, soy bean trypsin inhibitor, and lysozyme and were obtained from BioRad.

OTHER ASSAYS

Protein was determined by the method of Lowry *et al.* (15) using crystalline BSA as the standard. DNA was determined by the fluorescence method of Kissane and Robbins (16) as modified (6,17) and using calf thymus DNA as the standard.

RESULTS

The ability of pFSH, hCG, epinephrine, and cholera toxin to stimulate cAMP production in day 0 and day 6 cells was examined by incubating the cells at 37° C for 2 hours with maximally effective

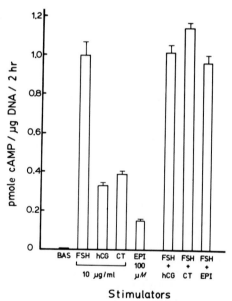

Fig. 1. Basal and pFSH-, hCG-, cholera toxin-, and epinephrine-stimulated cAMP production by day 0 granulosa cells. 18×10^7 cells in 0.5 ml were incubated for 2 hours at 37°C as described in Materials and Methods in the presence of 0.4% BSA, 1 mM methyl isobutylxanthine and FSH (10 μg/ml), hCG (10 μg/ml), cholera toxin (10 μg/ml), epinephrine (100 μM), or various combinations of the above stimulators at the above concentrations. The incubations were terminated by the addition of 1 volume ice-cold 10% TCA and the amount of cAMP produced determined as described in Materials and Methods. DNA in the pellet from each incubation was measured as described in Materials and Methods. Results are expressed as pmole cAMP produced per μg DNA and represent the mean ± SE of all determinations for two or more experiments.

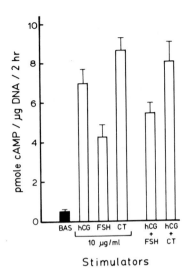

Fig. 2. Basal and pFSH-, hCG-, and cholera toxin-stimulated cAMP production by day 6 cultured cells. 8.0×10^5 cells were incubated and treated as described in Fig. 1. The results are expressed in the same manner as those of Fig. 1.

doses of the various stimulants and measuring the amount of cAMP in cells and medium. Basal cAMP production was lower in day 0 cells (Fig. 1) than in day 6 cultured cells (Fig. 2). Day 0 cells were stimulated maximally by pFSH, to a lesser extent by hCG and cholera toxin, and the least by epinephrine (Fig. 1). The combined effects of maximally stimulating doses of FSH plus one at the other three stimulants were not additive over the 2-hour incubation period (Fig. 1). Day 6 cells were stimulated maximally by hCG or cholera toxin, to a lesser extent by epinephrine (not shown), and to the least extent by pFSH. The combined effects of maximally stimulating doses of hCG and either cholera toxin or pFSH were not additive (Fig. 2).

Figures 3 and 4 summarize the data obtained when day 0 and day 6 cells, respectively, were incubated with maximally stimulating doses of FSH, hCG, or cholera toxin in the presence of increasing concentrations of TLCK. In all cases TLCK had a biphasic effect on cAMP production. At low concentrations ($2-100 \mu M$) there was a potentiation of cAMP accumulation, while at higher concentrations ($> 100 \mu M$) maximal cAMP production was reduced (Figs. 3 and 4). The potentiation of pFSH-stimulated cAMP accumulation was approximately three-fold in day 0 cells (Fig. 3). This was similar to the two- to threefold potentiation of cholera toxin stimulated cAMP production by both day 0 (Fig. 3) and day 6 (Fig. 4) cells. On the other hand, hCG-stimulated cAMP production in day 6 cells was increased five-fold by 100 μM TLCK (Fig. 4).

The effect of TLCK on day 0 and day 6 cultured cells was further investigated by incubation of the two cell types at 37°C with ^{125}I-labeled TLCK, with or without hormone, followed by extraction of the cells with 0.1% Triton X-100 and analysis of the extracted proteins by SDS-polyacrylamide gel electrophoresis. In the day 0 cells in the absence of hormone the label was associated with one major peak, MW_r 43,000, and several minor peaks (Fig. 5, Table I). Likewise, in the day 6 cultured cells, in the absence of hormone, the labeled inhibitor was associated with one major and several minor peaks (Fig. 6, Table I);

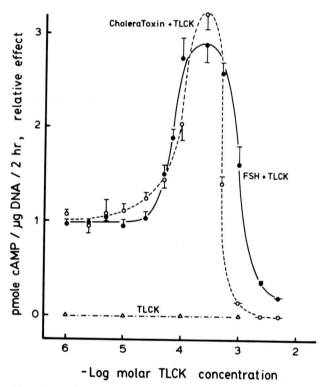

Fig. 3. The effect of increasing concentrations of TLCK on pFSH- and cholera toxin-stimulated cAMP production by day 0 cells. Day 0 cells were incubated as described in the legend of Fig. 1 in the presence of the indicated concentrations of TLCK. Results are expressed as pmole cAMP per μg DNA relative to that produced by a control incubation containing the appropriate stimulator but no TLCK and are the mean ± SE of all determinations for two experiments. O---O, Cholera toxin (10 μg/ml); ●——●, pFSH (10 μg/ml).

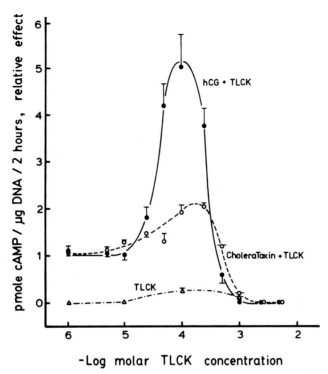

Fig. 4.   The effect of increasing concentrations of TLCK on hCG- and cholera toxin-stimulated cAMP production in day 6 cultured cells. Day 6 cultured cells were incubated as described in the legend of Fig. 3 with the substitution of hCG for pFSH. The results are expressed in the same manner as those of Fig. 3. O---O, Cholera toxin (10 μg/ml); ●——●, hCG (10 μg/ml).

however, the major peak in these cells was significantly smaller, MW_r 28,000, than that in the day 0 cells and incorporated three times as much label per incubation. This increase in labeling was not due to an increased amount of protein in the day 6 cultured cell incubations since the total protein in those incubations was only one-third that of the day 0 incubations (Table I). If the data were normalized to cpm per peak per incubation, the increase in the amount of label was 25-fold. Of the several minor radioactive peaks in the day 6 cultured cell, one, MW_r 54,000, is of interest since in the presence of unlabeled TLCK (1 mM) it bound more label than in the absence of unlabeled TLCK (Fig. 6, Table I). All other radioactive peaks in both the day 0 and day 6 cultured cells were displaced or remained the same in the presence of 1 mM TLCK (Figs. 5 and 6, Table I). The results of labeling experi-

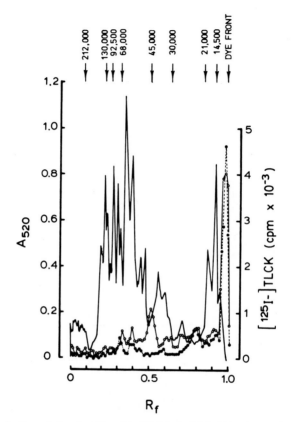

Fig. 5. Labeling of day 0 cells with ^{125}I-labeled TLCK. 2.0×10^7 cells in 0.5 ml were incubated for 10 minutes at 37°C as described in Materials and Methods in the presence of ^{125}I-labeled TLCK (5×10^5 cpm) with and without 1 mM TLCK. The incubations were terminated by the addition of 6 volumes of ice-cold MEM and the cells washed three times with MEM. Proteins were extracted at 0°C with 0.1% Triton X-100 (w/w) in 0.14 NaCl, 0.01 M H_3PO_4, pH 7.4, and the cells removed by centrifugation at 1000 g for 5 minutes. The extracted proteins were subjected to SDS-polyacrylamide gel electrophoresis and analyzed as described in Materials and Methods. A_{520} (——), ^{125}I-labeled TLCK incorporation in the absence (●---●), and presence (○——○) of 1 mM TLCK.

ments conducted in the presence of hormone, 10 μg/ml pFSH for day 0 cells and 10 μg/ml hCG for day 6 cultured cells, were identical to those described above in the absence of hormone (Table I).

In addition, variations on the above experiments were carried out, incubation at 0°C instead of 37°C and homogenization and centrifugation of the cells instead of Triton X-100 extraction. The only significantly labeled protein peak that was found after incubation of cells at 0°C was the major one, MW_r 28,000, found in day 6 cultured cells, which incorporated approximately half as much label as at 37°C (data not shown). This label was also displaced by 1 mM TLCK under these conditions. The radioactive peak found at MW_r 54,000 previously discussed was not evident at 0°C incubation for 10 minutes. In the day 0 cells there was no significant incorporation of label into proteins at 0°C (data not shown).

When the cells were homogenized and separated into 5000 g particulate and supernatant fractions prior to analysis on gels, the principal labeled protein peak in the day 0 cells, MW_r 43,000, was found exclusively in the particulate fraction (Table I). Under the same conditions, the main labeled protein peak, MW_r 28,000, of the day 6 cultured cells was distributed equally between the supernatant and particulate fractions, and the MW_r 54,000 protein was found only in the particulate fraction (Table I).

TABLE I
Incorporation of ^{125}I-Labeled TLCK into Various Protein Peaks from Day 0 and Day 6 Cultured Cells[a]

	Total protein (mg)	0.1% Triton X-100 extract (cpm/peak)	5000 g fractions (cpm/peak)	
			Supernatant	Particulate
Day 0 cells	1.02			
MW_r 43,000 protein				
−FSH		4,140	490	3,500
+FSH		4,510	460	4,060
Day 6 cells	0.34			
MW_r 54,000 protein				
−hCG, −TLCK		1,000	200	1,050
+TLCK		1,950	375	1,600
+hCG, −TLCK		1,000	300	700
+TLCK		1,800	300	1,500
MW_r 28,000				
−hCG		12,300	6,120	6,200
+hCG		11,200	5,850	4,700

[a] The cells were incubated as described in the legend of Fig. 5 and either extracted with 0.1% Triton X-100 as described in Materials and Methods or homogenized and centrifuged at 5000 g (avg) to yield a supernatant and a particulate fraction. The various fractions were analyzed by SDS-polyacrylamide gel electrophoresis and sliced as described in Materials and Methods and the ^{125}I cpm in protein peaks of interest summed. The results are expressed as "total ^{125}I cpm per peak."

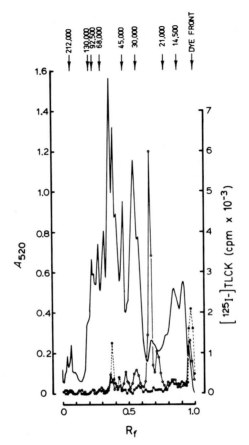

Fig. 6. Labeling of day 6 cells. 10^6 cells were incubated and treated as described in Fig. 5. A_{520} (—); ^{125}I-labeled TLCK incorporation in the absence (●——●) and presence (●---●) of 1 mM TLCK.

DISCUSSION

As has been shown previously (6,7) granulosa cells from porcine small follicles cultured as suspensions for 6 days in the presence of pFSH luteinize morphologically and have increased numbers of hCG binding sites. Another aspect of this differentiation was demonstrated in the present study by the reversal of sensitivity of day 0 and day 6 cultured cells to pFSH and hCG stimulation. pFSH was more effective in stimulating cAMP production in day 0 cells and hCG was more effective in day 6 cultured cells (Figs. 1 and 2). Cholera toxin and epinephrine stimulatability followed the same pattern as the hCG stimulatability; it was less effective than pFSH in day 0 cells and more effective than pFSH in day 6 cultured cells (Figs. 1 and 2). The various stimulators appeared to act upon the same adenylate cyclase enzyme since maximally effective doses of more than one stimulator were not additive (Figs. 1 and 2).

The biphasic effect of TLCK, [an irreversible inhibitor of trypsin-like proteinases, which covalently attaches to the active site histidyl residue (18)] on cAMP production in both day 0 and day 6 cultured cells has not been reported previously. Studies on the role of degradation of receptor-bound hCG in the mechanism of action of gonadotropins in cultured Leydig tumor cells (19,20) have shown that various protease inhibitors, including some chloromethyl ketones, block degradation of receptor bound ^{125}I-labeled hCG, and hCG-, cholera toxin-, or 8-Br-cAMP-stimulated steroid production; however, cAMP production was not examined. In broken cell preparations TLCK and other proteinase inhibitors have been shown to inhibit adenylate cyclase activity (3–5,21). TLCK has been tested in adenylate cyclase assays at concentrations as low as 1 μM and at no time has any potentiation of activity, such as that shown in Figs. 4 and 5, been seen (3; P. J. McIlroy and R. J. Ryan, unpublished observations). Kinetic analysis of adenylate cyclase activity indicates that low molecular weight proteinase inhibitors have a twofold effect; at low concentrations they inhibit only hormonal stimulation of adenylate cyclase, and at high concentrations the active catalytic moiety (4,5). The dose at which TLCK was effective in inhibiting hCG-stimulated adenylate cyclase in rat luteal tissue by 50% in a 20-minute assay (ID_{50}) was 0.4 mM (3,4) compared to the 0.25 mM ID_{50} (at maximal hCG-stimulation) in day 6 cultured cells (Fig. 4). At higher doses (ID_{50} of 1 mM) the inhibitors had a direct action on the active catalytic subunit of adenylate cyclase as indicated by their inhibition of NaF-stimulated cyclase (3,4).

Whether the inhibitory effect of TLCK on cAMP production in cells reported here was due to its acting directly on the catalytic moiety or in the stimulatory pathway cannot be determined since the intracellular concentration of TLCK in the incubated cells could not be determined. A comparison of ID_{50}s would suggest that the inhibitor was affecting the hormonal stimulatory pathway but this is uncertain since TLCK inhibits irreversibly (4,5) and ID_{50} dose levels are time-dependent for irreversible inhibition.

Since the biphasic effect of TLCK was seen with three different stimulators, all with different binding components, it is probable that it was reacting with some nonreceptor component. This view is supported by previous experiments in which it was shown that proteinase inhibitor effects on adenylate cyclase in broken cell preparations could not be explained by alterations in hormone binding (3,4).

It would appear that the potentiation of adenylate cyclase activity by TLCK required the presence of an integral cell structure, since this was the most obvious difference between this and previous studies (3–5,21); however, none of the previous studies have been conducted with a broken-cell preparation of porcine tissue. There are two possible explanations of the biphasic effect of TLCK on day 0 and day 6 cultured cells. Either it is due to two different concentration-related effects on the same component or to effects on two or more different components. The former is difficult to conceive of given the lack of a potentiating effect of the inhibitor in broken-cell preparations.

The above argument suggests that either intact lysosomes or an intact cytoskeletal system is necessary for the potentiating effect of TLCK, and that inhibition of the removal of hormone–receptor complex might be responsible; however, chloraquine, at concentrations shown to inhibit lysosomal degradation of receptor-bound hCG (18), did not potentiate hCG activation of cyclase (A. R. LaBarbera and R. J. Ryan, unpublished observations).

Other possible sites of action for TLCK include cAMP-dependent protein kinase which has been shown to be alkylated by the compound (22). Inhibition of this enzyme could prevent a negative feedback inhibitory pathway from turning off activated adenylate cyclase.

Examination of the data for the binding of ^{125}I-labeled TLCK to day 6 cells supports the hypothesis that there are two sites of action for TLCK, the higher affinity site being the MW_r 28,000 protein and the lower affinity site the MW_r 54,000 protein; however, the lack of a second binding site and the lack of identity of any of the proteins found to bind ^{125}I-labeled TLCK in day 0 and day 6 cells is against it.

The ^{125}I-labeled TLCK binding data did show that a distinct differentiation had occurred in the day 6 cultured cells. The MW_r 28,000 protein which was labeled in day 6 cultured cells (Fig. 6) was not present in the day 0 cells (Fig. 5). The identity and function of this protein has yet to be determined, but it could be a plasminogen activator. The evidence for this is varied and circumstantial; pregnant hog ovaries contain a large amount of plasminogen activator (23); plasminogen activator has been shown to be produced in the rat granulosa cell in response to FSH stimulation (24), and a bioassay based upon this observation has been developed (25); the protein appears to be produced in cultured granulosa cells in response to FSH (Fig. 6); and the size of the protein in question (MW_r 28,000) is the same as that found for the subunit of a number of plasminogen activators from a variety of sources (26). Whether this protein plays any role in the activation of adenylate cyclase has yet to be determined, but it is interesting to note that the best proteinase inhibitor of hCG-stimulated adenylate cyclase activity that was found in a recent study (4) was dansyl-Glu-Gly-Arg-CH$_2$Cl, an inhibitor of plasminogen activator.

SUMMARY

The sensitivity of freshly harvested or cultured porcine small follicle granulosa cells to gonadotropin-, cholera toxin- and epinephrine-stimulation of cAMP production has been examined. Freshly harvested cells are stimulated best by pFSH, to a lesser extent by hCG and choler toxin and least by epinephrine. After 6 days in culture in the presence of pFSH, the cells are most sensitive to hCG-and cholera toxin-stimulation, less sensitive to epinephrine-stimulation, and the least sensitive to pFSH-stimulation. In addition, the effect of tosyllysine chloromethylketone on cAMP production has been examined. In both freshly harvested and cultured granulosa cells TLCK has a biphasic effect. At low concentrations, less than 100 μM, it potentiates cAMP production, and at higher concentrations it inhibits production of the nucleotide. Examination of the possible sites of action of TLCK with an analog of high specific radioactivity revealed that the analog bound to a number of proteins. In freshly harvested cells the binding occurred principally to a protein of MW_r 43,000 while in cultured cells the principal binding protein was smaller, MW_r 28,000, and bound much more of the analog. The above binding of the labeled analog could be prevented by the presence of 1 mM tosyllysine chloromethylketone. One labeled analog binding peak, MW_r 54,000, in the cultured cells bound more label in the presence than in the absence of 1 mM tosyllysine chloromethylketone.

ACKNOWLEDGMENTS

This work was supported by funds from the National Institute of Child Health and Human Development (HD 9140) and the Mayo Foundation. We thank Mrs. E. R. Bergert for excellent technical assistance.

REFERENCES

1. Ryan, R. J., Birnbaumer, L., Lee, C. Y., and Hunzicker-Dunn, M. (1977) *Int. Rev. Physiol.* **13**, 85–152.
2. Lacombe, M.-L., Stengel, D., Haguenauer-Tsapis, R., and Honoune, J. (1979) *In* "Proteases and Hormones" (M. K. Agarwal, ed.), pp. 227–302. Elsevier/North-Holland Biomedical Press, Amsterdam.
3. Richert, N. D., and Ryan, R. J. (1977) *Biochem. Biophys. Res. Commun.* **78**, 799–805.
4. McIlroy, P. J., Richert, N. D., and Ryan, R. J. (1980) *Biochem. J.* **188**, 423–435.
5. McIlroy, P. J., and Ryan, R. J. (1979) *In* "Proteases and Hormones" (M. K. Agarwal, ed.), pp. 175–199. Elsevier/North-Holland Biomedical Press, Amsterdam.
6. LaBarbera, A. R., and Ryan, R. J. (1981) *Endocrinology*, in press.
7. LaBarbera, A. R., and Ryan, R. J. (1981) *Amer. J. Physiol.: Endocr. & Metab.*, in press.
8. Whitley, R. J., Keutmann, H. T., and Ryan, R. J. (1978) *Endocrinology* **102**, 1874–1886.
9. Harper, J. F., and Brooker, G. (1975) *J. Cyclic Nucleotide Res.* **1**, 207–218.
10. Steiner, A. L., Kipnis, D. M., Utiger, R., and Parker, C. W. (1969) *Proc. Natl. Acad. Sci. U.S.A.* **64**, 367–373.
11. Steiner, A. L., Parker, C. W., and Kipnis, D. M. (1972) *J. Biol. Chem.* **274**, 1106–1113.
12. Bolton, A. E., and Hunter, W. M. (1973) *Biochem. J.* **133**, 529–539.
13. Laemmli, V. K. (1970) *Nature (London)* **227**, 680–685.
14. Fairbanks, G., Steck, T. L., and Wallach, D. F. H. (1971) *Biochemistry* **10**, 2606–2617.
15. Lowry, O. H., Rosebrough, N. J., Farr, A. L., and Randall, R. J. (1951) *J. Biol. Chem.* **193**, 265–275.
16. Kissane, J. M., and Robins, E. (1958) *J. Biol. Chem.* **233**, 184–188.
17. Lohr, D., Kovacic, R. T., and Van Holde, K. E. (1977) *Biochemistry* **16**, 463–471.
18. Shaw, E. (1970) *Physiol. Rev.* **50**, 244–296.
19. Ascoli, M., and Puett, D. (1978) *J. Biol. Chem.* **253**, 7832–7838.
20. Ascoli, M. (1978) *J. Biol. Chem.* **253**, 7839–7843.
21. Abramowitz, J., and Birnbaumer, L. (1979) *Biol. Reprod.* **21**, 213–217.
22. Kupfer, A., Gani, V., Jimenez, J. S., and Shaltiel, S. (1979) *Proc. Natl. Acad. Sci. U.S.A.* **76**, 3073–3077.
23. Kok, P., and Astrup, T. (1969) *Biochemistry* **8**, 79–86.
24. Strickland, S., and Beers, W. H. (1976) *J. Biol. Chem.* **251**, 5694–5702.
25. Beers, W. H., and Strickland, W. H. (1978) *J. Biol. Chem.* **253**, 3877–3881.
26. Christman, J. K., Silverstein, S. C., and Acs, G. (1977) *In* "Proteinases in Mammalian Cells and Tissues" (A. J. Barrett, ed.), pp. 91–149. Elsevier/North Holland Biomedical Press, Amsterdam.

PART IV

NONSTEROIDAL GONADAL HORMONES

Selective Suppression of Follicle-Stimulating Hormone by Folliculostatin: A Proposed Ovarian Hormone

ROSEMARY R. GRADY, RUTH T. SAVOY-MOORE,
AND NEENA B. SCHWARTZ
Department of Biological Sciences
Northwestern University
Evanston, Illinois

INTRODUCTION

Our understanding of hypothalamic–pituitary–gonadal function has expanded greatly over the past decade. In simplest terms, we can think of this neuroendocrine axis as a negative feedback system. Inputs to the hypothalamus modulate synthesis, storage and release of GnRH (LHRH). GnRH reaches the anterior pituitary in a pulsatile pattern, stimulating the release of both gonadotropins, LH and FSH. These latter two hormones reach the gonads via the systemic circulation. FSH regulates spermatogenesis and follicular development while LH commands ovulation and steroidogenesis. Increased gonadal steroid synthesis and secretion elevate circulating steroid concentrations, which in turn decrease circulating gonadotropins by negative feedback. Evidence suggesting that steroids are a necessary, but possibly not a sufficient, feedback signal for the control of FSH will be discussed later.

At first glance this cascade of endocrine events beginning at the hy-

BIOREGULATORS OF REPRODUCTION

pothalamus would appear to dictate simultaneous and parallel release of LH and FSH in response to GnRH. Yet serum LH and FSH can differ markedly. During the rat estrous cycle both gonadotropins are elevated on the afternoon of proestrus during the period of the primary surge. Serum LH has declined to basal values by midnight while serum FSH remains elevated through estrus morning (the secondary surge of FSH) (1–3). While the secondary FSH surge in the rat is the most striking example of the divergent patterns of serum LH and FSH, other instances of independent secretion of these two hormones have been observed during the reproductive cycle of hamsters (4), ewes (5), primates (6), and humans (7,8).

To explain separate and joint secretion of the two gonadotropins, several hypotheses based on pituitary responsiveness to GnRH can be proposed (9). One explanation suggests that the two gonadotrophs respond to both frequency and amplitude of GnRH pulses. Some GnRH patterns may favor LH release and others, FSH. Support for this hypothesis is provided by several elegant experiments in the female monkey (10,11). Alternative hypotheses to explain differential secretion of the gonadotropins arise from the gonadal component of the axis.

Bilateral ovariectomy on the morning of proestrus resulted in an increase in serum FSH at 0800 on expected estrus while serum estradiol remained constant (12; serum estradiol concentrations were maintained by adrenal secretion.) This acute rise in serum FSH can not be inhibited by exogenous estradiol (13). In long-term ovariectomized rats, when both serum FSH and LH are elevated, high serum estradiol (200 pg/ml, maintained by Silastic capsules) returned serum LH to baseline while serum FSH remained 3–4 times basal values (14,15).

Following unilateral ovariectomy in the rat, serum FSH, but not LH, increases transiently between 1 and 24 hours, without a concommitant drop in serum estradiol (16). Moreover, administration of estradiol does not prevent this elevated serum FSH (16,17).

The data cited above indicate that estradiol exerts both necessary and sufficient negative feedback on LH, but not FSH. The existence of a second gonadal signal may explain the differential control of FSH/LH secretion.

Experiments by Uilenbroek and co-workers (18) suggest that the ovary secretes a substance with specific FSH-suppressing activity. When rats of both sexes were given an ovarian transplant under the kidney capsule two weeks after gonadectomy, serum LH and FSH returned to basal values. However, male and female rats receiving ovarian transplants in the spleen 2 weeks after gonadectomy showed a continuing elevation in serum LH and a decrease in serum FSH. Observations in male rats confirmed that ovarian steroids from the splanchnic site were inactivated by the liver before reaching the peripheral circulation. Serum estradiol did not rise in males having the transplanted ovary in the spleen, but did increase in those having the ovary implanted in the kidney. These experiments clearly indicate that a substance of ovarian origin, probably not a steroid inactivated by the liver, exerts selective suppression on FSH.

The following section outlines the evidence that folliculostatin, a nonsteroidal substance found in follicular fluid, exerts significant and selective suppression on serum FSH.

ADMINISTRATION OF FOLLICULAR FLUID SUPPRESSES SERUM FSH

Exogenous follicular fluid can suppress blood levels of FSH without any effect on LH. The suppression is not due to steroids, since the fluid is pretreated with charcoal to remove estradiol, progesterone, and testosterone (19). Follicular fluid or ovarian extracts from several species have been shown to suppress FSH: pig (20), cow (21–23), horse (24), mouse (25), hamster (26), and humans (27). Similarly, successful suppression of serum FSH following follicular fluid or ovarian extract administration has been demonstrated in numerous mammals: monkey (28), rat (20,21), mouse (25), hamster (26), horse (24), cow (29), and sheep (29). In the discussion that follows, we will concentrate on our observations in the rat.

In one of our first experiments with porcine follicular fluid (pFF), we demonstrated that folliculostatin injected intraperitoneally on metestrus suppressed serum FSH in a dose-dependent manner 5.5 hours later in rats which had been ovariectomized or sham-operated that morning (30). That the day of the cycle is not a critical factor is indicated by the results depicted in Fig. 1, when we gave pFF using intravenous injection to metestrous, diestrous, and estrous rats. Folliculostatin suppressed serum FSH on each day (Fig. 1a) regardless of the fluctuating steroid concentrations known to occur during the cycle (3). Serum LH was not affected significantly by folliculostatin (Fig. 1b).

We have also examined the effects of folliculostatin on the primary LH and FSH surges on proestrus (32). As can be seen in Fig. 2, serum FSH was significantly suppressed when folliculostatin was injected at least 5 hours prior to sacrifice. Serum LH was unaffected. These data

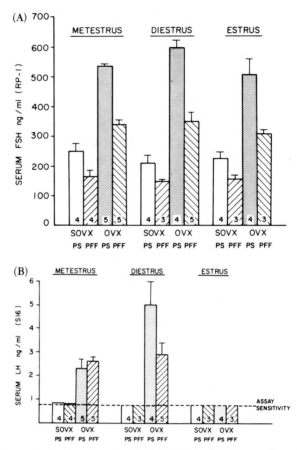

Fig. 1. Serum FHS (A) and serum LH (B) at 1700 of metestrus, diestrus, and estrus following surgery and injection that morning. Surgery was performed at 0800. SOVX, Sham ovariectomy; OVX, ovariectomy. 62.5 μl of either PS (porcine serum) or pFF (porcine follicular fluid) were injected intravenously at 1130, 5.5 hours before sacrifice by decapitation. The number of rats per group is shown at the bottom of each bar. Group means plus standard errors are depicted. LH assay detectability was 0.75 ng/ml; FSH assay detectability was 130 ng/ml. As can be seen, serum FSH responded briskly to ovariectomy on all three days, while serum LH did not rise on estrus. This discrepancy in LH and FSH response to ovariectomy has been subjected to intense scrutiny (17,31). Only serum FSH was suppressed by pFF.

are powerful evidence for the specific action of folliculostatin on FSH release.

The responsiveness of rats to folliculostatin in two situations in which FSH secretion is enhanced, is the absence of elevated LH,

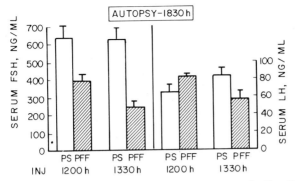

Fig. 2. Serum FSH (RP-1 as standard) and LH (S16 as standard) at 1830 on proestrus. PS or pFF was injected intraperitoneally at 1200 or 1330; the dose was 0.5 or 1.0 ml. Mean plus standard errors are shown. The number of rats per group ranged from 4 to 17. These data appeared in tabular form in Hoffmann *et al.* (32).

has also been tested. The first is the secondary FSH surge (20). As shown in Table I, this FSH surge (measured at 0400 estrus) can be blocked by folliculostatin administration. Second, Welschen and co-workers (23) showed that increased FSH secretion following unilateral ovariectomy could be blocked by injection of bovine follicular fluid. When both serum FSH and LH are elevated, in chronically ovariectomized rats (34) and mice (25), administration of follicular

TABLE I
Effect of Porcine Follicular Fluid Given Early or Late on the
Day of Proestrus on the Secondary FSH Surge[a]

| | Proestrus | | | |
Group	Time of injection	Treatment	n	Serum FSH at 0400 estrus
A	1545 hr; 1830 hr	PS (2 × 0.5 ml)	6	594 ± 33
B	1545 hr; 1830 hr	pFF (2 × 0.5 ml)	6	55 ± 5[b]
C	2230 hr	PS (1 ml)	10	551 ± 53
D	2230 hr	pFF (1 ml)	10	275 ± 53[b]

[a] All injections are intraperitoneal. Half of each treatment group A through D were allowed to manifest normal primary LH and FSH surges; the other half were blocked with pentobarbital, then received exogenous LH to produce an artificial LH surge (33). As can be seen, rats which were treated with pFF early (A,B) showed complete suppression of serum FSH at 0400h, while a delay in pFF treatment (C,D) rendered suppression less effective.

[b] $P < .05$; mean ± Se.

fluid returned FSH to basal values while LH remained elevated (25,34).

The response of the male rat to folliculostatin has also been assessed. DeJong and Sharpe (21) blocked increased serum FSH following castration with bovine follicular fluid. As shown in Fig. 3, we have obtained similar results. Porcine follicular fluid partially suppressed the acute rise in FSH 24 hours after orchidectomy, while serum LH rose unabated. Thus, it is possible to selectively alter FSH in the male with follicular fluid. However, large amounts of the fluid are required

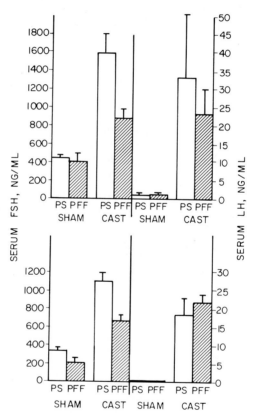

Fig. 3. Serum FSH (RP-1 as standard; left side of graph) and LH (S16 as standard; right side) 24 hours after surgery (sham, sham castration; cast, castration). Adult male rats were orchidectomized or sham operated at 2000. They received a total of 1 ml PS or pFF in three injections. Sacrifice was +24 hours after surgery, 5 hours after the last injection. This protocol was followed for both experiments, depicted separately in the top and bottom panels. N = 4/group. Group means plus standard errors are plotted. These data appeared in tabular form in Lorenzen *et al.* (35).

for reliable suppression. Furthermore, the degree of suppression of FSH secretion by this substance is not as great in the male as it is in the female either in our own hands (35) or in the hands of others (36).

The effects of follicular fluid have also been examined *in vitro*. When added to pituitary cell cultures, folliculostatin suppressed FSH release, although inhibition of LH release has also been reported (37–40).

CHARACTERIZATION OF FOLLICULOSTATIN

Hudson and co-workers (41) have pointed out that the failure to isolate testicular inhibin after more than 50 years of work may have been due to the lack of a reliable and precise bioassay. Darrell Ward, in the following chapter, has discussed the little we know about the chemical nature of folliculostatin. To assay pFF-derived materials, we use rats ovariectomized on the morning of metestrus. Test preparations are injected 3.5 hours after surgery and the animals are sacrificed 4.5–5.5 hours following injection. Four rats are injected with a given fraction, and individual serum FSH values are measured by radioimmunoassay. Originally, an intraperitoneal injection route was employed (19,30). We have increased the bioassay sensitivity by substituting intravenous injection. As indicated in Fig. 4, FSH was suppressed significantly by as little as 31.3 μl of follicular fluid, by the same volume of the $\geq 10,000$ MW fraction of pFF (PM 10), or by 4.2 mg of the ethanol-precipitated protein fraction of PM 10. The index of precision of the bioassay, 0.24, is very good. The assay is expensive, and turnaround time can be long, but the reliability is outstanding. Use of indirect bioassays, like those using ovarian or uterine weight as an endpoint for FSH secretion, are faster than the method described above. However, they may be misleading, since FSH and LH binding inhibitors are known to be present in follicular fluid (42,43).

Another problem in isolating an active fraction has been the definition of inhibin/folliculostatin activity. As originally proposed, these materials exert selective FSH suppression. As has been documented here, unfractionated follicular fluid does not possess LH suppressing activity *in vivo*. Many attempts at purification have resulted in materials which suppressed both LH and FSH, or stimulated LH (36). Routine purification procedures either may render materials less specific, or the particular bioassays used may not be able to distinguish specific FSH suppression from suppression of both gonadotropins. Pituitary cell culture assays seem particularly susceptible to suppression of ei-

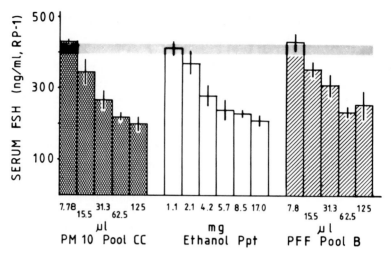

Fig. 4. Serum FSH in rats ovariectomized at 0730–0930 metestrus and injected i.v. with pFF, the ≥ 10,000 MW fraction of pFF (PM 10), or the ethanol-precipitated protein fraction of PM 10 (ethanol ppt). Control animals received porcine serum (mean ± SE; indicated by the horizontal shaded area; n = 8). Injections were administered 3.5 hours following ovariectomy and animals were sacrificed 4.5 hours later. N = 4/group; mean ± SE is plotted.

ther gonadotropin, although low doses of folliculostatin incubated for 48 hours will specifically suppress FSH. It seems imperative that we retain specific FSH suppression as the endpoint of fractionation. However, we should also recognize that under some conditions the active fraction from follicular fluid may be nonspecific .

IS FOLLICULOSTATIN A HORMONE?

Classical endocrinology is based on the observation that following the removal of a specific gland, a measurable alteration in a physiological variable occurs which can be reversed by treatment with the glandular extract. Ovariectomy leads to a rise in serum FSH which can be prevented or reversed successfully by nonsteroidal factors contained in follicular fluid. The source of folliculostatin may be the granulosa cells, since they secrete folliculostatin in culture (37). To be defined as a hormone, the glandular secretion must reach its target organ via the bloodstream. DePaolo and co-workers (44) reported that they can detect FSH-suppressing activity in ovarian venous blood, assayed with pituitary cell cultures. Yet without a widely accepted and available RIA for measuring folliculostatin in serum, its status as a hormone is retarded.

That folliculostatin plays a role in normal ovarian function is suggested by the fact that injection of follicular fluid suppressed serum FSH, which resulted in retarded follicular growth in rats (45) and in sheep and cows (29). Definitive proof of endocrine status for folliculostatin lies in its isolation and purification, so that an assay measuring its circulating concentrations can be validated. This critical step awaits future work. However, at present we are compelled by the observations cited in the last two sections to say "Yes! folliculostatin *is* a hormone," while we continue to pursue the chemical nature of this molecule.

ACKNOWLEDGMENTS

The authors gratefully acknowledge the support of Northwestern University Cancer Center and of Public Health Service grants AM06129 (RRG), HD05561 (RTS-M), and HD07504 (NBS). We also wish to thank William Talley, Brigitte Mann, and Sheri Veren for their excellent technical assistance; National Institutes of Health, Endocrinology Study Section, for gonadotropic hormones used as standards and for the FSH kit; Dr. L. E. Reichert, Jr. for the LH used for radioiodination; Dr. G. D. Niswender for contributing the antiserum used for the LH radioimmunoassay. NIH-LH-S16 was used as the standard for the LH assay, while NIH-FSH-RP-1 was used as the standard for the FSH assay.

REFERENCES

1. Butcher, R. L., Collins, W. E., and Fugo, N. W. (1975) *Endocrinology* **96**, 576–586.
2. Smith, M. S., Freeman, M. A., and Neill, J. D. (1975) *Endocrinology* **96**, 219–226.
3. Nequin, L. G., Alvarez, J., and Schwartz, N. B. (1979) *Biol. Reprod.* **20**, 659–670.
4. Bast, J., and Greenwald, G. S. (1974) *Endocrinology* **94**, 1295–1299.
5. Salamonsen, L. A., Jonas, H. A., Burger, H. G., Buckmaster, J. M., Chamley, W. A., Cumming, I. A., Findlay, J. K., and Goding, J. R. (1973) *Endocrinology* **93**, 610–618.
6. Knobil, E. (1974) *Recent Prog. Horm. Res.* **30**, 1–46.
7. Ross, G. T., Cargille, C. M., Lipsett, M. B., Rayford, P. L., Marshall, J. R., Strott, C. A., and Rodbard, D. (1970) *Recent Prog. Horm. Res.* **26**, 1–62.
8. Yen, S. S. C., Lasley, B. L., Wang, C. F., Leblanc, H., and Siler, T. M. (1975) *Recent Prog. Horm. Res.* **31**, 321–357.
9. Savoy-Moore, R. T., and Schwartz, N. B. (1980) *In* "Reproductive Physiology III (R. O. Greep, ed.) Vol. 22 pp. 203–248. University Park Press, Baltimore, Maryland.
10. Belchetz, P. E., Plant, T. M., Nakai, Y., Keogh, E. J., and Knobil, E. (1978) *Science* **202**, 631–633.
11. Wildt, L., Marshall, G., Hausler, A., Plant, T. M., Belchetz, P. E., and Knobil, E. (1979) *Fed. Proc., Fed. Am. Soc. Exp. Biol.* **38**, 978, Abstr. No. 3942.

12. Campbell, C. S., Schwartz, N. B., and Firlit, M. G. (1977) *Endocrinology* **101**, 162–172.

13. Chappel, S. C., and Barraclough, C. A. (1977) *Endocrinology* **101**, 24–31.

14. Campbell, C. S., and Firlit, M. G. (1976) *3rd Annu. National Center for Toxicological Research Horm. Res. Symp.* Abstract.

15. Campbell, C. S., and Schwartz, N. B. (1977) *J. Toxicol. Environ. Health* **3**, 61–95.

16. Butcher, R. L. (1977) *Endocrinology* **101**, 830–840.

17. Ramirez, V. D., and Sawyer, C. H. (1974) *Endocrinology* **94**, 475–482.

18. Uilenbroek, J. T. J., Tiller, R., deJong, F. H., and Vels, F. (1978). *J. Endocrinol.* **78**, 399–406.

19. Lorenzen, J. R., Channing, C. P., and Schwartz, N. B. (1978) *Biol. Reprod.* **19**, 635–640.

20. Schwartz, N. B., and Channing, C. P. (1977) *Proc. Natl. Acad. Sci. U. S. A.* **74**, 5721–5724.

21. DeJong, F. H., and Sharpe, R. M. (1976) *Nature (London)* **263**, 71–72.

22. Hopkinson, C. R. N., Duame, E., Sturm, G., Fritze, E., Kaiser, S., and Hirschhauser, C. (1977) *J. Reprod. Fertil.* **50**, 93–96.

23. Welschen, R., Dullaart, J., and deJong, F. H. (1978) *Biol. Reprod.* **18**, 421–427.

24. Miller, K. F., Wesson, J. A., and Ginther, O. J. (1979) *Biol. Reprod.* **21**, 867–872.

25. Bronson, F. H., and Channing, C. P. (1978) *Endocrinology* **103**, 1894–1898.

26. Chappel, S. C., Acott, T., and Spies, H. G. (1979) *In* "Ovarian Follicular and Corpus Luteum Function" (C. P. Channing, J. Marsh, and W. D. Sadler, eds.), pp. 361–371. Plenum, New York.

27. Chappel, S. C., Holt, J. A., and Spies, H. G. (1980) *Proc. Soc. Exp. Biol. Med.* **163**, 310–314.

28. Channing, C. P., Anderson, L. D., and Hodgen, G. D. (1979) *Adv. Exp. Med. Biol.* **112**, 407–415.

29. Miller, K. F., Critser, J. K., Rowe, R. F., and Ginther, O. J. (1979) *Biol. Reprod.* **21**, 537–544.

30. Marder, M. L., Channing, C. P., and Schwartz, N. B. (1977) *Endocrinology* **101**, 1639–1642.

31. Brown-Grant, K., and Greig, F. (1975) *J. Endocrinol.* **65**, 389–397.

32. Hoffmann, J. C., Lorenzen, J. R., Weil, T., and Schwartz, N. B. (1979) *Endocrinology* **105**, 200–203.

33. Schwartz, N. B., and Talley, W. L. (1978) *Biol. Reprod.* **18**, 820–828.

34. Campbell, C. S., and Schwartz, N. B. (1979) *Biol. Reprod.* **20**, 659–670.

35. Lorenzen, J. R., Dworkin, G. H., and Schwartz, N. B. (1981) *Am. J. Physiol.* (in press).

36. DeJong, F. H., Welschen, R., Hermans, W. P., Smith, S. D., and Van der Molen, H. J. (1978) *Int. J. Androl., Suppl.* **2**, 125–138.

37. Erickson, G. F., and Hsueh, A. J. W. (1978) *Endocrinology* **103**, 1960–1963.

38. DeJong, F. H., Smith, S. D., and Van der Molen, H. S. (1979) *J. Endocrinol.* **80**, 91–102.

39. Lagacé, L., Labrie, F., Lorenzen, J. R., Schwartz, N. B., and Chaining, C. P. (1979) *Clin. Endocrinol.* **10**, 401–406.

40. Scott, R. S., and Burger, H. G. (1979) *Proc. 61st Annu. Meet. Endocr. Soc.* Abstract No. 836.

41. Hudson, B., Baker, H. W. G., Eddie, L. W., Higginson, R. E., Burger, H. G., de Kretser, D. M., Dobos, M., and Lee, V. W. K. (1979) *J. Reprod. Fertil., Suppl.* **26**, 17–29.

42. Reichert, L. E. (1978) *In* "Novel Aspects of Reproductive Physiology" (C. H. Spilman and J. W. Wilks, eds.), pp. 355–368. S. P. Medical and Scientific Books, New York.
43. Yang, K. P. P., Gray, K. N., Jardine, J. H., Yen, H. L. N., Samaan, N. A., and Ward, D. N. (1978) *In* "Novel Aspects of Reproductive Physiology" (C. H. Spilman and J. W. Wilks, eds.), pp. 61–76. S. P. Medical and Scientific Books, New York.
44. DePaolo, L. V., Shander, D., Wise, P. M., Barraclough, C. A., and Channing, C. P. (1979) *Endocrinology* **105,** 647–654.
45. Hoak, D., and Schwartz, N. B. (1980) *Proc. Natl. Acad. Sci. U.S.A.* **77,** 4953–4956.

This indeed presented the ingredients for an interesting biochemical isolation study. Accordingly, we organized our approach to what we hoped would be the isolation of inhibin from ovarian sources. However, since it was not clear, and still is not clear, whether inhibin from the ovary was identical with inhibin from the testes, my colleagues coined the name "folliculostatin" for the material from the ovary. This term was first used in papers published in 1977 and 1978 (17,19). The term has taken the scientific world by storm and is widely used in all three of our laboratories and will be used in this paper.

In all of our studies with follicular fluid, the material used is charcoal-treated and filtered for the retentate on a PM-10 Amicon membrane. This is because my colleague, Dr. Channing, is collecting the low molecular weight fraction for her studies on the OMI. Moreover, we have shown early that all of the folliculostatin activity is retained in the high molecular weight fraction.

Our early studies were designed to assess the stability of the folliculostatin activity in the crude follicular fluid concentrates with which we were working. Some of these data have been reported in a publication by Lorenzen et al. (19). As shown in Table I (19,20), folliculostatin activity is remarkably stable in the follicular fluid as we obtain it. In the frozen state activity was retained for at least 1 year storage. At 4°C, the activity is unchanged for at least 2 months, and at room temperature, for at least 4 days. When heated at 60°C for 20 minutes approximately 50% of the activity is lost and at 80°C for 30 minutes the activity is totally destroyed. Digestion with trypsin also completely inactivated the folliculostatin. The pH stability was tested for 24 hours, and in some instances for even longer, for the pH range of 2.5–9.6. At pH 2.5 there was detectable loss of activity; at pH 4–5.4 the activity precipitates and, therefore, the isoelectric point must be in this vicinity. The folliculostatin is stable at pH 4–9.6. Some of the pH stability studies were indirectly obtained from other experiments. However, the pH studies were usually done at room temperature for 24 hours before evaluation.

It is conceivable that a neuraminidase activity in follicular fluid could suppress FSH levels by splitting sialic acid from FSH, thus causing a more rapid clearance of FSH from the serum. Therefore follicular fluid was tested for neuraminidase activity and no evidence was found that the enzyme is present in follicular fluid. Under the conditions tested as little as 5 Warren units/ml could have been detected.

Since some investigators had used chaotropic agents such as urea to dissociate a low molecular weight inhibin from high molecular weight

TABLE I
Properties of PM-10 Membrane-Filtered Porcine Follicular Fluid

Property tested	Treatment	Notes
A. Folliculostatin activity		
	(1) Storage 1 year, frozen	Stable
	(2) Storage, 4°C, 2 months	Stable
	(3) Room temperature, 4 days	Stable
	(4) 60°C, 20 minutes	50% inactivation (19)
	(5) 80°C, 30 minutes	Inactivated (19)
	(6) Trypsin, 100 μg/ml, 37°C	Inactivated (19)
	(7) pH 2.5, 24 hours	Partial inactivation
	(8) pH 4.0, 24 hours	Stable, but ppts.
	(9) pH 5.25, 24 hours	Stable, but ppts.
	(10) pH 5.4, 24 hours	Stable, but ppts.
	(11) pH 6.0, 24 hours	Stable
	(12) pH 7.0, 24 hours	Stable
	(13) pH 8.1, 24 hours	Stable
	(14) pH 9.6, 24 hours	Stable
	(15) Guanidine hydrochloride, 24 hours	
	(a) 5 M	Inactivates
	(b) 2.5 M	Inactivates
	(c) 1.0 M	Inactivates
	(d) 0.5 M	50% inactivation
	(e) 0.25 M	Stable
B. Proteolytic activity	(1) Chymotryptic-like activity (BTEE)	<0.16 μg/ml
	(2) Tryptic-like activity (TAME)	<0.04 μg/ml
C. Neuraminidase activity	Tested on bovine fraction VI (serum) or bovine submaxillary mucin as substrates	Activity absent, <5 Warren units/ml (20)

material, we tested a 5 M guanidine hydrochloride solution for its ability to dissociate a possible low molecular weight activity. A 5 M guanidine hydrochloride solution completely inactivates the folliculostatin activity. The activity was titrated with various concentrations of guanidine hydrochloride and only at 0.25 M guanidine hydrochloride was the activity stable. At 0.5 M inactivation was about 60% complete in 24 hours.

For reasons which will be discussed it was of interest to know if there was any proteolytic activity in follicular fluid. Using sensitive spectrophotometric assays neither chymotryptic-like or tryptic-like activity could be detected in follicular fluid. The data are expressed relative to the solids precipitable with 90% ethanol. The value given for each activity is that maximum sensitivity of enzyme activity detectable under the conditions of sampling employed. Although these figures do not completely exclude the possibility of very small quantities of proteolytic activity present, they certainly do indicate that any of this type protease activity detectable by these substrates would be in very low concentration.

Since there was accumulating in the literature a fair body of evidence which indicated that inhibin-M had a molecular weight of approximately 20,000, our initial experiments were designed to favor the isolation of a molecule in this molecular weight range. To summarize experiments conducted over a period of $2\frac{1}{2}$ years our follicular fluid preparations were submitted to chromatography initially on BioGel P-30. When all of the activity appeared to be in the higher molecular weight fraction on this gel we turned to a P-60 chromatography and again observed that all of the activity ran at the front of the chromatogram. So Sephadex G-100 was used and then Sephadex G-200, and evidence of a high molecular weight product was always obtained.

With the use of ion-exchange chromatography procedures (employing carboxymethylcellulose and DEAE-cellulose in the early experiments) considerable difficulty with the loss of activity upon fractionation of the follicular fluid preparations was experienced. At about that point we adopted the procedure of estimating theoretical potency based on the amount of starting material involved and then testing at a fourfold higher dose. Our rationale was that if more than 75% of the activity was being lost, there was no point in using that procedure.

Since the ion-exchange procedures seemed to be giving us a problem ammonium sulfate fractionation and ethanol precipitation were used. Of these two procedures the ethanol precipitation was preferred, and we now routinely precipitate the protein from follicular fluid concentrates with 90% ethanol. This gives maximum recovery of protein and virtually quantitative recovery of the folliculostatin activity.

Shortly after we had developed this approach the report by Chari *et al.* (13) appeared on the purification of folliculostatin from human follicular fluid. Her procedure employed an 86% ethanol precipitation in the presence of an added 0.1 *M* sodium chloride. Since we had already developed our own set of conditions we did not directly compare the two initial treatments. However, it seems likely that the initial procedure used by Chari *et al.* (13) is comparable to that which we employ.

The claim for the isolation of a homogeneous, 19,000-dalton inhibin from human follicular fluid is impressive. Using our assay and attempting to follow the procedure described by Chari (13), except to modify the initial step as noted, we have been thwarted by the fact that the only place the porcine activity fractionates is as a high molecular weight material.

The bioassay we are employing has only a fivefold dose–response range, thus perhaps our assays are overly sensitive to losses of activity. It will not be particularly instructive to recount several chromatographic procedures that we have attempted to employ, but with which a loss of activity was encountered. In fact, our experience seems to run counter to that of Baker *et al.* (21), who reported poor recovery from ethanol fractionation of rete testis fluid or testicular lymph, but very satisfactory recoveries from DEAE-Sephadex or CM-Sephadex.

As our studies on folliculostatin progressed—or more realistically, did not progress—it became of increasing importance to know if we were pursuing a high molecular weight, a medium molecular weight protein molecule, or a tiny peptide. The literature on inhibin is filled with data bearing on molecular weight. The range of suggested values is staggering, however, and there is no final basis for selection. In Table II (11–13,19,22–26), a sample of indicated molecular weights that have been suggested is presented. The list is far from complete, but selected to give a representative sampling of the range.

Reports range from the smallest molecular weight claimed as 1500. The highest reported is 160,000. There are also data which suggest even higher molecular weights (e.g., 25,26) although the authors do not necessarily indicate the higher values in their interpretations. This has led some investigators to propose that there are several nonsteroidal factors, which can influence the release of gonadotropins from pituitary cells. DeJong and collegues (23) have presented very

TABLE II
Representative Molecular Weight Reported for Inhibin-M or Folliculostatin

Report cited	Source of preparation	Molecular mass (daltons)
Thakur *et al.* (11)	Seminal Plasma (human)	19,000
Chari *et al.* (12)	Seminal Plasma (bovine)	19,000
Chari *et al.* (13)	Human follicular fluid	23,000
Cahoreau *et al.* (22)	Rete testis fluid (ovine)	160,000
deJong *et al.* (23)	Bovine follicular fluid	>10,000
	(according to treatment)	<10,000
Lorenzen *et al.* (19)	Porcine follicular fluid	>10,000
	(retained by PM-10 membrane)	
Shashidhara Murthy *et al.* (24)	Testicular extract (ovine)	20,000
Moodbidri *et al.* (25)	Testicular extract (ovine)	<5,000
	cited at this size later (ref. 11)	1,500
deJong (26)	Various (a review), 6 citations on this subject	5,000 to greater than 100,000

convincing data in support of this thesis. To avoid confusion, "inhibin" should be defined as a substance which specifically regulates FSH. Not all investigators have maintained this distinction. On the other hand, the use of the term "folliculostatin" has always been applied in this restricted sense. As deJong et al. state (23) "decisions on the presence of inhibin in gonadal preparations can only be derived from a combination of data—which yield information on the specific regulation of the release of FSH from the pituitary gland." They advocate the use of both in vivo and in vitro test systems. I favor this suggestion. Had all investigators applied this approach it may have forestalled much of the present confusion in the inhibin arena.

Thus, at this point it seemed extremely important to clarify, for our own studies, the molecular weight of folliculostatin. A method of estimation which would not require a purified product was desired. The first procedures which come to mind in this category would be bioassay of fractions obtained from molecular exclusion processes. However, since most of the wide variety of reported molecular weight studies had in fact employed such techniques, e.g., Sephadex chromatography or membrane exclusion procedures, another approach was needed which might provide new insights to the problem.

We turned to the estimation of molecular weight by radiation inactivation. The theoretical basis for the methodology is simple. One assumes that any ionizing radiation that strikes a molecule will inactivate that molecule. This has been referred to as the single target theory. The next assumption is that the probability of a hit is a function of the target volume and that this target volume is a function of the molecular weight of the protein involved. Kempner and Schlegel (27) have recently provided an excellent review of this methodology. It is essential that one have a means of measuring the activity of the protein involved. In this case then the basic equation is as follows:

$$A = A_o e^{-kD} \tag{1}$$

The activity, A, after any given dose, D in rads, is related to the initial activity, A_o, and the constant, k, in the exponent, which is related to the target size. Experimentally k may be estimated from the dose of radiation required to reduce the activity to 37% of the initial activity. Kempner and Macey (28) have provided an empirical equation which amounts to an evaluation of the factor k based on determinations of enzyme or hormonal activities of substances of known molecular weight. Thus as shown in Eq. (2) the only factor needed to

$$\text{Molecular weight} = (6.4 \times 10^{11})/D_{37} \tag{2}$$

estimate molecular weight is an estimation of the D_{37} value for a given activity. Thus the higher the molecular weight of the material involved the smaller the D_{37} in rads that will be required to produce this degree of inactivation.

There is one other requirement for the application of this technology which should be indicated. It is necessary that the protein be in a dried state in order to apply the theory, since in aqueous solutions the radiation effects are transmitted through much greater volumes due to effects on the solvent. In other words, the single target theory would not apply. For this purpose our 90% ethanol precipitates are readily dried and provide suitable material for the molecular weight estimation of folliculostatin by this methodology.

For our initial studies it was assumed that the molecular weight would probably be in the 20 to 30 thousand molecular weight range. Accordingly, the number of rads irradiation that would be required to reach 37% inactivation was estimated and the first experiment initiated. It was surprising to find that all of the samples were so near completely inactivated that we were beyond our dose range for estimating potency. Thus, the only thing learned from our first experience was that the material behaved as if it were a much larger molecule than had been assumed. Accordingly, our irradiation treatment periods were shortened and inclined toward the higher molecular weight estimates that were provided in the literature. As shown in Fig. 1 we

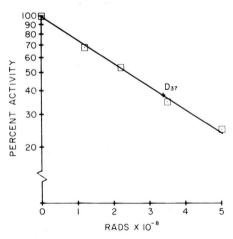

Fig. 1. Irradiation inactivation curve for folliculostatin. Irradiation was delivered from a ^{137}Cs source generating a dose of 5490 rads/minute. The folliculostatin preparation was the 90% ethanol precipitate described in the text.

were able to estimate a D_{37} of 3.5 million rads for folliculostatin inactivation. From Fig. 1 a molecular weight of 182,000 plus or minus 14,000 could be estimated.

This can be interpreted to mean that with the assay employed the activity is associated with a large molecule. This does not preclude the possibility that the folliculostatin molecule may not have subunits or some other type of aggregated structure. It does, however, tell us that the entire complex is required for biological activity in our assay system.

To relate this to a system which may be more familiar, two papers by Bill Odell and his colleagues in the 1960s using this technique to estimate the molecular weight of the pituitary glycoprotein hormones will be cited. These estimates were made in 1964, before the purification procedures and characterizations of these hormones had advanced to the state recognized today. In those studies Dr. Odell and his colleagues (29,30) estimated molecular weights of approximately 30,000. This tells us that a hit, in terms of our present knowledge, in either the α- or β-subunit was sufficient to inactivate the hormone.

This information, relative to the molecular weight of folliculostatin, has allowed us a re-orientation of our approach to the fractionation of this material. Unfortunately these studies are too early in their staging to indicate what the ultimate value of this re-orientation might be.

LH-RBI*

We reported in 1976 (9), a factor extractable from heavily luteinized rat ovaries which would inhibit the binding of LH to its receptors in the ovary. We called this material LH-RBI for receptor binding inhibitor. It was subsequently shown that this activity resided in a dialyzable and nondialyzable fraction. The nondialyzable fraction was approximately 4000 molecular weight. A similar factor is extractable from the ovaries from all of the species we have tested, which include goat, sheep, pork, dog, and cat. These findings have been confirmed by Sakai et al. (31), who also showed that the factor was derived from corpora lutea and not the interstitial tissue or the follicle. The properties of rat LH-RBI are summarized in Table III (9,32–34).

* This section was prepared in collaboration with Stephan D. Glenn, Hiromu Sugino, Hyun S. Nahm, and Kuo-Pao Yang (The University of Texas M.D. Anderson Hospital, Houston, Texas); and Cornelia P. Channing (University of Maryland, Baltimore, Maryland).

TABLE III
Properties of Rat LH-RBI[a]

1. Inhibits binding of LH or hCG to ovarian receptors
2. Inhibits LH or hCG stimulated steroidogenesis in the ovary in a dose-dependent fashion
3. Is present as a dialyzable (3800 dalton) and nondialyzable (>10,000 dalton) form
4. Inhibition of LH binding could not be demonstrated in testicular homogenates

[a] Summarized from references 9, 32–34.

Kumari *et al.* (35) found that in the porcine ovary extracts from the mid-cycle or old corpora lutea had greater ability to inhibit hCG binding than did extract of the early luteal phase corpora lutea.

Dr. Yang is continuing his characterization of the rat LH-RBI but studies are difficult since the amount of material available is small. In my laboratory we turned to the porcine corpora lutea, provided by Dr. Channing, in order to run parallel studies on a material which we felt would be in much greater supply. These studies have not progressed as rapidly as had been anticipated, however, since the material from the porcine corpora lutea seems to behave somewhat differently from the fractions from the rat ovary. The first difference observed was that a dialyzable LH-RBI in the porcine extracts could not be detected. We have had an occasional suggestion that there was such material but at

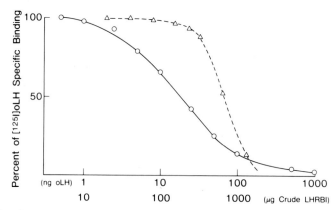

Fig. 2. Competitive inhibition curves from a rat ovarian homogenate receptor preparation (25 mg) with 2.5 ng ^{125}I-oLH as the trace. The ovaries were obtained from rats made pseudopregnant by PMSG-hCG treatment. The highly purified unlabeled oLH in the quantities indicated was added at the same time as the labeled preparation and the 2-hour incubation (37°C) initiated; open circle, solid line. The crude LH-RBI preparation, triangles, dashed line, was handled in the same way. For further details see Yang *et al.* (9).

TABLE IV
Summary of Purification Studies for Porcine LH-RBI

Purification step	Yield (329g C.L.) (mg)	ID$_{50}$ (μg)	Specific activity (μ/g)	Fold-purification	Total units	Percent recovery
(1) C.L. Extract[a]	18,200	1,080	13.9	1.0	253,000	100
(2) DEAE-Cellulose (fraction 7)	902	1,400	10.7	0.76	96,500	38
(3) Sephadex G-100	199	540	27.8	2.6	5,530	2.2
(4) DEAE-Cellulose (repeat)	88	250	60.0	5.6	5,268	2.1
(5) Sephadex G-75	41	185	81.1	7.6	3,285	1.3

[a] The extraction procedure consists of homogenization in 6 volumes of 0.02 M ammonium bicarbonate, followed by addition of solid phenylmethanesulfonyl fluoride to provide an initial concentration of 0.02 M. The extract was clarified, after 5 hours stirring, by centrifugation at 10,000 g. We have recently extracted the C.L. extract preparation with cold butanol and found a major portion of the activity is removed. Solubility is poor for aqueous-system testing, but the amount of butanol-soluble activity is substantial.

a far lower level than had been experienced in the case of the rat extracts. So our attention was turned to the nondialyzable LH-RBI.

As shown in Fig. 2 the LH-RBI provides a somewhat more precipitous decline in the competitive binding curve than does competition with unlabeled ovarian-luteinizing hormone (oLH) when iodinated oLH is used as the trace with an ovarian receptor system. In order to have some basis for estimating potency the ID$_{50}$ for the inhibition of the crude LH-RBI is compared with the ID$_{50}$ for purified oLH. This has the disadvantage that parallel slopes are not being dealt with, but it is convenient and gives some basis for estimation. Ultimately it would be desirable to have a purified LH-RBI as a reference standard. Thus one provisional unit of LH-RBI activity is taken as that which provides the same inhibition as 1 ng of purified oLH under these conditions.

In Table IV the purification procedures that have been applied to LH-RBI extracted from porcine corpora lutea are summarized. This fraction, after clarification by centrifugation, is applied to a DEAE-cellulose. The majority of the activity recovered from the DEAE-cellulose column (Fig. 3) is in fraction 7, which is eluted with 0.5 M ammonium bicarbonate buffer. There was a slight activity in the peak labeled fraction 5. Recovery of activity in fraction 7 was only 40% of the starting material in the corpora lutea extract. Attempts to fractionate the fraction 7 further using Sephadex, followed by DEAE-cellulose

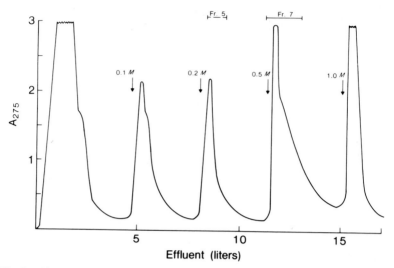

Fig. 3.   Chromatography of an extract from 329 g of frozen porcine corpora lutea; see Table IV. The extract in 0.02 M ammonium bicarbonate buffer was applied to a 5 × 20 cm column of DEAE-cellulose (Whatman DE-32) developed with stepwise increases of ammonium bicarbonate concentration, as indicated by the arrows. Temperature, 4°C; flow rate, 123 ml/hour. The LH-RBI activity was in fraction 7 (Fr. 7), with slight activity also detected in fraction 5.

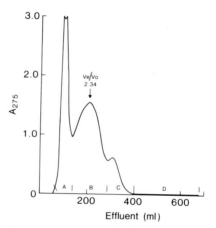

Fig. 4.   Gel filtration of 153 mg of Fr. 7 (Fig. 3), on a column of Sephadex G-100 (2 × 85 cm) developed with 0.2 M ammonium bicarbonate. Temperature, 5°C; flow rate, 42 ml/hour. LH-RBI activity was in fraction B.

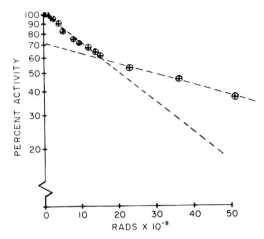

Fig. 5.   Irradiation inactivation study of LH-RBI (initial extract, Table IV). Conditions as per Fig. 1. The apparent biphasic inactivation is indicated by the dashed lines.

once again or Sephadex G-75, led to a very poor recovery (approximately 2% overall). As shown in Fig. 4 what activity was seen appeared to chromatograph on the Sephadex G-100 with a V_e/V_0 ratio of 2.34. Polyacrylamide gel electrophoresis of this fraction showed at least three components were present. The V_e/V_0 value suggests a molecular weight of the order of magnitude for the subunits of ovine LH. Indeed the major component in this fraction runs in the same area as the LH subunits on SDS-gel electrophoresis.

We thought it might be advisable to verify this molecular weight with the radiation inactivation approach which had been applied to folliculostatin. The starting material employed was the crude corpora lutea extract which had been clarified by centrifugation and lyophilized. However, as shown in Fig. 5, the inactivation curve in this instance proved to be biphasic. In order to analyze this curve a program which had been devised to sort out two different isotopes with different radioactive decay rates was borrowed from our Biomathematics department. As shown in Fig. 6 the computer sorted out the two different components and plotted them as two different inactivation curves for a low molecular weight and a higher molecular weight material. The calculated molecular weights from these curves would be 66,000 (range 46,000–85,000) for the high molecular weight component and 6800 (range 3500–10,000) for the low molecular weight component.

Thus, although we seemed to be observing in the porcine material a low and high molecular weight component as was reported previously for the rat LH-RBI, neither of the molecular weight estimates corre-

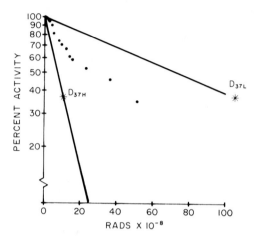

Fig. 6. Computer resolution of the apparent biphasic inactivation curves seen in Fig. 5. Graphic estimation of the D_{37} dose for a high molecular weight component (37L) and low molecular weight component (37H) is indicated.

late well with the G-100 value for the V_e/V_o ratio. If the decay curve is recalculated as a single linear regression the fit on the line is less satisfactory as shown in Fig. 7. The D_{37} estimate in this instance gives a calculated molecular weight of 16,000 with a 14,000 to 18,000 molecular weight range. This, in fact, would correlate better with the G-100 data obtained with the more purified preparation. Thus it is not cer-

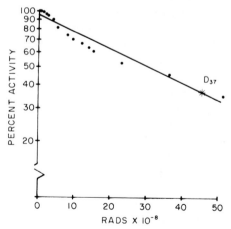

Fig. 7. Irradiation inactivation study of LH-RBI as in Fig. 5, but plotted as a single active substance.

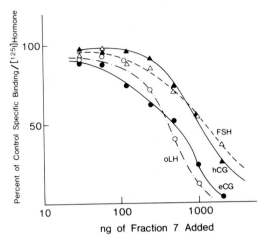

Fig. 8. Inhibition of binding of ^{125}I-labeled gonadotropins in a rat ovarian homogenate system (eCG, solid circles, solid line) or rat testicular homogenate system (oLH, hCG, or oFSH) by a crude porcine LH-RBI preparation. This type of preparation (Fr. 7) lacks the specificity reported for the rat LH-RBI preparations (32), but retains some specificity since other fractions from the same preparation (Fig. 3) failed to inhibit binding.

tain that the last three points on the inactivation curve (Fig. 5), which suggested the two phase inactivation, are real. Obviously there is a need to repeat the radiation inactivation studies since, as the old German dictum states, *Einmal ist keinmal*. Thus these observations are only preliminary at this point.

Although the rat LH-RBI apparently was effective only in an ovarian receptor system and did not inhibit in a testicular crude homogenate system, this behavior is not shared by the porcine LH-RBI preparations. Fig. 8 shows that the fraction 7 of the partially purified LH-RBI acts as a binding inhibitor for FSH, hCG, oLH, and PMSG using either ovarian or testicular systems. The oLH, PMSG, and oFSH results were obtained with testicular systems and the hCG data were obtained with an ovarian system, as were the oLH data in Fig. 2.

In summary, although an inhibitor fraction can be obtained from corpora lutea from several species, properties for the two examined the most extensively, i.e., rat and porcine, do not appear to parallel each other totally, thus they may not be identical materials. Moreover, a claim cannot be made that the LH-RBI has any significance at all for a physiological role. At this point it is being studied purely as an interesting phenomenon and without prejudice as to whether or not it may be important.

ACKNOWLEDGMENTS

This work was supported in part by grants AM-09801 and HD-08338 (Project 14) from the National Institute of Arthritis, Metabolism and Digestive Diseases, and National Institute for Child Health and Human Development, National Institutes of Health, respectively; the Ford Foundation, Grant No. 790-0656; and from the Robert A. Welch Foundation, Grant G-147.

REFERENCES

1. Chang, M. C. (1955). *J. Exp. Zool.* **128**, 378–386.
2. Jagiello, G., Miller, W. A., Ducayen, M. B., and Lin, J. S. (1974). *Biol. Reprod.* **10**, 354–363.
3. Jagiello, G., Graffeo, J., Ducayen, M., and Prosser, R. (1977). *Fertil. Steril.* **28**, 476–481.
4. Gwatkin, R. B. L., and Anderson, O. F. (1976). *Life Sci.* **19**, 527–536.
5. Tsafriri, A., and Channing, C. P. (1975). *Endocrinology* **96**, 922–927.
6. Channing, C. P., Stone, S. L., Kripner, A. S., and Pomerantz, S. H. (1978). *In* "Novel Aspects of Reproductive Physiology" (C. H. Spilman and J. W. Wilks, eds.), pp. 37–59. Spectrum Publ. Inc., New York.
7. Ledwitz-Rigby, F., Rigby, B. W., Gay, V. L., Stetson, M., Young, J., and Channing, C. P. (1977). *J. Endocrinol.* **74**, 175–184.
8. Darga, N. C., and Reichert, L. E., Jr. (1978). *Biol. Reprod.* **19**, 235–241.
9. Yang, K.-P., Samaan, N. A., and Ward, D. N. (1976). *Endocrinology* **98**, 233–241.
10. McCullagh, D. R. (1932). *Science* **76**, 19–20.
11. Thakur, A. N., Vaze, A. Y., Dattatreyamurty, B., Arbatti, N. J., and Sheth, A. R. (1978). *Indian J. Exp. Biol.* **16**, 854–856.
12. Chari, S., Duraiswami, S., and Franchimont, P. (1978). *Acta Endocrinol. (Copenhagen)* **87**, 434–448.
13. Chari, S., Hopkinson, C. R. N., Daume, E., and Sturm, G. (1979). *Acta Endocrinol. (Copenhagen)* **90**, 157–166.
14. deJong, F. H., and Sharpe, R. M. (1976). *Nature (London)* **263**, 71–72.
15. Hopkinson, C. R. N., Daume, E., Sturm, G., Fritze, E., Kaiser, S., and Hirschhauser, C. (1977). *J. Reprod. Fertil.* **50**, 129–131.
16. Welschen, R., Hermans, W. P., Dullaart, J., and deJong, F. H. (1977). *J. Reprod. Fertil.* **50**, 129–131.
17. Marder, M. L., Channing, C. P., and Schwartz, N. B. (1977). *Endocrinology* **101**, 1639–1642.
18. Miller, K. F., Wesson, J. A., and Ginther, O. J. (1979). *Biol. Reprod.* **21**, 867–872.
19. Lorenzen, J. R., Channing, C. P., and Schwartz, N. B. (1978). *Biol. Reprod.* **19**, 635–640.
20. Warren, L. (1959). *J. Biol. Chem.* **234**, 1971–1975.
21. Baker, H. W. G., Burger, H. G., deKretser, D. M., Eddie, L. W., Higginson, R. E., Hudson, B., and Lee, V. W. K. (1978). *Int. J. Androl., Suppl.* **2**, 115–124.
22. Cahoreau, C., Blanc, M. R., Dacheux, J. L., Pisselet, C., and Courot, M. (1979). *J. Reprod. Fertil., Suppl.* **26**, 97–116.
23. deJong, F. H., Welschen, R., Hermans, W. P., Smith, S. D., and van der Molen, H. J. (1979). *J. Reprod. Fertil., Suppl.* **26**, 47–59.

24. Sashidhara Murthy, H. M., Ramasharma, K., and Moudgal, N. R. (1979). *J. Reprod. Fertil., Suppl.* **26**, 61–70.
25. Moodbidri, S. B., Joshi, L. R., and Sheth, A. R. (1976). *IRCS Med. Sci.* **4**, 217.
26. deJong, F. H. (1979). *Mol. Cell. Endocrinol.* **13**, 1–10.
27. Kempner, E. S., and Schlegel, W. (1979). *Anal. Biochem.* **92**, 2–10.
28. Kempner, E. S., and Macey, R. I. (1968). *Biochem. Biophys. Acta* **163**, 188–203.
29. Odell, W. D., Swain, R. W., and Nydick, M. (1964). *J. Clin. Endocrinol. Metab.* **24**, 1266–1270.
30. Odell, W. D., and Paul, W. E. (1965). *J. Biol. Chem.* **240**, 2043–2046.
31. Sakai, C. N., Engel, B., and Channing, C. P. (1977). *Proc. Soc. Exp. Biol. Med.* **155**, 373–376.
32. Yang, K.-P., Samaan, N. A., and Ward, D. N. (1976). *Proc. Soc. Exp. Biol. Med.* **152**, 606–609.
33. Yang, K.-P., Samaan, N. A., and Ward, D. N. (1979). *Endocrinology* **104**, 552–558.
34. Yang, K.-P., Gray, K. N., Jardine, J. H., Yan, H. L. N., Samaan, N. A., and Ward, D. N. (1978). *In* "Novel Aspects of Reproductive Physiology" C. H. Spilman and J. W. Wilks, eds.), pp. 61–80. Spectrum Publ. Inc., New York.
35. Kumari, G. L., Tucker, S., and Channing, C. P. (1979). *Biol. Reprod.* **21**, 1043–1050.

Gonadostatins and Gonadocrinin: Peptides from the Gonads Regulating the Secretion of Gonadotropins

SHAO-YAO YING, NICHOLAS LING,
PETER BÖHLEN, AND ROGER GUILLEMIN

Laboratories for Neuroendocrinology
The Salk Institute for Biological Studies
La Jolla, California

INTRODUCTION

Ever since the isolation and total synthesis of luteinizing hormone releasing factor (LRF) in early 1970s, the neurohormonal substance of the hypothalamus capable of stimulating the synthesis and release of the pituitary gonadotropins was unequivocally ascertained. Subsequently, hundreds of LRF analogs possessing useful biological properties were synthesized, some being more potent, having a longer duration of action, others behaving as antagonists of the native LRF decapeptide. All LRF analogs examined, agonists, stimulate the secretion of LH as well as FSH from the pituitary gland, and antagonists bind competitively to the pituitary cells so that they inhibit the secretion of FSH and LH in the presence of native LRF. However, there are circumstances in which differential secretion of LH and FSH occurs. LRF cannot be the sole releasing factor that regulates the secretion of gonadotropin. Although a hypothalamic releasing factor specifically stimulating the secretion of FSH (FSH-RF) has been proposed, to this date a hypothalamic FRF is neither characterized nor even unequivocally demonstrated. Thus, some nonsteroidal proteina-

389

BIOREGULATORS OF REPRODUCTION
Copyright © 1981 by Academic Press, Inc.

ceous substance of gonadal origin has been suggested to play a role in modulating the gonadotropin secretion.

The concept that gonads secrete peptides that play a role in reproductive function is by no means a new one. Relaxin was first observed by Hisaw and his students in ovaries of late pregnant sow, and considered to be a polypeptide affecting the connective tissue and smooth muscle of reproductive tract. In fact, we have recently reported that side fractions of relaxin contain some peptidic substances specifically inhibiting release of LH at the level of the pituitary by antagonizing the effect of the hypothalamic LRF (1). That nonsteroidal extracts of the gonad are involved in the regulation of secretion of gonadotropin was originally reported by McCullagh. He had observed that extracts of the testes can decrease the elevated levels of plasma FSH following castration in laboratory animals and he named this nonsteroidal substance inhibin which, presumably, selectively and preferentially inhibits the secretion of FSH but has no effect on that of LH from the pituitary. Similar inhibin activity was observed in extracts of various parts of male reproductive system such as seminal plasma (2); testis (3–7); rete testis fluid (8,9); spermatozoa (10,11). Recently inhibin-like activity from ovarian follicular fluid was also reported (12–16) and some authors referred to it as folliculostatin (16). To this day, inhibin or inhibin-like substances have not been characterized; it appears to be a medium-sized polypeptide obtained by several groups in purified form but never obtained as a homogeneous material.

Work on the isolation of inhibin has slowed for two major reasons: one, lack of a simple, sensitive and practical, reliable and consistent biological screening system so that most precious materials isolated were exhausted for verification of biological activities. The biological activities of inhibin have been determined based on their ability to inhibit the hCG-induced ovarian or uterine weight increase in mice, to suppress the postcastration rise of serum FSH levels in pubertal or adult rats or to abolish the secondary rise in serum FSH levels in cycling rats following a timely ovariectomy. Recently, several laboratories, including our own, have reported an *in vitro* bioassay in which inhibin or an inhibin-like substance prevents the secretion of gonadotropin from a pituitary monolayer culture system. Second, some stages in the purification do pose difficulties and the pure inhibin is not yet available in sufficient quantity for standardization of basic studies from different laboratories, to say nothing regarding the much greater amounts so badly needed for characterization and identification of the primary structure.

For inhibin *in vitro* bioassay, Barraclough *et al.* (17) have adopted the method of dissociated pituitary cells originally developed in our laboratory (18): porcine follicular fluid preincubated for 26 hours, then challenged with LRF for 4 hours, and the tissue culture fluid measured by RIA for FSH. This method was also used by Hsueh and Erickson (19) and Scott and Burger (20). We have recently modified our original method by using immature female rats as the donors of pituitary based on earlier observations (21) that cells prepared from these rats have the advantage over those from young adult, immature male, or progesterone–estrogen-treated ovariectomized rats as to their response to LRF in secretion of gonadotropins (Fig. 1). Inhibin or inhibin-like substances from different sources available to us have been examined in this in vitro bioassay system. Briefly, immature female rats of 21 days of age are obtained from Holtzman, Madison, Wisconsin; pituitaries are collected on day 22 and dissociated enzymatically according to Vale *et al.* (18). After 3 days, various doses of LRF are added to culture dish after change of fresh medium thrice: after a 4-hour further culture, tissue culture fluid is collected for radioimmunoassay of pituitary hormones using *Staphylococcus aureus* as the

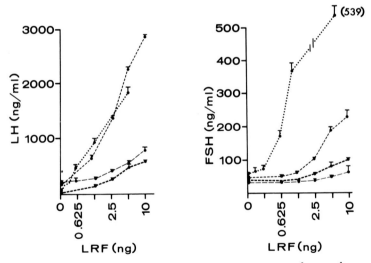

Fig. 1. Comparison of biological screening system using monolayer culture system of pituitary cells from four different donors. Cells from immature female rats are most sensitive to LRF.

(---------) ov + E, ovariectomized rats treated with estrogen and progesterone.

(············) imm ♀, immature female rats.

(————) imm ♂, immature male rats.

(— — — —) young ♂, young male rats.

TABLE I

**Inhibition of Secretion of Both LH and FSH by Various Preparations of
Inhibins or Gonadostatins in a Pituitary Monolayer Culture**

Type of gonadostatin	Source	Response[a]
Testicular extracts		
Bovine	Ying	−
Ram	Sheth	−
RTF	Hudson	+
Seminal plasma		
Bovine	Watkins	+
Porcine	Ford	+
Follicular fluid		
Porcine	Channing	+
Porcine	Weick	+
Porcine	Ying	+
Rat	Ying	+

[a] As the suppression of both LH and FSH secretion when gonadostatins was co-cultured simultaneously with synthetic LRF.

separating agents (22,23). When inhibin is examined, it is added along/simultanously with LRF and the resulting decrease in LH and FSH is the end point. For the inhibin or inhibin-like substances available to us as well as our own preparations, porcine follicular fluid of three different sources, bovine follicular fluid, rat follicular fluid and tissue extract (22), seminal plasma of bovine, porcine and human origin and ram rete testis fluid inhibited the secretion of both LH and FSH, whereas two testicular extracts showed no effects on either se-

TABLE II

Inhibition of Secretion of Both LH and FSH by Various Gonadostatins

Type of gonadostatins	Measured		References
	In vivo	*In vitro*	
RTF (rete testis fluid)	+		Cahoreau *et al.*, 27
RTF		+	Davies *et al.*, 28
Seminal plasma			
Bovine	+		Chari *et al.*, 25
Bovine	+		Peck and Watkins, 24
Bovine		+	Franchimont *et al.*, 26
Follicular Fluid			
Human	+		Chari *et al.*, 29
Bovine		+	de Jong *et al.*, 30

cretion of FSH or that of LH (Table I). While most authors emphasized the selective inhibition of FSH as the prominent characteristic of inhibin or inhibin-like substance, simultaneous inhibition
of LH and FSH by bovine seminal plasma (24–26), rete testis fluid
(27,28), and follicular fluid (29,30) was also reported (Table II). Further, inhibin or inhibin-like substances that showed inhibition of the
secretion of gonadotropins in our *in vitro* system always demonstrate
simultaneous inhibition of secretion of both LH and FSH. Whether it
is one single peptide having the ability to inhibit the secretion of both
FSH and LH needs to be ascertained. For operational facility in this
presentation, we will refer to substances of gonadal origin that inhibit the secretion of both FSH and LH as *gonadostatins*.

SEMINAL PLASMA GONADOSTATIN

Bovine seminal plasma (BSP)–gonadostatin, which probably has its
origin in the testis or spermatozoa, was collected from ejaculates and
spermatozoa were separated by centrifugation, then the supernatant
was precipitated with 86% ethanol. Such an ethanol-precipitate
preparation of seminal plasma is referred to as crude BSP–gonadostatin. When BSP-gonadostatin ranging from 50 μg to 200 μg
co-cultured with an optimal dose of LRF, which stimulates a 10-fold
increase of secretion of both LH and FSH, the gonadotropin level in
culture fluid was markedly inhibited and a dose–response curve was
observed (Table III). The amount of 200 μg BSP-gonadostatin was
referred to as 1 unit of gonadostatin activity. When BSP-gonadostatin
was applied to a Sephadex G-50 column (5.2 × 145 cm) and aliquots

TABLE III
Effect of BSP–Gonadostatin on Gonadotropin Secretion in
Pituitary Monolayer System

Treatment	N	LH (ng/ml)	FSH (ng/ml)
Control	3	454 ± 61	581 ± 78
1.25 ng LRF Control	3	3756 ± 178	1842 ± 31
1.25 ng LRF + 200 μg BSP	3	929 ± 124[a]	733 ± 119[a]
1.25 ng LRF + 100 μg BSP	3	1246 ± 175[a]	757 ± 21[a]
1.25 ng LRF + 50 μg BSP	3	3478 + 343	1532 ± 31

[a] Statistically significant from LRF controls: ($P < .01$).

of fractions tested in our *in vitro* biological system, one area of stimulatory and two areas of inhibitory activities were observed (Fig. 2). When the eluate corresponding to these three biological activities were measured with radioimmunoassays of FSH and LH, no immunoreactive gonadotropin was detected, suggesting the stimulating activity is not due to immunoactive LH and FSH in BSP-gonadostatin. The molecular weight of small BSP-gonadostatin has been estimated as approximately 1000 d. Thirteen grams of crude BSP-gonadostatin have been processed on Sephadex G-50 column and 169 mg of small molecular weight BSP–gonadostatin was recovered. We are in the process of purifying this small molecular weight BSP–gonadostatin with carboxylmethyl cellulose, partition, and high performance liquid chromatography. Hopefully, we will determine its primary structure and achieve the complete synthesis of its replicate in the near future.

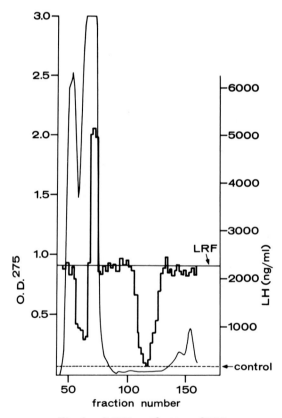

Fig. 2.   G-50F purification of BSP.

TABLE IV

Effects of Porcine and Human Seminal Plasma Gonadostatins on the Secretion of FSH and LH in Pituitary Monolayer Culture System

	N	LH (ng/ml)	FSH (ng/ml)
Control	4	233 ± 89^a	658 ± 50^a
LRF 1.25 ng	4	2450 ± 125	2070 ± 242
LRF 1.25 ng + HSP 200 μg	4	1006 ± 76^a	1349 ± 74^a
LRF 1.25 ng + PSP 200 μg	4	934 ± 43^a	1164 ± 77^a

[a] Statistically different from the LRF controls ($P < .01$).

Similar gonadostatin activities were observed in crude porcine seminal plasma and crude human seminal plasma (Table IV).

FOLLICULAR FLUID GONADOSTATIN

Table V demonstrates that three crude preparations of porcine follicular fluid (PFF)–gonadostatin at low doses inhibit the secretion of both LH and FSH in an *in vitro* system (Table V). However, when high amounts of PFF-gonadostatin were added, stimulation of the gonadotropin secretion was observed. Measurement of crude PFF–gonadostatin preparations with RIAs of gonadotropins showed immunore-

TABLE V

Effects of PFF (Porcine Follicular Fluid) Gonadostatin on the Secretion of LH and FSH in Pituitary Monolayer Culture System

	LH (ng/ml)	FSH (ng/ml)
Control	624 ± 83	532 ± 42
LRF 1.25 ng	2151 ± 83	1119 ± 77
LRF + PFF-c 80 μl	4831 ± 254^a	4722 ± 159^a
LRF + PFF-c 20 μl	2692 ± 198	1431 ± 124
LRF + PFF-c 5 μl	387 ± 42^a	219 ± 49^a
LRF + PFF-c 2.5 μl	700 ± 130	308 ± 8
Control	130 ± 10	253 ± 21
LRF 1.25 ng	1024 ± 30	877 ± 48
LRF 1.25 ng + PFF-w 80 μl	3491 ± 363^a	3590 ± 314^a
LRF 1.25 ng + PFF-w 20 μl	805 ± 40	3990 ± 390
LRF 1.25 ng + PFF-w 5 μl	387 ± 30^a	556 ± 51
LRF 1.25 ng + PFF-w 2.5 μl	381 ± 29	561 ± 39

[a] Statistically significant from the LRF controls ($P < .05$); PFF-c, porcine follicular fluid provided by Channing; PFF-w, porcine follicular fluid provided by Weick.

TABLE VI
Inhibition of Gonadotropin Secretion by Bovine Follicular Fluid (BFF)
Gonadostatin in a Monolayer Pituitary Culture System

	N	LH (ng/ml)	FSH (ng/ml)
Control	3	72 ± 4[a]	518 ± 39[a]
LRF 1.25 ng	3	3444 ± 109	2651 ± 46
LRF 1.25 ng + BFF 25 μl	3	1965 ± 119[a]	1461 ± 96[a]

[a] Statistically significant from LRF controls ($P < .01$).

active FSH and LH, which accounts for the elevated levels of gonadotropin secretion with high doses of PFF-gonadostatin resulting in
apparent "stimulation."

The bovine follicular fluid gonadostatin prepared in our laboratory
also inhibits the secretion of both LH and FSH (Table VI).

Rat follicular fluid (RFF)–gonadostatin was extracted with 0.02 N
acetic acid from PMSG (pregnant mares serum gonadotropin)-
primed ovaries (22,23). A dose–response curve of gonadostatin activity in RFF is shown in Fig. 3. The specificity of RFF-gonadostatin was
examined by measuring other pituitary hormones with radioimmuno-

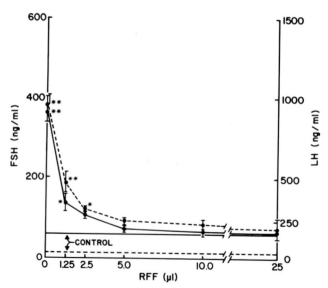

Fig. 3. Dose–response curve of gonadostatin (RFF) on suppression of FSH and LH
secretion. All cells were treated with 5 ng LRF with various amounts of gonadostatin.
The gonadotropin levels shown at 0 represent the LRF-treated group. Controls indicate
the saline-treated basal line. (---)LH; (——)FSH.

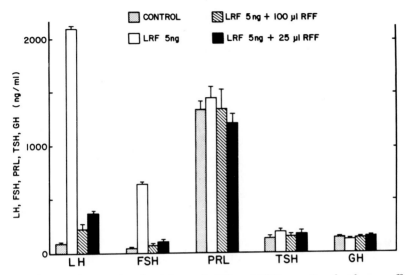

Fig. 4. Gonadostatin (RFF) inhibits only LH and FSH secretion, but has no effect on PRL, TSH, or GH.

assay in the tissue culture fluid when the cells were co-tested with gonadostatin and LRF, TRF, or IBMX (isobutyl-methylxanthine) (Fig. 4, Tables VII and VIII). The results indicate that RFF-gonadostatin specifically inhibits the secretion of LH and FSH but not that of other

TABLE VII
Gonadostatin and Gonadocrinin Affect Only LH and FSH
Secretion by the Pituitary Cells

Treatment	N	LH (ng/ml)	FSH (ng/ml)	PRL (ng/ml)	GH (ng/ml)	TSH (ng/ml)
Control	3	93 ± 4	141 ± 14	730 ± 19	40 ± 0.5	64 ± 5
IBMX[a] 1.0 nM	3	348 ± 10[b]	198 ± 34	950 ± 44[b]	228 ± 2[a]	146 ± 9[b]
IBMX 1.0 nM + gonadostatin 125 mf	3	319 ± 17[c]	175 ± 49	911 ± 39[c]	211 ± 1[c]	150 ± 8[c]
IBMX 1.0 nM + gonadocrinin 125 mf	3	497 ± 215	1022 ± 84	888 ± 35	204 ± 4	164 ± 18

[a] IBMX, 3 Isobutyl-1-methylxanthine.
[b] Statistically significant from the controls.
[c] Statistically significant from the controls but not from the IBMX controls.

TABLE VIII
Effects of Gonadostatin and Gonadocrinin on the
Secretion of TSH by the Pituitary Cells

Treatment	N	TSH (ng/ml)	LH (ng/ml)	FSH (ng/ml)
Control	3	54 ± 6	193 ± 4	146 ± 7
TRF 5 ng	3	358 ± 40[a]	185 ± 17	152 ± 31
TRF 5 ng + RFF 125 mf	3	396 ± 9[a]	153 ± 83	124 ± 31
TRF 5 ng + RFF-D$_2$ 125 mf	3	392 ± 18[a]	5198 ± 189[a]	1183 ± 76[a]

[a] Statistically significant from the controls.

pituitary hormones such as prolactin, GH, and FSH. Inhibin or inhibin-like substances, folliculostatin, or gonadostatin tested in our *in vitro* system showed no preferential inhibition of the secretion of FSH as claimed by others; the inhibition of both LH and FSH secretion always goes hand in hand. The conclusion of preferential suppression of FSH by others appears to have been based on testing systems designed with biological reaction to manifest the response of FSH but showing only marginal LH sensitivity such as reversed Steelman–Pohley bioassay, suppression of the post castration of FSH increase in male or female, long-term preincubation of gonadostatin to inhibit the response of pituitary culture cells to LRF treatment. If it turns out to be true that the suppression of FSH is always accompanied by an equivalent decrease of LH as presented here, the classic concept of inhibin would indeed need to be modified.

GONADOCRININ

While polypeptides or peptides of gonadal origin inhibiting the secretion of gonadotropins were the main themes of gonadostatin research, Ying and Guillemin (22) drew attention to the existence of peptides of small molecular weight (≤ 3500 d) extracted from rat follicular fluid referred to as gonadocrinin. Contrary to the activity of inhibin or gonadostatin, those stimulated the secretion of both LH and FSH from the pituitary gland (Fig. 5). Tissue such as liver, heart, similarly extracted showed no gonadocrinin activity. Gonadocrinin specifically stimulates the secretion of gonadotropins, but it has no effect on the secretion of other pituitary hormones such as prolactin, TSH, and GH (Tables VII, VIII, IX). Tryptic digestion completely abolishes the biological activity of gonadocrinin. The biological activity of gonadocrinin was found to be parallel to that of synthetic LRF. LRF

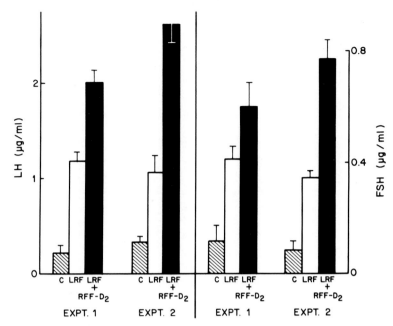

Fig. 5. Gonadocrinin at a dose of 40 millifragments (mf) stimulates the secretion of both LH and FSH in the *in vitro* bioassay system. Striated bars, control; white bars, LRF; solid bars, LRF plus 40 mf gonadocrinin.

antagonists competitively inhibit gonadocrinin activity, describing a linear dose–response curve, in the same manner as the antagonist inhibits the LRF activity. However, with various preparations of antibodies to LRF developed in our laboratory, we were not able to detect LRF in purified gonadocrinin preparations. When gonadocrinin was purified with Sephadex gel filtration columns, CMC and HPLC, the biologically active gonadocrinin was eluted at a position different

TABLE IX
Gonadocrinin Only Stimulates Secretion of LH and FSH but Has No
Effect on the Secretion of PRL, GH, or TSH

Treatment	N	LH (ng/ml)	FSH (ng/ml)	PRL (ng/ml)	GH (ng/ml)	TSH (ng/ml)
Control	3	93 ± 4	141 ± 14	730 ± 19	40 ± 0.5	64 ± 5
Gonadocrinin 125 mf	3	2971 ± 112[a]	978 ± 64	747 ± 12	46 ± 2	62 ± 6

[a] Significance level is .01, as calculated by the multiple comparison test following analysis of variance. This description of analysis applies to all other tables of data.

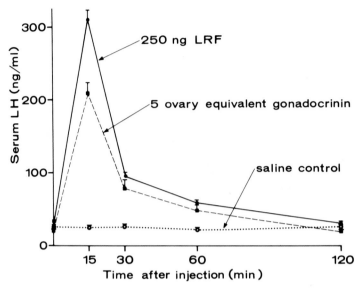

Fig. 6. Serum Levels after i.v. injection of gonadocrinin.

from that of LRF under identical conditions, indicating that gonado-crinin possesses LRF-like activity but could be a novel peptide. A pre-liminary amino acid analysis also indicates that gonadocrinin is differ-ent from LRF. Intravenous injection of gonadocrinin to rats on the sec-ond day of diestrus stimulates the serum LH levels in a profile similar to that of LRF injection (Fig. 6). Such a gonadocrinin was also ex-tracted from the media of rat granulosa cell culture while media of 3T3–fibroblast culture so extracted showed no gonadocrinin activity, suggesting that the granulosa cell may be the source of ovarian gona-docrinin. Furthermore, gonadocrinin activity was also extracted from porcine follicular fluid, rat testicular extract, and bovine testicular ex-tract. The evidence presently available shows that a novel peptide with LRF-like activity, but obviously different from LRF, was isolated from rat follicular fluid. Such observation of a gonadal peptide activat-ing the secretion of pituitary gonadotropins calls for a complete reap-praisal of all the present thinking on physiological relationships be-tween hypothalamus, pituitary, and gonad.

REFERENCES

1. Guillemin, R., Ying, S. Y., Dubois, M., and Picaper, G. (1979) *Endocrinology* **104,** 921A.

2. Franchimont, P., Chari, S., Hagelstein, M. T., and Duraiswami, S. (1975) *Nature* (*London*) **257**, 402
3. Lee, V. W. K., Keogh, E. J., Kretser, D. M., and Hudson, B. (1974) *Res. Commun. Chem. Pathol. Pharmacol.* **2**, 1406.
4. Keogh, E. J., Lee, V. W. K., Rennie, G. C., Burger, H. G., Hudson, B., and De Dretser, D. M. (1976) *Endocrinology* **98**, 997.
5. Moodbidri, S. D., Joshi, L. R., and Sheth, A. R. (1976) *IRCS Med. Sci.: Libr. Compend.* **4**, 217.
6. Nandini, S. G., Lipner, H., and Moudgal, N. R. (1976) *Endocrinology* **98**, 997.
7. Baker, H. W. G., Bremner, W. J., Burger, H. G., De Kretser, D. M., Dulmanis, A., Eddie, L. W., Hudson, B., Keogh, E. J., Lee, V. W. K., and Rennie, G. C. (1976) *Recent Prog. Horm. Res.* **32**, 429.
8. Setchell, B. P., and Sirinathsinghji, D. J. (1972) *J. Encocrinol.* **53**, LX-LXI.
9. Setchell, B. P., and Jacks, F. (1974) *J. Endocrinol.* **62**, 675.
10. Lugaro, G., Carrea, G., Casellato, M. M., Mazzola, G., and Fachini, G. (1973) *Biochim. Biophys. Acta* **304**, 719.
11. Lugaro, G., Casellato, M. M., Mazzola, G., Fachini, G., and Currea, G. (1974) *Neuroendocrinology* **15**, 62.
12. Hopkinson, C. R. N., Fritze, E., Sturne, S., and Hirschauser, C. (1977) *IRCS Med. Sci.: Libr. Compend.* **6**, 83.
13. de Jong, F. H., and Sharpe, R. H. (1976) *Nature* (*London*) **263**, 71.
14. Welschen, R., Hermans, W. P., Dullaart, J., and de Jong, F. H. (1977) *J. Reprod. Fertil.* **50**, 129.
15. Marder, M. L., Channing, C. P., and Schwartz, N. B. (1977) *Endocrinology* **101**, 1639.
16. Schwartz, N. B., and Channing, C. P. (1977) *Proc. Natl. Acad. Sci. U.S.A.* **74**, 5721.
17. Barraclough, C. A., Wise, P. M., Turgeon, J., Shander, D., Depaulo, L., and Rance, N. (1979) *Biol. Reprod.* **20**, 86.
18. Vale, W., Grant, G., Amoss, M., Blackwell, R., and Guillemin, R. (1972) *Endocrinology* **91**, 562.
19. Erickson, G. F., and Hsueh, A. J. W. (1978) *Endocrinology* **103**, 1960.
20. Scott, R. S., and Burger, H. G. (1979) *Endocrinology* **104**, 281A.
21. Ying, S. Y., and Guillemin, R. (1980) *Proc. Int. Cong. Endocrinol., 6th,* 1980.
22. Ying, S. Y., and Guillemin, R. (1979) *C. R. Hebd. Seances Acad. Sci., Ser. D* **289**, 943.
23. Ying, S.Y., and Guillemin, R. (1980) *Endocrinology* **106**, 114A.
24. Peck, J. C., and Watkins, W. B. (1979) *J. Reprod. Fetil.* **57**, 281.
25. Chari, S., Duraiswami, S., and Franchimont, P. (1978) *Acta Endocrinol.* (*Copenhagen*) **87**, 437.
26. Franchimont, P., Desnoulin, A., Verstraclen-Proyard, J., Hazee-Hagelstein, M. T., Walton, J. S., and Waites, G. M. H. (1978) *Int. J. Androl. Suppl.* **2**, 69.
27. Cahoreau, C., Blanc, M. R., Dacheux, J. L., Pisselet, C., and Courot, M. (1979) *J. Reprod. Fertil.*, Suppl. **26**, 97.
28. Davies, R. V., Main, S. J., Young, M. G. W. L., and Setchell B. P. (1976) *J. Endocrinol.* **68**, 26p.
29. Chari, S., Hopkinson, C. R. N., Daume, E., and Sturm, G. (1979) *Acta Endocrinol.* (*Copenhagen*) **90**, 157.
30. de Jong, F. H. (1979), R. Welschen, W. P. Hermans, S. D. Smith and H. J. van der Molen. *J. Reprod. Fert.*, Suppl. 26, **47**.

Dissociation of Luteal Progesterone and Relaxin Secretion: Modulation by Ovarian Factors

GERSON WEISS AND LAURA T. GOLDSMITH

Department of Obstetrics and Gynecology
New York University School of Medicine
New York, New York

INTRODUCTION

In the nonpregnant state, progesterone is the major luteal product. Since the corpus luteum is the only significant source of progesterone in the nonpregnant state, luteal activity can be inferred from the observation of progesterone in peripheral blood. In some species, most notably primates, study of luteal function in pregnancy has been hampered by the fact that progesterone is also a secretory product of the placenta. In these species, since serum progesterone has two sources, changes in serum progesterone levels are a poor indicator of luteal activity. However, it has been recognized that serum relaxin levels in human pregnancy result solely from luteal secretion (1). Thus, relaxin in peripheral blood can be used to observe luteal activity. This chapter describes some of these observations.

RELAXIN

Relaxin is a peptide hormone with a molecular weight of approximately 6000. It is composed of two peptide chains joined by disulfide

BIOREGULATORS OF REPRODUCTION

linkages (2). It is one of a class of structurally similar growth factors, which include insulin, nerve growth factor, epidermal growth factor, and the nonsuppressible insulin-like activity substances. There is remarkable tertiary structural similarity to insulin but no insulin activity and little direct amino acid homology (3). In women, relaxin can be measured in pregnancy sera from the time of the missed menses (4) using a radioimmunoassay which employs an antisera raised in a rabbit to purified porcine relaxin (5). Evidence that relaxin is a luteal product includes the observation that relaxin is found in ovarian vein blood in higher concentrations than in either peripheral blood or the contralateral ovarian vein blood (6). Lutectomy results in a prompt disappearance of circulating relaxin (1). Immunoreactive relaxin extracted from human corpora lutea of pregnancy is also active in the guinea pig pubic symphysis palpation assay, the classical bioassay for relaxin (7).

During human pregnancy serum relaxin levels rise from the time of the missed menses. After a peak in the first trimester of pregnancy, there is a 20–30% decline (8). Levels then remain stable for the remainder of pregnancy. Serum levels become undetectable 2–3 days after delivery (9).

The functions of relaxin are poorly understood and vary from species to species. In mice and guinea pigs relaxin is involved in formation of the intrapubic ligament which enlarges the diameter of the birth canal before delivery (2). This is not a significant action in rats or primates. Relaxin is involved in myometrial activity inhibition in rats and humans (10,11). It is also involved in cervical changes in many species (2).

CONTROL OF RELAXIN SECRETION IN WOMEN

Since relaxin is usually detectable in sera only during pregnancy and since it is present from the fourteenth day after conception, it is likely that an early signal from the blastocycst induces luteal relaxin secretion. Recently, Quagliarello et al. (12) have shown that hCG given on day 8–10 of the luteal phase is capable of inducing relaxin secretion. Although this treatment produces an abrupt rise in progesterone, relaxin does not become detectable for 2–6 days. Figure 1 depicts the dynamics of this reaction. It can be seen that progesterone rises promptly after hCG injection. Levels of serum progesterone are already falling when relaxin levels are still rising, suggesting different control mechanisms of both hormones, even though their secretion is stimulated by the same exogenous stimulus.

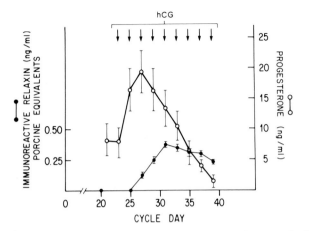

Fig. 1. Progesterone and relaxin secretion after hCG stimulation in the luteal phase in women (mean ± SEM). Vertical arrows indicate injection of 2500 IU hCG i.m.

The timing of the hCG is critical to relaxin secretion. When the hCG injections were given on day 2–3 of the luteal phase, no relaxin was detectable. In studies in which hCG was used to induce ovulation after human menopausal gonadotropin treatment to mature a follicle, we could not detect relaxin in the luteal phase. However, if these women conceived during the teatment cycle, then relaxin is detected at the time of the missed menses, presumably due to endogenous luteal stimulation from the blastocyst. Since the hCG stimulus was given in all these experiments but the response was variable, appropriate ovarian conditions are also necessary for relaxin secretion.

RHESUS MONKEY

It has been shown that the monkey corpus luteum of pregnancy is active in progesterone secretion on day 22 of pregnancy but shows little progesterone secretion on day 42 of pregnancy (13). We have been able to detect low levels of immunoreactive relaxin in pregnancy in rhesus monkeys using the same RIA that is used to measure circulating relaxin in women. On day 22 of pregnancy, relaxin was not detected in serum. In contrast, relaxin was present in serum on day 42 of pregnancy, at a time when the luteal production of progesterone is decreased. This suggests that there is dissociation of luteal relaxin and progesterone secretion in the rhesus monkey.

RAT

Using the same RIA to measure immunoreactive relaxin in the rat, we have shown that relaxin is not detectable in pregnancy on day 8, becomes detectable on day 10, and rises to maximal levels by day 13. These levels are maintained until delivery. If the fetus is removed on day 16 of pregnancy, relaxin levels in serum are unaffected. However, removal of both fetus and placenta or hysterectomy on day 16 result in a prompt early fall of circulating relaxin. This procedure did not significantly alter progesterone levels in the serum. The data suggest that either the placenta is also a source of circulating relaxin or that there is dissociation of luteal relaxin and progesterone secretion. Since ovariectomy on day 16 produces a rapid disappearance of circulating relaxin, the latter explanation is the correct one.

CONCLUDING REMARKS

The data presented show that, in all three species studied, there is dissociation of relaxin and progesterone secretion by the corpus luteum. While this dissociation in the rat may be due to either intraovarian factors or different tropic stimuli for relaxin and progesterone it is clear from the human studies that ovarian factors are controlling the differential secretion of these hormones. It is also clear that the endogenous condition of the corpus luteum is an important determinant of its responsiveness. Given appropriate permissive luteotropic stimuli, the ovary modulates the secretion pattern of its products. These caveats should be kept in mind when future studies are designed. The local ovarian factors modulating luteal function are as yet not understood. These factors should be better defined by extensive future research.

ACKNOWLEDGMENTS

This work is supported in part by United Cerebral Palsy Grant R-288-79 and the National Institutes of Health Grant HD 12395.

REFERENCES

1. Weiss, G., O'Byrne, E. M., Hochman, J., Steinetz, B. G., Goldsmith, L., and Flitcraft, J. G. (1978) *Obstet. Gynecol.* **52**, 569–570.

2. Schwabe, C., Steinetz, B., Weiss, G., Segaloff, S., McDonald, J. K., O'Byrne, E., Hochman, J., Carriere, B., and Goldsmith, L. (1978) *Recent Prog. Horm. Res.* **34**, 123–211.
3. Schwabe, C., and McDonald, J. K. (1977) *Science* **197**, 914–915.
4. Quagliarello, J., Steinetz, B. G., and Weiss, G. (1979) *Obstet. Gynecol.* **53**, 62–63.
5. O'Byrne, E. M., and Steinetz, B. G. (1976) *Proc. Soc. Exp. Biol. Med.* **152**, 272–276.
6. Weiss, G., O'Byrne, E. M., and Steinetz, B. G. (1976) *Science* **194**, 948–949.
7. O'Byrne, E. M., Flitcraft, J. F., Sawyer, W. K., Hochman, J., Weiss, G., and Steinetz, B. G. (1978) *J. Clin. Endocrinol. Metabl.* **102**, 1641–1644.
8. Quagliarello, J., Szlachter, N., Steinetz, B. G., Goldsmith, L. T., and Weiss, G. (1979) *Am. J. Obstet. Gynecol.* **135**, 43–44.
9. Quagliarello, J., Nachtigall, R., Goldsmith, L. T., Hochman, J., Steinetz, B. G., O'Byrne, E. M., and Weiss, G. (1979) *In* "Ovarian Follicular and Corpus Luteum Function" (C. P. Channing, J. M. Marsh, and W. A. Sadler, eds.), pp. 743–748. Plenum, New York.
10. Porter, D. G. (1979) *Anim. Reprod. Sci.* **2**, 77–96.
11. Szlachter, N., O'Byrne, E. M., Goldsmith, L., Steinetz, B. G., and Weiss, G. (1980) *Am. J. Obstet. Gynecol.* **136**, 584–586.
12. Quagliarello, J., Goldsmith, L., Steinetz, B., Lustig, D. S., and Weiss, G. (1980) *J. Clin. Endocrinol. Metab.* **51**, 74–77.
13. Walsh, S. W., Wolf, R. C., and Meyer, R. K. (1974) *Endocrinology* **95**, 1704–1710.

PART V

IN VITRO FERTILIZATION

In Vitro Fertilization
in the
Treatment of Human Infertility

ALEXANDER LOPATA, IAN W. JOHNSTON, IAN J. HOULT,
AND ANDREW L. SPEIRS

Department of Obstetrics and Gynaecology,
University of Melbourne
and
Reproductive Biology Unit,
Royal Women's Hospital,
Carlton, Victoria, Australia

INTRODUCTION

In vitro fertilization of human eggs and culture of the resulting embryos have become highly successful procedures. In contrast, the transfer of cultured embryos into the uterus has resulted in a disappointingly low number of term pregnancies. At present one live birth can be expected for approximately every 20 embryos placed in the uterus (1). It is envisaged, nevertheless, that the systematic evaluation and control of the factors responsible for this low efficiency of embryo transfer, will in time, make the procedure a generally accepted treatment for several types of human reproductive failure.

Infertility caused by irreparably damaged, or missing fallopian tubes, had been the only definitive indication for *in vitro* fertilization (IVF) and embryo transfer (ET). A fairly complete discussion of some current concepts in the management of patients who have these disorders, and consideration of the advantages and disadvantages of surgical removal of damaged tubes before IVF and ET, has been presented in a previous report (2). However, couples whose inability to conceive is unexplained, or is due to sperm antibodies in the female or the

411

BIOREGULATORS OF REPRODUCTION

male, cervical hostility, oligospermia, failed insemination by donor, and endometriosis are now included in the IVF program. In the unexplained infertility group preovulatory eggs obtained from over 50% of the patients are fertilizable *in vitro* and yield morphologically normal embryos in culture. In another group of infertile patients, some with unexplained but others with known causes of infertility, *in vitro* fertilization fails due to failed spermatozoal penetration through the zona pellucida. These patients should be investigated for the presence of zona antibodies in the circulation, and if possible in the zona pellucida of the patients' oocytes. If a zonal block to fertilization is diagnosed as the most likely cause of infertility the couple should be excluded from further attempts at IVF. It should be noted that in these instances IVF is not only a diagnostic test, but also a prognostic test which combined with the zona antibody results, accurately evaluates the cause of infertility, and may help the clinicians and the couple to accept the idea that further attempts at therapy are unwarranted.

The use of IVF and ET in women whose infertility is not due to tubal pathology raises the following clinical issues. It is known that some infertile patients can conceive naturally with the passage of time if they have patent fallopian tubes. In the event of a pregnancy following ET there would be some doubt as to whether conception occurred naturally or as a result of the inserted embryo. Such patients would need to abstain from intercourse during the treatment cycle and be admitted to hospital for monitoring several days prior to ovulation. In addition, if an infertile woman is known to have anatomically normal fallopian tubes, embryos produced *in vitro* could be placed in a fallopian tube at the pronuclear or 2-celled stage of development. This procedure would enable the early embryo to develop in its natural environment over almost its entire preimplantation stage. However, placement of the embryo into the tube would require a second laparoscopy with the disadvantage that the repeated general anaesthesia may impair the luteal phase (3).

PROTOCOL FOR IVF AND ET

SELECTION OF PATIENTS

Initially women whose tubal function has been irreversibly destroyed by infection, ectopic pregnancies, or by attempts at surgical repair were selected into the program. Currently, women unable to conceive due to a variety of conditions, as described in the introduction, are selected providing they are less than 35 years of age and have not had more than one child.

The infertile couple is fully investigated to ensure that ovarian and uterine function is normal, to assess the semen quality and to ascertain that the ejaculate is free of infection. A preliminary laparoscopy is carried out to evaluate any pelvic pathology and to determine whether the ovaries are accessible for oocyte collection. At a joint interview with the couple the current low chance of success of IVF and ET, the possibility of spontaneous abortion, and the incompletely known risks to the fetus are explained. In addition, it is pointed out that tests to detect fetal abnormalities would be offered if pregnancy occurred.

Women admitted into the program are required to have a cervical smear and culture to exclude *Mycoplasma, Candida, Trichomonas,* gonococci, and other pathogens, and some patients had serological screening for *Toxoplasma, Rubella,* cytomegalovirus, herpesviruses, hepatitis-B virus, and syphilis. Chromosome analysis of both partners to detect individuals at risk for producing aneuploid gametes has also been recommended, but we have not included this investigation in our protocol.

PRELIMINARY IVF TEST

In each infertile woman the first attempt at collection of preovulatory oocytes and *in vitro* fertilization is carried out following treatment with clomiphene citrate and human chorionic gonadotropin (hCG), as described previously (2,4). The aim is to assess the fertilizability of at least two of the wife's eggs in the presence of the husband's spermatozoa. If more than two preovulatory eggs are obtained the fertilization test is extended by using the spermatozoa of a fertile donor.

If one or two morphologically normal embryos are achieved by the infertile couple, each embryo is placed in the egg donor's uterus at the 8-celled stage of development. A third embryo produced by the infertile couple, or an embryo resulting from a donor fertilization, is cultured for 5 to 7 days to determine whether it has the potential for developing into a morphologically normal blastocyst capable of hatching from the zona pellucida. We also plan to study the chromosomal status of these additional embryos as well as their viability following storage at low temperatures.

However, if fertilization fails in two or more eggs, two supplementary tests may be carried out before the couple is excluded from the program. First, the zona pellucida of the unfertilized eggs, and the patient's serum and follicular fluid can be studied for the presence of zona antibodies (5,6). Second, the fertilizing capacity of the husband's spermatozoa can be evaluated by determining their capacity to penetrate the zona pellucida of salt-stored human eggs (7).

MONITORING OF PATIENTS DURING NATURAL CYCLES

Women selected from the waiting list, and assigned to a pool of patients participating in the program, notify the date of onset of their menses each month. Based on this information the coordinator of the program begins monitoring up to 10 patients per week. Patients who notify after this quota has been reached are asked to report during the next cycle.

Monitoring of the follicular phase begins on day 9 or 10 of the natural cycle when daily urinary estrogen excretion and daily ultrasound scanning of the ovaries are commenced. As a general rule a follicle diameter of 17 mm or more, together with an estrogen excretion of 30 to 40 μg per 24 hours, are critieria for admitting a patient to the hospital ward. However, a higher estrogen excretion in the presence of a smaller follicle, or a larger follicle combined with a lower estrogen output, are also end-points for admitting the patient. Upon admission the preovulatory phase is monitored by assaying luteinizing hormone (LH) excretion in 3 hour urine samples. The assays are carried out using a sensitive hemagglutination inhibition test (Hi-gonavis, Mochida Pharmaceuticals), which has been found to be most reliable when the patients' urinary output is between 150 and 200 ml during each 3-hour interval.

COLLECTION OF PREOVULATORY OOCYTES

At the outset of the program preovulatory oocytes were collected 24 hours after the beginning of the LH surge. Subsequently follicular aspirations were carried out at 26, 28, and 30 hours after the start of the LH surge. These intervals were timed from the midpoint of the first 3-hour period at which a definite LH rise was observed and was followed by a progressive increase of LH excretion over the next 2 or 3 assay intervals. Currently, most ovum collections are done 28 hours after the start of the LH surge.

It has been found that a small group of women ovulate between 26 and 27 hours after the onset of the LH surge. To detect this group, and prevent a needless laparoscopy, ultrasound scanning of the ovaries is carried out 1–2 hours preoperatively to determine whether the preovulatory follicle is still intact. In some patients, however, ovulation occurs after the sonar scan has been done, and in these cases a corpus hemorrhagicum is found at laparoscopy.

The technique of laparoscopy and the instruments used for follicular aspiration have been described in detail (8). If an oocyte is not obtained, the single lumen needle used for aspirating the follicular fluid is withdrawn and replaced with a blunted double-lumen needle. One channel of this needle is used for injecting culture medium into the follicle and the second for reaspirating the contents. Such irrigation of the follicle can be repeated a number of times and sometimes yields the trapped preovulatory egg.

In Vitro FERTILIZATION AND EMBRYO CULTURE

The insemination medium (IM) used for preparing a suspension of washed spermatozoa and for fertilizing the egg, and the growth medium (GM) used for embryo culture, were prepared by modifying Ham's F10 solution as outlined in Table I. The husband's semen is allowed to liquefy at room temperature and the seminal plasma is removed in two washings of IM. This is done by diluting 0.5 ml of semen in 2.5 ml of IM, centrifuging at 200 g for 10 minutes, removing the supernatant and dispersing the pellet in 3.0 ml of IM. After a similar gentle centrifugation the final pellet is dispersed in 1.5 ml of IM

TABLE I
Composition of Media Used for Human *in Vitro*
Fertilization and Embryo Culture

Media	
STOCK SOLUTION	
Ham's F10 powder with glutamine	9.81 g
Penicillin G	75 mg
Streptomycin sulfate	75 mg
Re-distilled water	1000 ml
CULTURE MEDIA	
To 100 ml STOCK SOLUTION add	
Calcium lactate—1.5 H_2O	24.52 mg
Sodium bicarbonate	210.6 mg
Adjust osmolarity to	280 mOsmoles/kg
FERTILIZATION MEDIUM	
Add IN NaOH to adjust pH (at 5% CO_2) to	7.50–7.60
Add human serum albumin	5 mg/ml
EMBRYO GROWTH MEDIUM	
Add IN HCl to adjust pH (at 5% CO_2) to	7.30–7.35
Add patient's serum (inactivated)	15% (vol:vol)

and about 1 ml of the sperm suspension is incubated in a Falcon tissue culture tube in a humidified atmosphere of 5% CO_2 + 5% O_2 + 90% N_2 at 37°C. All tissue culture and equilibration of media are carried out under the same conditions. The final sperm suspension is incubated for at least 30 minutes before it is used for inseminating the egg.

A preovulatory egg in cumulus is recovered from the aspirated follicular fluid and immediately rinsed in 1 ml of equilibrated IM and then transferred into 1 ml of IM in a Falcon tissue culture tube (type 2003). The egg is inseminated by adding about 10^6 motile spermatozoa from the preincubated sperm suspension. After 6 to 18 hours in the insemination culture the egg with its surrounding corona cells is transferred into 1 ml of equilibrated GM in a Falcon 2003 tube. If normal fertilization has occurred, and provided the corona cells are removed, a second polar body would be visible in the perivitelline space by 6 hours after insemination and 2 pronuclei would be seen in the ooplasm by 18 hours. However, to avoid damage to the egg the shell of corona cells is not removed at this early stage.

After culture in GM for 24 to 36 hours the corona cells are removed with fine needles to determine whether the egg is cleaving. Following a brief inspection the embryo, which is now at the 2-celled to 4-celled stage of development, is transferred into a 1 ml aliquot of freshly equilibrated GM for further growth. In some cases the detached corona cells are transferred with the embryo. When an embryo appears to be cleaving normally an 8-celled stage is generally observed by 68–78 hours after insemination. In most cases the culture is terminated at this stage as the embryo is prepared to be transferred into the uterus of the egg donor. Some embryos are cultured to the 12- to 16-celled stage before transfer.

The embryo is judged to be developing normally in tissue culture if the dividing cells are about equal in size, uniform in shape, and occupy most of the space within the zona pellucida. In addition cell division must be progressive and the rate of development should be within the time limits outlined by Edwards (9). Ideally it would also be important to know whether each blastomere contained a normal chromosome complement. However, this cannot be assessed in an embryo which is to be placed in the uterus.

EMBRYO TRANSFER

In preparation for transfer into the uterus the embryo is placed in a droplet of culture medium under sterile liquid paraffin oil, or alterna-

tively in 1 ml of equilibrated GM contained in the central well of a
Falcon organ culture dish. The patient is brought to the operating the-
atre for the transfer procedure but no premedication nor anesthesia is
used. She is placed in the left lateral position with the head of the
table tilted slightly downward. With a bivalve speculum in the vagina,
a fine cannula shaped like an uterine sound, with an ovoid tip, is
passed through the cervical canal until the tip is just within the uterus
(Fig. 1). The embryo is then drawn gently into the first 2 cm of a catheter, 1.4 mm in diameter, which has been previously filled with equilibrated culture medium at 37°C. The catheter containing the embryo
is threaded through the cannula, the latter is withdrawn from the
uterus and the embryo is released high into the fundus in about 50 μl
of culture medium. After about 20 seconds the catheter is withdrawn
and another 50 μl of medium is slowly injected as the catheter is
being pulled out from the uterine cavity. The lumen of the catheter is
then rinsed into a petri dish and inspected to ensure that the embryo

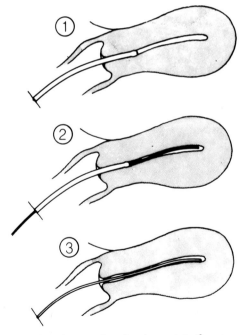

Fig. 1. The three steps in the transfer of embryos into the uterus. 1. The cannula is
inserted through the cervical canal until its tip is just inside the uterine cavity. 2. The
fine catheter containing the embryo is threaded to the fundus. 3. The cannula is withdrawn and then the embryo injected into the cavity in 50 μl of growth medium.

has been transferred. The patient remains in bed for about 24 hours and is discharged from the ward on the day after embryo transfer.

MONITORING OF PATIENTS AFTER ET

All patients collect a 24-hour specimen of urine on day 7 and day 14 after follicular aspiration for determination of total estrogen and pregnanediol excretion. In patients receiving an embryo, blood is collected on these days and on day 18 and 21 of the luteal phase for hCG assays.

If pregnancy occurs ultrasound examination of the pelvis is carried out at 3 weeks postconception to determine the location of the gestational sac. An ultrasound scan at 5 weeks postconception assesses the size of the embryo and detects the presence of an embryonic heart beat. At 10 weeks postconception a sonar scan is done to evaluate fetal growth and at 14 weeks an amniocentesis is carried out under ultrasound control. The amniotic fluid is assayed for α-fetoprotein and the fetal cells are cultured for chromosome analysis.

RESULTS

Some of the factors that prevented follicular aspiration during natural menstrual cycles are summarised in Table II.

Ultrasound examination of the ovaries revealed that in 5 patients the preovulatory follicle was developing in an ovary known to be inaccessible from a previous diagnostic laparoscopy. Ovulation was detected in 5 patients on sonar scanning of the ovaries at 1–2 hours before the scheduled operation. The use of ultrasound has, therefore, prevented needless laparoscopies in 10 patients. In 8 patients preoperative ultrasound scanning revealed an intact preovulatory follicle

TABLE II
Factors Which Prevented Follicular Aspiration
after Monitoring of the Preovulatory Phase

Number of cycles monitored	69
Follicle developing in inaccessible ovary	5
LH surge not detected	9
Ovulation detected by sonar	5
Ovulation occurred after sonar	8
Inadequate access due to adhesions	4

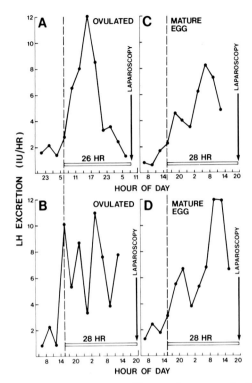

Fig. 2. The results of 3-hour urinary LH excretion assayed with Hi-gonavis in 4 patients. A: LH surge was considered to begin between 05.00 and 08.00, but at laparoscopy 26 hours later the patient was found to have ovulated; B and C: LH surge was considered to begin between 14.00 and 17.00, in B the patient had ovulated by 28 hours, in C a mature egg was obtained at 28 hours; D: LH surge was considered to begin between 14.00 and 17.00, a mature egg was recovered 28 hours later, and its fertilization produced an 8-celled embryo which resulted in a live birth.

but at laparoscopy an early corpus hemorrhagicum was found in six; the other two patients ovulated during laparoscopy. In one of the latter an ovulated oocyte was recovered from the cul-de-sac.

Representative charts of urinary LH excretion during the preovulatory phase of natural menstrual cycles are shown in Fig. 2. These illustrate the criteria which were used for judging the onset of the LH surge and for timing the interval for oocyte collection. As may be seen, timing began from the midpoint of the first 3-hour interval at which a rise in LH excretion above baseline levels (usually less than 2 IU LH per hour assayed with Hi-gonavis) was followed by successive rises (Fig. 2,A and D), or several distinctly higher than baseline levels (Fig.

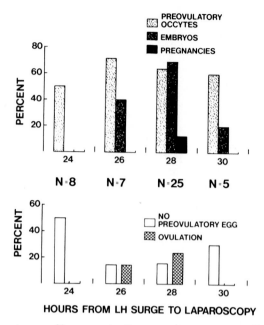

Fig. 3. The outcome of laproscopies for preovulatory oocyte collection carried out 24 to 30 hours after the beginning of the endogenous LH surge, and the results of in vitro insemination of eggs obtained at the various intervals after the onset of the surge.

2B and C), over 6 to 12 hours. An initial rise in LH excretion above the baseline, which was not sustained, was not used as the starting point.

Laparoscopy for collection of preovulatory oocytes was carried out 24 to 30 hours after the beginning of the LH surge (Fig. 3). Ovulation was not observed in 8 patients at 24 hours after the LH rise but occurred in one out of 7 patients by 26 hours. At 28 hours after the gonadotropin surge, 6 out of 25 patients had ovulated before, or at the time of, the laparoscopy. No ovulations occurred in the group of 5 patients who had a laparoscopy at 29 to 30 hours after the start of the LH surge.

Since over 20% of patients ovulated by 28 hours after the start of the endogenous gonadotrophin surge an analysis was made of the duration of the ascending and descending limbs of LH output, and of the peak LH values, as predictors of early or late ovulation. These results are presented in Table III. As may be seen, the ascending LH limb of the early ovulators ranged from 9 to 18 hours and that of late ovulators spanned 6 to 19.5 hours. There was an equally wide variation in the LH peak values and in the descending LH limb of the early and late ovulating groups. These analyses, therefore, did not prove to be of value for predicting the likely time of ovulation.

The recovery of oocytes from preovulatory follicles ranged from 50% when aspirations were carried out 24 hours after the LH surge, to 72% following the 26-hour interval; the retrieval rate being 64 and 60% at 28 and 30 hours, respectively (Fig. 3). However, the eggs recovered after the 28-hour interval produced the largest percentage (approx. 70%) of normally cleaving embryos following *in vitro* fertilization. None of the four eggs aspirated at 24 hours after the LH surge commenced cleavage following *in vitro* insemination.

A total of 14 embryos, ranging from the 8-celled to 16-celled stages, were transferred into the uterus of the egg donors during 1979. Two pregnancies ensued. In each case the pregnancy resulted from the transplantation of an 8-celled embryo. Both of these embryos developed from preovulatory eggs recovered at 28 hours after the beginning of the LH surge.

TABLE III

A Comparison of the Intervals from the Beginning of the LH Surge to the LH Peak, the Maximum LH Excretion, and the LH Peak to Operation Intervals, in a Group of Patients Who Had Ovulated before Ovum Collection and in a Group in Whom a Mature Egg Was Recovered

Patient	Onset of LH surge to peak (hour)	LH peak (IU/hour)	LH peak to laparoscopy (hour)	Total interval (hour)	Outcome
MIT	15	14	13	28	Ovulated
DRI	9	17.3	19	28	Ovulated
PED	15	9.3	13	28	Ovulated
TAY	18	9.3	10	28	Ovulated
LEE	12	12	15	27	Ovulated
SAM	14	10.7	14	28	Ovulated
DYS	9	13.3	19	28	Ovulated
Median values	14	12	14		
WHI	19.5	15.7	10	29.5	Mature egg
CHA	6	14.3	21	27	Mature egg
REE	18	12.6	10	28	Mature egg
HAS	8.5	28	19.5	28	Mature egg
KIR	9	9.3	19	28	Mature egg
CAM	18	10	10	28	Mature egg
COU	15	8.3	13	28	Mature egg
Median values	15	13	13		

TABLE IV

The Recovery of Preovulatory Eggs at Laparoscopies and the Outcome of *in Vitro* Fertilization, Embryo Culture, and Intrauterine Transfer of Embryos

Laparoscopies	52
Follicles aspirated	38
Preovulatory eggs	28
Immature/atretic eggs	2
Failed fertilization	6
Failed cleavage	8[a]
Embryos transferred into uterus	14
Pregnancies	2
Live births	1

[a] Two eggs remained at pronuclear stage; three embryos arrested at 3-celled stage; two embryos at 4-celled stage; one embryo at 6-celled stage.

Table IV shows the results of 52 laparoscopies. Two of these laparoscopies were done to confirm clinical findings suggesting the absence of a preovulatory follicle; in one case an LH surge was not detected with the Hi-gonavis assay and in the second ovulation was detected by sonar. Both findings were established to be accurate at laparoscopy. Twentyeight preovulatory eggs were recovered from 38 follicles which were accessible to aspiration. All of the preovulatory eggs were inseminated *in vitro* and 22 (78.6%) underwent fertilization. However in eight zygotes development arrested at stages ranging from the pronuclear ovum to the 6-celled embryo. The remaining 14 embryos appeared to cleave normally up to and beyond the 8-celled stage. Each was inserted into the uterus of the egg donor at the times shown in Table V. As may be seen, one of the pregnancies occurred after a daytime transfer and the second after an embryo was inserted at night.

TABLE V

The Time Intervals at Which Embryos Were Transferred into the Uterus

Time interval	Number of embryos	Pregnancies
06.00 to 12.00	4	0
12.00 to 18.00	4	1
18.00 to 24.00	6	1

Of the two pregnancies obtained by these procedures, one resulted in the birth of a normal female infant weighing 3580 g. The baby (Fig. 4) was found to be completely healthy as judged by comprehensive clinical assessment and has continued to develop normally. The second pregnancy resulted in spontaneous abortion of a normal male fetus at 20 weeks gestation. The abortion appeared to be due to a severe chorioamnionitis caused by an anaerobic gram negative bacillus. It is possible that this organism was introduced at an amniocentesis performed 5 days before the abortion. During this procedure the bowel may have been inadvertently transfixed by the needle which had to be passed through the uterine fundus due to an anterior placenta.

DISCUSSION

A prominent feature of the current method for treating infertility by IVF and ET is the low success rate. At present by far the greatest number of failures result from the low yield of preovulatory eggs from women having natural menstrual cycles. Thus 28 mature eggs were recovered from a total of 69 patients admitted for monitoring. Although Edwards *et al.* (10) did not use ultrasound to monitor the presence and location of preovulatory follicles their oocyte recovery rate was better; 44 mature eggs were collected from a total of 79 patients admitted for monitoring.

In our group of 69 patients 5 failures were unavoidable since ultrasound revealed that the preovulatory follicle was developing in an ovary known to be inaccessible. In four others the dominant follicle was found to be covered with adhesions at laparoscopy for ovum aspiration. A previous surgical attempt to free the ovaries from adhesions had been made in some of these patients but the adhesions had reformed. In others the reported accessibility of the ovaries was found to be inaccurate.

An LH surge was not detected in nine patients. The emotional stress associated with daily monitoring and admission to hospital may account for these anovulatory cycles. Persistent false negative assays are a less likely explanation since other patients monitored at the same time were found to have an LH surge and thus served as controls for the Hi-gonavis kits being used. In contrast, it has been reported that Hi-gonavis produced false positive results in 4 of 10 patients studied (11). This would result in the recovery of immature oocytes and may have occurred in two of our patients (Table IV). However, ovula-

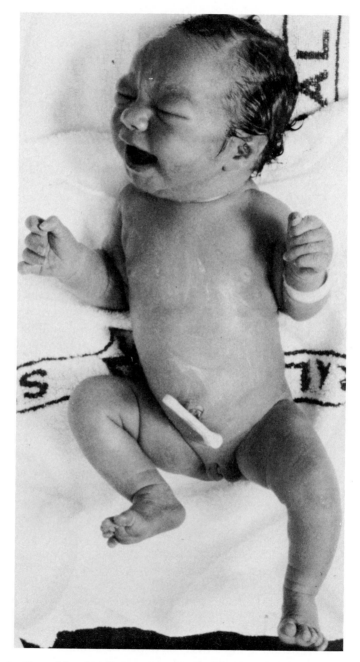

Fig. 4. Normal female infant conceived in the laboratory and born following an uneventful pregnancy and labor.

tion occurring 26 to 28 hours after a sequential rise in LH excretion, as detected with Hi-gonavis, was a commoner problem.

Thirteen patients ovulated before egg collection. In five ovulation was detected at the time of the sonar scan whereas eight ovulated after the scan. Since the ultrasound examination was carried out 1–2 hours before the scheduled laparoscopy, the five patients whose preovulatory follicles could no longer be detected probably ovulated at, or shortly before, 26 hours after the LH surge. If these five patients are allotted to the 26 hours post-LH group, the histogram in Fig. 3 would indicate that·50% of patients (6/12) ovulated within this interval. Such a high proportion of ovulations by 26 hours are difficult to explain. However, it is worth considering the possibility that a distended bladder, which is required for sonar scanning of the ovaries, may in some cases predispose to premature rupture of the ripe follicle.

At present the data indicates that preovulatory eggs, obtained 28 hours after the onset of the LH surge, give rise to the highest percentage of viable embryos following IVF. Some of these embryos have been shown to have the potential for producing live births after their transfer into the uterus of the egg donor. Viable embryos, defined as those capable of developing in culture to or beyond the 8-celled stage, have also been obtained from eggs recovered at 26 and 30 hours after the LH surge. This study will need to be extended since the numbers in the latter groups are too small to determine whether there is a statistically significant difference between the three post-LH intervals. It is clear, however, that two practical requirements will need to be balanced in a clinical program. First, the need to obtain mature eggs which will produce viable embryos and live births. Second, the need to minimize losses of preovulatory eggs due to spontaneous ovulation.

Human embryos grown in culture and transferred into the uterus through the cervix have a very low chance of establishing a pregnancy (1). The high wastage of transferred embryos may be due to defects in the embryo, endometrium, corpus luteum, or the transfer procedure. A cleaving embryo placed in the uterus may fail to develop into a blastocyst, or it may fail to implant, or its development may arrest after implantation if it carries a lethal chromosomal anomaly (12). Alternatively, the development of an apparently normal embryo may be retarded *in vitro* resulting in asynchrony between the endometrium and the stage of the embryo. Moreover, the endometrium may become nonreceptive due to the absence of hormonal factors, which are released by the embryo into the culture medium rather than into the genital tract. An early pregnancy may not be sustained due to an inadequately functioning corpus luteum following excessive drainage of granulosa cells during oocyte aspiration, or its function may not be maintained due to the absence of an embryonic signal. A technically difficult transfer may lead to damage of the embryo, or endometrium, or to expulsion of the embryo from the uterus. It is proposed that when these factors are evaluated and successfully controlled, IVF and ET will become an efficient method for treating human infertility.

ACKNOWLEDGMENTS

The secretarial assistance of Mrs. Anne McCartin throughout the program is gratefully acknowledged. The work was funded by the NH and MR.C of Australia, The Royal Women's Hospital, and generous donations from a Melbourne businessman.

References

1. Lopata, A. (1980) *Nature (London)* **288**, 642.
2. Lopata, A., Johnston, W. I. H., Leeton, J., and McBain, J. C. (1980) In "Assessment and Treatment of the Infertile Couple" (R. J. Pepperell, B. Hudson, and C. Wood, eds.), p. 209. Churchill-Livingstone, Edinburgh and London.
3. Soules, M. R., Sutton, G. P., Hammond, C. B., and Haney, A. F. (1980) *Fertil. Steril.* **33**, 364.
4. Lopata, A., Brown, J. B., Leeton, J. F., Talbot, J. Mc., and Wood, C. (1978) *Fertil. Steril.* **30**, 27.
5. Shivers, C. A., and Dunbar, B. S. (1977) *Science* **197**, 1082.
6. Mori, T., Nishimato, T., Kohda, H., Takai, I., Nishimura, T., and Oikawa, T. (1979) *Fertil. Steril.* **32**, 67.
7. Yanagimachi, R., Lopata, A., Odom, C. B., Bronson, R. A., Mahi, C. A., and Nicholson, G. L. (1979) *Fertil. Steril.* **31**, 562.
8. Lopata, A., Johnston, W. I. H., Leeton, J. F., Muchnicki, D., Talbot, J. Mc., and Wood, C. (1974) *Fertil. Steril.* **25**, 1030.
9. Edwards, R. G. (1973) *J. Reprod. Fertil., Suppl.* **18**, 87.
10. Edwards, R. G., Steptoe, P. C., and Purdy, J. M. (1980) *Br. J. Obstet. Gynaecol.* **87**, 737.
11. Djahanbakhch, O., Templeton, A. A., Hobson, B. M., and McNeilly, A. S. (1980) *Lancet* **I**, 1199.
12. Boué, J. G., and Boué, A. (1976) *Curr. Top. Pathol.* **62**, 193.

Current Problems in *in Vitro* Fertilization and Embryo Transfer

PIERRE SOUPART

Department of Obstetrics and Gynecology
Vanderbilt University School of Medicine
Nashville, Tennessee

INTRODUCTION

Born out of many years of investigation of the complex mechanisms of mammalian fertilization and implantation, the practical procedure of human *in vitro* fertilization (IVF) and embryo transfer (ET) slowly developed, by trial and error, over the past decade. During this period, technical problems had to be overcome: yield of preovulatory oocyte recovery, timing of such recovery, efficiency of fertilization, and embryonic development under tissue culture conditions. When improvement in these various areas had finally been achieved, systematic attempts at embryo transfer led to the recognition, several years later, that the very method used to improve egg recovery and its timing, namely, the hormonal induction of multiple follicle growth in normally cycling women, also altered the endocrine equilibrium in such a way that implantation of transferred embryos was most of the time compromised. When this difficulty was recognized, strategy for egg recovery in view of IVF-ET was modified. The objective now was to recover one single preovulatory egg in the course of a natural cycle, based on the assumption that the subsequent luteal phase would be most conducive of successful implantation of the transferred embryo. This new strategy has produced two successful births in the United Kingdom, and at the time of writing another one is ongoing in Australia. In India, there was a successful live birth, produced by an alledgedly different approach. Egg recovery was performed following multiple follicle growth induction. One, or several eggs, were fertil-

BIOREGULATORS OF REPRODUCTION

ized *in vitro,* and one, or several embryos, developing in culture were freeze-preserved. Then, one or several of these freeze-preserved embryos were transferred in a completely unmanipulated natural cycle. A live birth resulted. However, in all these attempts, the overall implantation success rate is still most disappointing, spontaneous abortions have been recorded, and abnormal pregnancies have been produced. Before getting to the center of the problems, it seems in order to briefly summarize the changes in reproductive medicine which favored the interest in the development of human IVF-ET.

Radical changes on the scene of reproductive medicine have strongly favored the development of this new procedure. Maternal and neonatal mortality and morbidity have been so drastically reduced by improved diagnostic and therapeutic procedures, that other problems of previously unrecognized magnitude, have now become prominent ones in the practice of obstetrics and gynecology. Infertility, of either male or female origin, is nowadays among the chief complaints presented to the practicing gynecologist. Adoption, a traditional palliative to infertility, has become increasingly difficult if not impossible to achieve over the years, owing to the widespread use of effective contraceptive methods, the liberalization of abortion laws, the tolerant attitude of society toward the single parent, and the incredibly complex regulations governing adoption in the United States. With regard to adoption for instance, a typical example of the ineptitude of current regulations is that of a family of a serviceman, otherwise satisfying all criteria of eligibility for adoption, which never meets the requirements for residence, simply because the man is constantly moved around, from one military installation to another, in the country or abroad. On the other hand, the advent and progressive acceptance of technological intervention in human reproduction, such as artificial insemination using the semen of the husband (AIH) or that of a donor (AID), has prompted many infertile couples to demand they be at least half if not full biological parents of their progeny. For many interviewed infertile couples, adoption is no longer an acceptable solution to their problems. The spectacular success of IVF-ET, with the birth of Louise Brown in England on July 25, 1978, and the attending ill advised publicity, have convinced many infertile couples that the procedure is simple and bound to be successful in most of the cases. Consequently, in the United States, clinics in the private and academic sectors of medicine, which have either announced their intent to offer this service or are known to have expertise in the techniques required by the IVF-ET procedure, have been flooded with requests for treatment of infertility resulting from tubal diseases. The volume of the demand is such that, considering the complexity of the IVF-ET procedure, clinics that conceivably could provide this service would be fully booked for the next 5–10 years.

Primarily, and most easily understood, IVF-ET is a procedure which permits the initiation of pregnancy when oviducts are absent or irreducibly blocked by pelvic inflamatory disease (PID) of various origin. What is less generally perceived, however, is that IVF-ET also offers a tremendous potential for the prevention of birth defects. In this particular instance, when it is known beforehand that a particular pregnancy will be at high genetic risk, the detection of the defect prior to implantation appears to be particularly important. The current technical possibility of performing harmless microbiopsy on the trophoblast of a preimplantation embryo developing in culture, and of using the few excised cells for both karyotype analysis and specific enzyme activity quantitative assays on single cell, would permit the screening out of defective embryos prior to implantation. As compared to the current practice of amniocentesis, diagnosis of an abnormal fetus, and the option of therapeutic abortion at mid-trimester, with the resulting terrible psychological stress on both parents, the same option offered prior to embryo transfer, would certainly represent a significant improvement. As stated before, no longer is the main objective of reproductive medicine only to deliver a live baby while optimally preserving the health of its mother, but also to promote the birth of a healthy baby. This specific goal, it should be stressed, can be largely achieved without recourse to genetic engineering, and has nothing to do with the irrational possibility, voiced by some, of creating a "superrace."

The purpose of this chapter is to evaluate the current status of IVF-ET in the light of knowledge gained over the past 10 years, to analyze the problems that were met over that period, and to define areas in which progress must be made, if human IVF-ET is to become a practical means for the alleviation of some type of infertility, for the prevention of birth defects, and, by using IVF as a research tool, for the acquisition of new fundamental knowledge, the significance of which may far outweigh the use of embryo transfer in its ultimate meaning.

While the development of such research progressed relatively unimpeded abroad (mainly in the United Kingdom and Australia), in the United States it has met with various circumstances, which transformed the scientific and medical problems into a controversial political issue, in that the appropriateness of federal support for such research has, in final analysis, to be decided on by a political individual, the Secretary of H.E.W. The analysis of these developments is beyond the scope of the present chapter, but a detailed account of the recent history of human *in vitro* fertilization research in the United States can be found in a current study (1).

INDICATIONS

For the sake of clarity the clinical indications of IVF-ET can be divided into two main categories, i.e., infertility problems and prevention of birth defects.

INFERTILITY PROBLEMS

Damaged, useless, or absent oviducts as well as failure of reversal of tubal sterilization constitute the major indication. Since IVF requires no more than 50,000–100,000 sperm in the fertilization droplet, oligospermia could be another important indication. However, oligospermia is often associated with asthenospermia and stockpiling sperm for AI rarely seems to be successful. It has been found (2) that a procedure, originally designed by Ericsson *et al.* (3) for the isolation of fractions enriched in Y-chromosome-bearing sperm, also extracts from the original population a fraction of sperm capable of withstanding freeze preservation and, after thawing up, retain a motility equal to, if not greater than, that of the original population. Thus, a method is available for segregating the most motile cells from an oligoasthenospermic population. It has been argued by some reviewers (4) that fertilization *in vitro* with sperm that have not passed through the female genital tract may be associated with an increased risk of fertilization with abnormal spermatozoa, since there is evidence that some types of abnormal spermatozoa are eliminated during the passage through the female tract (5). Conceivably, the Ericsson procedure (3) could be used as an substitute for the screening effect apparently exerted by the female genital tract. However, there is no evidence that spermatozoa of high motility are freer from chromosomal abnormalities than others. Quite recently a new *in vitro* fertilization system has been designed by Overstreet *et al.* (6), which somewhat mimics the conditions of the female genital tract, by placing oocytes in culture medium and semen on opposite sides of a barrier of cervical mucus in a flat capillary tube. No washing procedures are required and the spermatozoa reaching the medium are selected by the mucus for vigorous motility and normal morphology. Sperm numbers around the oocytes at the time of zona penetration were approximately one order of magnitude lower than in previously described systems. This system may increase the likelihood of generating normal human embryos *in vitro*.

Other indications are presence of antibodies against sperm in the female, abnormal cervical factors, genital tuberculosis in which tubal reconstruction is coutraindicated (7). IVF has also been used by Trounson *et al.* (8) in the investigation of idiopathic infertility.

PREVENTION OF BIRTH DEFECTS

When it is known that a pregnancy will be at high genetic risk, the karyotype of the embryo can be analyzed at the blastocyst stage, using a few cells obtained by microbiopsy of the trophoblast. Chromosome morphological and/or numerical abnormalities can be identified, and the defective embryo can be selected out. The same approach can be used for the sexing of embryos in view of controlling sex-linked diseases. Prediction of sex by this method, combined with embryo transfer in laboratory animals (rabbit) has been shown to be 100% accurate as well as harmless to the embryo (9).

CONDITIONS OF APPLICABILITY OF IVF-ET

The conditions of applicability of IVF-ET are quite simple. These include the presence of (1) at least one functional ovary, or an ovary that can be induced to ovulate in case of oligo- or amenorrhea; (2) a functional uterus free of synechiae; (3) cornua cauteriation at the time of or prior to oocyte recovery to prevent embryo migration in a remaining oviduct stump, leading to ectopic pregnancy; and (4) fertile semen, free of bacterial and viral infections.

STRATEGIES FOR OOCYTE RECOVERY AND THEIR RESULTS

BIOLOGICAL CONSIDERATIONS REGARDING FERTILIZABILITY OF MAMMALIAN OOCYTES

Owing to our current incomplete understanding of factors controlling oocyte maturation, oocytes are best obtained when they have completed much of their maturation *in vivo*. Triggered by the LH surge, the immature oocyte in the leading follicle has resumed meiosis, which has progressed up to metaphase of the second maturation division, where it has been physiologically arrested once again. This partial maturation is accompanied by the extrusion of the first polar body, which is present in the perivitellive space of ovulated eggs. The final stage of nuclear maturation will be triggered by the fertilizing sperm, and will culminate in the extrusion of the second polar body. Besides the morphological changes characterizing oocyte maturation, there are biochemical changes occurring in the ooplasm and known as "cytoplasmic maturation." Among these changes is the appearance of the "male pronucleus growth factor(s)" (MPGF) (1,10), without the presence of which the nucleus of the fertilizing sperm does not decondense and does not transform into a male pronucleus. The appearance of MPGF(s) is a late event in the oocyte maturation process. It occurs in oocytes maturing *in vivo* but not in those maturing *in vitro*, at least not under ordinary culture conditions (11). Finally, a third component of occyte maturation is the functional stimulation of follicular cell, cumulus oophorus, and corona radiata cells, which accompany the oocyte at the time of ovulation. Functional observations have strongly suggested that stimulation of these cells by gonadotropins facilitates the final acquisition of the sperm fertilizing ability, a phenomenon known as "sperm capacitation" (12,13).

TECHNIQUE FOR OOCYTE RECOVERY

Human oocytes can be recovered by preovulatory follicle aspiration in a variety of surgical situations giving access to the ovary (14). However, in view of IVF-ET, the current technique is laparoscopic aspiration of the preovulatory follicle contents. After initial aspiration of the follicular fluid with a single barrel needle, if the preovulatory oocyte has not been recovered, the follicle can be flushed with tissue culture medium adapted to support human oocytes (1), using a double-barrel needle. Culture medium is injected through one barrel while it is aspirated from the follicle through the second barrel. This a most useful technique, recently developed by the Australian teams, at Queen Victoria Hospital and Royal Women Hospital, Melbourne, in that the preovulatory oocyte is often found, not in the initial aspirate, but in one the several washings of the follicle. A most critical aspect of the logistics of oocyte recovery in view of IVF-ET is that the egg recovery laboratory be adjacent to the operating room, so that the laboratory and surgical teams are in direct voice and visual contact with each other, since follicle flushing must be repeated until the preovulatory oocyte is obtained. In case of egg recovery in the course of a natural cycle (see below), the operating room must be available around the clock, on an emergency basis. If the aspirated follicle is to be flushed with bicarbonate-buffered tissue culture medium, the pneumoperitoneum has to be established using a mixture of 90% N_2, 5% O_2, and 5% CO_2, which is the gas phase used in the culture of oocytes for fertilization and preimplantation development. At the end of a laparoscopic recovery, the gas mixture is flushed out using straight CO_2. Alternatively, the follicle may be flushed using phosphate buffered saline, which does not need a particular gas phase to maintain its pH.

The practical problems that have dominated human oocyte recovery in the early days as well as today are timing of recovery and an overall relatively low yield. These problems were overcome but it was then found that the solution was generating other problems. Hence, over the past 10 years, two different stategies were used for oocyte recovery, which will now be analyzed.

OOCYTE RECOVERY FOLLOWING INDUCTION OF MULTIPLE FOLLICLE GROWTH

In early work on oocyte recovery for IVF purpose, the recovery rate was relatively low. Edwards and Steptoe (15) reported a recovery rate of 31.8%, using a needle and syringe for laparoscopic recovery, and of 32.4%, when using a special aspiration apparatus. Morgenstern and Soupart, using a different approach (14), reported an overall recovery rate of 30.6%. Thus, in those two studies, three follicles had to be aspirated in order to obtain one oocyte. Another difficulty rested with proper timing of laparoscopic aspiration of follicle contents, so that preovulatory oocyte be recovered just prior to ovulation. Those problems were solved by adapting to cyclic women the method designed to induce ovulation in anovulatory women, i.e., administration of gonadotropins. The regime for priming of ovaries consisted of intramuscular injections of 3 vials of postmenopausal gonadotropins (hMG, menotropins, Pergonal, Serono Laboratories, Inc., Braintree, Massachusetts), containing each 75 IU FSH and 75 IU LH, starting on day 2 or 3 of the cycle and repeated 3 times every other day, up to a total of 12 vials, i.e., a total of 900 IU. An adequate preovulatory phase in these patients was indicated by a rise in 24-hour urinary estrogen excretion up to 50–100 mg (16). Then an ovulatory intramuscular injection of 5000 IU hCG (APL, Ayerst Laboratories, Inc., New York, New York) is administered on day 11 or 12 following onset of menses to just precede the natural LH surge. Ovulation is expected 36–40 hours after hCG injection. Thus, laparoscopy is timed to take place 32–34 hours after the hCG injection, at a time when follicles should be ripe but not yet ruptured. Using this regimen, it was found that the mean number of developing follicles on ovaries was 10.6 ± 0.4 (SE). Yet, this mean number was not statistically different from the mean number of 9.2 follicles found when using much lesser doses (300–375 IU) of hMG. Thus, increasing the dose of hMG in cyclic women did not increase the number of developing follicles found on ovaries after priming with gonadotropins (17). Using this gonadotropin regime, Edwards and Steptoe (18) reported that in prolonged trials involving some 100 cyclic women, no side effects (ovarian overstimulation) have been observed. Alternatively, clomiphene citrate can be used for priming of the ovaries, using the following schedule and doses, starting day 2 or 3 for 5 days: 100 mg, 50 mg, 100 mg, 50 mg, 100 mg. Then hCG is administered (5000 IU) on day 11 or 12 following onset of menses, to coincide with the estrogen rise. Lopata et al. (19) have conducted extensive studies on superovulation induction using clomiphene citrate and hCG. They recovered an average of one preovulatory oocyte per patient, with a recovery ranging from 0 to 3 preovulatory ova.

Using ova obtained by superovulation procedures, although fertilization did occur and some fertilized ova exhibited preimplantation development, none of the transferred embryos resulted in a durable implantation. Reportedly (20), in a series of 77 patients, and despite various treatments aiming at supporting the luteal phase (repeated injections of hCG, with or without progesterone and Primolut, bromocryptine, and even clomiphene citrate), only three implantations were observed, in two of which the level of endogenous hCG fell, and one ended up in an ectopic pregnancy (21). The latter observation led to the recommendation that cornua be cauterized to prevent migration of a transferred embryo into a remaining oviduct stump. It was concluded from these most disappointing results that the principal difficulty lays in abnormalities in the luteal phase following induction of follicular development with gonadotropins in cyclic women. Following stimulation with hMG and hCG, the follicular steroid patterns were bizarre. It seemed that the higher the estrogen concentrations, the shorter the luteal phase; many patients had only 9-day luteal phases. In the light of these disappointing results, Steptoe and Edwards decided to abandon gonadotropic stimulation of follicular development and to concentrate on normal follicles in the natural cycle. Short (20), reporting on the presentation by Steptoe and Edwards at the Royal College of Obstetricians in London on January 26, 1979, made the following comments: "In view of the high success rate achieved by many investigators who have used exogenous gonadotropins and/or clomiphene to obtain pregnancies in anovulatory women, Edwards and Steptoe's failures are unexpected. It would be surprising if abnormal follicular or a deficient luteal phase were the true explanation of their lack of success. One wonders why two of the pregnancies, which were detected by hCG levels, failed to go to term."

As far as the latter of Short's comments is concerned, the true explanation may rest with the natural embryonic loss, which occurs in spontaneous human pregnancies. A very recent study by Soules *et al.* (22) strongly suggests still another explanation for the experienced failures. The authors studied various hormonal parameters (E, P, LH, FSH, and PRL) in women of reproductive age undergoing a variety of operations under general anesthesia without compromise of ovarian vasculature. The collected evidence favors direct inhibition of ovarian steroidogenesis by (1) toxic effects of anesthetic agents or (2) stress-induced changes in other hormone levels, e.g., hyperprolactinemia.

OOCYTE RECOVERY IN THE COURSE OF NATURAL CYCLES

In the light of the above discussion, oocyte recovery in the course of a natural cycle seems to be a possible answer to previously experienced implantation failures. It has the apparent advantage of insuring a hormonally balanced luteal phase in the cycle of recovery, thought to be most favorable for implantation on embryo transfer. This, of course, assuming that the anesthesia itself does not inhibit ovarian steroidogenesis, which strongly suggests that egg recovery should be performed under regional or local rather than general anesthesia.

Oocyte recovery in a natural cycle requires precise determination of the LH surge, a critical factor, and currently the most difficult problem of laparoscopic aspiration of preovulatory follicle contents. Despite their high precision, currently available LH radioimmunoassay using blood serum are too time consuming to provide the almost instantaneous response needed for accurate timing of follicle aspiration. However, rapid radioreceptor assays (23) are being developed that may prove most useful in the near future. Ideally one should be able to follow the LH rise in peripheral blood on samples collected at 3-hour intervals, using an indwelling venous catheter to reduce the stress to the patient. In their recently reported (20) but still unpublished series, Steptoe and Edwards indicated that they used an immunologic test on urine (Hi-Gonavis, Mochida Pharmaceutical Co., Ltd., Tokyo, Japan) to approximate the time of the LH surge. So did Lopata *et al.* (24) to initiate the currently ongoing pregnancy in Australia. Using this immunologic test, results are obtained after 2 hours in a series of urine dilutions. The test is based on the binding of LH (or hCG) to anti-hCG sensitized erythrocytes, leading to hemagglutination. However, this test, originally designed for the detection of hCG in early pregnancy, is relatively insensitive as far as LH detection is concerned. In order to obtain a reading on 3-hour urine collections, patients must be put on restricted fluid intake to increase urinary LH concentration. Due to the low sensitivity of the test, baseline reading are extremely low, either nil or 0.5–1 IU LH excreted per hour. The beginning of the LH surge is assumed when LH excretion over a 3-hour period is double or significantly above the average baseline reading. The midpoint of that period is taken as time zero, to which 28 hours are added to determine the time of oocyte laparoscopic recovery. Thus, there is a minimum error margin of 1.5 hour, which is even greater at night, since there is no urine collection from 11 P.M. to 5 A.M. Thus, the true LH peak location may be missed. In addition many patients have diphasic or pulsatile LH surges. One must be ready to proceed with egg recovery around the clock when using the natural cycle. Dr. Ian Johnston, of the Royal Women Hospital, in Melbourne, has calculated from a series of 51 cases, the frequency of laparoscopic recoveries per 4-hour periods from midnight to midnight. The distribution was as follows: A.M.: 0–4: 3.92%; 4–8: 9.80%; 8–12 noon: 23.51%; P.M.: 12 noon–4: 13.73%; 4–8: 29.41%; 8–12: 19.61%. Johnston concluded that these data are most helpful for the surgical and laboratory teams in the planning of their social life: attending or giving a dinner party should be scheduled between midnight and 4 A.M. for minimum interference.

Steptoe and Edwards (20) reported that with use of this method in a series of 65 patients, LH surge determination was found in error in 9 cases, i.e., a failure rate of 13.8%, which, in retrospect, seems unacceptable for the recovery of one single preovulatory oocyte. They also observed that ovulation had already occurred 30 hours after the LH surge, thus a time interval significantly shorter in the natural cycle than that of 36 hours observed when ovulation is induced using hMG-hCG.

Despite the theoretical advantage of insuring a luteal phase most conducive of successful implantation, the use of the natural cycle for oocyte recovery has not yet been very productive. In their most recent series, Steptoe and Edwards (21) experienced 11 failures of oocyte recovery out of 56 favorable cases. Of the 45 recovered oocytes, 10 failed to become fertilized. Of the 35 fertilized ova, 3 failed to cleave. Among the 32 presumably transferable embryos, 4 were lost due to reportedly "poor" transfer technique. Of the 28 embryos thought to have been successfully transferred, only 4 did implant and of those 4, only 2 led to live births. Since this may seem to be a somewhat negative view, these results can be recalculated as follows: (1) correct timing of LH surge, 86% (56/65); (2) oocyte recovery rate, 80% (45/56); (3) fertilization rate, 78% (35/45); (4) cleavage rate, 91% (32/35); (5) presumably optimal transfer rate, 87% (32–4/32); (6) implantation rate, 14% (4/28); and (7) live birth, 50% (2/4). From these figures it can be seen that there are problems at all levels of the IVF-ET procedure. Improvement of LH surge timing can most probably be achieved, desirably to reach 100% accuracy. A very useful adjunct method will be the measurement of ovarian follicle growth by ultrasound scan (25). The method will also prevent unnecessary laparoscopies, by indicating that ovulation had already occurred at the scheduled time of egg recovery. With accurate timing of follicle contents aspiration, the oocyte recovery should also improve. It may not be possible to improve upon the fertilization and cleavage rates, because of the natural incidence of such failures (to be reviewed later), which may be beyond control. Transfer errors can certainly be eliminated with increasing practice. Thus, the main problem remains to insure implantation. The observed implantation success rate of 14% is considerably lower than the natural implantation rate of 69% (to be reviewed later). It is, therefore, possible that aspiration of the leading follicle contents in the course of a natural cycle traumatizes the follicle most of the time (4 out of 5 times, according to available data, 20), and/or that general anesthesia used for oocyte recovery interferes with steroidogenesis, both factors resulting in a possibly inefficient corpus luteum.

Yet, 4 pregnancies were successfully initiated in Edwards and Steptoe's series, using oocyte recovered in a natural cycle. This represents a success rate of 8.8% (i.e., 4 out of 45 preovulatory ova), which led to 2 live births. However, considering that this series originally consisted of 79 hopeful, infertile couples, it can also be said that the incidence of cruel disappointment was 97%. Qualitatively, and regardless of its current low yield, the possibility of initiating pregnancy by IVF-ET has been definitively established.

FUTURE STRATEGY FOR OOCYTE RECOVERY IN VIEW OF IVF-ET

Regardless of the type of strategy used for recovering preovulatory oocytes, the above analysis clearly shows that neither procedures are conducive to optimal reimplantation conditions in the luteal phase immediately following oocyte recovery. Early menstruation or fluctuation of steroidogenesis can occur; hence, the success of implantation is low (26).

Despite of the current lack of detailed information, the reported Indian experience (27) indicates that there is already some experimental support for a different strategy. This new approach was anticipated several years ago, both by Edwards and Steptoe (26) and this reviewer, in a research grant proposal to the National Institutes of Health (HD-08837-04) which has been the object of the first report of the National Ethics Advisory Board to the United States Public Health Service (28). Thus, there are valid reasons for predicting that the yield of human IVF-ET will be made more practical by combining superovulation techniques, IVF, embryo culture, and freeze-storage of preimplantation embryos, thus making it possible to delay embryo transfer to subsequent and completely unmanipulated menstrual cycles. The only invasive procedure required in such cycles would be accurate monitoring of the LH surge, in order to precisely schedule the reimplantation of a freeze-stored embryo in synchrony with the development of a normal luteal phase endometrium. In the case of anovulatory women eligible for IVF-ET, it would still be necessary to induce ovulation in order to perform the delayed transfer, but follicle aspiration trauma and the effects of general anesthesia would be avoided.

The current status of freeze preservation of mammalian preimplantation embryos is beyond the scope of this chapter but can be found in two recent and extensive reviews of the problems of IVF-ET (1,29). Preliminary work on freeze preservation of human preimplantation embryos is currently in progress at Monash University, Melbourne, Australia, under the direction of Dr. A. O. Trounson (personal communication).

EMBRYO TRANSER

Although surgical transfer of the preimplantation embryo has been tried, it was concluded that a nonsurgical approach was the best and simplest (20,21,30). The nonsurgical technique for embryo transfer is very similar to that used for artificial insemination. A fine catheter of about 1.5 mm in diameter is used for this purpose. The simple embryo transfer apparatus consists of a 1-ml disposable tuberculine syringe, graduated in 0.01 ml, a hypodermic needle, and a transparent indwelling venous catheter. The embryo is taken up in 0.05 ml of transfer medium in the distal end of the catheter and delivered into the uterine cavity by emptying the syringe, which was first loaded with about 0.2 ml of air. The transfer catheter is then slowly withdrawn from the uterus and immediately checked under the microscope to insure that the embryo has indeed been delivered to the uterine cavity. Just prior to transfer, the cervical os is swabbed with transfer medium, which contains antibiotics. Despite its apparent simplicity, embryo transfer is a delicate operation. Bleeding, although very slight may prevent implantation since a layer of fibrin deposited on the outer aspect of the zona pellucida would make blastocyst hatching impossible. Overall, however, embryo transfer should be completed in a matter of minutes.

A simple rule for successful mammalian embryo transfer is that "the embryo will wait for the endometrium, but the endometrium will not wait for the embryo." Thus, in order to insure successful implantation, perfect synchony of embryonic and endometrium development is of the essence. The human preimplantation embryo enters the uterus approximately 72 hours after ovulation, when the embryo is at the very early morula stage, consisting of 8–16 cells. Literature survey shows that only 15 human preimplantation embryos have been recovered from the genital tract, 9 from the oviduct and 6 from the uterus. The most advanced development stage recovered from the oviduct was a 7-cell embryo (31) and the earliest development stage recovered from the uterus was a 12-cell embryo (32), the age of both specimens was estimated at about 72 hours. The most advanced stage of development ever recovered from the human uterus was a blastocyst expanded in the zona pellucida, consisting of 186 cells and of an age estimated at more than 120 hours (33). Thus, it seems that preimplantation embryos can be transferred to the uterine cavity at anytime from the 8-cell stage up to the blastocyst stage. Edwards and Steptoe (26) reported having transferred embryos at the 6- to 8-cell, 8-cell, and morula stages. They also reported successful implantation only when transferred embryos were at 8- to 16-cell stage, and when the transfer was performed late at night. There is no physiological evidence in support of the latter statement, except perhaps the patient being asleep in bed. In the ongoing Australian pregnancy, the embryo was transferred at the 8-cell stage, at 10:45 P.M., 74 hours after fertilization. The obvious advantage of transferring a 8-cell embryo is that it cuts down on the need for culture in the laboratory.

Over the years, in series of embryo transfers following oocyte recovery from superovulation (hMG-hCG treatment), a variety of supportive therapies have been tried, but apparently without significant impact (20). Repeated injections of hCG, hCG and progesterone, hCG and Primolut, hCG–progesterone–Primolut, clomiphene citrate, bromocryptine, all were tried in order to support or substitute for possibly deficient corpora lutea. In the most recent series of transfers, following ovum recovery in natural cycles, no such therapies appear to have been used.

QUALITY CONTROL PROCEDURES

The interested reader will find a detailed description of the mechanisms involved in human fertilization, of its fine morphology, and of preimplantation development in recent reviews (1,29).

Advancing technologies provide us with quality control methodologies applicable at all steps of *in vitro* fertilization and preimplantation development. The use of such methodologies may not only prove to be a powerful tool for retrospective analysis of current data but it may also provide objective information that may prove determinant in case of possible litigation. Despite the modest history of IVF-ET at the present time, there has already been a malpractice suit in this area (e.g., Del Zio versus Columbia Presbyterian Hospital and Dr. R. Vande Wiele, New York, 1978).

To begin with, videotaping microscopy will permit dynamic and permanent record of motility characteristics in the fertilizing sperm suspension, a record that can be used for instant playback as well as retrospective computerized analysis.

Second, it must be realized that mammalian ova and embryos are exquisitely sensitive to exposure to most of the range of the visible and ultraviolet light spectrum, being most affected by the ubiquitous fluorescent light, and are repeatedly exposed to such radiations in the course of frequent and necessary examination (34,35). Light that appears less damaging to cells, ova, and embryos is from the red and infrared bands of the spectrum (35). There are two complementary ways of reducing the detrimental influence of visible light on ova and embryos: (1) conduct all manipulation under red light and (2) make all observations using video intensification microscopy (VIM, 36). In VIM, a silicon intensifier target (SIT) videocamera is used, which is 1000 to 10,000 times more sensitive to available light than conventional video cameras. In practical terms, this means that ova scored to be submitted to IVF and preimplantation development in culture can be examined in time-lapse mode for extended periods of time. An example of the application of such technology is provided by Fig. 1. Figure 1 is the photograph of the screen of a TV monitor connected to the SIT camera attached to a Zeiss microscope equipped with differential interference contrast (Nomarski's optics). Focusing was done as rapidly as possible, using red light. Then, the light source (tungsten filament bulb) was turned down completely without switching off, and the red filter was removed. Neutral density filters were then interposed on the light beam. As a result, no light whatsoever was perceptible to the eye when looking down the microscope eyepiece. Yet, the TV monitor connected to the SIT camera gave the brilliant picture shown in Fig. 1. This picture was taken on March 1, 1979, by Dr. Lennart Nilsson and myself, in Dr. Nilsson's laboratory, at the Karolinska Institute, in Stockholm. In this particular instance, randomly recovered human oocytes were used and the specimen shown is an immature oocyte. This picture clearly demonstrates the analytical power of the technique. This human egg is in the dictyate stage, exhibiting a germinal vesicle, and the uniform distribution of organelles throughout the ooplasm, as well as the tightly packed follicular cells surrounding the oocyte. It powerfully illustrates the dynamic potential of the method for (1) evaluation of morphological quality of preovulatory oocytes; (2) recording the actual fertilization, i.e., the fusion of the fertilizing sperm to an egg in metaphase II, exhibiting a first polar body in its perivitelline space; (3) recording the extrusion of the

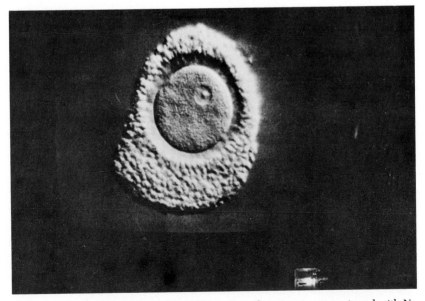

Fig. 1.   Picture of the screen of the TV monitor of a microscope equipped with Nomarski's optics and a video intensification camera (see text for explanation).

second polar body following oocyte activation; (4) recording the development of only two pronuclei, i.e., determining whether eventual polyspermy as well as retention of the second polar body may occur, both of which are possible abnormalities of fertilization; and (5) recording the whole preimplantation development, its precise timing, eventual abnormalities of successive cell divisions, the occurrence of compaction of the embryo, cavitation, as well as blastocyst hatching. Thus, in each instance of *in vitro* fertilization and preimplantation development in culture, a complete, permanent, and dynamic record of all significant events would become available, automatically, for instant and retrospective analysis.

Another important level of quality control rests with the microbiopsy of the mural trophoblast. As previously stated, karyologic and biochemical analyses carried out on a few cells excised from the mural trophoblast would add a new dimension to reproductive medicine, by the routine detection of chromosomal abnormalities (karyotype) and by screening for genetic malfunction, not recognizable by karotype analysis (quantitative assays of enzyme activity in single cell, 37). Owing to the delay imposed by such analyses, the need for freeze preservation of preimplantation embryos pending transfer becomes even more imperative.

EVALUATION OF WORLD RECORD AND SAFETY OF IVF-ET: WHAT TO EXPECT

If one looks critically at the current world record of IVF-ET, the success rate is not high, abnormal pregnancies have been produced, and spontaneous abortions, both clinical and preclinical have been recorded. When all reported and published data are combined (as of May 1, 1980), including both gonadotropins—induced and natural cycles, the current score is shown in Table I. The total number of pregnancies detected by sustained elevated titer of urinary gonadotropin amounts thus far to 11. Of these 11 pregnancies, 3 resulted in term, live birth, 1 is expected to be a term, live birth in early June 1980, 3 terminated as preclinical abortions, i.e., the sustained high titer of gonadotropin suddenly faded away, and 4 terminated as clinical abortions. The first of the 3 reported clinical abortions in the United Kingdom (21) was due to an ectopic pregnancy, presumably due to the migration of a transferred embryo from the uterine cavity to a remaining oviduct stump. The second one occurred 10 weeks after embryo transfer. The embryo was karyotyped and was found to be 69,XXX. It was

TABLE I
World Record of Pregnancies Established by IVF-ET[a] (as of May 1, 1980)

Country	Pregnancies	Live births	Sex[b]	Spontaneous abortions Clinical	Spontaneous abortions Preclinical
Australia	3	(1) June 1980	F	1	1
India	1	1	F	—	—
United Kingdom	7	2	M + F	3 (1 ectopic)	2
TOTAL	11	4	1M/3F	7	
Percent	100	36.4	25/75	63.6	

[a] As of May 1, 1980.
[b] Determined either at birth only or by karyotyping amniocentesis material and at birth.

not possible to determine from banding studies whether the additional autosomal set was maternally or paternally derived. The third one occurred 20.5 weeks after embryo transfer. A karotype test, performed on amniocentesis material at 16 weeks, exhibited a large Y chromosome, together with an additional fragment on one chromosome 15. Both of these anomalies were found to be present in the father. The infant was born alive, but it died after 2 hours. It weighed 200 g and measured 18 cm in crown–rump length. No abnormality could be detected at autopsy in either the baby or its placenta. A fourth clinical abortion occurred in Australia, following amniocentesis. The karyotype was that of a normal male (A. Lopata, personal communication).

Thus, from these 11 pregnancies, only 4 (36.4%) resulted in term, live births. This success rate has to be evaluated in the light of what is presently known of natural embryonic loss in women. The fact that embryonic loss occurs in women was first recognized by Hertig and Rock in 1949 (38). Only recently has it been recognized that this natural embryo loss may be high. Leridon (39) used data on the incidence of blighted human ova (40) together with data on fetal mortality (41), to construct a life-table of intrauterine mortality (Table II).

The results show that 69% of human ova exposed to spermatozoa are lost by the expected time of birth. The results also show a large incidence of failure of fertilization (16%) and a large incidence of embryo loss during the first 2 weeks following fertilization. Other series of independent evidence support the conclusion that high embryonic loss occurs spontaneously in the human (42). An estimate between 69%

TABLE II
A Life Table for Intrauterine Mortality in the Human
(per 100 Ova Exposed to Risk of Fertilization)[a]

Week after ovulation	Death (expulsion of dead embryos)	Survivors
—	16 (not fertilized)	100
0	15 (failed to cleave)	84 (fertile)
1	27	69 (implanted)
2	5.0	42
6	2.9	37
10	1.7	34.1
14	0.5	32.4
18	0.3	31.9
22	0.1	31.6
26	0.1	31.5
30	0.1	31.4
34	0.1	31.3
38	0.2	31.32
Life births (including birth defects)		31
Natural wastage		69

[a] From Leridon (39) by permission of the University of Chicago Press.

and 78% embryonic loss, however, is reasonably consistent with data showing that it takes an average of 4 months to achieve pregnancy by artificial insemination. Thus, it may take an average of 4 months of continual sexual activity to establish a pregnancy capable of producing a normal offspring (43). Embryonic loss also increases significantly with the age of the mother, particularly after the age of 35 years (39). Unfortunately, this is a circumstance much too frequent among patients eligible for IVF-ET.

The death of embryos may arise from two primary causes: intrinsic abnormalities in the embryo that are lethal (such as unmasked recessive genes and chromosomal aberrations) and lethal environmental effects mediated via the female genital tract. The effects may be due to the normal aging process in the female tract, disease of the genital tract, or transmission of exogneous teratogenic agents. Studies on incidence of cytogenetic aberrations in spontaneous abortions show that a major factor in embryonic loss is chromosomal imbalance that arises during the maturation (meiosis) of both types of germ cells and during fertilization. It has been argued that chromosomal aberrations that arises during gametogenesis and fertilization account for a loss of 50% in human embryos that are potentially existent at the time of fertilization (44). The cause of the 25% deficit between the estimate of 69%

(39) and 78% (42) and that of 50% (44) is presumably due to unmasked recessive genes and environmental factors of nongenetic origin. The true contribution of these factors is presently unknown. Much more is known, however, about cytogenetic factors involved in the loss of human embryos.

During meiosis, several accidents may occur, resulting in sperm and ova with abnormal numbers of chromosomes. Sex chromosomes may not separate, resulting in sperm that contain both X- and Y-chromosomes or no sex chromosomes at all or in ova containing two X chromosomes or no sex chromosomes at all. In the same way, any of the 22 pairs of autosomes may fail to separate. This type of aberration is called "nondisjunction." Estimates of nondisjunction for chromosomes 1, 9, and Y in human spermatozoa have been found to be 3.5%, 5.0%, and 2.0%, respectively (45). These are considered high rates. Fertilization involving any of these abnormal sperm or ova can result in abnormal embryos. For example, if a normal ovum is fertilized by a sperm without a sex chromosome, an XO embryo is produced, which is affected by Turner's Syndrome. Such an individual has only 45 chromosomes (karyotype: 45,XO) and is an example of a general class of aberration called *monosomy*. If an ovum with 2X chromosomes is fertilized by a normal Y-bearing sperm, an XXY individual is produced, who has Klinefelter's Syndrome. Such an individual has 47 chromosomes (karyotype: 47,XXY) and is an example of another general class of aberration called *trisomy*. Nondisjunction of the G class of chromosomes, i.e., chromosomes 21 or 22, can result in trisomy G, which causes Down's Syndrome (mongolism).

Other types of accidents can happen. Failure to complete meiosis may occur, so that an ovum or a sperm is produced that has the full diploid set of chromosomes. If, for example, a diploid ovum is fertilized by a normal sperm, a triploid embryo is produced (karyotype: 69,XXY or 69,XXX).

Normally, only one sperm enters the ovum at fertilization. Then, entry of more than one sperm is prevented by the *block to polyspermy*. If this mechanism fails, one or more sperm may enter the ovum at fertilization, giving triploids, tetraploids, and so on. Fortunately, much abnormal fertilization does not result in viable embryos in man. Recent studies (46,47) suggest that most human triploid embryos are formed naturally by dispermic fertilization as the result of failure of the block to polyspermy. There is a significant absence of autosomal monosomies in spontaneous human abortions (44). Boué and Boué (44) argue that these aberrations must be produced in numbers equivalent to the trisomies, but that they cause embryonic death so early that they cannot be detected. Their elimination may in fact occur before the first missed menstrual period (preclinical spontaneous abortions). It is the strong contention of this reviewer that, when we get to systematically study the cytogenetics of human preimplantation embryos, we shall find out that such aberrations actually occur and we shall be able to determine their frequency. Moreover, this will not be an artifact of IVF and preimplantation development, but will reflect the natural incidence of these aberrations.

What is the fate of cytogenetic aberrations? The presence of an abnormal number of chromosomes may or may not be lethal. For example, the XXY trisomy is compatible with postnatal life, the XO monosomy, as well as trysomy G, is predominantly lethal in fetal life, but some are born. Triploidy, however, is nearly always lethal in embryonic life and those that are born only survive for a short time. Studies on the chromosome complements in spontaneous abortions in women have provided information on when embryos die (44). Some types, such as tetraploidy (karyotype: 92), trisomy C, and trisomy E, are, on average, lethal a few weeks earlier than other types, such as monsomy X, triploidy, trisomy D, and trisomy G. Nevertheless, nearly all of them become developmentally arrested by the 8th week of pregnancy.

Is there such a thing as maternal selection against malformed embryos? We think we can say "Yes, there is." In all species, reproductive performance decreases with maternal age. And this is a major concern we have to deal with in sensibly answering most of the abundant mail we receive daily from infertile, aging women inquiring about their chances of being helped. In species that normally deliver several offsprings, this decline is also associated with a decrease in the incidence of congenital abnormalities in the newborn (48,49). A recent study (50) on the incidence of cleft lip-palate and open eyelid in litters of A/JKt mice suggests that deformed embryos are more likely to die *in utero* in older females. This is the first evidence that advanced maternal age can lead to differential death of malformed fetuses. It has been suggested (48) that the cause of selection is the competition between fetuses for the limited resources of the uterus. Such competition would not occur in species bearing a single offspring, like the human, and this may be the reason why increase in the incidence of several congenital abnormalities, such as mongolism, central placenta preavia, malformation of the central nervous system, and cleft lip and palate, occurs with advancing age.

Thus, there is strong evidence that there is a high incidence of embryonic death in the normal reproductive process in man. A large component of this arises from errors in meiosis in the male and female and in errors of fertilization, such as failure of the *block to polyspermy*. Normally, most of the abnormal embryos die and are eliminated early in pregnancy. Nevertheless, a few do not die and are eventually born with congenital abnormalities. The incidence of these abnormalities at birth increases with maternal age. Most of the evidence leading to the above conclusions has been collated in a report prepared by Biggers (4) for the Ethics Advisory Board.

Obviously, there are irreducible factors, the effects of which cannot reasonably be expected to be overcome by human *in vitro* fertilization and embryo transfer. One has to be prepared to repeat embryo transfer in order to initiate a pregnancy since the natural implantation success rate is only 69%. In this respect, freeze preservation of preimplantation embryos, following superovulation, would certainly improve the efficiency of the procedure, in that it would permit serial transfer without a need for repeated laparoscopies and would allow for delaying transfers to completely unmanipulated natural cycles. It can also be reasonably expected that advances in quality control procedures, such as the monitoring of failure of the block to polyspermy, karyotyping the blastocyst, and perhaps, in the not-too-distant future, quantitative enzyme activity assays on single cells, which have been previously discussed, will definitely help avoiding the transfer of defective embryos, especially when it is already known that a projected pregnancy will be at high genetic risk.

Biggers (4) has made some interesting statistical calculations regarding the efficiency of *in vitro* fertilization and embryo transfer. Starting with Leridon's life-table (see Table II), he figured out that the probability of obtaining a live baby from a blastocyst is 31/69 =0.45. If it is assumed that the production of blastocysts and transfer of embryos is fully efficient, the probability of obtaining live babies after the transfer of 1, 2, or 3 blastocysts can be calculated using the binomial distribution (Table III). The number of oocytes that need to be collected from the ovary to give 1, 2, or 3 blastocysts can also be calculated. Since it is unrealistic to suppose the transfer technique is 100% efficient, similar calculations have been done assessing 25, 50, and 75% efficiencies (Table IV). From experience with embryo transfer in animals, it is more realistic (and conservative) to assume an efficiency of about 50%. Thus if 1 blastocyst is transferred, the chances of obtaining a live baby is about 1 in 4. If 3 blastocysts are transferred in a single procedure, the chance of producing a live baby is raised to about 1 in 2, but this involves about a 1 in 100 chance of triplets. Please note that the terminology of "live baby" has been used and keep in mind

TABLE III
Probabilities of Failure and the Birth of Singletons, Twins, and
Triplets Following Human Blastocysts Transfer (4)
(Calculated from the Life Table of Leridon)[a]

No. blastocysts transferred	Required no. of oocytes	Probability			
		Failure	Singleton	Twins	Triplets
1	2	0.55	0.45	—	—
2	3	0.30	0.50	0.20	—
3	5	0.17	0.41	0.33	0.09

[a] Assumes efficiency of oocyte *in vitro* fertilization, embryo culture, and transfer technique.

that the 31 live babies that can be born alive out of 100 fertilizable ova will still contain a percentage of birth defects, unless advanced technology if applied for selecting out abnormal embryos prior to implantation and unless the pregnancy is carefully monitored afterward. The problem with increasing the efficiency of the technique by transferring more than one blastocyst at a time would arise from the added difficulty of monitoring the normality of more than one fetus and then deciding what to do if abnormal and normal fetuses are developing together. Thus, it would seem simpler, and perhaps as efficient, although it may require more time to initiate pregnancy, to proceed with serial transfer of a single blastocyst, following superovulation, IVF, embryo development in culture, and freeze storage of several embryos. Thus, clearly, cryobanking of human preimplantation embryos is a most important area for research and development related to human IVF-ET. The spectacular results achieved in laboratory and farm animals in this respect are most encouraging.

Yet, an important question remains open: "How does one assess the risk of abnormalities from human *in vitro* fertilization?" Under this

TABLE IV
Probability of Having a Child (Singleton, Twin, or Triplet) Following Human
Blastocyst Transfer Assuming Different Efficiencies of Transfer[a]

No. blastocysts transferred	Transfer efficiency (%)			
	25	50	75	100
1	0.11	0.23	0.34	0.45
2	0.21	0.40	0.56	0.70
3	0.30	0.53	0.71	0.83

[a] Source: Biggers (4).

title, Dr. J. J. Schlesselman, from the Biometry Branch, N.I.C.H.D., has published an in-depth statistical analysis of the problem (51). He concluded that:

> A major increase in the frequency of chromosomal abnormalities at the time of implantation which is attributable to *in vitro* fertilization seems likely to have a comparatively minor effect on both abnormalities among live births and the indications for elective abortion at amniocentesis. On the other hand, the induction of more abnormalities by *in vitro* as opposed to natural fertilization would result in more spontaneous abortions and require more attempts at *in vitro* fertilization to achieve a normal live birth. Because of this, the implications of *in vitro* fertilization appear to be much greater for the mother than for the child, in that the mother would be repeatedly subjected to the cost and risks associated with the surgical procedure for the collection of mature ova and the hormonal treatment to induce superovulation and achieve implantation. (51)

In his analysis, Dr. Schlesselman has not taken into account the technological developments that were discussed in this chapter. All of these are designed to reduce the risk to the mother. It remains probable, as Dr. Schlesselman stated (51) that "unless *in vitro* fertilization in humans strongly contradicts the experience in domestic animal reproduction, which suggests no increased risk of abnormalities at birth, a large number of births would be required to provide a definitive assessment of risk." This, from the part of an objective and independent biostatistician, is a most encouraging statement.

In the matter of human *in vitro* fertilization and embryo transfer, as in any other matter of deep human concern, only experience will tell. Progress should not be curbed, but investigations should be conducted with utmost caution.

RESEARCH APPLICATION OF IVF, NOT INVOLVING ET

This review would be incomplete without mentioning conceivable uses of human IVF, not involving ET. Roger V. Short (20) has listed some of these applications and commented that "In contrast to the obvious clinical applications of human IVF-ET for treating infertility in women with bilateral occlusion of the fallopian tubes, there are significant applications of this technique for fundamental research in a number of areas. Indeed, it seems probably that these fundamental discoveries will far outweigh the rather restricted use of embryo transfer in their ultimate clinical significance." To the number of specific examples quoted by Short (20), identified by an asterisk (*) at the beginning of a paragraph, more can be added, identified by a double asterisk (**).

CONTRACEPTIVE RESEARCH

*The mammalian oocyte is surrounded by a glycoprotein "shell," the zona pellucida. This shell contains specific binding sites for the spermatozoa of closely related species; unless the spermatozoa first bind to the zona, they will not be able to penetrate it and reach the vitelline membrane. If the glycoproteins of the zona pellucida of hamsters are injected into mice, antibodies are formed that render the mice infertile (52), and passive transfer to mice of rabbit antibodies raised against mouse eggs will make the mice temporarily infertile (53). In vitro, it can be shown that the antibody works as predicted by preventing attachment of spermatozoa to the zona pellucida (53). However, there may be an additional antifertility effect, since even if fertilization did occur, implantation would be prevented because the antibodies around the zona are known to prevent the blastocyst from "hatching" (54). These studies in laboratory animals, therefore, show considerable promise as a novel form of immunologic contraception. If research is to proceed in a logical manner toward the evaluation of this technique for human clinical use, the first step will be to see if antisera raised against the zonal glycoproteins of a variety of species, including primates and the human, are able to block the fertilization of human eggs by human spermatozoa in vitro. If this effect can be demonstrated in man, the next step will be to characterize and, if possible, synthesize the zonal glycoprotein, so that enough antigen can be produced for human clinical trials. Antisera raised in human would initially be screened for their antifertility action in an IVF system, before proceeding to clinical trials in vivo.

*Another area of contraception research where human IVF can provide an invaluable if not essential test system, relates to the development of male contraceptives. There is now abundant evidence to show that a variety of steroids (synthetic androgens, antiandrogens, or mixtures of androgens and gestagens) can be used to suppress sperm production by the testis (55). Although it is a relatively easy matter to produce severe oligospermia with sperm densities of less than 5 million per milliliter, it is extremely difficult to produce complete azoospermia. As long as there are still some motile sperm in the ejaculate, it will not be possible to reassure the man that he is indeed sterile. It would seem unethical to put the matter to the test by encouraging the man to have unprotected intercourse with his wife, who would then have to recourse to abortion to make up for any failures of the male contraceptive. Yet, one such clinical trial, sponsored by the National Institutes of Health, is currently going on at my own Institution. Abortion, not therapeutic, but corrective, in this case, is an officially approved procedure, while IVF technology is not. If it could be shown beforehand by IVF tests that the few spermatozoa produced by men on steroid suppression therapy were incapable of fertilizing the human egg, this would provide sufficient reassurance, to principal investigators and institutional review boards as well, to allow one to embark on a limited clinical trial. With some such IVF testing, it is difficult to see how it will ever be possible to develop chemical approaches to male contraception, unless they result in complete azoospermia.

INFERTILITY RESEARCH

*In contrast to the great research advances that have been made in the diagnosis and treatment of infertility in women over the past decade, there has been little or no progress in our understanding of male infertility. It is generally accepted that about 10% of married couples have an infertility problem, and although we cannot know for certain, it seems likely that the man is at fault in a significant proportion of such cases. The most useful index of male infertility is still the sperm count, but even this is an extremely imprecise guide. Nobody knows what a "normal" human spermatozoon looks like, and although much effort is devoted to scoring the proportion of morphologically "abnormal" spermatozoa in the ejaculate, we have no idea whether abnormal shape reflects abnormal function, apart from the fact that excessively large spermatozoa are diploid and hence incapable of hormal fertilization (56). However, detailed studies of the chromosomes of early human abortuses show that in 60% of cases there is a grossly abnormal karyotype that is presumably the cause of abortion. These abnormalities are mainly due to errors of gametogenesis, and many are paternally derived (57). Thus, it must follow that there are many genetically defective spermatozoa in the ejaculate, although with the present techniques we have no way of detecting them. It is also generally believed that if a man is oligospermic, with a sperm density of less than 20 million per milliliter, his fertility if greatly reduced. This is presumably not due to the low sperm count per se, since "bulking" a number of ejaculates in the deep-freeze and inseminating an increased number of spermatozoa at one time rarely seem to improve the fertility of those men. The likely explanation is that whatever factor is responsible for the inhibition of spermatogenesis was also responsible in most cases, for introducing some genetical, morphological, or biochemical lesions into the few sperm that were produced, thus rendering them infertile. Even considering current advances that make it possible to "reveal" the karyotype of human spermatozoa by such techniques as their fusion to zona-free hamster ova (58), it is only possible at best to test the karyotype of a few hundred human spermatozoa out of about some 200 million present in the ejaculate. It is not yet known whether such limited sampling will be of statistically significant diagnostic value.

**In idiopathic infertility, when all diagnostic resources of the art have failed to indicate the cause of the problem, IVF testing may be the last look at the cause of infertility. Trounson et al. (8) have conducted some preliminary studies on this aspect of infertility, encountered both in IVF-ET and AI programs. Their preliminary conclusion is that in idiopathic infertility, IVF testing reveals a high rate of fertilization failure and severe polyspermy, as compared to a control group of patients with tubal infertility, in which 83% of preovulatory ova led to apparently normally developing embryos.

CANCER RESEARCH

*One of the most fascinating tumors is the hydatidiform mole. It is a benign placental tumor, formed after fertilization of a "blighted ovum," following which the embryo itself fails to develop at all, while the placenta continues to grow as a cystic, grape-like structure, which secretes, among other things, greatly increased quantities of hCG. The mole usually reveals itself by hemorrhage and if the uterus is not completely evacuated surgically, there is a risk that some of the molar tissue will go on to develop into one of the most malignant tumors, a choriocarcinoma. The incidence of hydatidiform moles varies greatly in different areas of the world (e.g. highest in the Philippines), although the reason for these local differences in incidence rate is completely unknown. Recently, Kajii and Okama (59) have made a discovery of the utmost significance in our understanding of the genesis of human cancer. They investigated the karyotype of a number of moles and confirmed that they were invariably diploid and XX. Using chromosome banding techniques, they were able to deduce in a number of cases which of the individual chromosomes in the mole were derived from the father and which from the mother. They made the amazing discovery that *both* sets of chromosomes in the mole are always derived from the *father*, with no maternal contribution to its genotype whatsoever. Therefore, it seems likely that the mole is caused by fertilization of an oocyte with a defective nucleus by a haploid X-bearing spermatozoon. There is then a failure of the first cleavage of the egg, so that the cell becomes diploid and homozygous for all the paternal genes. Since a cell needs at least one X chromosome to survive, no mole would result from a defective oocyte fertilized by a Y-bearing spermatozoon. This exciting discovery opens up many promising lines of investigation. It should be possible to recreate *in vitro* the conditions necessary for the formation of a mole and then to investigate the way in which this bizarre, benign placental tumor eventually becomes malignant. It might be possible to explain the geographic variations in incidence rates in terms of some environmental factor that influences the production of defective ova. The fact that defective human fertilization can give rise to such an unpleasant tumor should sound a note of caution to those who seek to exploit human IVF-ET without adequate safeguards.

BASIC RESEARCH INTO MAN'S EVOLUTIONARY ORIGIN

*Evolutionary biologists have always been fascinated by man's affinities with his four closest living relatives, the chimpanzee, pygmy chimpanzee, orangutang, and gorilla, and it has recently been suggested that on anatomical and biochemical grounds, the pygmy chimpanzee is most likely the common ancestor from which man, the chimpanzee, and the gorilla take their origin (60). However, studies of the morphology of the spermatozoon in the four species, and spermatozoal DNA content, show that the spermatozoa of man and the gorilla are virtually indistinguishable from one another, although differing in a number of important respects from those of the orangutang and the two chimpanzee species (56,60). Since spermatozoal morphology has proven to be an excellent taxonomic guide in other, more closely related, species, there is a real possibility that man and the gorilla are far more closely related than has hitherto been suggested. One way of investigating this possibility would be to carry out a series of *in vitro* experiments to assess the ability of spermatozoa from the four great apes to bind to the zona pellucida of the human egg, to penetrate the zona, and to effect fertilization. Such an experiment, with its undertones of human–animal hybrids and genetic manipulations in a new sense of the word, would be abhorrent to many, and it is undoubtedly fear of public reaction that has prevented the experiment being performed to date. But the topic is mentioned here as it probably raises the greatest ethical dilemmas and the scientific community at large would appreciate some guidance. The obvious fear would be that if fertilization occurred *in vitro*, somebody would be tempted to implant the human–great ape hybrid embryo back into the uterus of an ape, or even a human, or more simply, to inseminate a female great ape with human semen. Some day, no doubt such experiments will be attempted, and it is impossible to forecast their outcome. The ethical implication could be minimized if the experiment was strictly confined to an *in vitro* situation; a further safeguard would be to use immature human oocytes aspirated from nonovulatory follicles, those that are capable of being fertilized by human spermatozoa *in vitro*, but incapable of subsequent normal development. One could even irradiate the human oocytes prior to fertilization, thereby guaranteeing that no postfertilization development would occur (61), or one could perform the experiment on dead oocytes recovered from a cadaver at autopsy, when fertilization would be impossible but the zonal sperm-binding mechanism would remain intact. Whatever the ethical implications of such experiments, the results would be of utmost significance in the assessment of man's phylogenetic origins.

BASIC RESEARCH ON THE CAUSES OF SPONTANEOUS HUMAN EMBRYONIC WASTAGE

**A most important aspect of IVF research, not involving ET, concerns the elucidation of the causes of massive embryonic wastage characterizing animal and human reproduction. Chromosomal abnormalities, numerical as well as morphological, do occur during gametogenesis and affect both spermatogenesis and oogenesis. And these are occurrence on which we have presently no control whatsoever. The frequent occurrence of chromosomal aberrations is suspected only by inference, based on the analysis of products of clinical spontaneous abortion (44) and defective offsprings. Spontaneous preclinical abortions, which never come to medical attention, must be extremely frequent too. The analysis of the cytogenetics of human preimplantation embryos, obtained by IVF techniques, is the only possible way to gain knowledge of the true incidence of embryonic wastage in the human as well as of its mechanimss. Detailed metabolic studies on human preimplantation embryos would also indicate the relative significance of one given chromosome missing from, or supplementary to, the normal chromosome balance. Such an approach, in the long run, could help clarify the role of each chromosome in the determination of normal embryonic development.

FURTHER RESEARCH ON FACTORS REGULATING HUMAN OOCYTE MATURATION

**Obviously, studies on *in vitro* maturation of human oocytes under various influences, using IVF and preimplantation development as end points, are needed in view of improving our understanding of the factors involved and of their regulatory functions.

ACKNOWLEDGMENTS

In the preparation of this chapter, large excerpts were taken from two previous reviews prepared by the author (see refs (1) and (29). Permission to use these excerpts was granted by the respective publishers, Year Book Medical Publishers, Inc., Chicago-London, and Harper and Row, Publishers, Inc., Hagerstown, Maryland. Other material, some of which was quoted verbatim, was taken from reference (20).

The expert typing skills of Mrs. Angela Sullivan in the preparation of this manuscript are also gratefully acknowledged.

REFERENCES

1. Soupart, P. (1979) *Curr. Probl. Obstet. Gynecol.* **3**, Part I, No. 2, 1–46; **3**, Part II, No. 3, 1–43.
2. Glaub, J. C., Mills, R. N., and Katz, K. F. (1976) *Fertil. Steril.* **27**, 1283.
3. Ericsson, R. J., Langevin, C. N., and Nichino, M. (1973) *Nature (London)* **246**, 421.
4. Biggers, J. D. (1979) *In* "Appendix, HEW Support of Research Involving Human in vitro Fertilization and Embryo Transfer," Stock No. 017-040-00454-1. Paper No. 8. US Govt. Printing Office, Washington, D.C.
5. Ahlgren, M. (1975) *Gynecol. Invest.* **6**, 206.
6. Overstreet, J. W., Gould, J. E., Katz, D. F., and Hanson, F. W. (1980) *Fertil. Steril.* **34**, 606.
7. Gomel, V. (1978) *Curr. Probl. Obstet. Gynecol.* No. 10.
8. Trounson, A. O., Leeton, J. F., Wood, C., Webb, J., and Kovacs, G. (1980) *Fertil Steril.* **34**, 431.
9. Gardner, R. L., and Edwards, R. G. (1968) *Nature (London)* **218**, 346.
10. Thibault, C. (1973) *In* "The Regulation of Mammalian Reproduction" (S. Segal *et al.*, eds.), p. 231. Thomas, Springfield, Illinois.
11. Soupart, P. (1975) *In* "La Fécondation" (C. Thibault, ed.), p. 81. Masson, Paris.
12. Soupart, P., and Morgenstern, L. L. (1973) *Fertil. Steril.* **24**, 462.
13. Soupart, P. (1975) *In* "The Biology of Spermatozoa" (E. S. E. Hafez and C. Thibault, eds.), p. 182. Karger, Basel.
14. Morgenstern, L. L., and Soupart, P. (1972) *Fertil. Steril.* **23**, 751.
15. Edwards, R. G., and Steptoe, P. C. (1970) *Lancet* **1**, 683.
16. Brown, J. B., Evans, T. H., Adey, F. D., Taft, H. P., and Townsend, L. (1969) *J. Obstet. Gynaecol. Br. Commonw.* **76**, 289.

17. Steptoe, P. C., and Edwards, R. G. (1970) *Lancet* **1**, 683.
18. Steptoe, P. C. (1973) *IRCS Libr. Compend.* (73-3), 15-14-4.
19. Lopata, A., Brown, J. B., Leeton, J. F., Talbot, J. M., and Wood, C. (1978) *Fertil. Steril.* **30**, 27.
20. Short, R. V. (1979) *In* "Appendix, HEW Support of Research Involving Human In Vitro Fertilization and Embryo Transfer," Stock No. 017-040-00454-1, Papers No. 10 and No. 11. US Govt. Printing Office, Washington, D.C.
21. Steptoe, P. C., and Edwards, R. G. (1976) *Lancet* **1**, 810.
22. Soules, M. R., Sutton, G. P., Hammond, C. B., and Haney, A. F. (1980) *Fertil. Steril.* **33**, 364.
23. Schmidt-Gollwitzer, M., Eiletz, J., Sackmann, V., and Nevinny-Stickel, J. (1978) *J. Clin. Endocrinol. Metab.* **46**, 902.
24. Lopata, A., Johnston, I. E. H., Hoult, I. J., and Speirs, A. J. (1980) *Fertil. Steril.* **33**, 117.
25. Hackelöer, B. J., Fleming, R., Robinson, H. P., Adam, A. H., and Coutts, J. R. (1979) *Am. J. Obstet. Gynecol.* **135**, 122.
26. Edwards, R. G., and Steptoe, P. C. (1977) *Ciba Found. Symp.* **52** (new ser.), 235.
27. Tayaraman, K. S. (1978) *New Sci.* **80**, 159.
28. Protection of Human Subjects; HEW Support of Human In Vitro Fertilization and Embryo Transfer: Report of the Ethics Advisory Board (1979) *Fed. Regist.* **44**, No. 118 35033.
29. Soupart, P. (1980) *Clin. Obstet. Gynecol.* **23**, 683.
30. DeKretzer, D., Dennis, P., Hudson, B., Leeton, J. F., Lopata, A., Outch, K., Talbot, J., and Wood, C. (1973) *Lancet* **2**, 728.
31. Pereda, J., and Croxatto, H. B. (1978) *Biol. Reprod.* **18**, 481.
32. Hertig, A. T., Rock, J., Adams, E. C., and Mulligan, W. J. (1954) *Contrib. Embryol. Carnegie. Inst.* **35**, 199.
33. Croxatto, H. B., Diaz, S., Fuentalba, B., Croxatto, H. D., Carrillio, D., and Fabres, C. (1972) *Fertil. Steril.* **23**, 447.
34. Daniel, J. C. (1964) *Nature (London)* **201**, 317.
35. Hirao, Y., and Yanagimachi, R. (1978) *J. Exp. Zool.* **206**, 365.
36. Willingham, M. C., and Pastan, I. (1978) *Cell* **13**, 501.
37. Hösli, P. (1977) *Clin. Chem.* **23**, 1476.
38. Hertig, A. T., and Rock, J. (1949) *Am. J. Obstet. Gynecol.* **58**, 968.
39. Leridon, H. (1977) "Human Fertility: The Basic Components." Univ of Chicago Press, Chicago, Illinois.
40. Hertig, A. T., Rock, J., Adams, E. C., and Menkin, M. C. (1959) *Pediatrics* **23**, 203.
41. French, F. E., and Bierman, J. (1962) *Public Health Rep.* **77**, 835.
42. Roberts, C. J., and Lowe, C. R. (1954) *Lancet* **1**, 498.
43. McLeod, J., and Gold, R. Z. (1953) *Fertil. Steril.* **4**, 10.
44. Boué, J. G., and Boué, A. (1976) *Curr. Top. Pathol.* **62**, 193.
45. Pearson, P. L., Gezaedts, J. P. M., and Pawlowitzki, I. H. (1973) *In* "Les accidents chromosomiques de la réproduction" (A. Boué and C. Thibault, eds.), p. 293. Centre International de l'Enfance, Paris.
46. Beatty, R. A. (1978) *Ann. Hum. Genet.* **41**, 299.
47. Jacobs, P. A., Angell, R. R., Buchanan, I. M., Hassold, T. J., Matsuyama, A. M., and Manuel, B. (1978) *Ann. Hum. Genet.* **42**, 49.
48. Parson, P. A. (1963) *Nature (London)* **198**, 316.
49. Kalter, H. (1971) *J. Dent. Res.* **50**, 1442.
50. Kalter, H. (1978) *J. Reprod. Fertil.* **53**, 407.

51. Schlesselman, J. J. (1979) *Am. J. Obstet. Gynecol.* **135,** 135.
52. Gwatkin, R. B. L., Williams, D. T., and Carlo, D. T. (1977) *Fertil. Steril.* **28,** 871.
53. Tsunoda, Y. (1977) *J. Reprod. Fertil.* **50,** 353.
54. Dudkiewicz, A. B., Noske, I. G., and Shivers, C. A. (1975) *Fertil. Steril.* **26,** 686.
55. DeKretser, D. M. (1976) *Proc. R. Soc. London* **195,** 161.
56. Senanez, H. M., Carothers, A. D., Martin, D. E., and Short, R. V. (1977) *Nature (London)* **270,** 345.
57. Short, R. V. (1979) *Ciba Found. Symp.* **64** (new series) Elsevier Holland, p. 377–394.
58. Rudak, E., Jacobs, P. A., and Yanagimachi, R. (1978) *Nature (London)* **274,** 911.
59. Kajii, T., and Okama, K. (1977) *Nature (London)* **268,** 633.
60. Zihlman, A. L., Cronin, J. E., Cramer, D. L., and Sarich, V. M. (1978) *Nature (London)* **275,** 744.
61. Baker, T. G. (1971) *Am. J. Obstet. Gynecol.* **110,** 746.

Factors Affecting Mammalian *in Vitro* Fertilization

B. JANE ROGERS

Department of Obstetrics and Gynecology
and Pacific Biomedical Research Center
University of Hawaii
Honolulu, Hawaii

INTRODUCTION

In considering factors that affect *in vitro* fertilization we must of course encompass the processes of capacitation and acrosome reaction. For fertilization to be successful the spermatozoa must undergo the poorly understood capacitation process and the ensuing morphological change referred to as acrosome reaction. The completion of capacitation is marked by the acrosome reaction, which results in the loss of the outer acrosomal membrane and the plasma membrane associated with it. This acrosome reaction releases and exposes enzymes which are instrumental in the fertilization process. Penetration of the cumulus oophorus is presumably facilitated by the enzyme hyaluronidase which is released during the acrosome reaction while penetration of the zona pellucida is aided by the enzyme acrosin which apparently remains bound to the inner acrosomal membrane. Any factor that affects capacitation, acrosome reaction, or actual egg penetration would be important in the successful occurrence of fertilization *in vitro*. The factors affecting fertilization can be divided into the following three categories for purposes of discussion: physical factors, biochemical factors, and sperm quality factors.

The area of physical factors refers to conditional and environmental parameters and will be dealt with most briefly. It includes methodological and logistical considerations associated with *in vitro* fertilization. The area of biochemical factors includes molecular effects and will be covered most extensively. Much of the information in this area

BIOREGULATORS OF REPRODUCTION
Copyright © 1981 by Academic Press, Inc.
All rights of reproduction in any form reserved.
ISBN 0-12-379980-5

comes from animal studies where acrosome reaction is more easily visualized and fertilization more readily achieved than in human. However, human data will be included where biochemical information is available. The area of factors affecting sperm quality contains human sperm data since human is the species where sperm quality is so heterogeneous and, thus, this becomes a factor in the ability to achieve *in vitro* fertilization. The relationship of sperm quality (as judged by parameters such as count, motility, and morphology) to fertilization in a cross-species zona-free egg system will be included in this section.

PHYSICAL FACTORS

Physical or methodological factors affect fertilization *in vitro* in an almost "black magic" fashion. These factors are of critical importance in the success of fertilization but are most often poorly understood or appreciated. Factors in this area are (1) sperm source, (2) sperm preparation, (3) sperm concentration, (4) medium, (5) incubation volume and container, (6) preincubation time, (7) condition of eggs, (8) natural fluids or components present, (9) insemination conditions, and (10) period of time sperm and eggs are in contact (1).

The *sperm source* refers to whether the sperm are epididymal or ejaculated. This can be a significant consideration with regard to the time and conditions required for capacitation. Ejaculated sperm appear to have more inhibitory components on their surface or in the fluid than epididymal sperm. Historically it is noteworthy that rabbit sperm was one of the most difficult species to capacitate *in vitro* even though numerous workers selected it as the model of choice. The sperm were easily obtained but not readily capacitated. Hamster, mouse, rat, and guinea pig were more easily capacitated, but in each case the sperm were epididymal instead of ejaculated. In human studies ejaculated sperm are almost always used. Therefore, procedures which take into consideration these sperm surface components should be employed. *Sperm preparation* ideally should include washing the sample in some manner such as by centrifugation or by dilution. Washing removes inhibitory components and in general facilitates capacitation. If the washing step is extremely detrimental to sperm in terms of motility and survival some compromise must be made even though this may lengthen the time required for capacitation and reduce the number of sperm that ultimately undergo acrosome reaction. The *sperm concentration* can be a critical factor in any fertilization

system. In most animal systems concentration generally range between 1×10^6 and 1×10^7 sperm/ml. Below this range survival is generally impaired and above this range acrosome reaction is somewhat
reduced. Most studies on the effect of concentration have used animal
sperm samples which contain a majority of actively motile and morphologically homogeneous sperm. Such homogeneity and high percentages of motile sperm are not usually found in human samples so
some thought is often given to the number of motile sperm in addition
to the total sperm concentration. At a concentration of 1×10^7 human
sperm per ml if 50% are motile that would give 5×10^6 motile sperm
per ml which is within the optimal range. Fertilization rates do not
appear to be enhanced significantly by concentrations higher than 1×10^7 sperm/ml. After washing and counting the sperm must ultimately
be suspended in a *medium* that supports survival, capacitation, acro-
some reaction, and fertilization. Certain components in the media are
essential and these will be discussed in more detail under biochemical factors. However, suffice it to say here that culture media such as
Tyrode's solution and Biggers Whiten and Whittingham's medium
(BWW) have been used successfully with both human and animal
sperm. Aside from having the proper pH and osmolality the medium
selected should contain sufficient levels of exogenous energy sources
such as glucose, pyruvate, and lactate as well as albumin. Modifications in the type or condition of albumin have been shown to enhance
capacitation somewhat in some species but the effect of various types
or concentrations of albumin has not yet been demonstrated in
human. We use bovine serum albumin (fraction V) at a concentration
of 3 mg/ml, but this has not been proven to be optimal.

The incubation conditions with regard to *volume of sperm, container,* and *preincubation time* are arrived at empirically. The volume
of sperm suspension in animal studies has varied from 50 μl to 2000
μl. Although the volume and container may seem somewhat arbitrary
they can affect the capacitation time. In human our incubation conditions consist of a 0.5 ml volume in a capped falcon tube placed hori-
zontally in an air incubator. The horizontal placement of the tube
gives a more desireable surface to volume ratio. A shorter capacitation
time can be achieved using a 100 μl drop covered with oil. The time
required to give 50% acrosome reaction is a reasonable preincubation
time prior to addition of eggs. This has not been ascertained in human
since visualization of acrosome reaction is virtually impossible on live
sperm. Five to seven hours preincubation time for human sperm gives
adequate capacitation for most individuals. However, after considering the total time required for sample collection, the time of sperm

with the eggs and examination of the eggs in addition to preincubation
we have opted for a longer preincubation time for logistical reasons.
Preincubation for 18 hours is greatly in excess of the minimal time required for capacitation.

The factors previously discussed have pertained primarily to the
sperm even though the medium and the container also affect the egg.
The *condition of the eggs* is of great importance in the attainment of
fertilization and even more so in the subsequent development. Media
found to support sperm survival have been found to be suitable for the
initial stages of *in vitro* fertilization. The source of eggs can vary from
cultured ovarian eggs from the same species to superovulated zona-
free eggs from a different species. In human experimentation in spite
of restrictions that are rather limiting, experiments have been carried
out with human eggs taken from developing follicles just prior to ovulation and from superovulated follicles. These eggs generally have
some degree of cumulus around them, which seems to be directly related to the health of the egg. The cumulus is generally left intact for
the *in vitro* fertilization procedure since it has been found to be bene-
ficial. In doing cross-species fertilization with hamster eggs and
human sperm both the cumulus and the zona pellucida are removed.
This creates a rather unnatural fertilization situation as one of the barriers to fertilization, the zona, is gone.

Natural fluids or components are often present in the *in vitro* fertilization environment. Fluids from both the male or female tract can either enhance or inhibit the fertilization process. Follicular fluid, oviduct fluid, uterine fluid, and cumulus cells are considered to be positive factors to fertilization whereas seminal fluid or epididymal fluid
retards or inhibits processes associated with fertilization. When unwashed eggs in cumulus or unwashed sperm are placed in a defined *in
vitro* fertilization medium this medium is no longer defined and the
effect the factors in the fluids have on fertilization must be considered.
The most desirable conditions for *in vitro* fertilization would be an ap-
proximation of the natural (*in vivo*) situation. Eggs in cumulus obtained immediately prior to ovulation with a small amount of follicular
fluid and oviduct fluid would be inseminated by washed sperm which
retained none of the seminal or epididymal fluid components.

The *insemination conditions* and the time of sperm and egg contact
have been rather variable both in human and animal studies. In the
human–hamster system the eggs are added to a 0.1 ml volume of
sperm suspension and maintained together for 2 hours to allow sperm
–egg fusion and sperm head swelling (nuclear decondensation).
About 25 eggs in a minimal volume are added to the sperm drop

which contains 1×10^6 sperm. An alternative technique is to place the eggs in a 50 or 100 μl drop to which an aliquot of sperm is added. Using this procedure the sperm are more dilute. Two hours appears to be an adequate minimal time for sperm–egg interaction. Since the eggs are zona-free extensive polyspermy has been observed at 2 hours.

Optimal physical factors for *in vitro* fertilization appear to vary from species to species although some basic considerations may be universal. Unfortunately it appears that it is not possible to ascertain precise optimal physical factors from theoretical considerations. Certainly more work needs to be done to establish optimal conditions especially in human *in vitro* fertilization.

BIOCHEMICAL FACTORS

Hyaluronidase is an acrosomal enzyme which facilitates the passage of sperm through the hyaluronic acid matrix of the cumulus surrounding the egg. The efficacy of the enzyme hyaluronidase is obviously a key factor in fertilization both *in vivo* and *in vitro*. If this enzyme is prevented from acting by the presence of an inhibitor or by failure to

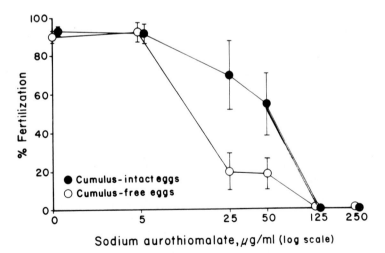

Fig. 1. Effect of sodium aurothiomalate (Myocrisin) on hamster fertilization. Hamster spermatozoa which had been capacitated by incubation for 3 hours with heat-treated human serum were used to fertilize cumulus-intact and cumulus-free hamster eggs in the presence of varying concentrations of the hyaluronidase inhibitor Myocrisin. Each point is the mean of 4–7 separate experiments, ± the standard error.

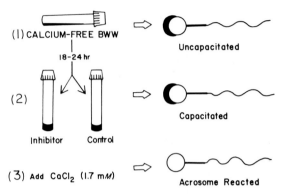

Fig. 2. Synchronous acrosome reaction of guinea pig spermatozoa. The protocol for testing the effect of trypsin inhibitors on acrosome reaction per se involves capacitating the washed guinea pig spermatozoa in 0.5 ml of Biggers, Whitten, and Whittinghams (BWW) medium in the absence of calcium to prevent acrosome reaction. The sample is divided into 0.25 ml aliquots to which inhibitor or saline is added prior to induction of the acrosome reaction with the addition of calcium.

be released from the acrosome, fertilization should be effectively blocked if the cumulus stays intact during the fertilization process. Some interesting results have been obtained in the hamster *in vitro* fertilization system using the low molecular weight hyaluronidase inhibitor sodium aurothiomalate, Myocrisin (2). Fertilization was

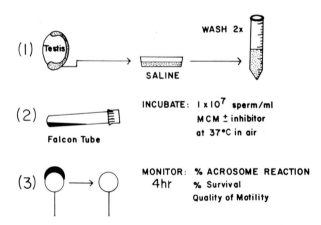

Fig. 3. Capacitation of guinea pig spermatozoa *in vitro*. Epididymal sperm are suspended in 4 ml saline and washed twice by centrifugation at 600 g. The sperm are resuspended to a final concentration of 1×10^7 sperm/ml and incubated with or without inhibitor in a 0.5 ml volume in a capped tube. The inhibitors are present throughout the capacitation period.

inhibited in the presence of cumulus cells at concentrations of 25–250 μg Myocrisin/ml (Fig. 1). Fertilization was also inhibited even in the absence of cumulus cells. This unexpected finding suggests that hyaluronidase may be involved in zona penetration or that other zona-penetrating enzymes such as acrosin may be inhibited by Myocrisin. Since acrosin is apparently not inhibited by Myocrisin the speculation that hyaluronidase is involved in zona penetration is favored. In any case the fertilization process is affected by the inhibition of hyaluronidase *in vitro*. *In vivo* fertilization was reduced from 100 to 37.5% by the presence of high levels of inhibitor (10 mg/ml) added to an epididymal sperm suspension prior to artificial insemination.

Acrosin, a trypsin-like enzyme in the sperm acrosome, is believed to be involved both in acrosome reaction and zona penetration. The evidence for both of these functions is reasonably convincing but has been questioned by some investigators. Therefore the action of acrosin is a vital factor in the fertilization process at two important levels. The involvement of acrosin in guinea pig acrosome reaction has been recently studied (3). Four different trypsin inhibitors were tested for

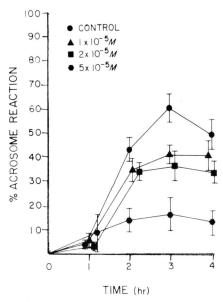

Fig. 4. Effect of p-aminobenzamidine on guinea pig sperm acrosome reaction. Sperm are incubated with varying concentrations of p-aminobenzamidine in the capacitation medium (MCM) and the effect on capacitation and/or acrosome reaction is monitored. Each point is the mean of 8 experiments ± the standard error.

their effectiveness in blocking acrosome reaction in both a synchronous and nonsynchronous system. The results were somewhat surprising in light of Meizel's previous work in hamster. We found inhibition by benzamidine, p-aminobenzamidine, and NPGB, but stimulation by TLCK whereas Meizel found inhibition in the hamster
system by all four inhibitors.

The two systems referred to as synchronous and nonsynchronous
indicate the way in which the acrosome reaction occurs. In the synchronous system the procedure (Fig. 2) is such that the acrosome reaction occurs almost simultaneously rather than spread over 2 or 3 hours.
The synchronous acrosome reaction is achieved by preincubating the
sperm in medium without calcium to allow capacitation but sus-
pending the occurrence of the acrosome reaction until the calcium is
added. This elegant method of separating capacitation and acrosome
reaction effects was devised by Yanagimachi. The trypsin inhibitors
could thus be tested in the nonsynchronous (Fig. 3) system where
acrosome reaction occurs in individual sperm at the time when they
have completed capacitation or in the synchronous system. Using
both methods allows a better differentiation between effects on ca-

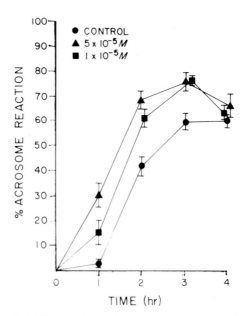

Fig. 5. Effect of TLCK on guinea pig sperm acrosome reaction. Sperm are incubated with two concentrations of TLCK to determine its effect on capacitation and/or
acrosome reaction. Each point is the mean of 14 experiments ± the standard error.

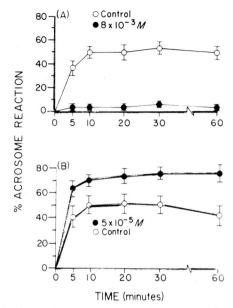

Fig. 6. Effect of NPGB and TLCK on guinea pig sperm synchronous acrosome reaction. Guinea pig sperm were preincubated in calcium-free BWW prior to the addition of inhibitor and calcium. The acrosome reaction was monitored over a 60-minute period in the presence and absence of NPGB (8×10^{-3} M) or TLCK (5×10^{-5} M). Each point is the mean of 6–10 experiments ± the standard error.

pacitation and acrosome reaction but cannot clearly show an effect on capacitation if both capacitation and acrosome reaction are affected.

In guinea pig sperm, benzamidine, p-aminobenzamidine, and NPGB were found to inhibit capacitation and/or acrosome in the nonsynchronous system when added to the incubation system at the outset (Fig. 4). TLCK, on the other hand, stimulated acrosome reaction with stimulation being most significant at the early time points (Fig. 5). In the synchronous system inhibitors were added to capacitated sperm prior to the addition of calcium. Benzamidine and p-aminobenzamidine produced inhibition that was transient such that there was essentially no difference at 60 minutes. With NPGB the inhibition in the synchronous system was sustained over the 1-hour period after the addition of calcium (Fig. 6). The acrosome reaction in the presence of lower concentrations of NPGB was atypical and often produced a crenulated membrane remaining attached to the sperm head. This was suggestive of a delay of acrosomal matrix dissolution. The cause of such a delay could be either an effect on acrosin or on the

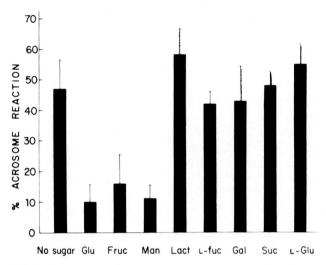

Fig. 7. Effect of sugars on guinea pig sperm acrosome reaction. Acrosome reaction at 3 hours in various sugars at a concentration of 5 mM. Pyruvate (0.25 mM) and lactate (20 mM) are present in all samples. The sugars tested are glucose (glu), fructose (fruc), mannose (man), lactose (lact), L-fucose (L-fuc), galactose (gal), sucrose (suc), and L-glucose (L-glu). Each bar is the mean of 4–7 experiments ± the standard error.

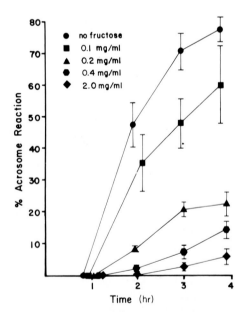

Fig. 8. Effect of fructose on guinea pig sperm acrosome reaction. Fructose was added to MCM in concentrations ranging from 0.1 mg/ml to 2.0 mg/ml. The sperm were at a concentration of 1 × 10⁷ sperm/ml. Each point is the mean of 4 experiments ± the standard error.

membrane directly. The TLCK in the synchronous system produced a stimulation of acrosome reaction that was sustained over the 60 minutes observation period after the addition of calcium (Fig. 6). The stimulation by TLCK appears to be a membrane effect since TLCK should inhibit acrosin and thus acrosome reaction if the enzyme inhibition was the single mode of action. The presence of inhibitors of acrosin can be a definite factor in fertilization whether by stimulating or inhibiting its occurrence. These effects appear to be at the level of the acrosome reaction at least in guinea pig and may be mediated by acrosin or direct membrane involvement.

Metabolism may be a key factor in the occurrence of capacitation and subsequent acrosome reaction and fertilization. The source of energy appears to be important in most species. In guinea pig an unusual phenomenon was observed (4) in which glucose was found to inhibit acrosome reaction. Other sugars were tested in the capacitation medium and it was found that only those sugars that were metabolized were able to inhibit acrosome reaction (Fig. 7). Glucose, fructose, and mannose caused significant reduction in acrosome reaction at 3 hours. Lactose, fucose, galactose, sucrose, and L-glucose did not cause signif-

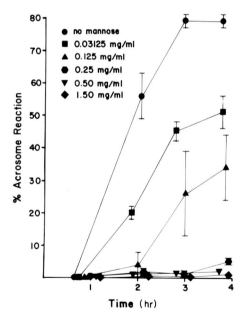

Fig. 9. Effect of mannose on guinea pig sperm acrosome reaction. Mannose was tested at concentrations from 0.03 mg/ml to 1.50 mg/ml. Each point is the mean of 4 experiments ± the standard error.

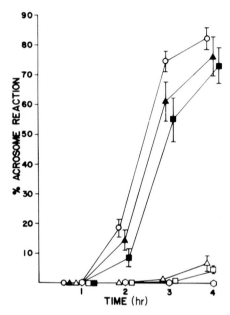

Fig. 10. Effects of G-6-P, F-6-P, and 2-deoxyglucose on guinea pig sperm acrosome reaction. Guinea pig spermatozoa were incubated in MCM with varying energy sources: ●, pyruvate (0.25 m*M*) and lactate (20 m*M*); ■, pyruvate (0.25 m*M*), lactate (20 m*M*) and glucose 6-phosphate (5 m*M*); ▲, pyruvate (0.25 m*M*), lactate (20 m*M*) and fructose 6-phosphate (5 m*M*); □, glucose 6-phosphate (5 m*M*); △, pyruvate (0.25 m*M*), lactate (20 m*M*) and ○, pyruvate (0.25 m*M*), lactate (20 m*M*), and 2-deoxyglucose (5 m*M*). Each point is the mean of 10 experiments ± the standard error.

icant reduction of acrosome reaction. Fructose caused significant reduction of acrosome reaction in a dose response fashion with 2 mg/ml giving less than 10% acrosome reaction at 4 hours (Fig. 8). Mannose also caused a dose-dependent reduction in acrosome reaction (Fig. 9). To ascertain if this effect was on acrosome reaction per se fructose was tested at various concentrations in the guinea pig synchronous acrosome reaction system. Even a concentration of 1 mg fructose/ml which produces significant reduction of acrosome reaction in the non-synchronous system produced no effect on acrosome reaction (5). These results are interpreted as an effect on capacitation rather than on acrosome reaction per se. Further exploration into this metabolic mechanism was carried out by testing glycolytic intermediates in the presence and absence of pyruvate and lactate. Glucose 6-phosphate and fructose 6-phosphate while supporting survival when present as the only exogenous energy source did not inhibit acrosome reaction when incubated in the presence of pyruvate and lactate (Fig. 10). If the occurrence of glycolysis had been the mechanism of glucose inhibition one might have expected G-6-P and F-6-P to exhibit a similar effect. The glucose analog, 2-deoxyglucose, did inhibit acrosome reaction in the presence of pyruvate and lactate. Since it does not proceed in the glycolytic pathway past the phosphorylation step it could be interpreted that this step is critical for inhibition of acrosome reaction.

Since the glucose inhibitory effect is so pronounced in guinea pig it seems attractive to postulate a similar effect in other species. To date this has not proved to be the case. Our recent studies with human sperm indicate that glucose appears to stimulate capacitation as demonstrated by *in vitro* fertilization studies. Based on preliminary data the fertilization rate at 6 hours was significantly lower in the absence of glucose (35.3% versus 1.5%). The results were variable from person to person suggesting that capacitation times can vary not only from person to person but also from ejaculate to ejaculate. Some samples gave fertilization with no preincubation in the presence or absence of

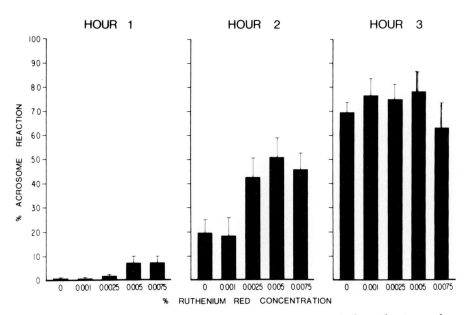

Fig. 11. Stimulation of guinea pig sperm acrosome reaction by ruthenium red. Guinea pig sperm were incubated in MCM at a concentration of 1×10^7 sperm/ml. Ruthenium red at concentrations from 0 to 0.0075% was present with the sperm from the start of incubation. Each bar is the mean of 5 experiments ± the standard error.

exogenous glucose suggesting that they were already capacitated upon ejaculation. This variability in human samples will make all metabolic studies more complex.

A possible mode of action of glucose on metabolism may be through an effect on respiration. Glucose has been shown to inhibit respiration in guinea pig (6). When glucose was added to sperm rapidly respiring in 5 mM pyruvate the oxygen uptake was reduced dramatically. Since stimulation of respiration has been linked to capacitation a mode for glucose inhibition in guinea pig could be the reduction of respiration.

The importance of metabolism in capacitation and acrosome reaction has been demonstrated in hamster sperm. Oligomycin, antimycin A, and rotenone, all oxidative phosphorylation inhibitors, were shown to inhibit acrosome reaction in a hamster capacitation system using heat-treated human serum as the capacitating agent (7). Therefore, it appears that oxidative phosphorylation is important in capacitation.

Certain ions have been found to be important factors in acrosome

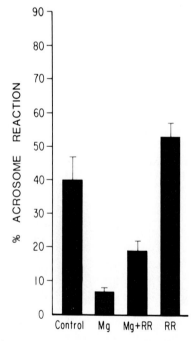

Fig. 12. Effects of magnesium and ruthenium red on guinea pig sperm acrosome reaction. Guinea pig sperm were incubated in MCM in the presence and absence of magnesium (3 mM) and ruthenium red (0.005%). Acrosome reaction at 3 hours is plotted; each bar is the mean of 5 experiments ± the standard error.

TABLE I
Effect of Glucose, Magnesium, and Potassium on Fertilization of Zona-Free Hamster Eggs by Guinea Pig Sperm[a]

Medium	Eggs fertilized/eggs inseminated	Fertilization (%)
MCM	0/78	0
MCM-G	0/40	0
MCM-GMg	0/36	0
MCM-K	40/40	100
MCM-GK	42/42	100
MCM-GMgK	34/34	100
Complete BWW	71/71	100
Mg-free BWW	44/44	100
K-free BWW	0/82	0

[a] Sperm were preincubated for 3 hours in each case in MCM to allow capacitation and acrosome reaction. The concentrations of substances tested were glucose (G) 5.56 mM, magnesium (Mg) 1.19 mM, and potassium (K) 4.78 mM.

reaction and fertilization. Calcium is essential for both acrosome reaction and fertilization. In the absence of calcium no acrosome reaction occurs in the guinea pig *in vitro* system. Three millimolar calcium gives higher levels of acrosome reaction than 1 mM but at 5 mM a reduction in acrosome reaction is observed due to precipitation in the medium. Magnesium has been found to be an inhibitor of acrosome reaction (8). This reduction in acrosome reaction is greater with increasing concentrations of magnesium and acrosome reaction is completely inhibited at 10 mM magnesium. Ruthenium red when added to the capacitation medium causes a stimulation of acrosome reaction (Fig. 11). Ruthenium red, which is a known inhibitor of mitochondrial calcium uptake, was found to stimulate calcium uptake in spermatozoa and thus stimulate acrosome reaction. Interplay between magnesium, ruthenium red, and acrosome reaction can be demonstrated

TABLE II
Fertilization of Zona-Free Hamster Eggs by Guinea Pig Spermatozoa as a Function of Potassium Concentration

Potassium (mM)	Eggs fertilized/eggs inseminated	Fertilization (%)
1	0/84	0
2	87/130	67
3	33/33	100
4	37/37	100
5	38/38	100

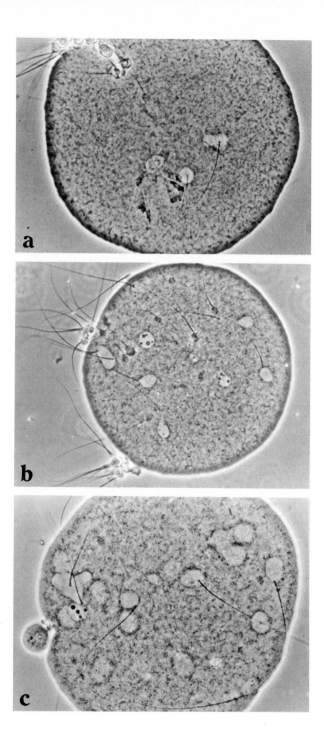

(Fig. 12). At a time when about 40% acrosome reaction occurs in the control having 1.71 mM calcium, ruthenium red stimulates the acrosome reaction to over 50%, magnesium inhibits it to less than 10% and a combination of magnesium and ruthenium red gives an intermediate level of acrosome reaction, 20%. This could be interpreted as a balance between stimulation of calcium uptake by ruthenium red and competitive inhibition of calcium uptake by magnesium.

Another ion essential for fertilization is potassium (9). Potassium was recently found to be required for fertilization of both zona-free hamster eggs and zona intact guinea pig eggs by guinea pig spermatozoa. Minimal capacitation medium (MCM) is incapable of supporting fertilization even though it supports acrosome reaction of guinea pig spermatozoa. The substances absent from MCM which were suspected of playing a key role in fertilization were glucose, magnesium, and potassium. Each of these was added to MCM separately and in combinations to see the effect on fertilization. The addition of glucose or magnesium to MCM still resulted in no fertilization (Table I). When potassium was added with or without glucose or magnesium the fertilization rate using the zona-free hamster eggs was 100%. Potassium is normally included in culture media at a concentration of about 5 mM. This concentration is sufficient to allow fertilization. The lowest concentration of potassium at which 100% fertilization was obtained was 3 mM and the minimal concentration for fertilization was between 1 and 2 mM (Table II). The number of swelling heads in the eggs was found to be a function of potassium concentration (Fig. 13) with 2 mM potassium giving an average of 3.0 sperm/egg (range 1–6) while 3 mM gave an average of 9.4 sperm/egg (range 3–20). Above 3 mM the number of sperm per egg was 10 or more. When guinea pig eggs were used for *in vitro* fertilization a potassium requirement also existed. No fertilization was seen in cultured ovarian zona-intact guinea pig eggs when guinea pig sperm were used (0/88 eggs) in eight separate experiments. When potassium was in the medium (4.78 mM) the average fertilization rate was 74%. Fertilized guinea pig eggs were monospermic (Fig. 14). Potassium was not required for acrosome reaction and to our surprise inhibited guinea pig acrosome reaction significantly at concentrations above 2 mM (Fig. 15).

Fig. 13. Fertilization of zona-free hamster eggs by guinea pig spermatozoa. Sperm were capacitated in MCM prior to addition of eggs. Fertilization was performed in MCM supplemented with 1 mg/ml bovine serum albumin and different concentrations of potassium; (a) 2 mM, (b) 3 mM, (c) 5 mM.

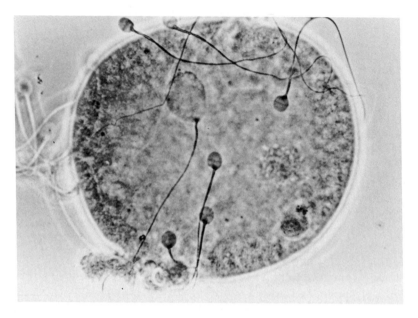

Fig. 14. Monospermic fertilization of a guinea pig egg *in vitro*. A cultured ovarian guinea pig egg is fertilized by capacitated guinea pig sperm. The swollen head in the vitellus is much larger than the acrosome reacted sperm on the surface of the egg. The zona pellucida was present during insemination but is not visible in this stained preparation as it was dissolved during fixation.

Cyclic AMP has been reported to be involved in capacitation and fertilization. Effects both in a positive and a negative sense have been reported when inhibitors of phosphodiesterase (PDE) are added to spermatozoa. In spite of the fact that PDE inhibitors do raise the level of cAMP there is no assurance that this is the only effect the PDE inhibitor is exerting or that this is the mode of action related to the effect on fertilization. Previously we reported an inhibitory effect on acrosome reaction by PDE inhibitors in guinea pig spermatozoa (10). Caffeine, theophylline, and MIX all inhibited acrosome reaction when sperm were incubated in a defined medium. The same effect was obtained using dibutyryl cAMP. The effect of imidazole, a PDE stimulator, was an increase in acrosome reaction over control levels. This data is all consistent with the concept that an increase in the levels of cAMP decreases acrosome reaction while a decrease in cAMP increases acrosome reaction.

The effect of PDE inhibitors was tested in the hamster *in vitro* fertilization system using heat-treated human serum as the capacitating agent. Inhibition of fertilization (10) was observed when these inhibitors were added to the medium from the start of the incubation. A significant reduction in fertilization from 76.1 to 3.2% was also observed in the presence of dbcAMP. These data are suggestive of changes in cAMP associated with capacitation and acrosome reaction.

To ascertain if changes in cAMP do occur during capacitation *in vitro* the actual levels of cAMP were measured by radioimmunoassay in guinea pig spermatozoa capacitating in a defined medium, MCM (Fig. 16). The levels of cAMP decreased from 5.37 pmole/10^7 sperm at the start of the incubation to 2.17 pmole/10^7 sperm by the end of the 4-hour incubation period (11). At first glance this decrease in cAMP over the period of capacitation seems to fit with the hypothesis that acrosome reaction is accompanied by a decrease in cAMP. However, when glucose was added to the medium at a concentration sufficient to inhibit acrosome reaction (1 mg/ml) a similar decline in the level of cAMP was observed. This suggests that the inhibition of acrosome

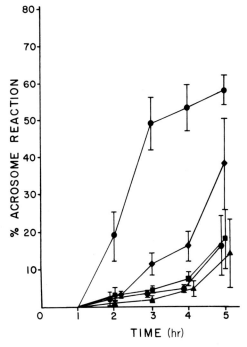

Fig. 15. Effect of potassium on guinea pig sperm acrosome reaction. Each point is the mean (± standard error) of 5 determinations in MCM with varying levels of potassium: ●, no potassium; ◆, 1 m*M*; ■, 2 m*M*; ●, 3 m*M*; ▲, 5 m*M*.

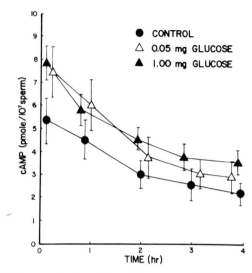

Fig. 16. cAMP in capacitating guinea pig sperm. cAMP was measured by radioimmunoassay in the presence and absence of glucose. Each point is the average of 6 experiments ± the standard error.

reaction in the presence of glucose is not mediated by increased levels of cAMP. It further suggests that cAMP changes are not a key factor in the occurrence of capacitation and acrosome reaction using these *in vitro* conditions.

Since the situation in guinea pig and hamster suggested an inhibitory effect of PDE inhibitors on acrosome reaction and fertilization the effect of these agents in human spermatozoa might be postulated to be similar. Since acrosome reaction is not readily visible in human spermatozoa fertilization of zona-free hamster eggs was used as an index of capacitation efficacy. Caffeine and theophylline were found to significantly stimulate fertilization in the human in contrast to the inhibitory effects in guinea pig and hamster spermatozoa (Fig. 17). At 6 hours the PDE inhibitor-treated spermatozoa fertilized over 60% compared to approximately 30% in the controls (12). The effect seemed to be an acceleration of capacitation since the controls would reach the same levels as the caffeine- or theophylline-treated samples if given sufficient time. Caffeine and theophylline apparently increased the level of acrosome reacted sperm in the medium. This is ascertained by the level of polyspermy (Table III). The amount of polyspermy at 6 hours was 2.41 decondensed sperm per fertilized egg in caffeine compared to 1.28 in the control.

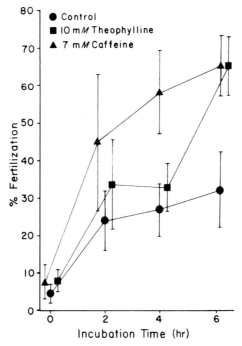

Fig. 17. Fertilization of zona-free hamster eggs in the presence and absence of caffeine and theophylline. Washed human spermatozoa were incubated in the presence of caffeine or theophylline for 0, 2, 4, or 6 hours prior to addition of zona-free hamster eggs. Each point is the mean of 5–10 separate experiments ± the standard error.

QUALITY OF SPERM

The third general area is referred to as quality of sperm or inherent fertilizing potential. The factors responsible for sperm quality continue to elude us. Even when all the physical and biochemical fac-

TABLE III
Effect of Caffeine and Theophylline on Polyspermy

	Average number of decondensed sperm/fertilized egg		
Time (hours)	Controls	Theophylline (10 mM)	Caffeine (7 mM)
0	1.00	1.00	1.00
2	1.00	1.25	1.40
4	1.25	1.16	1.47
6	1.28	1.97	2.41

tors are optimized a human sample may fertilize 100 or 0% in an *in vitro* fertilization test system. What then are the factors that make a given sample infertile? The three parameters that have been most frequently used a criteria in the past are count, motility, and morphology. More recently an *in vitro* fertilization test system has been implemented which allows evaluation of an additional parameter, fertilizing ability. Recent work has concentrated on the relationship between fertilizing ability, clinical fertility status, and routine semen analysis.

The fertilization assay is carried out with washed human sperm incubated at a concentration of 1×10^7 sperm/ml. The sperm are processed keeping in mind the physical factors discussed above. An aliquot (0.1 ml) is placed in a Falcon dish and covered with oil prior to the addition of superovulated cumulus-free, zona-free hamster eggs. The eggs are examined for the presence of swelling sperm heads 2 hours after insemination. Semen from clinically fertile and infertile

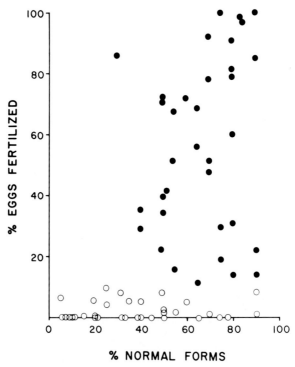

Fig. 18. Fertilization of zona-free hamster eggs by human sperm as a function of morphology. Two categories of patients are plotted: ○, "infertile" men (whose wives have been pregnant by a previous partner), ●, "fertile" men (who have fathered a child). Normal forms is the percent of oval shaped heads in the semen sample.

TABLE IV
Relationship of Morphology to Clinical Status of Fertility

	Proportion of males with greater than 50% abnormal forms	
Fertile	4/35	11.4%
Fertility unknown	6/41	14.6%
Wife has evidence of infertility	9/24	37.5%
Both have evidence of infertility	4/10	40.0%
Wife has no evidence of infertility	19/39	48.7%
Wife has been pregnant by other partner	22/33	66.7%

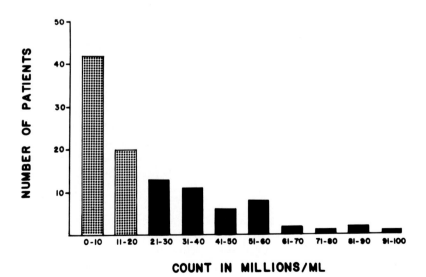

Fig. 19. Distribution of count in an infertile group. Men from infertile couples who fertilized less than 10% in the *in vitro* fertilization test are sorted according to count. Stippled bars represent abnormal level (less than 20 million sperm/ml). $n = 112$.

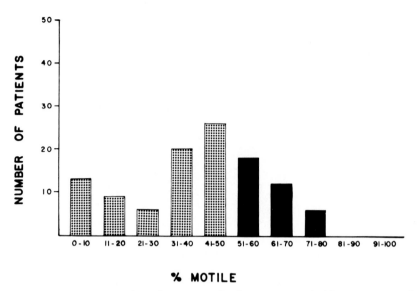

% MOTILE

Fig. 20.   Distribution of motility in an infertile group. Stippled bars represent abnormal level (less than 50% motile).

men were evaluated for fertilizing ability using this *in vitro* fertilization system. Men from a group of known fertility were found to have a high fertilization rate 56.4% (range 12.1–100%) whereas men from an infertile group had a very low fertilization rate, 2.2% (range 0–9.1%) (13). This infertile group was taken from infertile couples in which the wife had previously had a pregnancy by another partner. Another infertile group that was tested consisted of men whose wives had no evidence of infertility. These men had a fertilization rate of 1.9% with a range of 0–8.9%. It is important to classify the infertile males carefully since there are obviously men whose partners are the cause of the infertility. A group of males in which the wives showed evidence of infertility had a fertilization average of 60.2% with a range of 16.7–100%, which is similar to the fertile males. This *in vitro* fertilization test system appears to have value in differentiating between fertile and infertile semen samples since the fertile and infertile fertilization ranges did not overlap. About 10% seems to be the breaking point between fertiles and infertiles using the present incubation conditions.

The fertilization test allows us to compare fertilizing ability with characteristics of the semen sample. When the percent eggs fertilized is plotted against sperm concentration of individuals from fertile and infertile groups (fertility based on clinical status) the average count in the infertile group is definitely lower than in the fertile group. However, count does not appear to correlate linearly with fertilizing ability (13).

Motility has been considered a key diagnostic factor in fertility evaluation. When looking at percentage motile in relationship to fertilization *in vitro* the percentage of eggs penetrated is not a simple function of the percentage of motile sperm. However, none of the fertile individuals had less than 20% motile (13). It appears that although extreme deficiencies in count and motility are indicative of infertility neither of these variables is particularly diagnostic when the count is above 20 million/ml and above 20% motile. The relationship between morphology and fertilizing ability was examined. The fertilization rates of the fertile and infertile groups plotted against normal forms (Fig. 18) shows a distinct relationship between fertility status and fertilizing ability (14). Only 11.4% of the fertile males had less than 50% normal forms whereas 66.7% of the infertile group had less than 50% normal forms. The percentage of individuals with greater than 50% abnormal forms increased as the fertility status decreased (Table IV).

A group of 112 men from infertile couples who fertilized in the infertile range (less than 10%) were analyzed with regard to count, motility, and morphology distribution. The count was less than 20 mil-

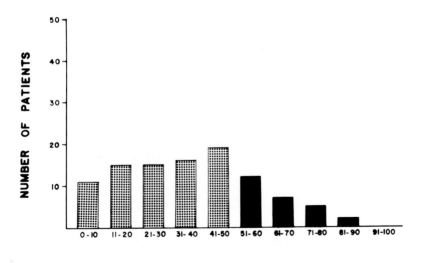

% NORMAL

Fig. 21. Distribution of morphology in an infertile group. Stippled bars represent abnormal (less than 50% oval forms).

TABLE V
Semen Analysis Parameters of Infertile Males[a]

	Count (millions/ml)	Percent (%)	Percent (%)	Fertilization
Average	27.1	42.9	39.2	1.3%
Range	(0.15–330.0)	(0–80)	(0–90)	(0–8.3)

[a] $n = 112$.

lion in over half of these samples, 62/112 (Fig. 19). The remaining 50
patients were distributed among the other groups with only 6 individuals with counts greater than 60 million/ml. Distribution with respect
to motility (Fig. 20) shows that the largest group of infertiles has motility of 41–50%. If below 50% motile is considered abnormal then
only 45.5% had abnormal motility. The number of patients in the infertile group possessing abnormal morphology (greater than 50% abnormal forms) was 63.4%. The morphology histogram (Fig. 21) shows
the largest group to be 41–50% normal and the distribution is definitely skewed to the lower percentage of normal forms.

The averages of the semen analysis parameters from this infertile
group of 112 individuals is shown in Table V. The average count, mo-

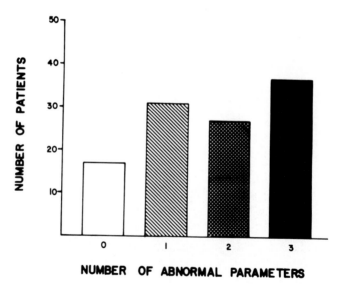

Fig. 22. Distribution of semen abnormalities in an infertile group. Men with count
< 20 million/ml, motility < 50%, and morphology < 50% normal forms are categorized as
abnormal parameters. Men with any one of three parameters below this range are categorized as 1, with two abnormal parameters as 2, and with all 3 abnormal, 3.

TABLE VI
Distribution of Abnormal Parameters

	One Abnormality (31 patients)	
Motility	8/31	(25.8%)
Count	7/31	(22.6%)
Morphology	16/31	(51.6%)
	Two Abnormalities (27 patients)	
Count and motility	9/27	(33.3%)
Count and morphology	10/27	(37.0%)
Morphology and motility	8/27	(29.6%)

tility, and morphology are low with a wide range and the fertilization rate is very low (1.3%). The distribution of abnormal parameters among the 112 infertiles (Fig. 22) shows that 17 individuals had none of the key parameters in the abnormal range, that is, below 20 million sperm/ml, less than 50% motile and less than 50% normal forms. Thirty-one had only one abnormal parameter, 27 had two abnormal parameters and 37 had all three parameters abnormal. The group with one abnormality showed a higher proportion of morphological abnormalities (Table VI). The 27 patients with two abnormalities showed no striking predominance of any pair (Table VI), however, the count and morphology category is highest. The group of 17 individuals who had normal count, motility, and morphology are especially interesting (Table VII) since despite a normal semen analysis their average fertilization rate was only 1.8%. What makes these men infertile both in life and in our *in vitro* fertilization test is the key question. These sperm have some biochemical lesion that is not demonstrated in their count, motility, or morphology, but is revealed when fertilizing capacity is

TABLE VII
Fertilization Rates of Males from Infertile Couples Who
Have Normal Routine Semen Analyses[a]

	Count (millions/ml)	Percent motile	Percent normal	Fertilization
Average	48.4	63.2	62.7	1.8%
Range	(20–101.5)	(50–80)	(50–90)	(0–6.5)

[a] $n = 17$.

measured. We may be at the point now that we can begin to ascertain what the actual factors are that differentiate a fertile from an infertile sperm sample. It is to this end that we must direct our attention to determine the *specific factors* that control the fertilizing capacity of human spermatozoa.

REFERENCES

1. Rogers, B. J. (1978) *Gamete Res.* **1**, 165–223.
2. Perreault, S. D., Zaneveld, L. J. D., and Rogers, B. J. (1980) *J. Reprod. Fertil.* (in press).
3. Perreault, S. D., and Rogers, B. J. (1980) *Biol. Reprod.* (submitted for production).
4. Rogers, B. J., and Yanagimachi, R. (1975) *Biol. Reprod.* **13**, 568–575.
5. Rogers, B. J., and Distor, E. (1980). *M. B. S. Biomed. Symp.*, 1980.
6. Rogers, B. J., Chang, L., and Yanagimachi, R. (1979) *J. Exp. Zool.* **207**, 107–112.
7. Rogers, B. J., Ueno, M., and Yanagimachi, R. (1977) *J. Exp. Zool.* **199**, 129–135.
8. Rogers, B. J., and Yanagimachi, R. (1976) *Biol. Reprod.* **15**, 614–619.
9. Rogers, B. J., Ueno, M., and Yanagimachi, R. (1980) *Biol. Reprod.* (submitted for production).
10. Rogers, B. J., and Garcia, L. (1979) *Biol. Reprod.* **21**, 365–372.
11. Rogers, B. J., and Jow, K. (1980) *Univ. Hawaii Sch. Med. Biomed. Symp.*, 1980.
12. Perreault, S. D., and Rogers, B. J. (1980) *Soc. Study Reprod.*, *13th Annu. Meet.*, 1980.
13. Rogers, B. J., Van Campen, H., Ueno, M., Lambert, H., Bronson, R., and Hale, R. (1979) *Fertil. Steril.* **32**, 664–670.
14. Rogers, B. J., Van Campen, H., Helmbrecht, G., and Soderdahl, D. (1980) *J. Androl.* **1**, 79.

Regulation of Epididymal Steroid Metabolizing Enzymes

B. ROBAIRE, H. SCHEER, AND C. HACHEY

*Department of Pharmacology and Therapeutics
and of Obstetrics and Gynecology,
McGill University and the Royal Victoria Hospital
Montreal, Quebec, Canada*

INTRODUCTION

Over the past 15 years, it has been well-established by a number of investigators that the mammalian epididymis plays important functional roles in addition to being a conduit between the testes and the vas deferens (1–4). The pioneering studies of Bedford (5) and Orgebin-Crist (6) have demonstrated that although spermatozoa have a relatively normal appearance when they leave the testes, they have neither motility nor the capacity to fertilize eggs, i.e., they are immature. The site where maturation has been found to take place is the caput region of the epididymis; by the time spermatozoa reach the corpus region of the epididymis a high percentage of them have already acquired their fertilizing potential (2,7,8). The caudal region of the epididymis seems to act as a site for storage of spermatozoa (1,9,10). Although a number of changes have been associated with the maturation of spermatozoa (11–13), the essential underlying changes are still poorly understood. It has, however, been clearly demonstrated that an epididymis that is not exposed to androgens will atrophy and will be unable to continue carrying out its functions of sperm maturation and storage (1,14–16). Evidence acquired over the past few years has suggested that it is not testosterone itself but rather its 5α-reduced metabolites, dihydrotestosterone (DHT) and/or 5α-androstan-3α,17β-diol (3α-diol), that may be the primary regulatory hormones for the two main epididymal functions of sperm maturation and storage (Fig. 1)

487

BIOREGULATORS OF REPRODUCTION

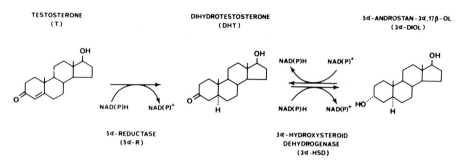

Fig. 1. Pathway of testosterone metabolism to dihydrotestosterone and 5α-andro-stan-3α,17β-diol in the rat epididymis.

(1,17–19). Orgebin-Crist has shown that, in an organ culture system, testosterone is unable to maintain the epididymal capacity for maturing spermatozoa whereas dihydrotestosterone is quite adept at maintaining this function (18). Lubicz-Nawrocki has shown that in the ligated cauda epididymis, 3α-diol is more efficient that DHT, which is in turn more efficient than testosterone, at maintaining spermatozoa fertile (19).

The two enzymes that catalyze the synthesis of DHT and 3α-diol, Δ⁴-5α-reductase and 3α-hydroxysteroid dehydrogenase (3α-HSD), respectively, have been shown by a number of investigators to be present in the epididymis of many different mammalian species (20–24). Due to the pivotal function of the products of these enzyme reactions we have focused our interest in the past few years on the regulation of these enzymes in the rat epididymis (24–27).

DIFFERENTIAL REGULATION OF EPIDIDYMAL Δ⁴-5α-REDUCTASE AND 3α-HSD

In order to reliably measure and compare the enzymatic activities (28) of Δ⁴-5α-reductase and 3α-HSD in the epididymis, conditions have been established whereby (1) single products are synthesized from the substrates provided, i.e., DHT from testosterone for Δ⁴-5α-reductase and 3α-diol from DHT for 3α-HSD, (2) the assays are linear with respect to both time and enzyme concentration, (3) the substrate concentrations are maintained between 0.1 and 10 times the K_m values, and (4) the percent products formed are maintained between 0.3 and 15. In order to attain these essential criteria, it was necessary to use the nuclear fraction to measure Δ^4-5α-reductase activity and the cytoplasmic fraction for 3α-HSD activity.

The results in Fig. 2 show that in control animals, 3α-HSD activity was found in the caput-corpus and cauda regions of the rat epididymis in approximately equal amounts. Δ^4-5α-Reductase activity, however,

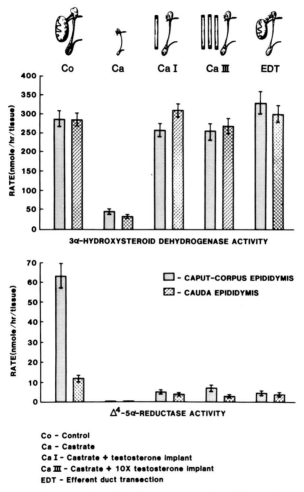

Fig. 2. 3α-Hydroxysteroid dehydrogenase and Δ^4-5α-reductase activities (nmole/hour/tissue) in the caput-corpus (dotted bars) and cauda (cross-hatched bars) regions of the rat epididymis. Rates are shown for control animals (Co), castrated animals receiving either empty polydimethylsiloxane (PDS) implants (Ca), or testosterone (T)-filled PDS implants measuring 2.2 cm (CaI) or 24.0 cm (CaIII) and animals whose efferent ducts were transected (EDT). Values represent the means ± SEM, $n = 5$.

was found to be selectively localized in the caput-corpus region as opposed to the cauda region of the epididymis. In addition, it was noted that the activity of 3α-HSD was 5 to 10 times higher than that of Δ^4-5α-reductase. Castration resulted in a decrease in both 3α-HSD and Δ^4-5α-reductase activities, the former to approximately 15% of control while the latter was reduced to nondetectable levels. Administration of testosterone at the time of castration via subdermal polydimethylsiloxane (PDS) implants of either a unit length that maintained serum testosterone in the normal control range (CaI, 3.6 ± 0.6 ng/ml) or of implants 10 times this length (CaIII, serum testosterone—36 ± 7.5 ng/ml) maintained 3α-HSD activity in both the caput-corpus and cauda regions of the epididymis; under these conditions however, Δ^4-5α-reductase was not maintained (15% of its control value in the caput region). It is interesting to note that even the high dose of testosterone, which approximates the concentration of androgens in rete testis fluid, did not cause an increase in 3α-HSD activity above its control value nor significantly further increase the activity of Δ^4-5α-reductase (24).

The data discussed above suggested the possibility that a factor coming directly from the testis was involved in regulating Δ^4-5α-reductase activity in the epididymis, whereas 3α-HSD activity was regulated directly by the concentration of androgens in serum. One approach taken to test this hypothesis was to ligate the efferent ducts (EDT) and to then assay for the two enzyme activities in the epididymis (Fig. 2). If indeed epididymal Δ^4-5α-reductase was regulated by a testicular factor, one would expect a selective decline in this enzyme and no significant change in 3α-HSD activity since Leydig cell function in the EDT animals is not known to be markedly affected by this procedure. The results shown in Fig. 2 are consonant with this prediction. Δ^4-5α-Reductase activity was decreased in the caput-corpus and cauda regions to values not significantly different from those obtained with castration and testosterone replacement therapy. 3α-HSD activity was not altered by this treatment. Neither serum testosterone nor accessory sex organ weights differed significantly between the efferent duct transected animals and the control animals (24).

The regulation of epididymal Δ^4-5α-reductase by a factor in the serum could not be ruled out on the basis of the above experiment since the possibility still remained that the critical substances secreted by the testes into the peripheral circulation was not being elaborated by testes whose efferent ducts had been transected. This possibility was tested by unilaterally castrating a group of rats. Animals had one testis removed and 5 weeks later, the activities of Δ^4-5α-reductase

toli cells. There is as yet no direct evidence of the nature of such a regulatory substance(s). It is possible, however, to piece together a testable hypothesis that is consistent with the data presented above and with recent observations obtained by a number of investigators.

The three major substances that have to date been identified as the secretory products of Sertoli cells are estradiol, inhibin, and androgen binding protein (ABP). Though there is clear evidence that estradiol may be elaborated by Sertoli cells, it now appears that this function is limited to the Sertoli cells of immature animals (29). It has now been shown by a number of investigators that Sertoli cells from rats 30 days of age or older do not secrete estradiol (29,30); rather, this function seems to be limited to Leydig cells in adult animals (31). The presence and nature of inhibin in males is still highly controversial (32,33). It has been clearly demonstrated by Steinberger and Steinberger (34) that secretions from cultured Sertoli cells can preferentially suppress the secretion of FSH from cultured pituitary cells. However, little information is available on the developmental pattern of this substance, on the effects of hypophysectomy and testosterone replacement or on the presence and the longitudinal distribution of inhibin in the epididymis; the lack of such information renders the incorporation of inhibin in the scheme of regulation of epididymal Δ^4-5α-reductase impossible at this time.

The third possible regulatory substance, androgen binding protein, was first found in the epididymis and later shown to be secreted by the testis and more specifically by Sertoli cells (35,36). The secretion of this protein is further found to be under the control of both FSH and testosterone (35,37). The developmental pattern of androgen binding protein in the epididymis, reported by Hansson and his colleagues (38) is quite similar to the one shown in Fig. 4 for Δ^4-5α-reductase in the epididymis. ABP was undetectable in the first 2 weeks of life in the rat; concentrations of ABP then increased, reaching a peak in the third month of life, and subsequently declined by somewhat more than 50%. The longitudinal distribution of ABP in the epididymis reported by these investigators (39) is somewhat different from that shown in Fig. 5 for Δ^4-5α-reductase in that the decrease along the length of the tissue is less dramatic. However, recent studies by Pelliniemi et al. (40) have demonstrated that ABP is internalized in the epithelial cells of the epididymis, exclusively in the initial segment of this tissue. This site for intracellular localization of ABP in the epididymis is nearly identical to the site where we have found the highest activity for Δ^4-5α-reductase.

Based on the above lines of evidence, it is possible to conjecture that Sertoli cells elaborate ABP, which then enters the epididymis; ABP charged with DHT is taken up by the epithelial cells of the initial segment of the epididymis, where the DHT molecule is donated to the cytoplasmic receptor. Lobl and his collaborators (41) have demonstrated that the face of the DHT molecule that binds to androgen binding protein is the opposite to that which binds to the epididymal cytosol receptors for DHT. The cytoplasmic receptor complex in turn is translocated to the nucleus to regulate gene expression; the synthesis of Δ^4-5α-reductase could then be the result of one such gene expression. The initial segment of the epididymis would thus be acting as the regulatory region that would synthesize and secrete the active androgen, dihydrotestosterone. Thus, the physiological function for the ABP–DHT complex may be to act as a messenger linking the testis and the epididymis. At present it is not possible to test this hypothesis with whole animal experiments since it is necessary to selectively expose the epithelial cells of the epididymis to different factors and to ascertain the specific products elaborated by these cells in response to different stimuli. This hypothesis can easily be tested in a cell or organ culture system; such systems are presently being established in our laboratory as well as in other centers. These experiments will hopefully permit the characterization of the Sertoli cell product(s) presently known, or yet to be identified, that regulates epididymal steroid metabolizing enzymes, and more specifically epididymal Δ^4-5α-reductase.

SUMMARY

Using a variety of endocrine manipulations including castration with testosterone replacement therapy, efferent duct transection, developmental studies, and hypophysectomy with testosterone replacement therapy, it has been possible to demonstrate that epididymal Δ^4-5α-reductase activity is controlled differentially from 3α-hydroxysteroid dehydrogenase activity, two sequential enzymes involved in the conversion of testosterone to its active metabolite(s). 3α-HSD activity is regulated by circulating androgen levels whereas Δ^4-5α-reductase activity is regulated primarily by a testicular factor, probably of Sertoli cell origin. A hypothesis concerning the nature of this factor(s) and the mechanism by which it could produce its regulatory effect on epididymal Δ^4-5α-reductase activity is presented.

ACKNOWLEDGMENTS

The unpublished work referred to in this article was supported by the Medical Research Council of Canada and the Fraser Memorial Fund of the Royal Victoria Hospital.

REFERENCES

1. Orgebin-Crist, M.-C., Danzo, B. J., and Davies, J. (1975) In "Handbook of Physiology" (D. W. Hamilton and R. O. Greep, eds.), Sect. 7, Vol. V, pp. 319–338. Williams and Wilkins, Baltimore, Maryland.
2. Bedford, J. M. (1967) J. Exp. Zool. 166, 217–282.
3. Lubicz-Nawrocki, C. M. (1974) J. Reprod. Fertil. 37, 251–255.
4. Blaquier, J. A., Cameo, M. S., and Burgos, M. H. (1972) Endocrinology 90, 839–842.
5. Bedford, M. J. (1966) J. Exp. Zool. 163, 319–330.
6. Orgebin-Crist, M.-C. (1967) Nature (London) 216, 816–818.
7. Orgebin-Crist, M.-C. (1969) Biol. Reprod., Suppl. 1, 155–175.
8. Blandau, R.J., and Rumery, R. E. (1964) Fertil. Steril. 15, 571–579.
9. Tesh, J. M., and Glover, T. D. (1969) J. Reprod. Fertil. 20, 287–297.
10. White, W. E. (1932) Anat. Rec. 54, 253–273.
11. Bedford, J. M., and Nicander, L. (1971) J. Anat. 108, 527–544.
12. Calvin, H., and Bedford, M. J. (1971) J. Reprod. Fertil,., Suppl. 13, 65–75.
13. Nicolson, G. L., Usui, N., Yanagimachi R., Yanagimachi, H., and Smith, J. R. (1977) J. Cell Biol. 74, 950–962.
14. Benoit, M. J. (1926) Arch. Anat. Histol. Embryol. 5, 173–412.
15. Lubicz-Nawrocki, C. M., and Glover, T. D. (1973) J. Reprod. Fertil. 34, 315–329.
16. Dyson, A. L., and Orgebin-Crist, M.-C. (1973) Endocrinology 93, 391–402.
17. Orgebin-Crist, M.-C., Jahad, N., and Hoffman, L. H. (1979) in "Androgens and Antiandrogens" (L. Martini and M. Motta, eds.), pp. 105–114. Raven, New York.
18. Orgebin-Crist, M. C., Jahad, N., and Hoffman, L. H. (1976) Cell Tissue Res. 167, 515—525.
19. Lubicz-Nawrocki, C. M. (1973) J. Endocrinol. 58, 193–198.
20. Inano, H., Ayoka, M., and Tamaoki, B.-I. (1969) Endocrinology 84, 997–1003.
21. Gloyna, R. E., and Wilson, J. D. (1969) J. Clin. Endocrinol. Metab. 29, 970–977.
22. Frankel, A. I., and Eik-Nes, K. B. (1970) Endocrinology 87, 646–652.
23. Djøseland, O. (1975) Steroids 27, 47–65.
24. Robaire, B., Ewing, L. L., Zirkin, B. R., and Irby, D. C. (1977) Endocrinology 101, 1379–1390.
25. Robaire, B., Covey, D. F., Robinson, C. H., and Ewing, L. L. (1977) J. Steroid Biochem. 8, 307–310.
26. Robaire, B. (1979) Can. J. Physiol. Pharmacol. 57, 998–1003.
27. Scheer, H., and Robaire, B. (1980) Endocrinology 107, 948–953.
28. Segal, I. H., (1975) "Enzyme Kinetics," pp. 18–99. Wiley, New York.
29. Dorrington, J. H., and Armstrong, D. T. (1979) Recent Adv. Horm. Res. 35, 301–333.
30. Pomerantz, D. K. (1979) Biol. Reprod. 21, 1247–1255.
31. Payne, A. H., and Valladares, L. E. (1980) In "Testicular Development, Structure and Function" (A. Steinberger and E. Steinberger, eds.), pp. 185–193. Raven, New York.

32. Franchimont, P., Chari, S., Hazee-Hagelstein, M. T., Debruche, M. L., and Duraisnvami, S. (1977) *In* "The Testis in Normal and Infertile Men" (P. Troen, and H. R. Nankin, eds.), pp. 253–270. Raven, New York.
33. Plant, T. M., Hess, D. L., Hotchkiss, J., and Knobil, E. (1978) *Endocrinology* **103**, 535–541.
34. Steinberger, A., and Steinberger, E. (1976) *Endocrinology* **99**, 918–921.
35. Hansson, V., Ritzén, E. M., French, F. S., and Nayfeh, S. N. (1975) *In* "Handbook of Physiology" (D. W. Hamilton and R. O. Greep, eds.), Sect. 7, Vol. V, pp. 173–202. Williams & Wilkins, Baltimore, Maryland.
36. Means, A. R., and Tindall, D. J. (1975) *In* "Hormonal Regulation of Spermatogenesis" (F. S. French, V. Hansson, E. M. Ritzen, and S. N. Nayfeh, eds.), pp. 383–398. Plenum, New York.
37. Tindall, D. J., and Means, A. R. (1976) *Endocrinology* **99**, 809–818.
38. Hansson, V., Reusch, E., Trygstad, O., Torgersen, O., French, F. S., and Ritzén, E. M. (1973) *Nature (London), New Biol.* **246**, 56–59.
39. Hansson, V., Trygstad, O., French, F. S., McLean, W. S., Smith, A. A., Tindall, D. J., Weddington, S. C., Petrusz, P., Nayfeh, S. N., and Ritzén, E. M. (1974) *Nature (London)* **250**, 387–391.
40. Pelliniemi, L. J., Dym, M., Durand, M., Gunsalus, G. L., Musto, N. A., Bardin, C. W., and Fawcett, D. W. (1979) *Am. Soc. Androl. 4th Annu. Meet.* Abstract 28.
41. Lobl, T. J., Campbell, J. A., Tindall, D. J., Cunningham, G. R., and Means, A. R. (1980) *In* "Testicular Development, Structure and Function" (A. Steinberger, and E. Steinberger, eds.), pp. 323–330. Raven, New York.

Sperm–Egg Recognition and Binding in Mammals

BELA J. GULYAS AND ELI D. SCHMELL

Pregnancy Research Branch
National Institute of Child Health and Human Development
National Institutes of Health
Bethesda, Maryland

INTRODUCTION

The cellular mechanisms of fertilization, particularly in invertebrates and lower vertebrates, have been the subject of numerous studies during the past century. These studies indicate that following binding of the spermatozoa to the outer investment of the egg a sequence of physiological and morphological changes occur culminating in formation of the zygote nucleus, or the intermixing of paternal and maternal chromosomes. These events have been divided into a number of steps, each categorized either by well marked cellular events or by some other operational demarcation. The initial interaction or recognition between sperm and egg, comprising sperm attachment and binding, may be considered the very first step in the sequence of events in fertilization. This is, however, not to exclude the maturation processes that occur to both the sperm and the egg in the female reproductive tract. The initial interactions between sperm and egg may be viewed as a form of cell–cell recognition and adhesion specific to fertilization. As such, it represents the first bioregulation step in the fertilization process, supposedly by limiting interaction to sperm and egg of the same species. The specificity of this regulatory process, sperm–egg binding, has been examined in a number of species. Although this phenomenon received considerable attention in recent years both in vertebrates and invertebrates, the content of this chapter will be restricted to observations in mammals with an occassional reference to lower vertebrates or invertebrates.

BIOREGULATORS OF REPRODUCTION

In a number of systems, particularly in the sea urchin, for example, where sperm–egg recognition has been studied extensively, all aspects of fertilization occur extracorporally. Thus in these species, where the natural habitat and site of fertilization can be closely reproduced, *in vitro* studies on sperm binding to the outer investment of the egg are probably of functional significance. The same claims cannot be made, however, in the case of mammalian reproduction. Because of the problems inherent in studying the internal site of fertilization, much of the work on fertilization in mammals must be explored *in vitro*. These conditions by no means resemble the *in vivo* environment. Observations on sperm binding to the zona pellucida of mammalian ova *in vitro* may represent a response to an unnatural environment. Furthermore, it must be remembered that the physiological significance of species-specificity of sperm binding in mammals, where species interbreeding occurs only in limited cases in nature (1, cited in 2), and even then with low frequency, may be of questionable importance. With these reservations in mind we shall review sperm attachment and binding to mammalian eggs as we understand this phenomenon mostly from *in vitro* studies. We will first summarize the physiological and morphological processes involved in mammalian sperm–egg interactions, that is sperm capacitation and the acrosome reaction. Second, we shall review relevant studies on mammalian gamete recognition and binding, and finally discuss most recent results from our laboratory on this topic. The purpose of this chapter is not to review the entire scope of sperm–egg interaction; instead, the discussion here will be limited to the problems of sperm binding to the zona pellucida and its significance to the fertilization process in mammals.

SPERM CAPACITATION

In many mammalian species spermatozoa must apparently undergo a physiological maturation, called capacitation, before they attain the ability to penetrate the ova (3–5). Under normal conditions this physiological change occurs while the spermatozoa ascend in the female genital tract to the site of fertilization. Although the biochemical details and the molecular biology of sperm capacitation remain to be completely elucidated, at least three changes are thought to be involved in the process, all of which appear to be prerequisites, or part, of the acrosome reaction. First, some reports indicate that as a result of capacitation there is an increase in sperm respiration (6–9). Second, recent electron microscopic studies have revealed subtle rearrangements of membrane particles in the outer acrosomal and plasma membranes which are observable only with freeze-fracture and freeze-etch techniques (10–12). Third, capacitation results in the removal of sperm surface components (13–16) including lectin and/or anti-sperm –antibody binding sites (17–19). It has also been demonstrated that sperm exposed to capacitating conditions exhibit a decreased net negative charge (14,20) that might be related to capacitation. That capacitation results in destabilization of the sperm membrane (14) was demonstrated by Davis *et al.* (21). They showed that serum albumin decreases the cholesterol to phospholipid ratio of the sperm plasma membrane, which in turn hastens spontaneous membrane fusion (acrosome reaction, see below), a precondition for mammalian fertilization. Regardless of the details of the mechanisms it entails, capacitation is considered to be a reversible process that renders the spermatozoa capable of undergoing the acrosome reaction, the second sperm modification necessary for successful fertilization.

ACROSOME REACTION AND ITS RELATIONSHIP TO SPERM BINDING

Capacitation renders the membranes of the spermatozoa capable of an acrosome reaction, resulting in obvious membrane changes. The acrosome reaction is initiated as a series of focal fusion points between the outer acrosomal and the sperm plasma membranes followed by vesiculation of these membranes (14,22–25). The reaction is complete when the inner acrosomal membrane is completely exposed. A criterion for the occurrence of a true acrosome reaction is the visualization of the fused ends of the inner acrosomal and plasma membranes (14,26). It has been suggested (15,27,28) that the function of the acrosome reaction is to allow certain lytic enzymes, such as hyaluronidase and acrosin, to be released. These enzymes presumably aid in sperm penetration through the cumulus oophorus cells and the zona pellucida.

Apparently, Ca^{2+} is essential for initiation of the acrosome reaction in mammalian spermatozoa. The precise mechanism by which Ca^{2+} alters sperm membranes culminating in the acrosome reaction is unclear. However, it has been proposed that Ca^{2+} influx occurs into the sperm during the acrosome reaction in rabbit (29), guinea pig (30,31), and hamster spermatozoa (32). For example, guinea pig spermatozoa capacitated in Tyrodes or Krebs-Ringer solution with 0.1% bovine serum albumin (BSA) in the absence of Ca^{2+} fail to undergo acrosome reaction. However, the acrosome reaction can be induced in these spermatozoa within a few minutes when Ca^{2+} is added to the incubation medium. These observations have been interpreted to indicate that Ca^{2+} is required for membrane fusion once the spermatozoa have undergone full capacitation (33). The results corroborate the observations that during capacitation BSA interacts with the sperm plasma membrane and the phospholipid bilayer becomes more permeable to Ca^{2+} (21), which could then initiate the acrosome reaction.

Of particular interest and importance to this discussion is the temporal and spatial relationship between the acrosome reaction and binding of the spermatozoa to the zona pellucida. It is well established that spermatozoa located within the perivitelline space have undergone the acrosome reaction (15,34,35). Moreover, under *in vivo* conditions only acrosome-reacted spermatozoa can penetrate the zona pellucida (14,22,25,36,37), whereas unreacted ones do not. Thus the critical question pertinent to sperm binding is whether the acrosome reaction occurs before, after, or during binding to the zona pellucida. The answer to this question will clarify, at least in part, whether it is the inner acrosomal membrane of the reacted spermatozoa or the plasma membrane of the intact spermatozoa that is responsible for sperm–egg recognition and binding to the zona pellucida in mammals.

With this question in mind, Saling and Storey (38), using a fluorescent probe, chlorotetracycline (CTC), developed an assay for determining the acrosome reaction in mouse sperm. The fluorescence signal in CTC is elicited upon chelation of Ca^{2+}, or Mg^{2+}, thereby recording the location of the divalent cations (38). Using the fluorescent technique, Saling and Storey demonstrated a bright fluorescence on the acrosomal region of the intact sperm, whereas acrosome reacted sperm did not fluoresce (39). Moreover, within 10 minutes of *in vitro* insemination only acrosome-intact spermatozoa were observed on the zona surface. Forty minutes later, half of the zona-bound spermatozoa had undergone acrosome reaction and the remainder initiated the acrosome reaction. Penetration of the zona pellucida by sperm that had undergone full acrosome reaction occured 90 minutes after *in vitro* insemination. These results confirm earlier observations that, in the mouse, the acrosome reaction occurs after binding to the zona pellucida (40). Furthermore, the results indicate that *in vitro* it is the plasma membrane of the fertile mouse sperm which is responsible for specific recognition of the zona. Thus it appears that at least in the mouse, the obligatory sequence for the initial steps of *in vitro* fertilization, before zona penetration can occur are (1) capacitation, (2) binding to the zona, and (3) acrosome reaction. Although indications are that acrosome reaction occurs on the zona surface it remains to be shown that zona components are responsible for initiating the acrosome reaction.

These recent *in vitro* observations on the sequence of events prior to penetration of the zona pellucida are at variance with previous *in vivo* accounts. Earlier studies have indicated that in mammals the acrosome reaction occurs in the vicinity of the ovum or after contact with the cumulus oophorus (14,22,41,42). Although it had been shown that acrosome-intact spermatozoa could reach the zona pellucida, it was demonstrated that only the acrosome-reacted sperm could penetrate it (35). Ultrastructural studies on rabbit (14,22) and hamster eggs (25) showed that spermatozoa lack the plasma membrane and outer acrosomal membrane prior to attachment, suggesting that zona recognition could occur at the inner acrosomal membrane or even at the equatorial segment of the spermatozoon (35). Reconciliation of the different views as to whether it is the inner acrosomal membrane or the plasma membrane that is involved in sperm–egg recognition will be difficult because both *in vivo* and *in vitro* observations have their inherent limitations in trying to ascertain this question.

It is possible, however, that "the" fertilizing sperm does not undergo the acrosome reaction before reaching the zona surface both *in vivo* and *in vitro*. *In vivo*, many sperm may undergo a "premature" acrosome reaction upon interaction with cumulus cells. However, the fertilizing spermatozoon may indeed reach the zona completely intact. This would suggest a cooperative dissolution of the cumulus by spermatozoa that can no longer fertilize the egg, but their efforts would allow the fertilizing sperm to reach the zona surface intact. This scenario would be consistant with both the *in vivo* and *in vitro* observations.

SPERM BINDING TO THE ZONA PELLUCIDA

One of the most intensely studied processes in fertilization is sperm–egg recognition and binding. It is generally accepted that both the egg investment and some portion of the spermatozoon play equal roles in the recognition and binding process. That is, a sperm surface molecule(s) recognizes a receptor(s) on the surface of the egg, resulting in binding.

BINDING BETWEEN HOMOLOGOUS GAMETES

Hartmann *et al.* (43,44) were the first to recognize that initially hamster spermatozoa adhere to the zona pellucida in a reversible manner,
such that the adherent sperm can be removed by repeated washings of
the eggs. This initial contact between homologous gametes is referred
to as "attachment." Subsequently, homologous gametes adhere in an
irreversible fashion called "binding," which is stable even after repeated washings. Attachment of capacitated hamster spermatozoa to
hamster eggs is a fairly rapid process that commences within 2–3 minutes after *in vitro* insemination (44). The more stable binding of spermatozoa occurs 30 minutes after insemination. Binding of hamster
spermatozoa to isolated zonae on the other hand occurs much more
rapidly (5–10 minutes) (33), and is linearly related to sperm concentration.

We have recently investigated homologous sperm–egg recognition
and binding *in vitro* (45), using capacitated spermatozoa from mouse,
hamster, and guinea pig with living or glutaraldehyde-fixed oocytes,

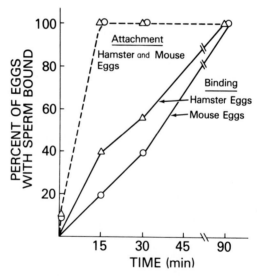

Fig. 1. Attachment and binding of mouse sperm to mouse and hamster eggs. Mouse
and hamster ova (100 each) were placed in separate watch glasses in 0.5 ml of modified
Krebs–Ringer solution. Mouse sperm (10^5 cells) were added to each sample of eggs and
at the indicated times eggs were removed to assess sperm attachment (dashed line) or
sperm binding (solid lines), between homologous gametes (○) and heterologous gametes. (△). (From Schmell and Gulyas, 45.)

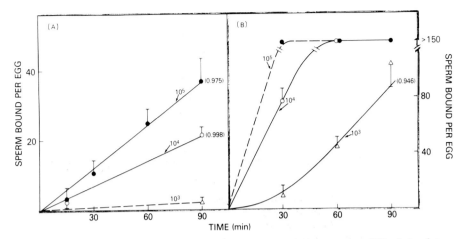

Fig. 2. Kinetics of homologous sperm–egg binding. Three series of 50 μl droplets were prepared containing either 10^3 (△), 10^4 (○), or 10^5 (●) sperm. Eggs were added to each droplet and at the indicated times they were removed, washed three times, and the number of sperm bound to each egg was determined. (A) Binding of mouse sperm to mouse eggs, using 15 eggs for each determination. (B) Binding of hamster sperm to hamster eggs, using 8–10 ova for each sample. The numbers in parentheses are the correlation coefficients of those curves which conform to linearity with time. The bars indicate one SD of the mean. (From Schmell and Gulyas, 45.)

obtained from superovulated females. In our experiments we attempted to adapt the washing procedures originally described by Hartmann *et al.* (43), with one major difference: the orifice of the micropipete was larger than the overall diameter of the eggs. Thus, the shearing forces applied during washing were probably somewhat gentler in our studies. Initial experiments revealed that after homologous insemination mouse and hamster gametes exhibit a rapid attachment followed by a slower binding (Fig. 1). These results are similar to those reported by Hartmann and co-workers (43,44) for homologous insemination. Moreover, kinetic studies revealed that binding of homologous gametes (mouse or hamster) is linear with time over a broad range of sperm concentrations (Fig. 2). In subsequent experiments it was determined that for a given preparation of spermatozoa and eggs, sperm–egg binding apparently is saturable (Fig. 3). Due to difficulties in obtaining guinea pig ova only qualitative observations of sperm–egg interactions were assessed. However, attachment and binding to homologous eggs were observed (Fig. 4c).

Saling and co-workers (46) examined the minimum *in vitro* requirements of sperm–egg binding in the mouse. They demonstrated that

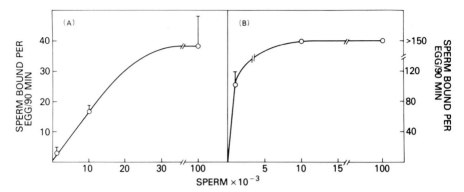

Fig. 3. Effect of sperm concentration on homologous sperm–egg binding. Saturation curves of sperm binding are presented for both mouse (A) and hamster (B) eggs. Curves were obtained by plotting the number of sperm bound per egg (mean ± *SD*) after a 90-minute incubation with homologous eggs. (From Schmell and Gulyas, 45.)

initial binding of mouse spermatozoa to the zona pellucida requires Ca^{2+} and is independent of the Ca^{2+} requirement for maintenance of motility (47). The binding exhibits Ca^{2+} specificity and Mg^{2+} substitution for Ca^{2+} is inadequate. The authors suggest that binding is dependent on Ca^{2+} *in vivo* as well. In support of this concept they note that Ca^{2+} levels of epididymal fluid are low in hamster and bull (48,49) where the acrosome reaction is not expected to take place. However, Ca^{2+} concentrations are relatively high in the oviducts (50) where

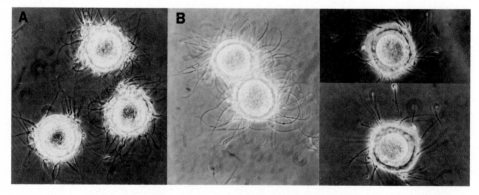

Fig. 4. Photomicrographs of sperm bound to homologous eggs. Following incubation with homologous sperm, eggs were washed, then fixed in 1.25% glutaraldehyde. (A) mouse sperm bound to mouse eggs, (B) hamster sperm bound to hamster eggs, and (C) guinea pig sperm bound to guinea pig eggs. (From Schmell and Gulyas, 45.)

sperm–egg binding and the acrosome reaction occur. Although the acrosome reaction and binding are both Ca^{2+} dependent and closely related events, several lines of evidence suggest that they are separable processes. First, binding is rapid (15 minues) (46), whereas the acrosome reaction requires at least 1 hour (32). Thus the acrosome reaction is much slower than binding. Second, Ca^{2+}-dependent binding is reversible, whereas the acrosome reaction is not. Lastly, whereas Ca^{2+} influx occurs into hamster (32) and guinea pig (30) during the acrosome reaction, it does not occur during binding in the mouse (46).

BINDING BETWEEN HETEROLOGOUS GAMETES

For the most part, sperm penetration of the zona pellucida is accomplished only by homologous sperm (2,35) and for this reason the zona pellucida has been considered as the single most important morphological barrier to interspecies fertilization. The fact that zona-free eggs of rat, mouse, guinea pig, and human are penetrable by heterologous spermatozoa (2) is usually presented in support of this hypothesis. But even in these instances successful penetration of eggs by a heterologous spermatozoon requires previous acrosome reaction (2).

A review of the literature on sperm binding in mammals reveals a lack of consensus regarding specificity of sperm binding to the zona pellucida. The findings of a number of studies on heterologous gamete interactions are summarized in Table I. Whereas some investigators have reported sperm binding to the zona pellucida to be highly specific (43,44,51,52), others described sperm–egg recognition of limited specificity (35,53,55). It should be noted, however, that in some instances the spermatozoa were capacitated *in vitro*, whereas in other studies uncapacitated spermatozoa were used.

In view of the conflicting reports concerning specificity of gamete binding, and because of the potential importance of the species specificity of sperm–egg binding as a natural bioregulator of mammalian fertilization, we reinvestigated the specificity of gamete interactions *in vitro* using several rodent species. Sperm–egg binding was examined using *in vitro* capacitated mouse, hamster, and guinea pig spermatozoa and either living or glutaraldehyde-fixed oocytes obtained after superovulation.

Initial qualitative observations on the specificity of sperm binding in homologous and heterologous inseminations are illustrated in Fig. 1. As mentioned earlier, *in vitro* capacitated mouse spermatozoa at-

TABLE I

Summary of Results from Homologous and Heterologous *in Vitro* Insemination[a]

Sperm \ Ova	Human	Gibbon	Baboon	Rhesus monkey	Squirrel monkey	Bovine	Porcine	Rabbit	Rat	Guinea pig	Hamster	Mouse	References
Human	+		−	−	−			−		−	−	−	53,54
Gibbon	+												
Baboon													
Rhesus monkey				+				+			+	+	53
Squirrel monkey					+			+			+	+	53
Bull						+					+		55
Boar							+				+		55
Rabbit				+	+			+	±	+	+	+	53
Rat							−	−	−		+		51,55
Guinea pig	(−)									(+)	(−)	(−)	53,55; (45), (35)
Hamster	(+)	+		+	+			+	+	(+)	(+)	(+)	53,54,55,(45); (35),43
Mouse	+		+		+			+		+	+, −	(+), +	40,53,54,(45); 51

[a] Each symbol represents an experiment from one of the references listed to the right. Any one reference may embrace more than one experiment. Circled symbols and references represent use of capacitated sperm. +, Binding; ±, weak binding; −, no binding.

tach rapidly to mouse oocytes, whereas binding to the zona pellucida is a slower process. Furthermore, *in vitro* capacitated mouse spermatozoa also attach and bind to hamster eggs at a similar rate (Fig. 1). In contrast to nonspecific binding observed between mouse and hamster gametes, binding of guinea pig sperm appears to be highly specific. Binding of spermatozoa in this species was observed only with homologous ova.

As shown in Fig. 5, quantitative assessment of mouse and hamster sperm binding to hamster eggs confirms the nonspecificity of binding in these two species. Although sperm concentration is limiting for both mouse and hamster, the kinetics of sperm binding to hamster eggs is similar for both mouse and hamster sperm. In contrast, guinea pig spermatozoa fail to bind to either mouse or hamster eggs even at

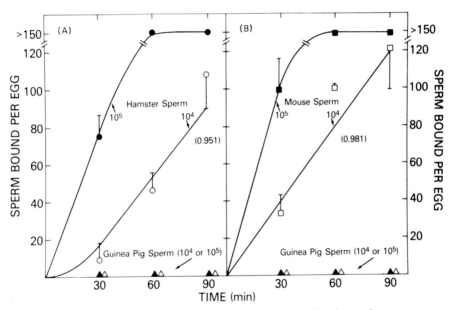

Fig. 5. Kinetics of hamster, mouse, and guinea pig sperm binding to hamster eggs. Several groups of 50 μl droplets of Biggers-Whitten-Whittingham medium were prepared with either 10^5 sperm (closed symbols) or 10^4 sperm (open symbols) and 8–10 hamster eggs were added to each droplet. At the indicated times the eggs were removed, washed three times, and the number of sperm bound to each egg was assessed in the phase contrast microscope. Sperm binding to hamster eggs was determined using (A) hamster sperm ($\bigcirc$,$\bullet$); (B) mouse sperm ($\square$,$\blacksquare$); and (A,B) guinea pig sperm ($\triangle$,$\blacktriangle$). The numbers in parentheses are correlation coefficients of those curves which conform to linearity with time. The bars represent one SD of the mean. (From Schmell and Gulyas, 45.)

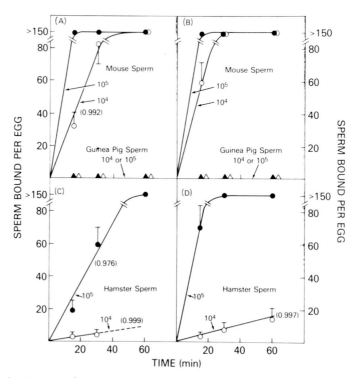

Fig. 6. Kinetics of sperm binding to fixed mouse and hamster eggs. The binding of mouse, hamster, and guinea pig sperm to fixed mouse eggs (A and C) and hamster eggs (B and D) was assessed with 15 ova for each determination. Binding was determined with 10^4 (○) or 10^5 (●) mouse or hamster sperm per 50 μl droplet, and with 10^4 (△) or 10^5 (▲) guinea pig sperm per droplet. The numbers in parentheses are correlation coefficients of those curves which conform to linearity with time. The bars represent one SD of the mean. (From Schmell and Gulyas, 45.)

very high concentrations. Similar specificity and kinetics were obtained when sperm binding to mouse eggs was analyzed using *in vitro* capacitated mouse, hamster, and guinea pig sperm (not illustrated).

Homologous and heterologous *in vitro* inseminations were also performed using previously fixed eggs. As with living eggs, mouse and hamster spermatozoa readily bind to homologous and heterologous fixed eggs (Fig. 6). Guinea pig spermatozoa, which were previously shown to bind only to guinea pig eggs, failed to bind to either fixed mouse or hamster eggs.

These observations indicate that *in vitro* binding of capacitated sperm to the zona pellucida of intact ova is not strictly a species-specific process among the three rodents examined. Whereas mouse and hamster spermatozoa bind to heterologous ova, binding of guinea pig spermatozoa is strictly species-specific. Furthermore, similar results were observed with fixed eggs, indicating that the zona sperm receptor retains its binding capacity in slightly aldehyde-fixed eggs. This observation should prove useful in studies where large numbers of binding assays must be performed with mammalian gametes.

SPERM RECEPTORS

Although the scope of this chapter is limited to studies on mammalian species it is appropriate to introduce the topic of sperm receptors with F. R. Lillie's (56) classic work on sea urchins. He proposed that the sea urchin egg surface contains a substance (fertilizin) which specifically interacts with a complementary sperm surface substance (anti-fertilizin) during the initial steps of fertilization. Thus Lillie introduced the concept of receptor molecules to the study of gamete recognition. Molecules, or receptors, involved in gametic recognition have since been identified in the vitelline membrane of several species of sea urchin (57,58). "Bindin," the sperm component that recognizes the sperm receptor on the vitelline membrane, has also been isolated from the sea urchin sperm (58–60). Several lines of evidence support the hypothesis that bindin, a species-specific agglutinin of unfertilized eggs, is the protein responsible for binding sperm to sea urchin eggs (60). These results form the basis for proposing a generalized mechanism of sperm–egg binding, where one gamete contains a protein which recognizes and binds to a carbohydrate moiety on the surface of the other gamete (58–62).

Despite the increased understanding of the molecular and biochemical events involved during gamete recognition in lower animals, only limited information is available pertaining to sperm–egg recognition in mammals. To date no information is available as to whether a protein similar to bindin exists in mammalian spermatozoa. More progress has been made however, regarding the zona pellucida receptor(s) for sperm. Several lines of evidence suggest that the zona pellucida possesses a receptor for sperm which is sensitive to pancreatic trypsin (51,63) and retains its sperm-binding property after heat treatment (64). Moreover, binding of spermatozoa to the zona pellucida is inhibited by antisera produced against whole ovary homogenates (65–69).

Most recently, Bleil and Wassarman (70) isolated three glycoproteins from mouse zona pellucida (ZP1, ZP2 and ZP3) and demonstrated that one of the glycoproteins, purified ZP3, inhibited binding of sperm to egg (71). Furthermore, ZP3 isolated from 2-cell embryos had no significant effect on sperm binding, which corroborates earlier reports on the lack of sperm binding to 2-cell embryos (72,73). These results indicate that ZP3 purified from unfertilized mouse eggs, possesses sperm receptor activity responsible for binding the sperm. (For further detail see Wassarman in this volume.)

The distribution of sperm receptors in the zona pellucida has not been determined with certainty. Whereas it would seem logical that the majority of the receptors are located on the outer surface of the zona pellucida, it is possible that they are distributed throughout the zona. In fact, presently available indirect evidence support both possibilities. In the hamster (54) capacitated sperm bind to both the inner and outer surfaces of the zona pellucida when binding was assessed by light microscopy. It has been shown that sperm receptor activity is present in the zonae pellucidae of growing mouse oocytes at a time when zona synthesis is incomplete (71). However, this observation does not demonstrate the localization of receptors in the zonae of mature eggs. On the other hand, studies with lectins suggest that lectin binding is localized predominantly on the outside surface of the zona pellucida (35,74,75). These observations may be the result of precipitation of lectins at the zona surface.

Recently, Phillips and Shalgi (76) have demonstrated that, in hamster, sperm receptors are predominantly localized on the outer zona surface. By scanning electron microscopy (SEM) they showed a distinct morphological difference between the inner and outer zona surfaces on intact eggs. Furthermore, sperm binding was predominantly limited to the outer surface of isolated zonae. When sperm were observed seemingly on the inner face of the zona, in fact SEM revealed that these zonae had turned inside out during isolation. Thus, the data apparently indicate that sperm receptors are enriched on the outer surface of the hamster zona.

In order to ultimately isolate a bindin-type molecule from mammalian sperm, experiments to fractionate egg-binding components of the sperm have been initiated. A rapid technique was devised to isolate sperm heads. Briefly, capacitated sperm were subjected to sonic oscillation to dissociate heads from tails and midpieces. The sperm heads were subsequently isolated (Fig. 7) by filtration through nitex nylon, followed by low-speed centrifugation. The purified sperm heads were routinely obtained in high yields (>80% for guinea pig, >60% for hamster and 20–60% for mouse). The isolated sperm heads bind to living or fixed eggs with the same specificity as the intact spermatozoa (Fig. 8). That is, mouse and hamster sperm heads bind to both mouse

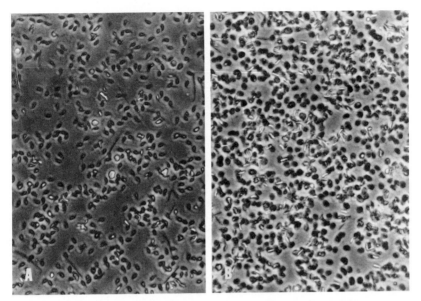

Fig. 7. Isolated mouse (A) and guinea pig (B) sperm heads.

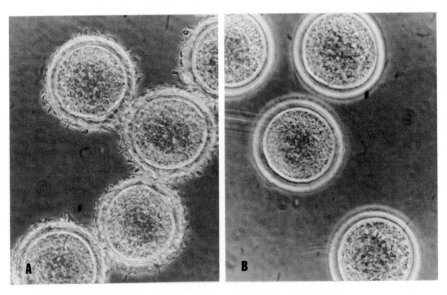

Fig. 8. Sperm heads (10^5) isolated from hamster or guinea pig sperm were incubated with 10 fixed hamster ova. After 30 minutes the ova were washed three times and observed in the microscope. Only homologous binding occurred (A), heterologous binding was not observed (B).

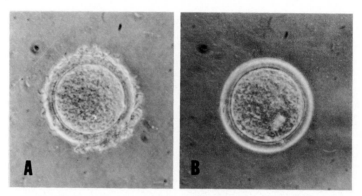

Fig. 9. Effect of trypsin treatment on the binding of isolated sperm heads to hamster eggs. Isolated hamster sperm heads (10⁶) were preincubated with trypsin (1 mg/ml) for 30 minutes, washed three times and incubated with ova. (A) Binding of sperm heads preincubated in buffer alone. (B) Binding of sperm heads preincubated in buffer containing trypsin.

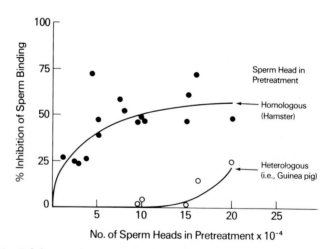

Fig. 10. Inhibition of sperm binding by isolated sperm heads. Following incubation of hamster ova with isolated sperm heads as in Fig. 8, the washed eggs were inseminated with a limiting quantity of hamster sperm. After 30 minutes the number of sperm bound per egg was assessed. The data presented are expressed as percent inhibition of binding, where 100% is binding observed with eggs that were preincubated in buffer alone. The data represent the cumulative results of four independent experiments. Inhibition of hamster gamete binding by pretreatment with hamster sperm heads (●---●) and guinea pig sperm heads (○---○).

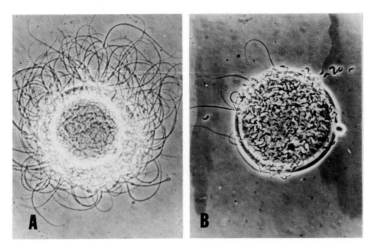

Fig. 11. Photomicrograph illustrating binding of intact hamster spermatozoa to eggs following pretreatment with isolated sperm heads. (A) Binding of intact sperm to eggs pretreated with guinea pig sperm heads or buffer alone and (B) binding of intact sperm to eggs pretreated with hamster sperm heads.

and hamster ova, whereas guinea pig sperm heads bind only to guinea pig eggs. Moreover, binding is apparently trypsin sensitive (Fig. 9). When isolated sperm heads are pretreated with trypsin, washed, and added to eggs, essentially no binding is observed. With the addition of both trypsin and trypsin inhibitor binding was uneffected. Finally, inhibition experiments indicate that the isolated sperm heads apparently compete for the zona sperm receptor, because pretreatment of living or fixed eggs with isolated heads from homologous sperm inhibits subsequent binding of intact spermatozoa (Figs. 10 and 11). Experiments are in progress to solubilize and purify the egg-binding component(s) of the sperm head.

CONCLUSION

The importance of the species-specificity of sperm binding to the zona pellucida *in vivo* is uncertain when one considers that "the primary mechanisms by which hybridization in mammals is prevented are the physiological and behavioral separation of males and females of different species" (2). Natural hybrids, although few in number, further reduce the importance of species-specificity of sperm receptors among mammals. This is not to say that differences in zona sperm receptors and their ability to recognize sperm of different species do not exist. Some species exhibit marked specificity in sperm–egg recognition. Therefore, while evaluating species-specificity of sperm–egg binding in mammals it must be remembered that specificity experiments were by necessity done *in vitro*, under different conditions in various laboratories. Some of the confusion and uncertainties might be clarified if more uniform procedures and conditions were established and applied in examining sperm binding to the zona pellucida. Whether sperm binding to the zona pellucida is strictly species-specific or not, the inability of spermatozoa to penetrate the zona pellucida during heterologous insemination might be a factor to examine more closely as a bioregulatory mechanism of interspecies fertilization. This is compatible with the earlier concept that the zona pellucida is the major barrier to interspecies fertilization (35,52).

Finally, regardless of the species-specificity of sperm–egg binding, this process remains of extreme interest and importance in terms of bioregulation of fertilization and fertility. Since productive incorporation of spermatozoa into female tissues is limited to ova, all aspects of sperm–egg recognition are of interest and potentially relevant. Thus, isolation of mammalian sperm receptors and "bindin" type molecules will provide information regarding the biochemical mechanism(s) underlying successful sperm–egg interations in mammals. The similarities as well as the differences between these molecules will provide an understanding of not only the fertilization process but also other biological recognition events as well.

SUMMARY

As a prerequisite for fertilization mammalian spermatozoa must undergo capacitation *in vivo* or *in vitro*. Following physiological changes induced during capacitation the spermatozoa are rendered capable of undergoing the acrosome reaction, which has been shown to be a Ca^{2+}-dependent process. During acrosome reaction the outer acrosomal and the plasma membranes fuse and form small vesicles and the inner acrosomal membrane becomes exposed. *In vivo* the acrosome reaction has been reported to occur in the proximity of the ovum after making contact with the cumulus oophorus. More recent *in vitro* observations suggest that the acrosome reaction of the potential fertilizing spermatozoon occurs only after attachment to the outer surface of the zona pellucida. These results indicate that *in vitro* it is the plasma membrane of the spermatozoa, rather than the inner acrosomal membrane, responsible for recognition and binding to the zona pellucida.

Sperm binding, to the zona pellucida does not appear to be strictly species-specific. In the hamster and the mouse, capacitated sperm first attach in a reversible manner, then bind to the zona pellucida in an irreversible manner. After heterologous insemination mouse and hamster spermatozoa attach and bind to both mouse and hamster eggs with similar affinities. Guinea pig sperm, on the other hand, bind only to homologous ova. The kinetics of mouse and hamster sperm–egg binding is similar using both fixed and live eggs. As with living eggs, guinea pig sperm failed to bind to fixed mouse or hamster eggs.

Recent observations indicate that the zona pellucida of mammalian eggs contains a sperm receptor glycoprotein. Isolated sperm heads bind to ova with a specificity similar to that of intact sperm. Furthermore, isolated sperm heads compete for zona sperm receptors and binding is trypsin sensitive.

ACKNOWLEDGMENT

The authors gratefully acknowledge the expert clerical assistance of Linda Baldwin.

REFERENCES

1. Gray, A. P. (1954) "Mammalian Hybrids." Commonw. Agric. Bur., Farnham Royal, Bucks, England.
2. Yanagimachi, R. (1978) *Curr. Top. Dev. Biol.* **12,** 83–105.
3. Austin, C. R. (1951) *Aust. J. Sci. Res., Ser. B* **4,** 581–596.
4. Austin, C. R. (1952) *Nature (London)* **170,** 326.
5. Chang, M. C. (1951) *Nature (London)* **168,** 697–698.
6. Hamner, C. E., and Williams, W. L. (1963) *J. Reprod. Fertil.* **5,** 143–150.
7. Mounib, M. S., and Chang, M. C. (1964) *Nature (London)* **201,** 943–944.
8. Murdoch, R. N., and White, I. G. (1967) *J. Reprod. Fertil.* **14,** 213–223.
9. Rogers, B. J., and Morton, B. (1973) *Biol. Reprod.* **9,** 361–369.
10. Friend, D. S., and Rudolf, I. (1974) *J. Cell Biol.* **63,** 466–479.
11. Friend, D. S., Orci, L., Perrelet, A., and Yanagimachi, R. (1977) *J. Cell Biol.* **74,** 561–577.
12. Koehler, J. K., and Gaddum-Rosse, P. (1975) *J. Ultrastruct. Res.* **51,** 106–118.
13. Oliphant, G., and Brackett, B. G. (1973) *Biol. Reprod.* **9,** 404–414.
14. Bedford, J. M. (1968) *Am. J. Anat.* **123,** 329–358.
15. Bedford, J. M., and Cooper, G. W. (1978) *In* "Membrane Fusion" (G. Poste and G. L. Nicolson, eds.), pp. 65–125. Elsevier/North-Holland Press, Amsterdam.
16. Oliphant, G. (1976) *Fertil. Steril.* **27,** 28–38.

17. Gordon, M., Dandekar, P. V., and Bartoszewicz, W. (1975) *J. Ultrastuct. Res.* **50,** 199–207.
18. Koehler, J. K. (1976) *Biol. Reprod.* **15,** 444–456.
19. Schwarz, M. A., and Koehler, J. K. (1979) *Biol. Reprod.* **21,** 1295–1307.
20. Vaidya, R. A., Glass, R. H., Dandekar, P., and Johnson, K. (1971) *J. Reprod. Fertil.* **24,** 299–301.
21. Davis, B. K., Byrne, R., and Bedigian, K. (1980) *Proc. Natl. Acad. Sci. U.S.A.* **77,** 1546–1550.
22. Bedford, J. M. (1972) *Am. J. Anat.* **133,** 213–254.
23. Barros, C., Bedford, J. M., Franklin, L. E., and Austin, C. R. (1967) *J. Cell Biol.* **34,** 1–5.
24. Franklin, L. E., Barros, C., and Fussell, E. N. (1970) *Biol. Reprod.* **3,** 180–200.
25. Yanagimachi, R., and Noda, Y. D. (1970) *J. Ultrastruct. Res.* **31,** 465–485.
26. Bedford, J. M. (1970) *Biol. Reprod., Suppl.* **2,** 128–158.
27. Meizel, S. (1978) *In* "Development in Mammals" (M. H. Johnson, ed.), Vol. 3, pp. 1–64. North-Holland Publ., Amsterdam.
28. Green, D. P. L. (1978) *In* "Development in Mammals" (M. H. Johnson, ed.), Vol. 3, pp. 65–81. North-Holland Publ., Amsterdam.
29. Oliphant, G., Cabot, C. L., and Singhaus, C. A. (1977) *J. Reprod. Fertil.* **50,** 245–250.
30. Yanagimachi, R., and Usui, N. (1974) *Exp. Cell Res.* **89,** 161–174.
31. Rogers, B. J., and Yanagimachi, R. (1975) *J. Reprod. Fertil.* **44,** 135–138.
32. Talbot, P., Summers, R. G., Hylander, B. L., Keough, E. M., and Franklin, L. E. (1976) *J. Exp. Zool.* **198,** 382–392.
33. Gwatkin, R. B. L. (1976) *In* "The Cell Surface in Animal Embryogenesis and Development" (G. Poste and G. L. Nicolson, eds.), pp. 1–54. Elsevier/North-Holland Biomed. Press, Amsterdam.
34. Chang, M. C., and Hunter, R. H. F. (1975) *Handb. Physiol., Sect. 7: Endocrinol.* **5,** 339–351.
35. Yanagimachi, R. (1977) *In* "Immunobiology of Gametes" (M. Edidin and M. H. Johnson, eds.), pp. 225–289. Cambridge Univ. Press, London and New York.
36. Yanagimachi, R., and Chang, M. C. (1964) *J. Exp. Zool.* **156,** 361–376.
37. Yanagimachi, R. (1966) *J. Reprod. Fertil.* **11,** 359–370.
38. Saling, P. M., and Storey, B. T. (1979) *J. Cell Biol.* **83,** 544–555.
39. Saling, P. M., Sowinski, J., and Storey, B. T. (1979) *J. Exp. Zool.* **209,** 229–238.
40. Wolf, D. P., and Inoue, M. (1976) *J. Exp. Zool.* **196,** 27–38.
41. Austin, C. R. (1961) "The Mammalian Egg." Thomas, Springfield, Illinois.
42. Yanagimachi, R., and Mahi, C. A. (1976) *J. Reprod. Fertil.* **46,** 49–54.
43. Hartmann, J. F., Gwatkin, R. B. L., and Hutchison, C. F. (1972) *Proc. Natl. Acad. Sci. U.S.A.* **69,** 2767–2769.
44. Hartmann, J. F., and Hutchison, C. F. (1974) *J. Reprod. Fertil.* **36,** 49–57.
45. Schmell, E. D., and Gulyas, B. J. (1980) *Biol. Reprod.* **23,** 1075–1085.
46. Saling, P. M., Storey, B. T., and Wolf, D. P. (1978) *Dev. Biol.* **65,** 515–525.
47. Heffner, L. J., Saling, P. M., and Storey, B. T. (1980) *J. Exp. Zool.* **212,** 53–59.
48. Morton, B., Harrigan-Lunn, J., Albagli, L., and Jooss, T. (1974) *Biochem. Biophys. Res. Commun.* **56,** 372–379.
49. Mann, T. (1975) *Handb. Physiol. Sect. 7: Endocrinol.* **5,** 461–471.
50. Borland, R. M., Hazra, S., Biggers, J. D., and Lechene, C. P. (1977) *Biol. Reprod.* **16,** 147–157.
51. Hartmann, J. F., and Gwatkin, R. B. L. (1971) *Nature (London)* **234,** 479–481.
52. Hamada, A., and Chang, M. C. (1977) *Biol. Reprod.* **6,** 300–309.

53. Bedford, J. M. (1978) *Anat. Rec.* **188**, 477–488.
54. Gwatkin, R. B. L., and Williams, D. T. (1977) *J. Reprod. Fertil.* **49**, 55–59.
55. Peterson, R. N., Russel, L., Bundman, D., and Freund, M. (1979) *Science* **207**, 73–74.
56. Lillie, F. R. (1919) "Problems of Fertilization," Univ. of Chicago Press, Chicago, Illinois.
57. Aketa, K. (1967). *Embryologia* **9**, 238–245.
58. Schmell, E., Earles, B. J., Breaux, C., and Lennarz, W. J. (1977) *J. Cell Biol.* **72**, 35–46.
59. Glabe, C. G., and Lennarz, W. I. (1979) *J. Cell Biol.* **83**, 595–604.
60. Vacquier, V. D. (1980) *Symp. Soc. Dev. Biol.* **38**, 151–168.
61. Vacquier, V. D., and Moy, G. W. (1977) *Proc. Natl. Acad. Sci. U.S.A.* **74**, 2456–2460.
62. Marchesi, V. T., Ginsburg, V., Robbins, P. W., and Fox, C. F. (1978) *Prog. Clin. Biol. Res.* **23**.
63. Oikawa, T., Nicolson, G. L., and Yanagimachi, R. (1975) *J. Reprod. Fertil.* **43**, 133–136.
64. Gwatkin, R. B. L., Williams, D. T., and Anderson, O. F. (1973) *J. Cell Biol.* **59**, 128a.
65. Shivers, C. A., Dudkiewicz, A. B., Franklin, L. E., and Fussell, N. E. (1972) *Science* **178**, 1211–1213.
66. Shivers, C. A., and Dudkiewicz, A. B. (1974) *Basic Life Sci.* **4**, Part B, 81–96.
67. Jilek, F., and Pavlok, A. (1975) *J. Reprod. Fertil.* **42**, 377–380.
68. Oikawa, T., and Yanagimachi, R. (1975) *J. Reprod. Fertil.* **45**, 487–494.
69. Sacco, A. G. (1977) *Biol. Reprod.* **16**, 158–163.
70. Bleil, J. D., and Wassarman, P. M. (1980) *Dev. Biol.* **76**, 185–202.
71. Bleil, J. D., and Wassarman, P. M. (1980) *Cell* **20**, 873–882.
72. Inoue, M., and Wolf, D. P. (1975) *Biol. Reprod.* **13**, 546–551.
73. Inoue, M., and Wolf, D. P. (1975) *Biol. Reprod.* **13**, 340–346.
74. Oikawa, T., Yanagimachi, R., and Nicolson, G. L. (1973) *Nature (London)* **241**, 256–259.
75. Nicolson, G. L., Yanagimachi, R., and Yanagimachi, H. (1975) *J. Cell Biol.* **66**, 263–274.
76. Phillips, D. M., and Shalgi, R. M. (1980) *J. Exp. Zool.* **213**, 1–8.

Membrane-Bound Sperm-Specific Antibodies: Their Role in Infertility

RICHARD BRONSON, GEORGE COOPER,
AND DAVID L. ROSENFELD

Division of Human Reproduction
Department of Obstetrics and Gynecology
North Shore University Hospital
Manhasset, New York

The role that antisperm antibodies play in infertility is controversial due to an almost complete reliance of prior studies on serologic tests for their detection. Attempts to correlate human infertility with the presence of circulating sperm-specific antibodies by indirect immunofluorescence, sperm agglutination, or complement-dependent cytotoxicity tests have been conflicting (1,2). As both fertile and infertile men and women can have high titers of humoral antisperm antibodies, and as the reported incidence of these varies widely, it has not been clear that such antibodies have a direct adverse affect on fertility. Indeed, immunity to spermatozoa becomes relevant to the question of fertility only when sperm-specific antibodies can be demonstrated within the reproductive tract secretions, and when these immunoglobulins, bound to spermatozoa, can be shown to hinder sperm transport in the female or subsequently alter sperm–egg interaction.

As a prerequisite for determining how sperm-specific antibodies might alter the physiology of reproduction, one needs an easy means of directly assessing the presence of immunoglobulins bound to the sperm surface. We have developed such a method for detecting plasma membrane-bound antibodies on motile spermatozoa, by use of Immunobeads (Bio-Rad). We have also correlated the presence of antibodies bound to spermatozoa in ejaculates with (1) the results of serologic tests, in these same men, for sperm agglutinins; (2) the finding of sperm-specific antibodies in serum, as determined by Immuno-

BIOREGULATORS OF REPRODUCTION

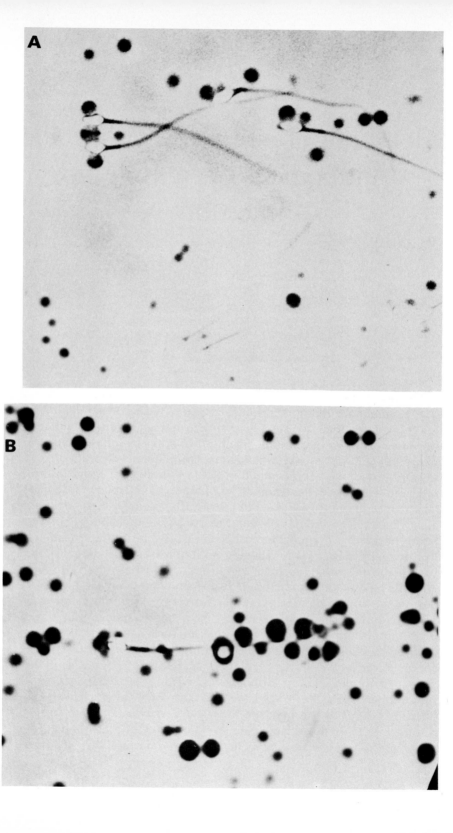

bead binding following passive transfer to antibody negative donor sperm; and (3) the ability of antibody positive spermatozoa to penetrate enzymatically denuded, zona-free hamster ova.

Sera were obtained from 73 men judged to be at high risk for antisperm autoantibodies, based on repeatedly poor postcoital testing, spontaneous sperm agglutination in semen, prior vasectomy, or infertility in spite of a complete normal evaluation. These sera were screened for antisperm antibodies by a modification tray agglutination test (3), the Franklin–Dukes test (4), and Immunobead binding following passive transfer to donor sperm.

Immunobeads (Bio-Rad) linked covalently to rabbit, antihuman IgA (α-chain specific) or IgG (γ-chain specific) antibody were suspended at 2.0 mg/ml in Dulbecco's phosphate buffered saline (PBS), with crystallized human serum albumin 10 mg/ml (Pentax, Miles Laboratories). Semen liquified at room temperature was filtered through pyrex glass wool (5). Filtered semen was diluted 1:5 v/v with PBS containing human serum albumin (HSA) 5 mg/ml (fraction V, Sigma), and washed twice, after which the final sperm pellet was resuspended in PBS/HSA to a final cell count of 10–20 million per cc.

Five microliters of this sperm suspension was added to 50 μl of immunobead suspension, added to a glass slide, mixed, and allowed to stand at room temperature for 5 minutes prior to counting. Immunobead-sperm binding commensed as soon as the two were mixed, with maximum binding essentially complete by 5–10 minutes (Fig. 1).

The regional sites of Immunobead binding were classified as follows: spermatozoa binding one or more Immunobeads exclusively to the tail end piece were designated as tail tip binders (tt). When Immunobeads bound to the principal piece of the tail (PP binders), special notation was also made as to the specific location of binding; namely, the zipper region immediately posterior to the annulus, or the proportion of the tail exhibiting binding, e.g., the distal one-fifth, etc. The designation mp was given to sperm demonstrating Immunobead binding to the mid-piece and neck region. H indicated head binding, with pac. and ac. designating postacrosomal or acrosomal locations (Tables I and II).

Sperm-specific antibodies were detected in the sera of 23 of the 73 men studied. Five sera contained sperm-specific antibodies that were solely of IgA class, seven solely IgG, and the remainder, both immu-

---

Fig. 1. (A.) Head specific IgG Immunobead binding following serum transfer—#227. (B.) Head and tail specific IgG following serum transfer—#25.

noglobulin classes. When sera contained sperm-specific antibodies of both immunoglobulin classes, the regional binding characteristics for anti-IgA beads did not correlate with that for anti-IgG beads. Thus head and principal piece binding might be present for anti-IgA but not for anti-IgG beads or vice versa (Table I).

Background levels of nonspecific bead binding to motile sperm were determined by examining semen of two categories of men: (1) semen donors participating in the AID program, who had fathered children, (2) men from infertile couples, whose sperm demonstrated normal *in vitro* cervical mucus penetration. The range of nonspecific Immunobead binding for various regions of the sperm plasma membrane varied from 0 to 13%, for each immunoglobulin class (Table II).

The distribution of immunoglobulins on the sperm plasma membrane did not correlate with the patterns of sperm-to-sperm agglutination observed by tray agglutination or Franklin–Dukes testing. In most cases in which tail-to-tail sperm agglutination was demonstrated by the serologic tests, immunoglobulins bound to the head were also detected. Sera giving head-to-head sperm agglutination frequently possessed tail specific antibodies as well.

The specific molecular events leading to sperm agglutination remain unclear. Extensive antibody binding, as detected by Immunobeads, was often found on motile, nonagglutinated sperm. Cross-linking of sperm by antibodies, a prerequisite for agglutination, may depend both on the spacial distribution of antigenic sites on the sperm

TABLE I

A Comparison of Immunoglobulins Detected on the Plasma Membrane of Sperm in an Ejaculate with Those Detected within Serum of the Same Individual by Passive Antibody Transfer to Known Antibody Negative Sperm[a]

Anti-Ig immunobead specificity	Immunobead binding[b]									
	Serum transfer					Patient semen				
	H	mp	PP	tt	NB	H	mp	PP	tt	NB
IgA	99	—	—	100	0	94	96	95	100	—
	99	—	—	100	0	96	96	96	100	—
IgG	100	100	100	100	0	100	—	100	100	0
	100	100	100	100	0	100	—	100	100	0

[a] Varying patterns of midpiece and tail binding were detected for IgA and IgG Immunobeads in serum and semen.

[b] See methods for binding nomenclature.

TABLE II
Immunobead Binding of Antibody-Free Ejaculate Sperm

Sperm donor[a] category	Number of men	Regional[b] binding location	Percent sperm binding immunobeads for each region and immunobead class[c]	
			IgA	IgG
Proven fertile	10	H	0 (0–4)	0 (0–1)
		mp	0 (0–2)	0 (0–1)
		tt	4 (1–13)	1 (1–6)
		NB	96 (84–99)	99 (94–100)
Normal *in vitro* mucus penetration	24	H	0 (0–6)	0 (0–1)
		mp	0 (0–1)	—
		tt	4 (0–13)	2 (0–7)
		NB	96 (87–100)	98 (93–100)

[a] Nonspecific binding was determined by examining sperm of two categories of men: (1) semen donors participating in the AID program, who had fathered children; (2) men from infertile couples, whose sperm demonstrated normal cervical mucus penetration and progressive motility.

[b] See methods for nomenclature of regional binding. NB indicates absence of Immunobead binding over any sperm region.

[c] Median (range).

surface, as well as the antibody concentration within semen or serum, and the immunoglobulin classes involved.

A divergence of immune events in serum and semen was found. Antibodies were either detected on sperm in the absence of circulating humoral antibodies, or sperm-specific immunoglobulins were present in sera but not detectable on spermatozoa. Specific immunoglobulin classes were also present on sperm while not in serum, and frequently a discrepancy of regional antibody binding was seen between serum and semen as well. This was especially the case for IgAs, indicating the likelihood of a source of immunoglobulins through local secretion within the male reproductive tract. Indeed, secretory IgA has been found in high concentration within seminal plasma relative to all other immunoglobulin classes (6). Antibodies may also appear in the seminal plasma as transudates from the prostate, although in concentrations low relative to serum (7). These two sources of immunoglobulin explain the apparent dichotomy between immune events in serum and seminal plasma.

Six sera were selected in which regional Immunobead binding occurred over the acrosomal and post acrosomal regions of the sperm head, following passive antibody transfer. As this region of the sperm is involved in the acrosome reaction and membrane fusion events between gametes, these sera were utilized to determine whether antibodies bound to the sperm plasma membrane might interfere with ovum penetration. Conditions were established such that all sperm were antibody bound over the head region, as confirmed by Immunobead binding. The penetrating ability of sperm from fertile donors, following preincubation in antibody positive or antibody negative sera, was assessed using the zona-free hamster egg, enzymatically denuded of its investments, as described by Yanagamachi *et al.* (8). In addition, the ejaculate of an infertile individual found to have Immunobead binding over the head region of all his sperm was also studied for the ability of these spermatozoa to penetrate hamster eggs.

Penetration rates of antibody coated sperm, in each instance, were not significantly different from those of antibody free sperm. The kinetics of sperm–egg interaction were also not altered

There is a wide variation in the percentage of sperm that possess antibodies bound to their plasma membrane, both between men and between repeated ejaculates of the same individual. Antibody free sperm within an ejaculate should be able to reach the distal ampulla, the site of fertilization, and to interact normally with ova. The likelihood of fertilization then depends upon the proportion of sperm that are antibody free, in any given ejaculate. Whether antibody bound sperm retain the ability to fertilize eggs is not known. It is possible that antibodies might prevent, through steric hindrance, the close apposition of membranes required for membrane fusion. This might be expected for the larger, mulivalent immunoglobulins (sIgA, IgM) that would allow association of several Ig molecules with the plasma membrane. Wolf has obtained evidence, in one instance, of a human serum which possessed sperm-specific antibodies and impaired the penetration of zona-free hamster eggs by antibody-coated sperm, with no loss of sperm motility (9). Menge has also prepared antisera, in rabbits, against human sperm and found that these interfere with penetration rates of zona-free hamster eggs without altering motility (10). As penetration rates of zona-free hamster ova, by antibody-bound sperm, did not differ from controls, our own preliminary data would suggest that membrane events—either the acrosome reaction or sperm–egg membrane fusion—are not altered by sperm-specific membrane bound autoantibodies.

A more likely site of interference with gamete interaction is at the level of the zona pellucida. Species-specific sperm acceptor sites are present on the zona, and sperm binding to the zona appears to be a prerequisite to subsequent zona penetration. Antibodies directed against the zona obscure the sperm acceptor sites and block both the sperm binding and fertilization (11). Heterologous antibodies have also been produced in rabbits against boar sperm membrane vesicles. Binding of boar sperm to the porcine zona pellucida was blocked by both whole antisera and univalent antibody prepared by papain digestion (12). Hence, it would not be unlikely that the sperm-specific autoantibodies detected in this study could impair binding to the zona pellucida and inhibit penetration. Studies are in progress to confirm this hypothesis.

The location of antibody binding upon the sperm plasma membrane may then be critical in determining the mode by which specific immunoglobulins impair fertility. Sperm-specific antibodies which bind to the tail region might be expected to alter sperm motion within cervical mucus, but could not otherwise impair gamete interactions should these sperm reach the ampulla, the site of fertilization. Antibody bound to the acrosome and postacrosome regions of the sperm head could theoretically interfere with the acrosome reaction, penetration of the zona pellucida, and sperm–egg membrane fusion. Success of fertilization by antibody bound sperm may then depend upon the location of antibody on the plasma membrane, the amount of antibody bound, and immunoglobulin class involved.

REFERENCES

1. Beer, A. E., and Neaves, W. B. (1978) *Fertil. Steril.* **29**, 3.
2. Boetcher, B., Hjort, T., Rumke, P., Schulman, S., and Vyazov, O. E. (1977) *Acta Pathol. Mocrobiol. Scand., Suppl.* **258**, 1–69.
3. Marmar, J. L., Praiss, D. E., and DeBenedictus, T. J. (1980) *Arch. Androl.* **4**, 347.
4. Rose, N. R., Hjort, T., Rumke, P., Harper, M. J. K., and Vyazov, O. (1976) *Clin. Exp. Immunol.* **23**, 175.
5. Paulson, J. D., Polakoski, K. L., and Leto, S. (1979) *Fertil. Steril.* **32**, 125.
6. Uehling, D. T. (1971) *Fertil. Steril.* **22**, 769.
7. Rumke, P. (1975) *Clin. Exp. Immunol.* **22**, 256.
8. Yanagimachi, R., Yanagimachi, H., and Rogers, B. J. (1976) *Biol. Reprod.* **15**, 471.
9. D. P. Wolf, personal communication.
10. Menge, A. C., and Black, C. S. (1979) *Fertil. Steril.* **32**, 214.
11. Trounson, A. O., Shivers, C. A., McMaster, R., and Lopata, A. (1980) *Arch. Androl.* **4**, 29.
12. Peterson, R. N., Russell, L., Bundman, D., and Freund, M. (1980) *Science* **207**, 73.

PART VI

POST-FERTILIZATION
PHENOMENA

Regulation of Pronuclear Development

FRANK J. LONGO

Department of Anatomy
University of Iowa
Iowa City, Iowa

INTRODUCTION

Investigations of pronuclear development have their origin well before the turn of the century. From these early studies emerged the basis for the chromosome theory of inheritance and a fundamental understanding of the mechanisms of heredity (cf. 1,2 for a review of these early investigations). Many investigations of pronuclear development since this early period have been descriptive, detailing morphological parameters associated with fertilization. Reviews and detailed observations at the light microscopic level of male and female pronuclear development in mammals and invertebrates have been published (1,3,4). Relatively few studies have been carried out delineating cellular mechanisms or controlling factors of pronuclear development. This is due not to a lack of interest in this aspect of fertilization but rather to technical limitations. Nevertheless, we are beginning to gain some understanding of the mechanisms and regulatory events involving the development of the male and female pronuclei.

In this chapter, events concerning the metamorphosis of the sperm nucleus into a male pronucleus are reviewed. Development of the female pronucleus has also been studied; many of the processes observed here are similar to those involving the metamorphosis of the sperm nucleus into the male pronucleus (cf. 5). How the mechanisms and regulators controlling the development of the male pronucleus relate to those involving the development of the female pronucleus remains unexplored.

529

BIOREGULATORS OF REPRODUCTION
Copyright © 1981 by Academic Press, Inc.
All rights of reproduction in any form reserved.
ISBN 0-12-379980-5

Although specific details involving the development of the male pronucleus vary from one organism to another, there are three basic features common to the organisms studied so far (Fig. 1) (5). (1) The earliest alteration of the sperm nucleus upon incorporation into the egg is the breakdown of its nuclear envelope. As a result of this process the condensed sperm chromatin is placed in direct association with components of the egg cytoplasm, i.e., without an intervening membranous boundary. (2) Dispersion of the condensed chromatin follows the loss of the sperm nuclear envelope, yielding a mass much larger in volume and more diffuse in composition than that taken into the egg with the sperm nucleus. (3) At the time of, or shortly after the dispersion of the sperm chromatin, a nuclear envelope is formed along the periphery of the dispersed chromatin, thereby separating the paternally derived, hereditary material from the zygote cytoplasm. As a result of these processes there is a dramatic transformation in the shape, volume, chromatin conformation, and nucleoprotein content of the former sperm nucleus (compare Fig. 2 and 3). Furthermore, the paternally derived chromatin of the male pronucleus becomes active with respect to DNA synthesis (6–9). There is also evidence that the transformed sperm chromatin is capable of RNA synthesis (10–12).

TRANSFORMATION OF THE SPERM NUCLEUS INTO A MALE PRONUCLEUS

In order to fully appreciate mechanisms regulating the development of the male pronucleus, events concerning the transformation of the sperm nucleus need to be considered. Electron microscopic observations of pronuclear development have been made employing the zygotes of a number of plants and animals (5,13–18). The following account is a general overview of these processes.

BREAKDOWN OF THE SPERM NUCLEAR ENVELOPE

Unlike the situation in most organisms, the sperm chromatin of some animals and plants is not bounded by a nuclear envelope (12,19). Following gamete fusion in these instances, the paternally derived chromatin becomes directly associated with the egg cytoplasm, without an intervening membranous layer. However, in the sperm of most organisms studied so far, a sperm nuclear envelope is present. Breakdown of the sperm nuclear envelope quickly occurs following the incorporation of the spermtozoon (5,15) and involves a ve-

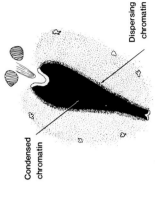

(B) CHROMATIN DISPERSION

Condensed chromatin

Dispersing chromatin

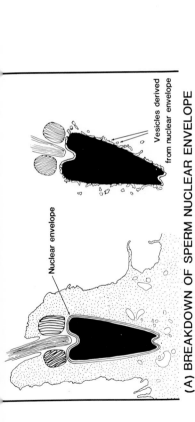

Nuclear envelope

Vesicles derived from nuclear envelope

(A) BREAKDOWN OF SPERM NUCLEAR ENVELOPE

(D) MALE PRONUCLEUS

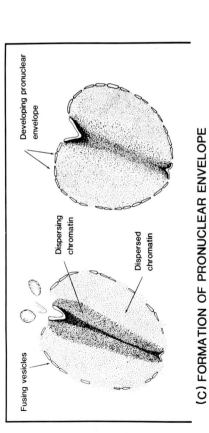

Developing pronuclear envelope

Fusing vesicles

Dispersing chromatin

Dispersed chromatin

(C) FORMATION OF PRONUCLEAR ENVELOPE

① **Fig. 1.** · Diagrammatic representation (not to scale) of the major events of pronuclear development in *Arbacia* zygotes. (A) The condensed chromatin of the sperm nucleus is surrounded by a nuclear envelope, which breaks down subsequent to sperm incorporation, forming numerous vesicles that are scattered within the cytoplasm. (B) This is followed by dispersion of the condensed chromatin. (C) Vesicles aggregate along the periphery of the dispersed chromatin and fuse together to form elongate cisternae, which in turn coalesce to form a nuclear envelope. (D) The result of these processes is the formation of a spheroid male pronucleus containing dispersed chromatin and surrounded by a nuclear envelope possessing pores.

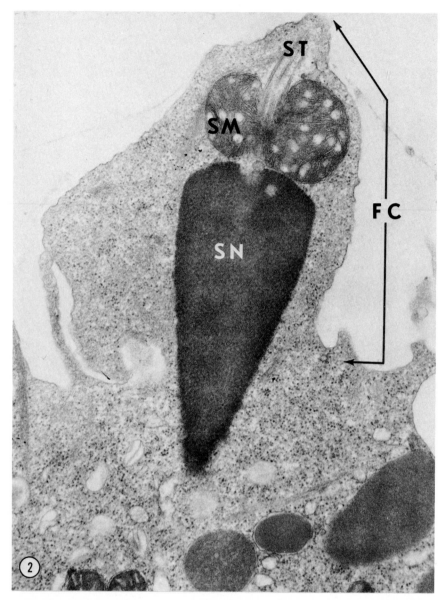

Fig. 2. Incorporated *Arbacia* spermatozoon, 1 minute after insemination. The cytoplasm in the region of gamete fusion has engulfed the spermatozoon, forming a fertilization cone (FC). ST, Portion of the axonemal complex of the sperm flagellum; SM, sperm mitochondrion; SN, sperm nucleus containing condensed chromatin.

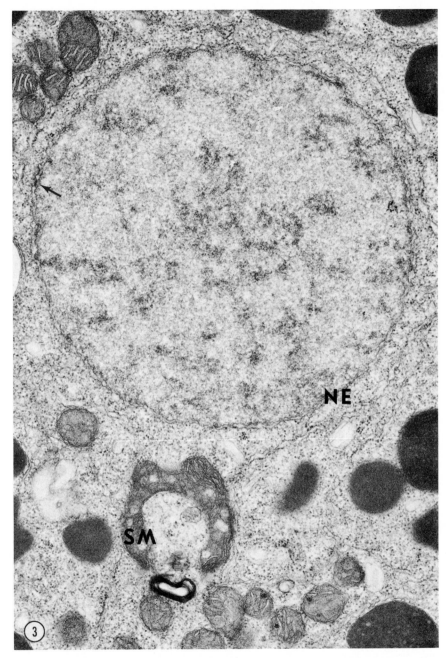

Fig. 3. Male pronucleus of an *Arbacia* zygote, 10 minutes postinsemination. The dispersed paternally derived chromatin is surrounded by a nuclear envelope (NE) possessing pores (arrow). SM, Sperm mitochondrion.

siculation of the inner and outer membranes comprising the nuclear envelope. This process is comparable to that described by Barros *et al.* (20) for the acrosome reaction. The inner and outer laminae of the sperm nuclear envelope fuse together at multiple sites, thereby forming vesicles that initially outline the condensed sperm chromatin but shortly are scattered into the surrounding cytoplasm (Fig. 1). Because the vesicles lack distinguishing features, they are soon lost in and among other vesicular elements of the zygote.

A number of observations have been made indicating that breakdown of the sperm nuclear envelope at fertilization is a highly regulated event. For example, (1) in the sea urchin, *Arbacia*, breakdown of the sperm nuclear envelope does not go to completion (cf. 5). Segments of the sperm nuclear envelope lining the apex and the base of the incorporated sperm nucleus are left intact; subsequently these become incorporated into the nuclear envelope of the male pronucleus. They are associated with some electron-dense material, presumably chromatin, and line areas of the sperm nucleus that become sculptured early during spermiogenesis, seemingly as a result of their association with the acrosomal vesicle and centriole (21). The function of those portions of the sperm nuclear envelope that remain intact is unknown. (2) In *Arbacia*, breakdown of the sperm nuclear envelope can occur in the immediate vicinity of the female pronucleus. In this instance there is no apparent effect on the nuclear envelope of the female pronucleus. The absence of such an effect, in this case, indicates the specificity of the mechanism concerning the breakdown of the sperm nuclear envelope.

Although factors regulating the breakdown of the sperm nuclear envelope have not been determined, it is possible that cytoplasmic processes similar to those involved with nuclear envelope disruption in other cells are involved (22–25). Wasserman and Smith (26) have demonstrated that mature amphibian ova contain a cytoplasmic factor which is able to induce germinal vesicle breakdown when injected into immature oocytes. The activity of this factor is quickly lost after fertilization but later reappears and cycles with development. Its appearance coincides with the G to M transition of cycling cells, indicating that this factor is not restricted to oocyte maturation but may play a more general role in regulating nuclear envelope breakdown during mitosis. Studies involving fusion of somatic cells at different stages of the cell cycle also demonstrate that factors inducing nuclear envelope breakdown and chromosome condensation appear in the cytoplasm at the end of S_2, persist through M and disappear as the cell enters G_1 (22,27).

As a result of the breakdown of the sperm nuclear envelope, the condensed sperm chromatin is directly exposed to the zygote cytoplasm (Fig. 1) (5,14,15,28–31). This presumably allows factors within the zygote cytoplasm to gain access to the chromatin and thereby alter its composition. If the membranes surrounding the sperm are not disrupted, cytoplasmic factors necessary for sperm transformation might not be able to gain access to the chromatin. In this regard sea urchin sperm nuclei incorporated into immature germinal vesicle eggs remain surrounded by membranous cisternae and fail to undergo chromatin dispersion suggesting that (1) the conditions necessary for chromatin dispersion are absent (or inactive) or (2) the agents are present but unable to gain access to the condensed chromatin and function (32). Furthermore, sperm mechanically injected into eggs (33) or phagocytized by somatic cells (34), in both cases surrounded by membrane, do not transform. The failure of the sperm nucleus to metamorphose in these instances may be due to an inability of cytoplasmic factors to gain access to the contents of the sperm nucleus.

CHROMATIN DISPERSION

Morphological transformation of the sperm condensed chromatin into the dispersed form of the male pronucleus is a dramatic event which has been examined by electron microscopy in a variety of organisms (5,12,17,28–31,35–40). In the organisms that have been studied so far, sperm chromatin generally disperses in a characteristic pattern. In many organisms morphological changes first occur along the peripheral aspect of the incorporated sperm nucleus where condensed, densely staining chromatin grades to a more dispersed and lightly staining mass (cf. 5). As this process continues, the peripheral dispersed zone increases in size, whereas the central dense portion gradually becomes smaller until it is no longer present. This pattern suggests that the agent(s) responsible for dispersion "migrates" from the periphery to the center of the sperm nucleus (5). Eventually all of the sperm chromatin becomes a morphologically homogeneous mass of dispersed chromatin (Fig. 1 and 3).

It has been suggested that the mechanism of sperm chromatin dispersion in the rat and rabbit may be the opposite of nuclear condensation during spermiogenesis (30,36). Comparisons of chromatin during pronuclear development and spermiogenesis in invertebrates (*Arbacia, Mytilus,* and *Spisula*) indicate that such is not the case, at least in these organisms (cf. 5). Further study is necessary to determine the relation, if any, between chromatin dispersion and condensation during pronuclear development and spermiogenesis(5).

It is not unreasonable to suggest that the dispersion of the condensed sperm chromatin is a morphological manifestation of a change in nucleoprotein content. How closely changes in nucleoprotein content are related to the pattern of chromatin dispersion remains to be determined.

Chemical changes attending the dispersion of the sperm chromatin have been studied, but there is a need for further investigations in this area (cf. 41 for a review). Studies of molecular changes in the incorporated sperm nucleus are formidable due to technical problems, e.g., isolation of pronuclei is made difficult due to an extremely high cytoplasm—nucleus ratio. Despite this and other difficulties, a number of studies have been performed yielding interesting results. These studies can be divided into three groups based on the method of analysis employed: (1) cytochemical, (2) autoradiographic, and (3) biochemical. In all three instances attention has been devoted to changes that the proteins associated with the DNA undergo.

In an effort to fully appreciate the importance and significance of nucleoprotein changes of the paternally derived chromatin at fertilization, one needs to first consider the state of the nucleoprotein within the mature sperm nucleus, its characteristics, and its similarities to nucleoproteins found in somatic cells. During the differentiation of the spermatogonium into a spermatozoon in many organisms, histones characteristic of somatic cells are replaced by a distinct group of basic proteins, often unique to the mature spermatozoon and much more basic than that found in somatic cells (sperm basic nuclear proteins, 42–50). It has been suggested that the complexing of the sperm DNA to these highly basic proteins permits condensation of the chromatin and repression of the DNA. In those cases where the sperm chromatin contains highly basic proteins and is repressed, a question remains as to how genetic activity is resumed after fertilization. Because the sperm basic nucleoproteins are often unique and tend to predominate in amount, the nonbasic nucleoproteins of the spermatozoon have not been as extensively investigated. Recent studies have examined the nonbasic proteins in the sperm nucleus and their changes at fertilization (51).

Cytochemical examination of fertilized eggs have demonstrated that the sperm basic proteins are replaced by different basic nucleoproteins (44,52–55). How this replacement is affected, i.e., whether it is a dissociation of the protein from the DNA or a masking of the protein could not be settled by existing cytochemical techniques. Nevertheless, these investigations demonstrate that the paternally derived chromatin stained differently subsequent to the metamorphosis of the sperm nucleus into a male pronucleus and support the idea that the DNA brought into the egg with the spermatozoon acquires a "new" set of basic nucleoproteins, presumably during the dispersion of the sperm chromatin.

Support for the idea that the basic proteins specific for the sperm nucleus are actually removed from the paternally derived DNA came from autoradiographic analysis of incorporated sperm labeled with amino acids (56–58). During the differentiation of the sperm nucleus into a male pronucleus there is a dramatic reduction in autoradiographic grains associated with the dispersing chromatin, Indicating that the basic proteins unique to the sperm nucleus are not simply "masked" but are most probably dissociated from the DNA.

More recent and direct studies of the transformation of the paternally derived chromatin at fertilization by Carroll and Ozaki (59) have shown that the basic proteins of the sperm nucleus are, in fact, lost at fertilization and the paternally derived DNA becomes associated with basic proteins similar to those found within the female pronucleus. Similar results have also been reported by Poccia *et al.* (60). Investigations of nonbasic nucleoproteins at fertilization have similarly demonstrated that the paternally derived chromatin undergoes considerable chemical reorganization following its incorporation into the egg. As in the case of basic nucleoproteins, the nonbasic nucleoproteins of the spermatozoon are replaced by ones that are similar to those found in the female pronucleus (61).

Although a number of mechanisms whereby the conversion in nucleoproteins may be brought about have been proposed, none have been shown to be correct. Frog and sea urchin eggs have been shown to contain DNA binding proteins and pronuclei are able to concentrate cytoplasmic nonhistone proteins (61–64). Interestingly, Barry and Merriam (62) showed that chick erythrocyte nuclei suspended in cytoplasm from *Xenopus* eggs swell, but do not change when mixed with cytoplasm from immature oocytes. Swelling of nuclei in this case was related to the concentration of magnesium ion.

A number of investigations have been carried out with mammalian sperm *in vitro*, demonstrating that cleavage of disulfide bonds is a requirement for decondensation, thereby permitting the disruption of the nucleoproteins bound to the DNA (65–69). Although there is a high concentration of thiol groups in eggs (70), there is no evidence to suggest that they do in fact participate in chromatin dispersion.

Phosphorylation as well as other enzymatic modifications of the nucleoproteins may also have a role in dispersion of the condensed sperm chromatin. Phosphorylation has been shown to be involved in the modification of basic nucleoproteins during spermatogenesis in salmonid fish (71); perhaps these modifications are reversed at fertilization (72,73). A high level of phosphorylation does occur in the mouse egg at fertilization (74). Whether or not this leads to the disruption of noncovalent binding and the reduction of the interactions between sperm basic proteins for DNA has not been demonstrated (cf. also 75–78).

Recent investigations have shown that the basic proteins of mammalian sperm nuclei are degraded when sperm or isolated sperm nuclei are incubated in vitro with sulfhydryl compounds and that substantial basic protein degradation must occur before sperm nuclei decondense. The possibility that sulfhydryl-induced proteolytic activity is also involved in sperm nuclear decondensation in vivo has been proposed (66,69,79,80). To date there is no evidence to indicate whether or not proteolysis, due to enzymes derived either from the sperm or from the egg, plays a role in sperm nuclear decondensation in vivo. An acrosin-like protease, associated with isolated rabbit sperm nuclei, has been found that is responsible for nucleoprotein degradation and decondensation in vitro (69). However, such proteolytic activity may have little importance in vivo, since Young (68) indicates that the decondensing activity intrinsic to isolated sperm nuclei is of acrosomal origin and is liberated from the acrosome during isolation and washing of the spermatozoon.

Motlik et al. (81) found a significant accumulation of label in male and female pronuclei of rabbit oocytes when incubated in vitro with [³H]lysine and subsequently fertilized. A similar incorporation of substances from the zygote cytoplasm has also been observed in experimental systems, where somatic cell nuclei are transferred to Xenopus eggs (62,82,83; cf. also 84,85). In these instances it has been demonstrated that the "state" of the egg cytoplasm has profound influences on the activity of the transplanted nucleus (82). For instance, when nuclei are microinjected into immature oocytes, which are characterized by high RNA and low DNA synthetic activities, the transplanted nuclei synthesize RNA. Conversely, when nuclei are injected to mature eggs, characterized by relatively high DNA and low RNA synthetic activities, the transplants synthesize DNA. These experiments clearly demonstrate the control of gene activity by elements within the egg cytoplasm (22,82,86). It is not unreasonable to presume that the changes exhibited by the sperm nucleus during pronuclear development, most likely initiated by egg cytoplasmic factors, also allow for its reprograming.

Based on observations demonstrating an absence of DNA polymerase activity in sea urchin sperm, it has been speculated that one of the substances acquired from the zygote cytoplasm at fertilization by the transforming sperm nucleus is DNA polymerase (87). The presence of DNA polymerase activity within the male promucleus indicates that sometime following the incorporation of the sperm nucleus, the enzyme is "unmasked" or obtained from the cytoplasm (87). Moreover, the cytoplasm of the sea urchin egg has been shown to contain abundant DNA polymerase activity. More recent investigations have demonstrated DNA polymerase activity in mature mammalian sperm (88,89; cf. also 90–92). Consequently, synthetic activities of the male pronucleus, such as DNA polymerase, may also arise from enzymes brought into the egg with the spermatozoon, which are in turn, activated by components of the egg cytoplasm.

FORMATION OF THE NUCLEAR ENVELOPE OF THE MALE PRONUCLEUS

Development of the nuclear envelope of the male pronucleus has been studied in a variety of organisms (cf. 5,13,31,39,40,93) and is similar to the series of events described for nuclear envelope formation in mitotic and meiotic cells (Fig. 1). The timing of the formation of the nuclear envelope that comes to surround the dispersed sperm-derived chromatin (male pronuclear envelope) appears to vary in those animals that have been studied thus far. For example, in the sea urchin, *Arbacia*, development of the male pronuclear envelope is initiated during the dispersion of the chromatin (94). In *Spisula*, formation of the male pronuclear envelope takes place after chromatin dispersion, apparently in concert with the formation of the nuclear envelope of the female pronucleus (95, cf. also 5). In either instance morphological events of the formation of the pronuclear envelope are similar. Vesicles coalesce along the periphery of the dispersed chromatin, and fuse to form elongate cisternae which develop pores. The cisternae then fuse together to enclose the dispersed chromatin and form a nuclear envelope (5). In those instances where portions of the sperm nuclear envelope are incorporated into the structure of the male pronuclear envelope, the elongate cisternae fuse with the sperm-derived membranes, such that they too become a part of the membranous boundary of the male pronucleus. Those regions of the sperm nuclear envelope incorporated into the male pronuclear envelope frequently retain distinctive morphological features, which allows them to be identified at later stages of fertilization or embryonic development, e.g., following the fusion of the male and female pronuclei (94,96).

Investigations have been carried out in an effort to determine the source(s) of membrane that comprises the male pronuclear envelope in the sea urchin (97). Possible sources include (1) the sperm nuclear envelope, (2) the endoplasmic reticulum of the egg, and (3) the *de novo* synthesis of membrane components. Studies with the sea urchin, *Arbacia,* have demonstrated that portions of the sperm nuclear envelope, specifically the apical and basal regions, are in fact incorporated into the male pronuclear envelope. This raises the question of whether the amount of nuclear envelope present within the incorporated sperm is sufficient to completely enclose the dispersed paternally derived chromatin. In other words, is the male pronuclear envelope comprised entirely of the sperm nuclear envelope? This question has been answered by a geometrical analysis of the surface area of the sperm nucleus and the male pronuclear envelope (97). Since in *Arbacia* all of the nuclear envelope within the spermatozoon surrounds the nucleus, the amount of sperm nuclear envelope can be determined by calculating the surface area of the sperm nucleus, which is approximately 14 μm^2. The surface area of the male pronucleus is variable. As the male pronucleus sits within the zygote cytoplasm it continues to enlarge and can increase in size to equal that of the female pronucleus (approximately 11 μm in diameter). Computation of the surface area of the male pronucleus based on a diameter of 5 μm yields a surface area of about 79 μm^2. Since the male pronuclear envelope has pores (approximately 14% of the total surface area) and the sperm nucleus does not, the total surface area of the male pronucleus needs to be adjusted to 68 μm^2. Assuming that all of the sperm nuclear envelope is incorporated into the male pronuclear envelope then only 14/68 or 21% of the pronuclear envelope can be made up of the sperm nuclear envelope (97).

As a source of membrane for the formation of the pronuclear envelope, the endoplasmic reticulum is a likely possibility based on its prevalence (98), continuity with the nuclear envelope (99) and involvement in nuclear envelope formation and repair in other cells (cf. 100,101). The possible role of the endoplasmic reticulum of the zygote in the formation of the male pronuclear envelope has been examined by an analysis of male pronuclear development in centrifuged *Arbacia* eggs. When sea urchin eggs are placed on a sucrose cushion of equivalent density and then centrifuged, their cytoplasmic components stratify into layers consisting of specific organelles (98,102). The stratified egg can in turn be further centrifuged to yield nucleate and anucleate halves, each consisting of a specific constellation of organelles. In the stratified egg, cytoplasmic components layer into the following zones from the centripetal to the centrifugal region: (1) the lipid zone, (2) the hyaline zone, containing the membranous organelles of the ovum, such as, endoplasmic reticulum, annulate lamellae, and Golgi bodies (situated within this region is also the female pronucleus), (3) the mitochondrial layer, (4) the yolk region, and (5) the pigment zone. The nucleate half contains the lipid, hyaline, and a portion of the mitochondrial layers. The anucleate half contains the remainder of the mitochondrial layer, the yolk, and pigment layers. Most important for these studies is that most, if not all, of the endoplasmic reticulum (as well as other membranous cisternae) becomes localized in a discrete region of the egg, the hyaline zone. Since sperm incorporation occurs randomly along the surface of the egg and because the organelles within the stratified and half-eggs are localized to specific regions, one can determine what effect the presence or absence of endoplasmic reticulum has on the development of the male pronucleus (97).

The results of ultrastructural analyses of male pronuclear development in centrifuged eggs indicate that the time required to form a male pronuclear envelope is prolonged in areas depleted of endoplasmic reticulum (Table I). Although such results do not prove unequivocally that endoplasmic reticulum directly contributes to the formation of the pronuclear envelope, they are highly suggestive of such an association (cf. 97).

Although the question of the involvement of membrane biosynthesis in the formation of the pronuclear envelope is a complex one, two

TABLE I

Estimated Amount of Endoplasmic Reticulum Present and the Time Required to Complete the Formation of the Male Pronuclear Envelope[a]

	Stratified egg			
	Centripetal region	Centrifugal region	Nucleate half	Nonnucleate half
Estimated amount of endoplasmic reticulum	Abundant	Sparse	Abundant	Negligible
Time required to complete the formation of the pronuclear envelope (minutes postinsemination)	4–6	12[b]	4	[c]

[a] Taken from Longo (97).

[b] Completed male pronuclear envelope first observed at 12 minutes postinsemination.

[c] Male pronuclear envelope not formed as late as 20 minutes postinsemination.

principals seem clear (103). (1) Membranes do not form *de novo* in cells; newly synthesized proteins and lipids are inserted into preexisting membranes. (2) Membrane components frequently are synthesized or inserted into sites distinct from their ultimate destinations (103). Investigations have been carried out examining membrane biosynthesis by measuring the appearance and activity of specific enzymes, the incorporation of labeled precursors into membrane components, and the effects of various inhibitory agents on this incorporation (104–109). Analyses comparable to those performed in somatic cells have been carried out with fertilized *Arbacia* eggs. These studies demonstrate that the incorporation of labeled leucine into TCA-precipitable material can be inhibited up to 80% of controls during the period of pronuclear development with puromycin. Electron microscopic observation of puromycin-treated specimens indicate that male pronuclear development is unaffected; the nuclear envelope that forms is morphologically similar to that of controls (97).

Consequently, it would appear that in the case of *Arbacia* zygotes, possibly as much as 20% of the pronuclear envelope may be derived from the sperm nuclear envelope, whereas the remainder comes from sources derived from the egg. The contribution of endoplasmic reticulum to the formation of the male pronuclear envelope may be as great or greater than 80% of the total membrane. What contribution the biosynthesis of membrane components makes is not known with certainty.

With the formation of the pronuclear envelope, transformation of the sperm nucleus into a male pronucleus is essentially concluded (cf. 5 for additional information on further morphogenesis of the male pronucleus). However, the male pronucleus does not remain static, but continues to undergo morphogenetic events, including its enlargement and migration to the female pronucleus. With the association of the male and female pronuclei there is the integration of the maternally and paternally derived chromosomes in order to form the hereditary complement of the embryo. As a result of this association of the two pronuclei the identity of the male pronucleus is lost.

ASPECTS REGULATING THE METAMORPHOSIS OF THE SPERM NUCLEUS INTO A MALE PRONUCLEUS

The time period required for male pronucleus formation varies considerably among animals that have been studied so far (cf. 5). In some animals, e.g., the sea urchin, this period is relatively brief, i.e., about 8 minutes (94). In the chicken it is approximately 25 minutes (14). In mammals it is 3–4 hours (4,110). The basis for this difference in time to form a male pronucleus may be dependent on (1) the size of the sperm nucleus and/or (2) the concentration or activity of the agents involved in pronuclear development.

In sea urchins the difference in size of the male and female pronuclei is great, the male pronucleus being much smaller than the female. In mammals, as well as many other organisms, this size differential is not as pronounced or, in fact, may be reversed, such that the male pronucleus is larger than the female (cf. 5). If pronuclear migration is inhibited in sea urchin zygotes, thereby preventing the fusion of the pronuclei, the male pronucleus continues to increase in size, often attaining the dimensions of the female pronucleus. In mammalian zygotes, under similar circumstances, continued enlargement of the male pronucleus is not as obvious (111). These observations suggest that (1) factors responsible for the continued enlargement of the male pronucleus are present in the zygote cytoplasm well after the normal period of fertilization and (2) the size the male pronucleus attains prior to its association with the female pronucleus is related to the period of time spent within the zygote cytoplasm.

Events involving the development of the male pronucleus do not appear to affect (involve) the maternally derived chromatin. That is, although both groups of chromatin are confined within the same cytoplasm, the two masses may be observed to undergo processes that are dissimilar or "antagonistic" to one another (4,11,110, cf. 5,112,113). In the case of sea urchins, the eggs are inseminated after the completion of meiosis, i.e., when the ovum has concluded its meiotic divisions and contains a female pronucleus. Sperm that enter such eggs are immediately transformed into male pronuclei with no apparent affect on the female pronucleus. In the molluscs, *Spisula* and *Mytilus*, sperm enter eggs that are in the germinal vesicle stage or at the first metaphase of meiosis, respectively (cf. 5). Hence, in both species, inseminated ova must complete meiosis and develop a female pronucleus. Development of a male pronucleus is initiated in the eggs of both species immediately after the incorporation of the sperm nucleus. Dispersion of sperm-condensed chromatin in both instances appears to have no affect on the condensed or condensing meiotic chromosomes of the egg which are involved in the completion of meiosis. Observations such as these help to demonstrate the specificity of processes concerning the regulation of the maternally and paternally derived chromatin and that the maternally derived chromatin is often unresponsive to conditions affecting the metamorphosis of the sperm nucleus.

Furthermore, the paternally derived chromatin is seemingly unaffected by conditions affecting the maternally derived chromatin during the completion of its meiotic events. Results of recent investigations by Hirao and Yanagimachi (114) employing polyspermic hamster eggs indicate that cytoplasmic factors controlling the development of the female pronucleus are not identical to those regulating the development of the male pronucleus.

There is a wealth of information originating from before the turn of the century which indicates that the transformations of the sperm nucleus into a male pronucleus are dependent upon the activation or appearance of factors that arise with the development of the ovum (cf. 1,25). That more than one factor is responsible for the transformation of the sperm nucleus into a male pronucleus has been assumed. Recent investigations by Hirao and Yanagamachi (114) indicate that the factor inducing dispersion of the sperm nucleus is different from the agent responsible for transforming the decondensed sperm nucleus into a male pronucleus. The identification of these factors has not

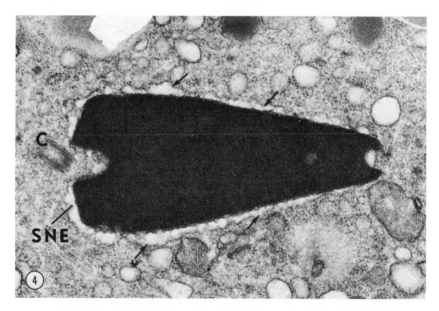

Fig. 4. Sperm nucleus incorporated into a immature *Arbacia* oocyte (germinal vesicle intact), 30 minutes postinsemination. The membrane lining the base of the sperm nucleus (SNE), and derived from the sperm nuclear envelope, is continuous with cisternae lining the lateral aspect of the sperm nucleus (arrows). The condensed chromatin of the sperm nucleus is morphologically unchanged. C, Sperm centriole. Taken from Longo (32).

TABLE II
Extent of Sperm Nuclear Transformation into Male Pronuclei
versus Stage of Egg Development[a,b]

	Stage of development			
	Germinal vesicle oocyte		Meiotically dividing oocyte	Pronuclear ova
	Previtellogenic	Vitellogenic		
Disappearance of sperm nuclear envelope	?	?	+	+
Cromatin dispersion	−	−	+	+
Formation of pronuclear envelope	−	−	−	+

[a] Taken from Longo (32).
[b] +, Takes place; −, does not take place; ?, not established.

been achieved and we have little insight into their chemical composition. Much of the work in this area of fertilization has been descriptive, demonstrating *a posteriori* that such factors exist in a wide variety of animals (25,32,115–122). The pattern of investigation in most of the organisms studied so far is very similar and one system, the sea urchin, will be described in order to highlight salient features of this regulatory aspect of pronuclear development.

Immature germinal vesicle eggs of the sea urchin can be inseminated, however, incorporated sperm remain essentially unchanged (32). [These results differ from those previously published by Franklin (123). The basis for this difference is unknown.] The perinuclear cisternae of the sperm nuclear envelope may enlarge and/or possibly vesiculate but further alterations of the sperm nucleus, such as loss of the nuclear envelope and chromatin dispersion, are not observed (Fig. 4; Table II). Sperm that enter sea urchin eggs at the time of their meiotic divisions, i.e., at the first or second metaphase division, undergo changes normally associated with sperm incorporated into mature eggs. In such instances there is a loss of the sperm nuclear envelope and the dispersion of condensed chromatin, but not to the same extent as observed in inseminated pronuclear ova (Fig. 5). Only with the completion of meiosis do sea urchin eggs become capable of supporting the complete development of the sperm nucleus into a male pronucleus. However, chromatin dispersion does not always go to completion in fertilized eggs that have recently completed meiosis. As indicated in Table II (cf. also Fig. 6) incorporated sperm nuclei exhibit greater differentration with increasing oocyte maturation. The rela-

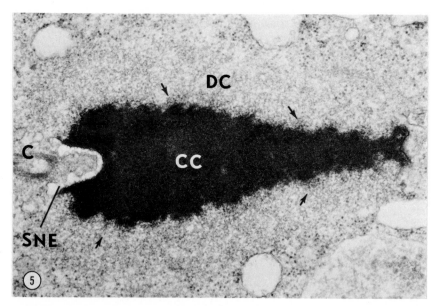

Fig. 5. Sperm nucleus incorporated into an *Arbacia* oocyte, which is undergoing its meiotic division (germinal vesicle broken down). The condensed chromatin (CC) is dispersing as indicated by the arrows. Portions of the sperm nuclear envelope (SNE) remain at the apex and base of the sperm nucleus. DC, Dispersed chromatin; C, sperm centriole. Taken from Longo (32).

tion of sperm nuclear transformation and egg maturation lends support to the notion that factors required for pronuclear development appear (or are activated) as the egg progresses through meiosis. Furthermore, a number of investigators have shown that material required for normal morphogensis of the oocyte, as well as the embryo are contributed by substances originating in the germinal vesicle (cf. 25).

Evidence has been presented to show that proteins synthesized during oogenesis are involved in the activation of genes essential for embryonic development (cf. 25). There are data to suggest that changes in activity of incorporated sperm nuclei, heterokaryons, and transplanted nuclei depend upon an exchange of proteins between cytoplasm and nucleus, which may be involved with nuclear enlargement and alterations in chromosome morphology and activity (82,86).

Studies by Hunter (124) with porcine ova also indicate the presence of factors within the egg cytoplasm that are instrumental in the transformation of the sperm nuclei into male pronuclei. Hunter (124) observed the presence of fully formed male pronuclei and undeveloped sperm nuclei within the same cytoplasm in polyspermic porcine ova

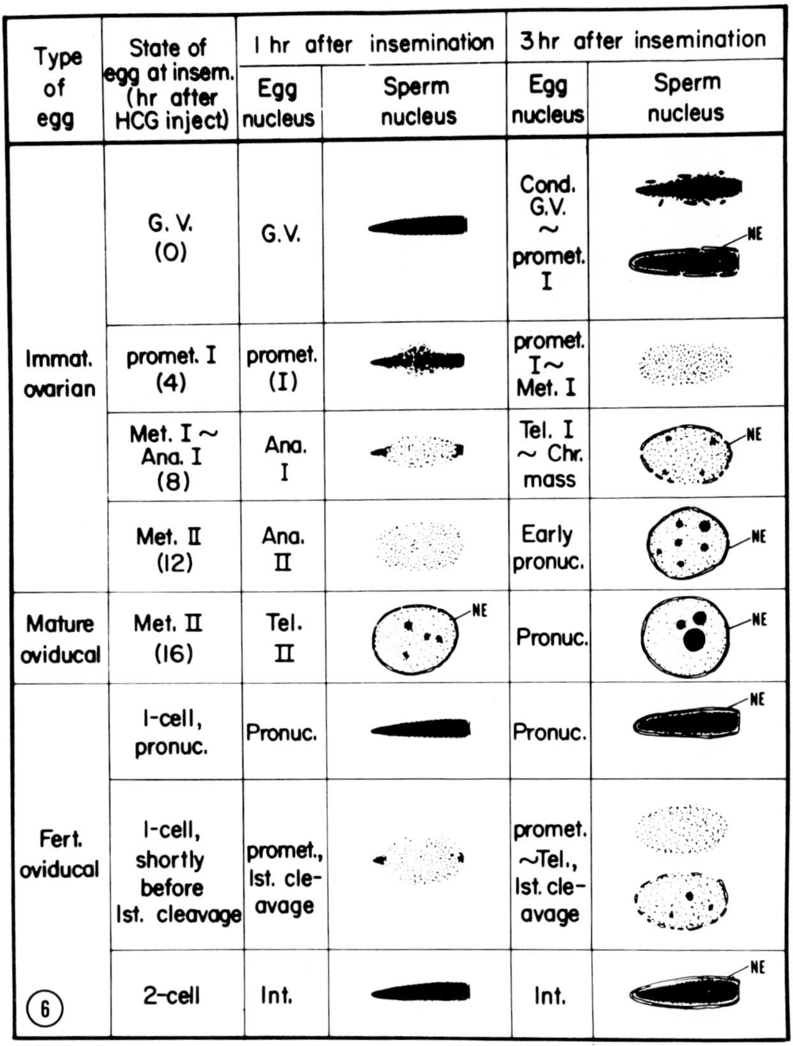

Type of egg	State of egg at insem. (hr after HCG inject)	1 hr after insemination		3 hr after insemination	
		Egg nucleus	Sperm nucleus	Egg nucleus	Sperm nucleus
Immat. ovarian	G. V. (0)	G.V.		Cond. G.V. ~ promet. I	NE
	promet. I (4)	promet. (I)		promet. I ~ Met. I	
	Met. I ~ Ana. I (8)	Ana. I		Tel. I ~ Chr. mass	NE
	Met. II (12)	Ana. II		Early pronuc.	NE
Mature oviducal	Met. II (16)	Tel. II	NE	Pronuc.	NE
Fert. oviducal	1-cell, pronuc.	Pronuc.		Pronuc.	NE
	1-cell, shortly before 1st. cleavage	promet., 1st. cleavage		promet. ~Tel., 1st. cleavage	
	2-cell	Int.		Int.	NE

Fig. 6. Changes in sperm nuclei incorporated into hamster eggs at various stages of maturation and early development. GV, Germinal vesicle; Cond GV, germinal vesicle, which contains condensing chromatin; Promet, prometaphase; Met, metaphase; Ana, anaphase; Tel, telophase; Chr mass, chromatin mass; Pronuc, pronucleus; Int, interphase; NE, new nuclear envelope. Taken from Usui and Yanagimachi (115).

and suggested that a factor in the egg cytoplasm, which is responsible for male pronuclear development, is present in limited quantities. In polyspermic eggs the material may have been exhausted or inactivated by developing male pronuclei and, therefore, was absent or unable to exert its influence on remaining incorporated sperm nuclei. Similar findings have also been reported by Hirao and Yanagimachi (114). The proposition of limited quantities of factors for pronuclear development is a reasonable one; however, further investigation is required in this area since other explanations can account for the simultaneous appearance of male pronuclei and sperm nuclei in the same zygote cytoplasm (cf. 41).

Although factors required for differentiation of the sperm nucleus into a male pronucleus appear with egg maturation, Thibault (125) suggests that conditions other than germinal vesicle breakdown are involved in the appearance of these substances. Rabbit eggs matured *in vitro* are capable of fertilization, however, incorporated sperm nuclei reportedly fail to transform into male pronuclei in rabbit eggs matured *in vitro*. On the basis of such results, Thibault (125) suggests that a male pronuclear growth factor, normally present during pronuclear development, is inactive or absent in *in vitro* matured ova. It is believed that this factor may be normally formed in surrounding follicle cells and then transported to the egg (125,126).

Despite the lack of information on their composition attempts have been made to determine the longevity of the cytoplasmic factors that might be involved with the tranformation of the sperm nucleus. That is, how long after insemination is the egg cytoplasm capable of supporting the development of a male pronucleus? This question implies that zygote cytoplasmic factors that are responsible for male pronuclear development have a finite life time or a limited period of activity. Investigations concerning the question of the longevity of these factors have also considered the possibility that those elements responsible for metamorphosis of the sperm nucleus into a male pronucleus are similar or identical to regulators of the cell cycle. Recent experiments by Wasserman and Smith (26) have uncovered possible relations between factors involved in oocyte development and mitosis. Perhaps agents involved in these processes are similar to those involved with morphogenesis of the sperm nucleus into a male pronucleus. Such as association is not difficult to formulate since many of the events of pronuclear development are, in fact, similar morphologically to events taking place during mitosis. For example, breakdown of the sperm nuclear envelope, chromatin dispersion, and formation of the pronuclear envelope are events similar to those that occur at prophase and telophase of mitotically active cells.

Studies concerning the longevity of the factors regulating pronuclear development primarily involve refertilization or sperm incorporation into somatic cells. Pronuclear development has been examined in the sea urchin (*Arbacia*) and hamster under conditions of re-fertilization (115,127). With proper manipulation of the *Arbacia* zygote, it is possible to fuse sperm with zygotes as late as 20–30 minutes after fertilization. This is well after the period of pronuclear fusion (approximately 15 minutes postfertilization) and at the time the zygote nucleus is replicating its DNA in preparation for the first cleavage division (8). Sperm incorporated into zygotes undergo male pronuclear development as observed in controls. Comparable results have also been reported by Poccia *et al.* (60) who inseminated ammonia-activated sea urchin eggs before G_2. In such cases the male pronucleus reportedly forms chromosomes in concert with the female pronucleus.

Similar results have been obtained by Usui and Yanagimachi (115) who have refertilized hamster zygotes at different times during fertilization and at different stages of cleavage (Fig. 6). The results of this study also suggest that regulators of sperm nuclear transformation may have a more general role, sharing some relation to factors involved with the cell cycle. For example, pronuclear development did not take place when sperm were incorporated into zygotes at the pronuclear stage, whereas sperm nuclear envelope breakdown and chromatin dispersion took place when sperm were incorporated into zygotes shortly before the first cleavage division, i.e., at prometaphase of mitosis.

Investigations have been carried out taking this type of experimentation one step further in that attempts have been made to incorporate sperm into cultured somatic cells (cf. 34,128). Results from such studies have been controversial due primarily to the question of whether sperm fuse with the plasmalemma of somatic cells or are, in fact phagocytized. In the former, the contents of the spermatozoon would gain access to the cytoplasm of the cell in much the same manner as they would during fertilization. In such instances, any changes the sperm nucleus would undergo would reflect those mediated by nucleocytoplasmic interactions. The possibility exists, then, that sperm nuclear transformation in such a case would be due to factors similar to those that are active at fertilization. Potentially such a system could provide further insights into the relation of factors involved in pronuclear development and the cell cycle. In those instances where the spermatozoon is phagocytized, changes in the sperm nucleus would most likely be indicative of degeneration, characteristic of the contents of a phagosome. Considerable evidence exists to demonstrate that, in fact, sperm are phagocytized by cultured cells and, although they may appear to undergo changes comparable to those observed at fertilization, they are, when closely examined, degenerative (cf. 34). There are instances, however, where sperm appear to fuse with cultured cells, and, consequently, the sperm nucleus establishes direct cytoplasmic contact (cf. 128). In such cases there is an apparent activation of the sperm nucleus in the form of chromatin dispersion. This is accompanied by a shift from the protamine- to the histone-type of basic protein associated with the transforming sperm nucleus. In some instances there is also the induction of RNA and DNA synthesis in the transformed sperm nucleus.

Investigations have been carried out examining the specificity of the factors involved in pronuclear development, i.e., are the factors responsible for sperm nuclear transformation in the egg of one species capable of interacting with the sperm nucleus of a different species to elicit pronuclear development? This particular aspect of pronuclear regulation has not been extensively studied, nevertheless the results of a limited number of investigations are interesting. The experimen-

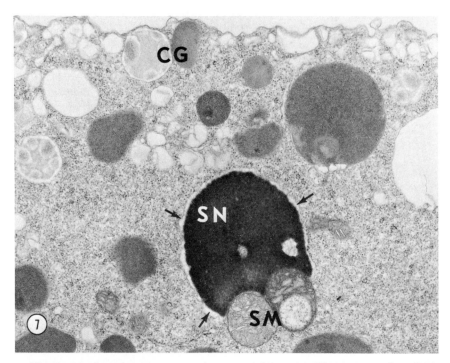

Fig. 7. *Mytilus* sperm incorporated into an *Arbacia* egg. The sperm nucleus (SN) contains condensed chromatin that is surrounded by a continuous nuclear envelope (arrows). SM, sperm mitochondria; CG, cortical granule. Taken from Longo (132).

TABLE III

Diameter and Volume of Male and Female Pronuclei in *Mytilus* and *Arbacia* Zygotes and Cross-Fertilized *Arabacia* Eggs (*Arbacia* ♀ × *Mytilus* ♂)[a]

	Nuclear diameter (µm)	Nuclear volume (µm³)
Mytilus sperm nucleus	2.2 ± 0.16	5.6
Mytilus male pronucleus in *Mytilus* zygote	10.7 ± 1.0	647.7
Arbacia male pronucleus in *Arbacia* zygote	4.5 ± 0.29	48.1
Mytilus male pronucleus in *Arbacia* zygote	5.8 ± 0.61	103.2
Arbacia female pronucleus in fertilized egg	10.9 ± 0.67	684.7
Arbacia female pronucleus in artificially activated egg	11.1 ± 0.48	723.1
Arbacia female pronucleus in cross-fertilized egg	12.2 ± 0.67	960.1

[a] Taken from Longo (132).

tal approach in this area of investigation has been one of cross-fertilization, in which the extent of the transformation of the sperm nucleus into a male pronucleus is determined. In those cases where it has been studied, i.e., *Mytilus* (mussel) ♂ × *Arbacia* (sea urchin) ♀ and hamster ♀ × human ♂, changes in the sperm nucleus, characteristic of pronuclear development, i.e., sperm nuclear envelope breakdown, chromatin dispersion, and formation of a nuclear envelope, do occur (129–132). In the two crosses cited above the incorporated sperm nucleus transforms into a male pronucleus (Fig. 7 and 8).

These observations indicate that factors involved in the transformation of the sperm nucleus into a male pronucleus are not species-specific and are capable of interacting with sperm nuclei of evolutionary divergent organisms. Interestingly, in the case of naturally fertilized *Mytilus* and *Arbacia* eggs the male pronuclei that normally develop differ considerably from one another when compared morphologically (Table III). In the cross of *Mytilus* ♂ × *Arbacia* ♀, the male pronuclei that form structurally resemble those that develop from *Arbacia* sperm, thus suggesting that cytoplasmic factors determine the form of the pronucleus (132).

In addition to investigations demonstrating the lack of specificity with respect to the factors involved in pronuclear development, experiments have been carried out where sperm nuclei have been microinjected into eggs (121,133–135). Moreover, frozen-thawed and freeze-dried human sperm have been injected into hamster eggs (135). In these cases, the injected sperm nucleus developed into a structure which morphologically resembled a male pronucleus. Fur-

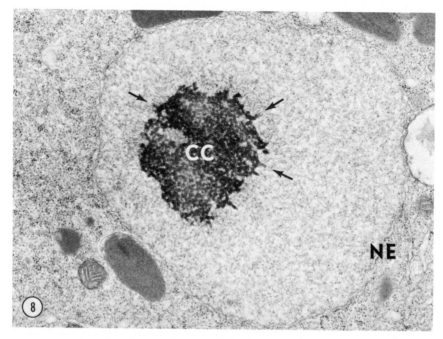

Fig. 8. Male pronucleus formed as a result of the reorganization of a *Mytilus* sperm nucleus that has become incorporated into an *Arbacia* egg. Emanating from the condensed chromatin (CC), which has persisted in this male pronucleus are fine filaments (arrows). This pattern of chromatin dispersion is characteristic of metamorphosing *Mytilus* sperm nuclei incorporated into *Mytilus* eggs and differs from that seen in male pronuclei derived from *Arbacia* sperm nuclei (cf. 5). NE, Nuclear envelope. Taken from Longo (132).

thermore, pronuclei that developed from sperm nuclei injected into mature amphibian eggs were shown to be capable of DNA synthesis (121,133). On the other hand, sperm nuclei injected into immature amphibian eggs do not transform into male pronuclei or synthesize DNA as long as the germinal vesicle remains intact (121,133). Moriya and Katagiri (133) report that the failure of sperm nuclei to synthesize DNA when injected into immature amphibian eggs is not due to a deficiency of DNA polymerase or an absence of deoxyribonucleotides. They suggest that additional cytoplasmic factors need to be present which make the DNA brought into the egg with the sperm accessible for replication. Furthermore, these investigations have shown that nonviable sperm, under appropriate conditions, are able to transform into pronuclei.

Recently it has been demonstrated that the elevation of intracellular pH that occurs in the ova of some organisms at fertilization is necessary for egg activation and development of the male pronucleus (136,137). In sea urchins, where it has been most extensively examined, if the alkalinization of the egg cytoplasm is inhibited, then the incorporated sperm nucleus fails to transform into a male pronucleus. Inhibition of male pronuclear development can be reversed in this instance by placing eggs in appropriate media which promote an increase in intracellur pH, e.g., sea water or sodium-free sea water containing ammonia. These results suggest that there is a rate-limiting step in the formation of the pronucleus, dependent in some manner upon cytoplasmic alkalinization of the zygote. The observations of Carron and Longo (137) reinforce the idea that the pH increase at fertilization (or a process accompanying this alteration) induces a single pervasive change within the egg cytoplasm which activates a series of independent events leading to the development of the male pronucleus. Furthermore, experiments with somatic cells also indicate that modulation of intracellular pH influences nuclear structure (109,112).

SUMMARY AND CONCLUSIONS

There is a need for further studies of pronuclear development, for this area is of considerable importance to our understanding of fertilization. Furthermore, results of experiments in this area have the potential of telling us much about the functioning of cells in general. After its metamorphosis into a male pronucleus the paternally derived chromatin becomes active in nucleic acid synthesis. It is reasonable to suggest that the nucleoproteins that become associated with the DNA during dispersion of the condensed chromatin are responsible for this change in activity.

Transformation of the sperm nucleus into a male pronucleus is a dramatic example of nucleocytoplasmic interaction, encompassing major alterations in chromatin composition and membrane biogenesis. Although few examinations of how these processes are regulated have been carried out we are beginning to achieve insights into the molecular events concerning structural and functional changes of the paternally derived chromatin. The relationship of factors involved with pronuclear development to those regulating events of the cell cycle are beginning to be explored. Research into this area holds promise of revealing similar regulators and common cellular mechanisms. Further investigation of pronuclear development will help to establish the mechanisms involving the transformations of the sperm nucleus at fertilization, and hence, enhance our knowledge of how the nucleus and cytoplasm interact with one another.

ACKNOWLEDGMENTS

Portions of the work cited here were supported by grants from the National Institutes of Health and the National Science Foundation. Appreciation is expressed to Alan Carroll, Christopher Carron, and Stephen Downs for their discussions and contributions to the preparation of this chapter.

REFERENCES

1. Wilson, E. B. (1925) "The Cell in Development and Heredity." Macmillan, New York.
2. Voeller, B. R. (1968) "The Chromosome Theory of Inheritance." Appleton, New York.
3. Sobotta, J. (1895) *Arch. Mikrosk. Anat.* **45**, 15–93.
4. McGaughey, R. W., and Chang, M. C. (1969) *J. Exp. Zool.* **170**, 397–410.
5. Longo, F. J. (1973) *Biol. Reprod.* **9**, 149–215.
6. Luthardt, F. W., and Donahue, R. P. (1973) *Exp. Cell Res.* **82**, 143–151.
7. Mintz, B. (1964) *J. Exp. Zool.* **157**, 85–100.
8. Longo, F. J., and Plunkett, W. (1973) *Dev. Biol.* **30**, 56–67.
9. Simmel, E. B., and Karnofsky, D. A. (1961) *J. Biophys. Biochem. Cytol.* **10**, 59–65.
10. Longo, F. J., and Kunkle, M. (1977) *J. Exp. Zool.* **201**, 431–438.
11. Kaulenas, M. S., and Fairbairn, D. (1968) *Exp. Cell Res.* **52**, 233–251.
12. Foor, W. E. (1970) *Biol. Reprod., Suppl.* **2**, 177–202.
13. Brawley, S. H., Wetherbee, R., and Quatrano, R. S. (1976) *J. Cell Sci.* **20**, 233–254.
14. Iwamatsu, T., and Ohta, T. (1978) *J. Exp. Zool.* **205**, 157–180.
15. Okamura, F., and Nishiyama, H. (1978) *Cell Tissue Res.* **190**, 89–98.
16. Austin, C. R. (1968) "Ultrastructure of Fertilization." Holt, New York.
17. Zamboni, L. (1971) "Fine Morphology of Mammalian Fertilization." Harper, New York.
18. Van Blerkom, J., and Motta, P. (1979) "The Cellular Basis of Mammalian Reproduction." Urban & Schwarzenberg, Munich.
19. Bell, P. R. (1975) *J. Cell Sci.* **17**, 141–154.
20. Barros, C., Bedford, J. M., Franklin, L. E., and Austin, C. R. (1967) *J. Cell Biol.* **34**, C1-C5.
21. Longo, F. J., and Anderson, E. (1969) *J. Ultrastruct. Res.* **27**, 486–509.
22. Johnson, R. T., and Rao, P. N. (1971) *Biol. Rev. Cambridge Philos. Soc.* **46**, 97–155.
23. Masui, Y., and Markert, C. L. (1971) *J. Exp. Zool.* **177**, 129–146.
24. Maruta, H., and Goldstein, L. (1975) *J. Cell Biol.* **65**, 631–645.
25. Masui, Y., and Clarke, H. (1979) *Int. Rev. Cytol.* **57**, 185–282.
26. Wasserman, W. J., and Smith, L. D. (1978) *J. Cell Biol.* **78**, R15–R22.
27. Ringertz, N. R., and Savage, R. E. (1977) "Cell Hybrids." Academic Press, New York.

28. Piko, L. (1969) *In* "Fertilization: Comparative Morphology, Biochemistry and Immunology" (C. B. Metz and A. Monroy, eds.), Vol. 2, pp. 325–403. Academic Press, New York.
29. Stefanini, M., Oura, C., and Zamboni, L. (1969) *J. Submicrosc. Cytol.* **1**, 1–23.
30. Szollosi, D., and Ris, H. (1961) *J. Biophys. Biochem. Cytol.* **10**, 275–283.
31. Yanagimachi, R., and Noda, Y. D. (1970) *J. Ultrastruct. Res.* **31**, 465–485.
32. Longo, F. J. (1978) *Dev. Biol.* **62**, 271–291.
33. Hiramoto, Y. (1962) *Exp. Cell Res.* **27**, 416–426.
34. Phillips, S. G., Phillips, D. M., Dev, V. G., Miller, D. H., Van Diggelen, O. P., and Miller, O. J. (1976) *Exp. Cell Res.* **98**, 429–443.
35. Bedford, J. M. (1968) *Am. J. Anat.* **123**, 329–358.
36. Bedford, J. M. (1970) *Biol. Reprod., Suppl.* **2**, 128–158.
37. Bedford, J. M. (1970) *In* "Mammalian Reproduction" (H. Gibian and E. J. Plotz, eds.), pp. 124–182. Springer-Verlag, Berlin and New York.
38. Foor, W. E. (1968) *J. Cell Biol.* **39**, 119–134.
39. Pasteels, J. J. (1963) *Bull. Cl. Sci., Acad. R. Belg.* **49**, 329–336.
40. Pasteels, J. J. (1965) *Bull. Soc. Zool. Fr.* **90**, 195–224.
41. Longo, F. J., and Kunkle, M. (1978) *Curr. Top. Dev. Biol.* **12**, 149–184.
42. Mayer, J. F., and Zirkin, B. R. (1979) *J. Cell Biol.* **81**, 403–410.
43. Marushige, Y., and Marushige, K. (1975) *J. Biol. Chem.* **250**, 39–45.
44. Bloch, D. P., and Hew, H. Y. C. (1960) *J. Biophys. Biochem. Cytol.* **7**, 515–530.
45. Loir, M., and Lanneau, M. (1978) *Exp. Cell Res.* **115**, 231–243.
46. Balhorn, R., Gledhill, B. L., and Wyrobek, A. J. (1977) *Biochemistry* **16**, 4074–4080.
47. Bellvé, A. R., Anderson, E., and Hanley- Bowdoin, L. (1975) *Dev. Biol.* **47**, 349–365.
48. Kistler, W. S., Geroch, M. E., and Williams-Ashman, H. G. (1973) *J. Biol. Chem.* **248**, 4532–4543.
49. Monfoort, C. H., Shiphot, R., Rozun, T. H., and Steyn-Parve, E. P. (1973) *Biochim. Biophys. Acta* **322**, 173–177.
50. Dixon, G. H. (1972) *In* "Gene Transcription in Reproductive Tissue" (E. Diczfahisy, ed.), pp. 128–154. Bogtrykkeriert Forum, Copenhagen.
51. Kunkle, M., Longo, F. J., and Magun, B. E. (1978) *J. Exp. Zool.* **203**, 371–380.
52. Bloch, D. P. (1969) *Genetics, Suppl.* **61**, 93–111.
53. Das, C. C., Kaufmann, B. P., and Gay, H. (1964) *J. Cell Biol.* **23**, 423–430.
54. Das, N. K., Micou-Eastwood, J., and Alfert, M. (1975) *Dev. Biol.* **43**, 333–339.
55. Das, N. K., and Barker, C. (1976) *J. Cell Biol.* **68**, 155–159.
56. Kopecny, V., and Pavlok, A. (1975) *J. Exp. Zool.* **191**, 85–96.
57. Kopecny, V., and Pavlok, A. (1975) *Histochemistry* **45**, 341–345.
58. Ecklund, P. S., and Levine, L. (1975) *J. Cell Biol.* **66**, 251–262.
59. Carroll, A. G., and Ozaki, H. (1979) *Exp. Cell Res.* **119**, 307–315.
60. Poccia, D., Krystal, G., Nishioka, D., and Salik, J. (1978) *In* "Cell Reproduction: Honoring Daniel Mazia" (E. R. Dirksen, D. M. Prescott, and C. Fred Fox, eds.), pp. 197–206. Academic Press, New York.
61. Kunkle, M., Magun, B. E., and Long, F. J. (1978) *J. Exp. Zool.* **203**, 381–390.
62. Barry, J. M., and Merriam, R. W. (1972) *Exp. Cell Res.* **71**, 90–96.
63. Hoffner, N. J., and DiBerardino, M. A. (1977) *Exp. Cell Res.* **108**, 421–427.
64. Claycomb, W. C., and Villee, C. A. (1974) *Exp. Cell Res.* **83**, 191–199.
65. Calvin, H. I., and Bedford, J. M. (1971) *J. Reprod. Fertil. Suppl.* **13**, 65–75.
66. Marushige, Y., and Marushige, K. (1978) *Biochim. Biophys. Acta* **519**, 1–22.

67. Mahi, C. A., and Yanagimachi, R. (1975) *J. Reprod. Fertil.* **44**, 293–296.
68. Young, R. J. (1979) *Biol. Reprod.* **20**, 1001–1004.
69. Zirkin, B. R., Chang, T. S. K., and Heaps, J. (1980) *J. Cell. Biol.* **85**, 116–121.
70. Barnett, R. J. (1953) *J. Natl. Cancer Inst.* **13**, 905–925.
71. Louie, A. J., Candido, E. P. M., and Dixon, G. H. (1974) *Cold Spring Harbor Symp. Quant. Biol.* **38**, 803–819.
72. Willmitzer, L., Bode, J., and Wagner, K. G. (1977) *Nucleic Acids Res.* **4**, 149–162.
73. Willmitzer, L., Bode, J., and Wagner, K. G. (1977) *Nucleic Acids Res.* **4**, 163–176.
74. Young, R. J., and Sweeney, K. (1978) *Eur. J. Biochem.* **91**, 111–117.
75. Benjamin, W. B., and Goodman, R. M. (1969) *Science* **166**, 629–631.
76. DeLange, R. J., and Smith, L. D. (1971) *Annu. Rev. Biochem.* **40**, 279–314.
77. Elgin, S. C. R., and Bonner, J. (1970) *Biochemistry* **9**, 4440–4447.
78. Kleinsmith, L. J., Allfrey, V. G., and Mirsky, A. E. (1966) *Science* **154**, 780–781.
79. Chang, T. S. K., and Zirkin, B. R. (1978) *J. Exp. Zool.* **204**, 283–289.
80. Zirkin, B. R., and Chang, T. S. K. (1977) *Biol. Reprod.* **17**, 131–137.
81. Motlik, J., Kopecny, V., Pivko, J., and Fulka, J. (1980) *J. Reprod. Fertil.* **58**, 415–419.
82. Gurdon, J. B., and Woodland, H. R. (1968) *Biol. Rev. Cambridge Philos. Soc.* **43**, 233–267.
83. Gurdon, J. B., DeRobertis, E. M., and Partington, G. (1976) *Nature (London)* **260**, 166–120.
84. Appels, R., Bolund, L., and Ringertz, N. R. (1974) *J. Mol. Biol.* **87**, 339–355.
85. Dupuy-Coin, A. M., Ege, T., Bouteille, M., and Ringertz, N. R. (1976) *Exp. Cell Res.* **101**, 355–369.
86. Gurdon, J. B. (1975) *In* "Cell Cycle and Cell Differentiation" (J. Reinert and H. Holtzer, eds.), pp. 123–131. Springer-Verlag, Berlin and New York.
87. Fansler, B., and Loeb, L. A. (1969) *Exp. Cell Res.* **57**, 305–310.
88. Witkin, S. S., and Bendich, A. (1977) *Exp. Cell Res.* **106**, 47–54.
89. Richards, J. M., and Witkin, S. S. (1978) *J. Reprod. Fertil.* **54**, 43–47.
90. Hecht, N. (1974) *J. Reprod. Fertil.* **41**, 345–354.
91. Hecht, N. B., and Williams, J. L. (1979) *J. Reprod. Fertil.* **57**, 157–165.
92. Chevaillier, P., and Philippe, M. (1976) *Chromosoma* **54**, 33–37.
93. Szollosi, D., and Hunter, R. H. F. (1973) *J. Anat.* **116**, 181–206.
94. Longo, F. J., and Anderson, E. (1968) *J. Cell Biol.* **39**, 339–368.
95. Longo, F. J., and Anderson, E. (1970) *J. Ultrastruct. Res.* **33**, 495–514.
96. Longo, F. J., and Anderson, E. (1970) *J. Cell Biol.* **46**, 308–325.
97. Longo, F. J. (1976) *Dev. Biol.* **49**, 347–368.
98. Anderson, E. (1970) *J. Cell Biol.* **47**, 711–733.
99. Fawcett, D. W. (1965) *In* "Intracellular Membranous Structure" (S. Seno and E. V. Cowdry, eds.), pp. 15–40. Jpn. Soc. Cell Biol., Okayama.
100. Feldherr, C. M. (1972) *Adv. Cell. Mol. Biol.* **2**, 273–307.
101. Flickinger, C. J. (1974) *J. Cell Sci.* **14**, 421–437.
102. Harvey, E. B. (1956) "The American Arbacia and Other Sea Urchins." Princeton Univ. Press, Princeton, New Jersey.
103. Rothman, J. E. (1980) *In* "Membrane-Membrane Interaction" (N. B. Gilula, ed.), pp. 1–9. Raven, New York.
104. Chlapowski, F. J., and Band, R. N. (1971) *J. Cell Biol.* **50**, 634–651.
105. Dallner, G., Siekevitz, P., and Palade, G. E. (1966) *J. Cell Biol.* **30**, 97–117.
106. Orrenius, S., Ericsson, J. L. E., and Ernster, L. (1965) *J. Cell Biol.* **25**, 627–639.
107. Korn, E. D. (1969) *Annu. Rev. Biochem.* **38**, 263–288.

108. Ray, T. K., Lieberman, I., and Lansing, A. I. (1968) *Biochem. Biophys. Res. Commun.* **31**, 54–58.
109. Obara, Y., Weinfeld, H., and Sandberg, A. A. (1975) *J. Cell Biol.* **64**, 378–388.
110. Zamboni, L., and Mastroianni, L. (1966) *J. Ultrastruct. Res.* **14**, 118–132.
111. Longo, F. J. (1976) *J. Cell Biol.* **69**, 539–547.
112. Obara, Y., Chai, L. S., Weinfeld, H., and Sandberg, A. A. (1974) *J. Cell Biol.* **62**, 104–113.
113. Krishan, A., and Ray-Chaudhuri, R. (1969) *J. Cell Biol.* **43**, 618–621.
114. Hirao, Y., and Yanagimachi, R. (1979) *Zool. Mag.* **88**, 24–33.
115. Usui, N., and Yanagimachi, R. (1976) *J. Ultrastruct. Res.* **57**, 276–288.
116. Iwamatsu, T., and Chang, M. C. (1972) *J. Reprod. Fertil.* **31**, 237–247.
117. Niwa, K., and Chang, M. C. (1975) *J. Reprod. Fertil.* **43**, 435–451.
118. Dettlaff, T. A., Nikitina, L. A., and Stroeva, O. G. (1964) *J. Embryol. Exp. Morphol.* **12**, 851–873.
119. Katagiri, C., and Moriya, M. (1976) *Dev. Biol.* **50**, 235–241.
120. Katagiri, C. (1974) *J. Embryol. Exp. Morphol.* **31**, 573–587.
121. Skoblina, M. N. (1976) *J. Embryol. Exp. Morphol.* **36**, 67–72.
122. Schuetz, A. W., and Longo, F. J. (1981) *J. Exp. Zool.* (in press).
123. Franklin, L. E. (1965) *J. Cell Biol.* **25**, 81–100.
124. Hunter, R. H. F. (1967) *J. Exp. Zool.* **165**, 451–459.
125. Thibault, C. (1973) *In* "The Regulation of Mammalian Reproduction" (S. J. Segal, R. Crozier, P. A. Corfman, and P. G. Condliffe, eds.), pp. 231–246. Thomas, Springfield, Illinois.
126. Thibault, C., and Gerard, M. (1973) *Ann. Biol. Anim., Biochim., Biophys.* **13**, 145–156.
127. Longo, F. J. (1980) *Dev., Growth & Differ.* **22**, 219–227.
128. Van Meel, F. C. M., and Pearson, P. L. (1979) *J. Cell Sci.* **35**, 105–122.
129. Yanagimachi, R., Yanagimachi, H., and Rogers, B. J. (1976) *Biol. Reprod.* **15**, 471–476.
130. Barros, C., and Herrera, E. (1977) *J. Reprod. Fertil.* **49**, 47–50.
131. Barros, C., Gonzalez, J., Herrera, E., and Bustos-Obregon, E. (1979) *Andrologia* **11**, 197–210.
132. Longo, F. J. (1977) *J. Cell Biol.* **73**, 14–26.
133. Moriya, M., and Katagiri, C. (1976) *Dev., Growth & Differ.* **18**, 349–356.
134. Graham, C. F. (1966) *J. Cell Sci.* **1**, 363–374.
135. Uehara, T., and Yanagimachi, R. (1977) *Biol. Reprod.* **16**, 315–321.
136. Chambers, E. L. (1976) *J. Exp. Zool.* **197**, 149–154.
137. Carron, C. P., and Longo, F. J. (1980) *Dev. Biol.* **79**, 478–487.

Control of Cell Fate during Early Mouse Embryogenesis

MICHAEL I. SHERMAN

Roche Institute of Molecular Biology
Nutley, New Jersey

INTRODUCTION

The nature and distribution of factors governing cell fate during embryogenesis is a subject that has been under investigation for more than a century (see Chap. 7 of Davidson, 1). The general concensus from countless studies on numerous submammalian species is that instructional factors become localized in different areas of the cytoplasm of either the unfertilized egg, the newly fertilized egg or the early cleavage stage embryo (depending upon the factor and/or the species); cells acquiring these instructional cytoplasmic factors during subsequent cleavages thereby come to possess information which ultimately influences their direction of differentiation.

The nature of the instructional factors, which are hereafter referred to as *determinants,* is largely a mystery. Determinants in some cases appear to reside in morphological structures: for example, polar granules in amphibian eggs are thought to contain germ cell determinants (2). Other studies (3,4) suggest that maternal mRNAs (i.e., mRNAs present in the egg prior to fertilization) are in some cases differentially distributed to cells during early cleavage stages, raising the possibility that such macromolecules can act as determinants. Finally, Davidson (1) has also pointed out the potential importance of small molecules such as ions in influencing determination by citing cases in which treatment with lithium chloride or sodium thiocyanate leads to disproportionate production of specific cell types in developing sea urchin embryos.

Until recently, studies on cell determination during embryogenesis

BIOREGULATORS OF REPRODUCTION

have been to a large degree restricted to nonmammalian species. The reasons for this include limited availability of mammalian embryos, difficulties in establishing satisfactory culture conditions for them and problems with their manipulation. As these obstacles have been progressively minimized by technical refinements, at least for rodent and lagomorph embryos, mammalian embryologists are now in a better position to learn about cell determination in their experimental systems. The studies described bear upon the issues of whether mammalian (primarily mouse) embryos possess cytoplasmic determinants and, if they do exist, when and how they become localized among the cells (called *blastomeres*) and what can be surmised about their nature.

ARE BLASTOMERES OF THE EARLY MAMMALIAN EMBRYO REGULATIVE OR MOSAIC?

A *regulative* blastomere is one that is totipotent; i.e., when disaggregated from neighboring blastomeres, it retains the ability to form an entire organism. Conversely, a *mosaic* blastomere is one whose developmental potential has been reduced so that it is capable of forming only a restricted and incomplete array of cell types. Davidson (1) has considered in some detail the regulative versus mosaic nature of early embryonic cells from embryos of several nonmammalian species. In some embryos, the blastomeres resulting from the first few cell divisions are regulative whereas in others the blastomeres become mosaic with the onset of cleavage. Eventually, all blastomeres become mosaic. The most logical explanation for these observations is that blastomeres will remain regulative so long as they acquire all the different cytoplasmic determinants; as soon as the cleavage planes become such that progeny blastomeres fail to receive all varieties of determinants, the developmental potential of the cells will become restricted (1).

In studies with rabbit embryos, Seidel (5,6) demonstrated that at least some blastomeres at the two-cell stage were regulative: After destroying one blastomere of the pair and transferring the other to a foster mother, he was able to obtain live young in a limited number of cases. In a more thorough study, Moore *et al.* (7) found that the success rate for live births was approximately 30%, 20%, and 10% when single blastomeres from two-, four-, and eight-cell rabbit embryos, respectively, were transferred to foster mothers. In experiments with mouse embryos, Tarkowski (8) found that less than 20% of individual blastomeres from two-cell embryos were able to develop in a morphologically normal manner beyond implantation stages when transplanted to foster mothers; in studies in which he allowed conceptuses to develop to term, he obtained six live young. In earlier studies with rat embryos, Nicholas and Hall (9) reported that individual blastomeres from the two-cell stage could give rise to morphologically normal postimplantation embryos, and they demonstrated further that both blastomeres from the same embryo were able to regulate to this degree. However, they did not obtain normal development beyond the first semester of pregnancy.

It would appear from these studies that at least some of the blastomeres of early rodent and lagomorph embryos are totipotent. For several reasons it would be invalid to assume from the low frequency at which blastomeres were actually shown to be regulative that some blastomeres have lost their totipotency by the two-, four-, or even eight-cell stage. Unlike simpler systems, to obtain the ultimate proof that a mammalian blastomere is regulative, i.e., that it can produce a complete organism, one must transfer the embryo to a foster mother; because of technical limitations, successful development to term of intact embryos transferred to foster mothers is often less than 50%. Even though periods of culture were relatively short in these experiments, brief exposure of very early embryos to inappropriate culture conditions might well have had adverse effects upon later development. Finally, most of these initial studies on cell potency were carried out by destroying sister blastomeres and leaving the cell debris in contact with the surviving blastomere, inside the zona pellucida; the detrimental consequences of this continued contact are unknown.

It appeared, therefore, that conclusive assessments could not be made in studies such as those described, and mammalian embryologists sought other experimental protocols in an effort to learn about the developmental nature of early blastomeres. It is indeed obvious from more recent experiments that studies on the regulative nature of blastomeres of the mammalian embryo inadequately defined the developmental lability of the blastomeres and did not provide meaningful information about the time at which lability is lost and blastomere fate becomes fixed.

AGGREGATION EXPERIMENTS

Tarkowski (10) and subsequently Mintz (11) observed that cleavage stage mouse embryos placed in apposition to each other could integrate into a single aggregate embryo. Normal offspring could be obtained when these aggregate embryos were transferred to foster mothers. Subsequently, it has been shown that aggregates containing as many as sixteen eight-cell embryos can form single enlarged but apparently normal blastocysts which can implant successfully in foster mothers and give rise to morphologically normal midgestation embryos (12). The production of such chimeras indicates that aggregated embryos form a single integrated organism rather than producing multiple ones, i.e., twinning. Integration of this sort would be expected to occur if (a) many cells of the aggregate died, leaving only a single organizing center, i.e., a group of blastomeres with information to form the embryo proper and its surrounding membranes; (b) cells within the aggregate embryo reassorted to take up their appropriate positions (i.e., cells destined to give rise to placental structures surrounding those determined to produce the embryo proper; see below); or (c) the cells were developmentally labile at the time of aggregation. Alternative (c) is the most likely explanation since there is no evidence of extensive cell death in chimeric embryos (see 10) and no reason to suspect extensive cell reassortment during early embryogenesis. Graham and his colleagues (13–15) have reported that in unperturbed embryos sister blastomeres remain adjacent to each other following each cell division and cinematographic and autoradiographic (15,16) analyses of composite embryos provide reason to suspect that cell movement is similarly restricted in chimeras.

DISAGGREGATION EXPERIMENTS

Tarkowski and Wroblewska (17) and subsequently Sherman (18) found that disaggregated blastomeres cultured at the four-cell stage (one-fourth blastomeres) formed primarily two types of structures: (a) miniblastocysts, containing fewer cells than normal blastocysts but nevertheless both components, i.e., an outer single layer of trophectoderm cells surrounding an enclosed cluster of cells called the inner cell mass (ICM) and (b) trophectodermal vesicles, structures containing only the outer single layer of cells. Pairs of blastomeres at the eight-cell stage (two-eighth blastomeres) formed fewer miniblastocysts and more trophectodermal vesicles. One-eighth blastomeres formed a still higher proportion of trophectodermal vesicles and a lower proportion of miniblastocysts. Sherman (18) demonstrated that during further culture under appropriate conditions, trophectodermal vesicles gave rise to cells which resembled giant trophoblast cells morphologically and biochemically. No ICM cell derivatives (e.g., endoderm) were observed. These latter results are consistent with earlier observations by Gardner (19,20) that trophectodermal vesicles obtained by microsurgery of blastocysts produced only giant trophoblast cells when transplanted to foster mothers or to ectopic sites. Disorganized structures containing vacuolated cells which do not enclose other cells also arise from disaggregated blastomeres (17,18). These nonintegrated structures can form apparently normal trophoblast cells but not ICM derivatives (18).

Tarkowski and Wroblewska (17) and Wudl and Sherman (21) carried out studies in which the fate of all disaggregated blastomeres from single eight-cell embryos was followed. It was found that in some cases, *all* one-eighth or two-eighth blastomeres gave rise to trophectodermal vesicles. Again, it was demonstrated that during culture all these trophectodermal vesicles could give rise to trophoblast cells but not to ICM derivatives (21). All blastomeres at the eight-cell stage are, therefore, capable of producing trophoblast derivatives. *In vitro* studies (18,21) as well as *in vivo* ones (19,20,22) thus indicate that cells identifiable as trophoblast morphologically, biochemically, and functionally can differentiate from trophectoderm cells in the absence of contact with ICM cells. In fact, Sherman and Atienza-Samols (23) have shown that one-sixteenth blastomeres can differentiate to trophoblast-like cells without cell division and without contact with any other cells. Finally, Rizzino and Sherman (24) have reported that the trophectoderm-to-trophoblast conversion can occur in a relatively simple serum-free medium; this reduces the likelihood that the elaboration of the trophoblast differentiation program is promoted by external effectors.

The reasonable conclusion from these experiments is that all eight-cell blastomeres can give rise to trophoblast cells in the absence of any external cues.

REAGGREGATION EXPERIMENTS

Hillman *et al.* (12) have demonstrated that disaggregated eight-cell blastomeres placed on the outside of intact eight-cell embryos tend to contribute to the trophectoderm layer of the blastocyst whereas blastomeres surrounded by others have a greater likelihood than peripheral blastomeres of contributing to the ICM. When composite embryos are analyzed at later stages, blastomeres placed on the outside of eight-cell embryos are found to contribute more often to the trophoblast and yolk sac than to the embryo proper. On the other hand, Kelly (25,26) has provided evidence from related reaggregation experiments that all blastomeres at the four-cell stage are capable of contributing to fetal tissues and that individual eight-cell blastomeres reaggregated with blastomeres from another embryo can give rise to progeny in both embryonic and extraembryonic tissues.

THE INSIDE–OUTSIDE HYPOTHESIS

Taken together, the results of aggregation, disaggregation, and reaggregation experiments support the view that all eight-cell blastomeres are labile and that their fate is influenced by their position relative to other blastomeres in the embryo. Thus, as elaborated in the "Inside–Outside Hypothesis" by Tarkowski and Wroblewska (17), blastomeres on the outside of an unperturbed embryo are fated to give rise to trophoblast cells whereas blastomeres can only acquire the instructional information necessary for production of embryonic tissues by assuming an internal position in the blastocyst, i.e., by becoming part of the ICM. The reaggregation studies support the Inside–Outside Hypothesis in a general way, although not always to the letter. For example, blastomeres placed on the outside of an eight-cell embryo contribute not only to the trophoblast layer but often also to the yolk sac and occasionally even to the embryo (12). Conversely, eight-cell blastomeres placed internally can produce progeny yolk sac and trophoblast cells (25,26). These observations do not reflect exceptions of the Inside–Outside Hypothesis in principle but are most likely consequences of cell lineage. As Graham and his colleagues have reported (14,27), "inside" blastomeres (those totally surrounded) arise only in embryos containing twelve or more cells. Although inside blastomeres do not predictably derive from the same progenitor blastomere(s), they are most likely to be descended from those blastomeres which (a) divided earliest and (b) had contacts with the greatest number of cells in the previous generation (13,14,28). There does, however, appear to be enough leeway in cell patterning such that a peripheral cell at the eight-cell stage can have one or more descendents which will reside in the ICM three divisions later; such a likelihood can undoubtedly be increased in reaggregation experiments since the blastomeres used are taken from at least two different embryos and the ones placed in an outside position might divide earlier than those internally. The result will be that the progeny of these earlier-dividing blastomeres, although they might initially have had fewer cell contacts than the other blastomeres in the composite, will soon come to occupy an inside position. In extreme cases in which the time of division of all outside blastomeres is considerably advanced over those of inside blastomeres, it is conceivable that by the blastocyst stage most ICM cells will have been derived from outside cells which had displaced those originally in an internal position. A conceptus could then arise whose embryo descended from the original outside cells of the composite and whose yolk sac and/or trophoblast derived at least partly from inside cells. This could account for the exceptional embryos of this type observed in the studies of Hillman *et al.* (12) and of Kelly (26). It is important to note, however, that such dramatic reorganizations would not be expected to occur in a normal, unperturbed embryo.

In summary, despite occasional apparent inconsistencies in experiments involving artificially constructed embryos, it is most reasonable to conclude from the studies described that blastomeres are labile at least to the eight-cell stage and that the ultimate fate of their progeny depends upon the position they assume through subsequent divisions.

WHEN DO BLASTOMERES LOSE THEIR LABILITY?

Gardner (19,29) was the first to produce chimeras by injecting cells from one blastocyst into the blastocoelic cavity of another. Using this technique, he demonstrated that injected cells from the ICM at the expanded blastocyst stage could contribute to the formation of the developing embryo whereas cells from the trophectoderm layer could not (19,30). On the basis of these studies and others described above, Gardner, concluded that trophectoderm cells lose their lability by the expanded blastocyst stage. We cannot yet be certain of the exact time that this loss of lability occurs. However, in recent experiements, Rossant and Vijh (31) were able to reconstruct complete embryos by combining only outer blastomeres from late morulae, inserting them into empty zona pellucidae and then transplanting these structures into foster mothers. Technical difficulties have so far precluded an extension of these studies to the early or mid-blastocyst stage. Presumably, lability of trophectoderm cells is lost at one of these two substages, i.e., at some time during the fourth day of pregnancy.

Although ICM cells from expanded blastocysts can contribute to virtually all tissues of resultant mice when injected into the blastocoel of other expanded blastocysts (32), several lines of evidence suggest that these cells have lost the ability to form trophoblast. First, Gardner and his colleagues (33–35), through injection of ICMs into the blastocoel, have demonstrated that these cells do not contribute to trophoblast giant cells or to the ectoplacental cone. Second, Solter and Knowles (36) have devised an immunological procedure for selectively killing the trophectoderm layer of the blastocyst, resulting in the isolation of an undamaged ICM. When expanded blastocysts are subjected to the immunosurgery procedure and the resultant ICMs are maintained in culture, they do not regenerate a trophoblast layer but rather give rise to an outer layer of primitive endoderm cells (36). Finally, Rossant (37,38) has aggregated isolated ICMs with morulae, and even though some of the ICM cells initially occupy an outside position of the aggregate, they are rarely found to contribute to the trophoblast layer when these composite conceptuses are analyzed after transfer to foster mothers.

Contrary to these results with expanded blastocysts, inner cells obtained by immunosurgery of early blastocysts and late morulae were first shown by Handyside (39,40) to be capable of regenerating an outer trophoblast layer. These observations were subsequently confirmed by Hogan and Tilly (41) and by Spindle (42). Rossant and Lis (43) demonstrated by experiments involving transfer to foster mothers that ICMs isolated from early blastocysts could regenerate an entire conceptus whereas similar structures from expanded blastocysts were much less likely to do so.

The conclusion from these experiments is that like trophectoderm cells, ICM cells appear to be pluripotent at the late morula stage, but their fate becomes restricted by the expanded blastocyst stage. In fact, studies with isolated ICMs indicate that in many cases these cells are still labile at the early blastocyst stage, suggesting a gradual loss of potential by these cells over an 8-hour period on the fourth day of gestation, between the early blastocyst and expanded blastocyst stages.

BIOCHEMICAL STUDIES ON INSIDE AND OUTSIDE CELLS

As mentioned above, the work by Graham and his colleagues (27) indicates that enclosed cells of the preimplantation embryo are likely to be faster dividing than peripheral cells. Ducibella (44) has described ultrastructural differences between outside and inside blastomeres. Most important, however, in the context of this discussion are the findings of Johnson and his colleagues in studies on polypeptide synthetic patterns by cells on the inside and outside of preimplantation mouse embryos. Van Blerkom et al. (45) incubated either intact expanded blastocysts or their trophectoderm and ICM moieties in the presence of [^{35}S]methionine, extracted the labeled polypeptides and analyzed them by two-dimensional polyacrylamide gel electrophoresis. Although most of the spots on the resultant gels were common to the two cell types, Van Blerkom *et al.* did observe populations of spots which appeared to be limited to ICM or trophectoderm preparations. In subsequent studies, Johnson *et al.* (39) and Handyside and Johnson (46) provided evidence that some of these trophectoderm-specific and ICM-specific polypeptides began to be synthesized as early as the morula stage, that is, *prior to the time at which trophectoderm and ICM cells lose their lability.* Futhermore, it was reported that inner cells at the morula stage synthesized ICM-specific polypeptides but not trophectoderm-specific ones (39,46). The production of some trophectoderm- and ICM-specific polypeptides can be reduced or eliminated by treatment of the embryos with α-amanitin, suggesting that these polypeptides are translated from mRNAs transcribed during embryogenesis (39). Most recently, Johnson and his colleagues (47) have generated trophectodermal vesicles by treating eight-cell embryos with cytochalasin D (48). Under these conditions blastomeres fail to divide, but upon removal of the cytochalasin D they form junctional complexes and subsequently the embryos cavitate. Since the cell number remains at eight, no blastomeres can be enclosed. The fate of these structures is to form only trophoblast (47,48), as was found for trophectodermal vesicles formed in other ways (18,19,22). However, when the protein synthetic profiles of these trophectodermal vesicles were analyzed, it was found that they produced trophectoderm-specific polypeptides, as expected, *but also ICM-specific polypeptides* (47). Longer exposures to cytochalasin D prevented normal compaction and cavitation leading to the generation of nonintegrated structures; the cells in these structures also synthesized both trophectoderm-specific and ICM-specific polypeptides.

The importance of these experiments by Johnson and his colleagues is such that they must be taken into account in any model purporting to explain the elaboration of the developmental program by early mouse embryos. However, certain caveats concerning their data merit consideration. Although the trophectoderm and ICM polypeptides are among the few available biochemical markers that can be used to distinguish between trophectoderm and ICM cells (for a review of this subject, see 49), it is disquieting that we know nothing about them other than their location as spots on a gel. What role do these polypeptides play in development and differentiation of trophectoderm and ICM derivatives? What, for example, is the significance of the production of ICM-specific polypeptides by trophectodermal vesicles whose cells will all ultimately differentiate as trophoblast (47)? Conversely, why do ICMs isolated from expanded blastocysts synthesize some "trophoblast-specific" polypeptides after they have lost the ability to give rise to morphologically recognizable trophoblast cells (50)? Even though production of these polypeptides might be delayed and quantitatively less than one would find in cells of the correct phenotype, it must be asked whether or not these markers are truly trophectoderm- or ICM-specific in unperturbed embryos. Attempts should be made to ascertain, for example, that cells in the trophectoderm do not normally acquire "ICM-specific" markers, and vice versa, shortly after the expanded blastocyst stage, the latest stage studied by Van Blerkom and Johnson (45).

Notwithstanding the above concerns, we shall assume in considering models to explain the loss of blastomere lability that the trophectoderm and ICM markers used by Johnson and his colleagues are indeed specific in unperturbed embryos and that their experiments are, therefore, valid.

A DETERMINANT MODEL

Although cytoplasmic determinants have long been considered to be involved in differentiation of nonmammalian embryos (see Introduction), we do not have any direct evidence for the existence of determinants in early mammalian embryogenesis. On the other hand, it is difficult to devise a satisfactory model explaining blastomere fate and behavior without the use of determinants. One might propose a simple cell contact extension of the Inside–Outside Hypothesis, which would predict that blastomeres with at least part of their surface on the outside of the embryonic mass (i.e., not in contact with other blastomeres) become programmed to differentiate to trophoblast cells whereas blastomeres whose surface is in contact with other cells on all sides (or ultimately with an outer surface exposed to the blastocoel) become programmed to form ICM derivatives. This is, in essence, what appears to happen during early mouse embryogenesis. However, this model does not explain why and when blastomere lability is lost: Why do exposed cells of ICMs isolated by immunosurgery regenerate trophoblast at early stages but not at later ones? Why do repositioned outside cells at the morula stage retain the capacity to contribute to the ICM whereas outside cells of the expanded blastocyst do not? Finally, the model does not explain why trophectodermal vesicles should synthesize ICM-specific polypeptides before the cells differentiate overtly to trophoblast. A somewhat different "micro-environmental" model (44) has been rejected for several reasons by Johnson *et al.* (47,51). At least one determinant model has already been proposed which is not contradicted by available data (47,51). The model described herein is built upon that proposal and most notably makes use of the concept of cell polarity envisaged by Johnson and his colleagues.

In the initial formulation of his model, Johnson (51) invokes the presence or both trophectoderm-type and ICM-type determinants, but in a later version (47), a single (unspecified) "radial gradient of information" is said to exist. I favor the earlier view in the model to be presented here, i.e., that there are two distinct types of determinants, namely trophoblast determinants (informational factors which guide the cell to differentiate as trophoblast) and ICM determinants (informational factors which guide the cell to participate in the formation of ICM-derived tissues, e.g., embryo proper or yolk sac). Details of the model are as follows: Trophoblast determinants are more influential than ICM ones. ICM determinants may either be absent or randomly distributed until the eight-cell stage, whereas trophoblast determinants are arrayed in a gradient in the uncleaved egg. The latter are present at a higher concentration in the peripheral cytoplasm than in the central cytoplasm. As cleavage occurs, individual blastomeres remain polarized with respect to the population of determinants. Thus, at the eight-cell stage each cell has a gradient of trophectoderm determinants with increasing concentrations toward the external surface. By this stage, there is also a reciprocal gradient of ICM determinants with the highest concentration in the part of the cell facing the inside of the embryo. At the next division, one or more blastomere(s) will give rise to both an internal daughter cell (which is totally enclosed by other blastomeres) and an external daughter cell (which has part of its surface on the outside of the embryo). As a result of the movement of determinants, the internal daughter blastomere will come to possess a disproportionately large number of ICM determinants and a disproportionately small number of trophoblast determinants. The opposite is the case for the external daughter. At each subsequent cell division, perhaps aided by the persistence of intracellular polarization of determinants (see below), their unequal distribution will become more pronounced until, at the expanded blastocyst stage, the external (trophectoderm) cells possess virtually no ICM determinants and, conversely, the concentration of trophoblast determinants in internal (ICM) cells is below the critical level required to influence the cell to differentiate as trophoblast. The cells have thus lost their lability.

DISCUSSION OF THE MODEL

TYPES OF DETERMINANTS

If determinants do indeed exist, it is most likely that they are cytoplasmic. It is, however, conceivable that the determinants lie within the cell surface membrane; there appears to be heterogeneity in the gross morphology (14,44,52) as well as antigen and enzyme distribution (see 49,52) of surface membranes in early mouse embryos, not only between inside and outside cells but also at different locations along individual blastomeres (52,53). A nuclear location for determinants would be inconsistent with the model described herein and with that proposed by Johnson *et al.* (47).

The model as presented involves both trophoblast and ICM determinants. The demonstration that disaggregated blastomeres have a strong disposition to form trophoblast cells suggests that trophoblast determinants exist and that models containing only ICM determinants are unlikely to be correct. On the other hand, the claim that trophectodermal vesicles produce ICM-specific polypeptides, at least transiently, argues for the existence of ICM determinants as well as trophoblast determinants. The ultimate formation of trophoblast by such cells leads to the conclusion that trophoblast determinants are more influential than ICM ones. The nature of the trophoblast and ICM determinants and the way in which they impart information are unknown.

TIME OF APPEARANCE OF DETERMINANTS

I have proposed the early existence of trophoblast determinants because several experiments already discussed suggest that the information necessary for differentiation to trophoblast is inherent to the blastomeres at very early stages of mouse embryogenesis. Trophoblast determinants are considered to be distributed in a gradient throughout early embryogenesis because studies in which oil droplets are injected into cells (13,54) suggest that there is not extensive reorganization of the cytoplasm beyond the two-cell stage. The existence of ICM determinants at early cleavage stages, perhaps in a polarized array, is not ruled out; however, since no one has devised a way to get early blastomeres to form only ICM cells, there is as yet no support for the initial presence of these determinants.

MOVEMENT OF DETERMINANTS

The determinant gradients must not be passive or frozen since this would be inconsistent with changes of cell fate in blastomere reaggregation experiments as well as the lack of evidence for twinning in embryo aggregation experiments. Instead, the determinants must possess the ability to redistribute following manipulation of blastomere position. Determinant movement might occur in two ways. The first is via junctional complexes between adjacent cells. Lo and Gilula (55) have demonstrated that following compaction of blastomeres at the morula stage, fluorescein injected into one blastomere can become distributed among all blastomeres via gap junctional complexes within a matter of minutes. If transmission of determinants is by this route, then determinant size is restricted, since molecules with molecular weights above 2000 are unable to penetrate such junctions. Alternatively, determinant movement might take place during cell division. Lo and Gilula (55) have demonstrated that intercellular transfer of horseradish peroxidase (MW 40,000) is detectable at most times during embryogenesis. In this case, transfer is assumed to take place via cytoplasmic bridges between daughter blastomeres since the enzyme is only passed from the injected blastomere to one additional one. However, the results obtained suggest that these cytoplasmic bridges exist for considerable periods, allowing ample time for determinants to redistribute among the daughter blastomeres as described in the model. If determinant movement occurs during cell division there would presumably be no restriction placed upon determinant size.

Recent experiments by Pedersen and Spindle (56) might have some bearing upon the location and movement of determinants. These investigators microinjected zona-intact or zona-free eight-cell embryos into the blastocoelic cavity of large aggregate blastocysts. The majority of zona-intact embryos formed morphologically normal blastocysts which, following recovery from the aggregate host embryos and further culture, gave rise to morphologically normal outgrowths containing a monolayer of giant trophoblast cells. On the other hand, most of the embryos whose zona pellucida had been removed by pronase treatment failed to form morphologically normal blastocysts. Rather, they usually adhered to the inside of the trophectoderm layer as a solid mass of cells resembling an ICM. When these masses were recovered by immunosurgery from the host blastocysts they too gave rise upon further culture to outgrowths morphologically similar to those obtained from normal blastocysts.

Results from experiments with zona-intact embryos suggest that either the concentration of ICM determinants in the blastocoelic fluid is
not high enough to override the influence of trophoblast determinants
in the injected embryo or ICM determinants cannot be taken up from
the blastocoelic fluid. Results with zona-free embryos suggest that
even though they are in apparent intimate contact with host trophectoderm cells and cannot form a normal blastocyst, the blastomeres of the
injected embryo do not lose their trophoblast determinants to these
outer host cells (since the recovered cell masses subsequently produce trophoblast cells). The retention of trophoblast determinants by
the injected embryos could be explained if determinant movement
occurs by cell division since blastomeres from the injected embryo do
not appear able to integrate into the trophectoderm layer of the host
blastocyst (56). It would be very interesting to determine whether
blastomeres from the injected embryo form gap junctional complexes
with trophectoderm cells of the host blastocyst. If such complexes do
form without loss of trophoblast determinants from the internal embryo, this would argue against determinant transmission via gap junctions.

CONSEQUENCES OF INTRACELLULAR POLARIZATION OF
DETERMINANTS

Polarization of determinants in blastomeres should serve to greatly
facilitate determinant movement. Because we are unaware of the
identity of the determinants, we are obviously unable to determine
whether or not they are polarized within individual blastomeres. Handyside (52) and Izquierdo *et al.* (53) have recently obtained evidence
that morphological, antigenic, and enzymatic polarities in surface
membranes of mouse blastomeres are not disrupted when blastomeres are disaggregated. This could reflect maintenance of determinant gradients if the determinants are membrane-associated. This
could also suggest that the cytoskeletal framework in these blastomeres (see 57) might be rigid enough to promote cytoplasmic compartmentalization [if such compartmentalization does exist, it does not
seriously impede the spread of injected horseradish peroxidase
throughout both the injected blastomere and the sister blastomere
(55); however, movement of larger macromolecules or subcellular particles might be affected].

The way in which intracellular polarization of determinants could
lead to the ultimate localization of determinants is best exemplified by
reference to the case presented in the model, namely that of an eight-

cell blastomere giving rise by division to an internal and an external blastomere. If determinants are polarized in the parental blastomere, the daughter blastomeres should automatically inherit an unequal supply of ICM and trophoblast determinants. Prior to the next cell division, the gradients of available ICM and trophoblast determinants will have become reestablished in both the internal and external daughter blastomeres. If the subsequent cleavage plane is approximately perpendicular to the axis of the gradient (e.g., an internal blastomere divides to give an internal daughter and an external daughter), then the distribution of trophoblast and ICM determinants will again be disproportionate: The internal daughter inherits a higher ratio of ICM : trophoblast determinants than the parental blastomere and the external daughter acquires a higher ratio of trophoblast : ICM determinants. On the other hand, if the cleavage plane is approximately parallel to the axis of the gradient, the ratio of ICM : trophoblast determinants will be approximately the same in the daughter blastomeres as in the parental blastomere. Provided that trophoblast and ICM determinants become polarized in blastomeres prior to each cell division, the cell lineage patterns described by Graham and his colleagues (13–15) should be adequate to allow the appropriate sequestration of determinants in the three- to four-cell doublings which occur between the eight-cell stage and the expanded blastocyst stage.

This section has focused upon ways in which division of blastomeres can help to distribute determinants in overall gradients throughout the embryo. In the example cited, the determinants are passively carried to their desired locations by cytoplasmic (and/or membrane) partitioning during cell division. A somewhat more unorthodox view would be that the determinant gradients within a blastomere are the driving forces which influence the location of subsequent daughter blastomeres. That is, when a polarized blastomere divides, the daughter blastomere which happens to contain a relative abundance of ICM determinants is carried toward a central position by virtue of its possession of these excess ICM determinants. Conversely, the other daughter blastomere is drawn toward an external site by virtue of its content of an excess of trophoblast determinants. In this way the determinants would be actively controlling their own distribution as well as influencing cell lineage.

IS THE MODEL VALID?

The model presented is not irrefutable and certain aspects have been chosen from a number of possible alternatives. Overall, the model is consistent with normal development as well as with the blastomere manipulation studies that have been described. Thus, the presence of ICM and trophoblast determinants in eight-cell blastomeres accounts for their lability and the ability of determinants to reestablish their characteristic gradients between the eight-cell and expanded blastocyst stages would explain the lack of twinning in chimeras. On the other hand, the dominance of trophoblast determinants correctly predicts that trophectodermal vesicles will ultimately differentiate as trophoblast even though they might transiently express ICM-specific polypeptides. The incomplete stratification of ICM and trophoblast determinants between the eight-cell and expanded blastocyst stages would account for the ability of outer cells of the morula or inner cells of the early blastocyst to regenerate a total blastocyst. Finally, the sequestration of determinants by the expanded blastocyst stage would result in loss of lability both by inside and outside cells at that time.

Determinants have been very diffusely defined in this model; the paucity of available information does not permit restriction of the nature of the determinants to a particular class of molecules or macromolecules (unless they are distributed via gap junctional complexes, in which case the determinants must have a relatively low molecular weight), or their localization to the cytoplasm or the cell membrane. In defense of the broad definition of determinant as used herein, it should be pointed out that researchers have been aware of the existence of determinants in nonmammalian embryos for many years, but none has yet been unequivocally isolated or identified. Of course, without knowledge of the identity of the determinants it becomes difficult to conclusively validate (or invalidate) the model. Nevertheless, it might be helpful to use the determinant model as a guide in the search for informational factors which control early mammalian embryogenesis.

REFERENCES

1. Davidson, E. H., (1976) "Gene Activity in Early Development," 2nd ed. Academic Press, New York.
2. Smith, L. D., and Williams, M. A. (1975) *In* "The Developmental Biology of Reproduction" (C. L. Markert and J. Papconstantinou, eds.), pp. 3–24. Academic Press, New York.
3. Donohoo, P., and Kafatos, F. C. (1973) *Dev. Biol.* **32**, 224–229.
4. Rodgers, W. H., and Gross, P. R. (1978) *Cell* **14**, 279–288.
5. Seidel, F. (1952) *Naturwissenschaften* **15**, 355–356.

6. Seidel, F. (1960) *Wilhelm Roux' Arch. Entwicklungsmech. Org.* **152**, 43–130.
7. Moore, N. W., Adams, C. E., and Rowson, L. E. A. (1968) *J. Reprod. Fertil.* **17**, 527–531.
8. Tarkowski, A. K., (1959) *Acta Theriol.* **3**, 191–267.
9. Nicholas, J. S., and Hall, B. V. (1942) *J. Exp. Zool.* **90**, 441–459.
10. Tarkowski, A. K. (1961) *Nature (London)* **190**, 857–860.
11. Mintz, B. (1962) *Am. Zool.* **2**, 541.
12. Hillman, N., Sherman, M. I., and Graham, C. F. (1972) *J. Embryol. Exp. Morphol.* **28**, 263–278.
13. Graham, C. F., and Deussen, Z. A. (1978) *J. Embryol. Exp. Morphol.* **48**, 53–72.
14. Graham, C. F., and Lehtonen, E. (1979) *J. Embryol. Exp. Morphol.* **49**, 277–294.
15. Kelly, S. J. (1979) *J. Exp. Zool.* **207**, 121–130.
16. Mulnard, J. G. (1971) *Adv. Biosci.* **6**, 255–277.
17. Tarkowski, A. K., and Wroblewska, J. (1967) *J. Embryol. Exp. Morphol.* **18**, 155–180.
18. Sherman, M. I. (1975) *In* "The Early Development of Mammals" (M. Balls and A. E. Wild, eds.), pp. 145–165. Cambridge Univ. Press, London and New York.
19. Gardner, R. L. (1971) *Adv. Biosci.* **6**, 279–301.
20. Gardner, R. L., and Johnson, M. H. (1972) *J. Embryol. Exp. Morphol.* **28**, 279–312.
21. Wudl, L. R., and Sherman, M. I. (1978) *J. Embryol. Exp. Morphol.* **48**, 127–151.
22. Snow, M. H. L. (1973) *In* "The Cell Cycle in Development and Differentiation" (M. Balls and F. S. Billett, eds.), pp. 311–324. Cambridge Univ. Press, London and New York.
23. Sherman, M. I., and Atienza-Samols, S. B. (1979) *Exp. Cell Res.* **123**, 73–77.
24. Rizzino, A., and Sherman, M. I. (1979) *Exp. Cell Res.* **121**, 221–233.
25. Kelly, S. J. (1975) *In* "The Early Development of Mammals" (M. Balls and A. E. Wild, eds.), pp. 97–105. Cambridge Univ. Press, London and New York.
26. Kelly, S. J. (1977) *J. Exp. Zool.* **200**, 365–376.
27. Barlow, P. W., Owen, D., and Graham, C. F. (1972) *J. Embryol. Exp. Morphol.* **27**, 431–445.
28. Kelly, S. J., Mulnard, J. G., and Graham, C. F. (1978) *J. Embryol. Exp. Morphol.* **48**, 37–51.
29. Gardner, R. L. (1968) *Nature (London)* **220**, 596–597.
30. Gardner, R. L. (1974) *In* "Birth Defects and Fetal Development, Endocrine and Metabolic Disorders" (K. S. Moghissi, ed.), pp. 212–233. Thomas, Springfield, Illinois.
31. Rossant, J., and Vijh, K. M. (1980) *Dev. Biol.* **76**, 475–482.
32. Ford, C. E., Evans, E. P., and Gardner, R. L. (1975) *J. Embryol. Exp. Morphol.* **33**, 447–457.
33. Gardner, R. L., Papaioannou, V. E., and Barton, S. C. (1973) *J. Embryol. Exp. Morphol.* **30**, 561–572.
34. Gardner, R. L., and Johnson, M. H. (1973) *Nature New Biol.* **246**, 86–89.
35. Gardner, R. L. (1975) *In* "The Developmental Biology of Reproduction" (C. L. Markert and J. Papaconstantinou, eds.), pp. 207–236. Academic Press, New York.
36. Solter, D., and Knowles, B. B. (1975) *Proc. Natl. Acad. Sci. U.S.A.* **72**, 5099–5102.
37. Rossant, J. (1975) *J. Embryol. Exp. Morphol.* **33**, 979–990.
38. Rossant, J. (1976) *J. Embryol. Exp. Morphol.* **36**, 163–174.
39. Johnson, M. H., Handyside, A. H., and Braude, P. R. (1977) *In* "Development in Mammals" (M. H. Johnson, ed.), Vol. 2, pp. 67–97. North-Holland Publ., Amsterdam.

40. Handyside, A. H. (1978) *J. Embryol. Exp. Morphol.* **45**, 37–53.
41. Hogan, B., and Tilly, R. (1978) *J. Embryol. Exp. Morphol.* **45**, 93–105.
42. Spindle, A. I. (1978) *J. Exp. Zool.* **203**, 483–489.
43. Rossant, J., and Lis, W. T. (1979) *Dev. Biol.* **70**, 225–261.
44. Ducibella, T. (1977) *In* "Development in Mammals" (M. H. Johnson, ed.), Vol. 1, pp. 5–30. North-Holland Publ., Amsterdam.
45. Van Blerkom, J., Barton, S. C., and Johnson, M. H. (1976) *Nature (London)* **259**, 319–321.
46. Handyside, A. H., and Johnson, M. H. (1978) *J. Embryol. Exp. Morphol.* **44**, 191–199.
47. Johnson, M. H., Pratt, H. P. M., and Handyside, A. H. (1981) *In* "Cellular and Molecular Aspects of Implantation" (S. R. Glasser and D. W. Bullock, eds.). Plenum, New York (in press).
48. Surani, M. A. H., Barton, S. C., and Burling, A. (1980) *Exp. Cell Res.* **125**, 275–286.
49. Sherman, M. I. (1979) *Annu. Rev. Biochem.* **48**, 443–470.
50. Johnson, M. H. (1979) *J. Embryol. Exp. Morphol.* **53**, 335–344.
51. Johnson, M. H. (1979) *J. Reprod. Fertil.* **55**, 255–265.
52. Handyside, A. H. (1980). *J. Embryol. Exp. Morphol.* **60**, 99–116.
53. Izquierdo, L., Lopez, T., and Marticorena, P. (1980) *J. Embryol. Exp. Morphol.* **59**, 89–102.
54. Wilson, I. B., Bolton, E., and Cuttler, R. H. (1972) *J. Embryol. Exp. Morphol.* **27**, 467–479.
55. Lo, C. W., and Gilula, N. B. (1979) *Cell* **18**, 399–409.
56. Pederson, R. A., and Spindle, A. I. (1980) *Nature (London)* **284**, 550–552.
57. Lehtonen, E., and Badley, R. A. (1980) *J. Embryol. Exp. Morphol.* **55**, 211–225.

Index